The Arming and Fitting of English Ships of War
1600–1815

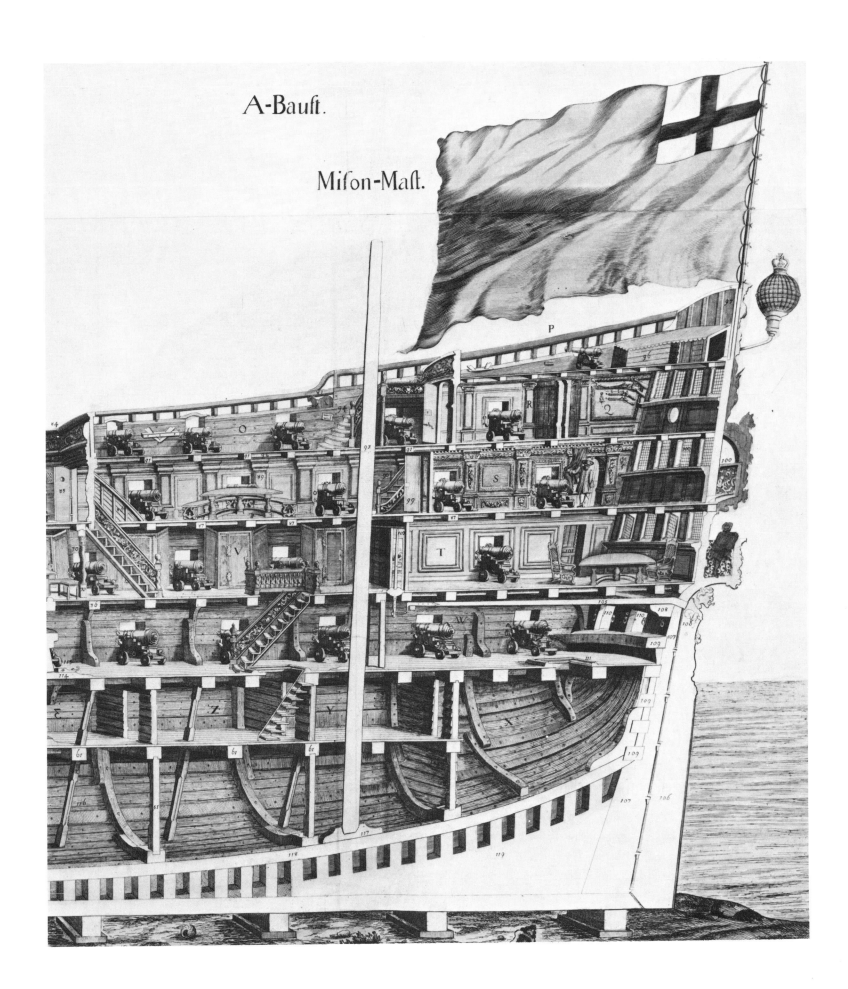

A-Bauſt.

Miſon-Maſt.

THE ARMING AND FITTING
OF ENGLISH SHIPS OF WAR
1600–1815

BRIAN LAVERY

CONWAY
MARITIME PRESS

© Brian Lavery 1987

First published in Great Britain 1987 by
Conway Maritime Press
24 Bride Lane
Fleet Street
London EC4Y 8DR

ISBN 0 85177 451 2

Designed by Roger Lightfoot

Typesetting and page make-up by Eta Services (Typesetters) Ltd, Beccles, Suffolk
Printed and bound in Great Britain by R J Acford, Chichester

Frontispiece. *The stern of a First Rate, from the Phillips print c1690.* NMM.

CONTENTS

Acknowledgements

I would like to thank the following for help with this work: past and present members of the staff of the National Maritime Museum, who have offered many useful comments, in particular Roger Knight, David Lyon, John Munday, Rina Prentice, Simon Stevens, Alan Stimson, and Chris Ware; Robert Gardiner and Rosie Ford of Conway Maritime Press; John Cox, Frank Fox, John Franklin, Peter Goodwin, Colin Martin, Rudi Roth, and Roderick Stewart; the members of the Invincible (1744–58) Committee. Also, the staff at the following institutions: The Science Museum, London; The London Library; The British Library, London; The Public Record Office, Kew and Chancery Lane, London; The Pepys Library, Magdalene College, Cambridge; HMS *Victory*, Portsmouth; TS *Foudroyant*, Portsmouth Harbour; Frigate *Unicorn*, Dundee; Merseyside Maritime Museum, Liverpool.

INTRODUCTION

This book is intended to serve two main purposes. The first is to provide ship-modellers, marine archaeologists, and historians with a guide to how English ships of war were fitted out during the great age of the sailing ship. In this respect I hope it will follow in the traditions of James Lees' *Masting and Rigging*, and Peter Goodwin's *Construction and Fitting of the Sailing Man of War 1650–1850*. However, the reader will notice some differences from these works. I do not claim to have provided every piece of data on all the fittings of the years in question, nor have I attempted to draw up tables of proportions for various ships and periods. Instead, in the main text, I have described the general principles which affected the design of each fitting, and in the appendices provided material from contemporary sources which have been selected largely to provide detailed information and specific dimensions. I have not attempted to interpolate from these to provide proportions which might cover other cases, preferring to leave this to the reader.

The second purpose is broader: to study the development of a particular technology for its own sake. The book is almost entirely confined to the Royal Navy, mainly because there are sources, in the form of manuscripts, plans and models, for this body, while those relating to merchant shipowners are rare, for few records were kept in the first place, and those that were have largely perished. However, there is an obvious correlation between the Navy and other operators of ships, and the gap in their technological development was probably not very great.

There is a popular myth that the Royal Navy in the age of sail was an innately conservative body, which only adopted new technology as a last resort, after it had been tried by others. I hope that this book will show how mistaken this notion is. Steering wheels, copper sheathing, and many other innovations were first tried out aboard naval ships, in advance of the rest of the world, and many less dramatic inventions were tested thoroughly over the years. Certainly there were times, such as the first half of the eighteenth century, when the Navy was absurdly afraid of change, but in general it is no exaggeration to say that the sailing navy was in the forefront of new technology. Its ideas were eventually adopted by other navies, and also by merchant ships, for it did not operate in a vacuum. As a rough rule of thumb the development of merchant ships lagged about twenty years behind that of naval ships. Though it is not possible to write a coherent history of merchant ship fittings of this period, because sources are so sparse, this work should give some indication of the 'state of the art' at a given time.

The application of new technology to sailing ships has broad implications. The Navy in wartime was the largest single employer in the country, not only of seamen, but of those who built and maintained ships, and supplied them with all their fittings, from ships' boats to barrel staves, from copper sheets to anchors. This book is not intended to be an industrial history, but it does reflect the wide range of skills required to keep the Navy afloat, and the vast amounts of raw materials which were needed.

General historians are coming to believe that 'wars are too important to be left to military historians'. Likewise, technology is too important to be left to pure technological historians, and it is necessary to approach the subject on a broad front to understand its development. The men who built the ships, and those who fitted them out and directed the efforts of others, were products of their societies, and it would be foolish to ignore this aspect.

The term 'fittings' can be taken to mean those items essential to the ship which were not a permanent part of the structure. I have interpreted the term 'fittings' rather liberally, including items of varying permanence. I have written nothing about rigging, for the simple reason that it is covered in other works, and I have included hammocks which were obviously not part of the ship, but dealt with consumable stores, such as food and spare parts, only in reference to the way they were stored, or when they throw light on other items, such as pumps. Some fittings, such as capstans, are virtually integral parts of the ship, but have been included as they have a history of their own. I have considered the underwater protection of the hull, but not that above the water. Though the painting or paying of the sides had considerable importance as a protection, it might also be considered part of the decoration of the ship, and that is a subject which deserves separate study.

The chronological boundaries of this work are matters of convenience rather than historical significance. Most would date the beginning of the supremacy of sail at 1588, if not earlier; 1600 was not a year of any great significance. But records of the sixteenth century are sparse, and comparatively well explored and from 1600 there is a steady growth in the amount of material available, which gains in momentum over the years. Nevertheless the sources, in the form of manuscripts, draughts and models, are still quite sparse until the second half of the seventeenth century, and some aspects of the early history have to be neglected because no records seem to exist. This is partly because of the tradition of craftmanship. Shipwrights and other skilled workers did not record their practices, and did not encourage outsiders to observe them. Often it is only by chance that we can find out what they did. In later years, as the number of inventions and innovations grew, and as society became gradually more literate, more and more was written down, or represented in the form of draughts or models, but for the first half of the seventeenth century we often have only rather vague answers to some of our questions.

This is less so in some areas than others. In the case of gun-making, the development of iron ordnance, and the rivalry between the Admiralty and the Ordnance Board, led to quite substantial records being kept. On the other hand, the whole century provides little information about the insides of ships, except for the Pepysian reforms which mainly affected officers' cabins, rather than the seamen. Ordinary mariners rarely wrote autobiographies in those days, and those who did tended to concentrate on exotic places visited. The day-to-day details of shipboard life were taken for granted.

The close of the book at 1815 is no less convenient. It was obviously not the end of the age of sail, though it was not long before steam tugs came into use, and these had many effects on anchors, boats, and other fittings even before steam was applied to the ships themselves. The date 1815 is largely of political significance as it marked the end of the long series of wars with France, and the beginning of a longer period of peace than Europe had known for centuries. The effect of this on the Navy is obvious enough – few ships were fitted out for sea. But this did not affect the pace of technological change. By about 1810 the number of inventions submitted annually to the Navy for consideration was increasing rapidly, as a study of the Admiralty indexes will show. A substantial proportion of these were accepted for trial or even for standard use, so that those few ships which were fitted out after 1815 probably had a great variety of fittings. Already some innovations, for instance round-crown anchors, chain cables and iron water tanks, were on the verge of becoming standard, and others were soon to follow.

The period after 1815 becomes increasingly complex, as numerous inventions were tested on a small number of ships, so that it becomes difficult to tell what was standard at any given time. It is a period which contrasts strongly with the relative stability of the previous centuries, and as such it deserves to be treated separately.

Notes on the Text

I have used the original weights, measures and prices in all cases. Many of these are no longer familiar to readers, so the adjacent list shows their values in the metric system. Obviously it is not practical to attempt to convert money to its 'present' value, but I have included a note on the £.s.d system, which went out of use more than 15 years ago.

For those who are not familiar with the structure of naval administration, I will briefly explain the status of the Navy Board and the Admiralty. The Admiralty was in overall charge of all matters relating to the Navy, while the Navy Board was responsible for more technical matters, such as shipbuilding and the supply of naval stores. Relations between the two bodies were often very complex. Though the Ordnance Board was essentially part of the Army administration, it dealt with naval guns, while other boards, such as the Victualling Board and the Sick and Hurt Board, fulfilled other specialised roles under the Admiralty. All these boards tended to believe that their knowledge and experience gave them certain rights independent of the Admiralty, and sometimes they resisted its authority. The reader is directed to Baugh's *British Naval Administration in the Age of Walpole* for the best account of relations between the different boards.

The main building yards were Deptford, Woolwich, Chatham, Sheerness and Portsmouth, which were the oldest dockyards; Plymouth was added to the list at the end of the seventeenth century; and Pembroke Dockyard at the beginning of the nineteenth. There were overseas bases, such as Gibraltar and Port Royal, Jamaica, but these are not of such importance, for the British Navy did not build ships in the colonies, except for those built at Bombay from 1801. There were also a few home bases which were not developed to full dockyard status. Deal was the most important of these, in relation to this book.

The dockyard was usually headed by the commissioner, who was technically a member of the Navy Board, but whose real power was limited. Under him was a committee of the senior officers, of whom the master shipwright had the greatest effect on shipbuilding and fitting. Under him were several other officers who controlled much of the detail of the fitting out of ships: the assistant master shipwrights, the master boatbuilder, master mastmaker, master smith, and so on.

Measures

Weight

1 pound (lb) = 0.454 kilogrammes
1 quarter (qr) = 28lbs
1 hundredweight (cwt) = 4qrs or 112lbs
1 ton = 20cwt or 2240lbs

Length

1 inch (in) = 2.54 centimetres
1 foot (ft) = 12in
1 yard (yd) = 3ft or 36in

Money

12 pence (12d) = 1 shilling (s)
20 shillings = 1 pound (£1)
Sums of money are written in the form £3/2/0, or 3/6. Eg, £2/15/6 = two pounds, fifteen shillings and six pence; 7/8 = seven shillings and eight pence.

Other measures

1 gallon = 4.456 litres
1 quire = 24 sheets of paper
1 ream = 480 sheets of paper
1 ell = 45in
1 bushel = 8 gallons (of dry goods)
1 chaldron = 36 bushells
1 cord = a pile of wood, usually 8ft x 4ft x 4in

PART I

Steering

Chapter 1. Rudders

Basic Principles

The stern rudder began to replace the side rudder (also known as the steering oar) in the thirteenth century, and it had almost completely superseded it by 1500. The side rudder had some advantages, in that it was balanced. It rotated near its centre line, so that the movement of its fore edge counteracted that of its after edge, and little effort was needed to move it. The stern rudder, on the other hand, was hinged at its fore edge, and all the force of the water had to be counteracted by the effort of the helm. However, it was much more robust, and could be better adapted to make use of the mechanical advantage of a long tiller.[1]

The stern rudder had important effects on ship design. If it was to be fitted with more than two hinges, its fore edge had to be straight, as had the sternpost of the ship to which it was attached. Moreover, the shape of the underwater hull had to be sharp enough to allow the water to flow to the rudder. Sir Anthony Deane claimed that 'the shape and run abaft is only for bringing the water the quicker to the rudder'.[2] Much of the design of the underwater hull aft of midships was based on the need for the rudder to be able to operate efficiently. Double-ended ships were no longer common, because the lines aft had to be finer than those forward.

The biggest advantage of this type of rudder was that it was placed where its effect was greatest, near the extremity of the ship. It was impossible to have a forward rudder, for the pressure of the water, or the slightest yaw would have forced it off the centre line and made it very difficult for the helmsman to restore it to the neutral position. At the stern, the rudder stayed in the neutral position unless considerable force was exerted to displace it. It was comparatively strong, because it could be held to the sternpost by several hinges and it was better protected from the dangers of storm and grounding than a rudder in any other position. Thus the non-balanced stern rudder, hinged to the sternpost by its fore edge, remained supreme in European waters and on European ships until it began to be replaced by the balanced rudder, the product of a new technology, in the middle of the nineteenth century.

The Shape of the Rudder

The most important determinant of the shape of the rudder was the sternpost. This was straight, and slightly at an angle from vertical. This angle varied from ten to fifteen degrees on British warships (in French ships it tended to be nearer to the vertical), and tended to decline slightly over the years. The sternpost was of course fixed, being an integral part of the ship's design.

The rudder was slightly less thick than the sternpost to which it was attached. It was relatively thin at its foot, but like the sternpost became thicker nearer its head. It did not usually become thinner in the fore and aft direction, so it was still quite thick at its after edge. On a First Rate of around 1670, for example, it was 11in thick at the lowest part of its foot and slightly thicker at the waterline, above which great thickness did not matter.[3] The thickness of the rudder below the waterline had some disadvantages. When the ship was moving ahead, it would have caused a certain amount of water resistance by creating eddies. When going astern the after face of the rudder would be in the opposite direction and would thus tend to counteract its main effect. Nevertheless it was important that the wood was thick, for the rudder had to have considerable strength.

The rudder was not particularly wide in its fore and aft direction. 'The narrower the rudder is the better, if the ship do feel it; for a broad rudder doth hold much dead water, if the helm be put over to any side.'[4] Furthermore, a rudder that was too broad would be rather weak, partly because of the method of construction. The rudder compensated for its lack of width by its great length. In most cases it began at the lowest level of the keel, or the false keel. It had to extend above the top of the sternpost, so the tiller could be fitted. After 1754 it was carried up even further, above the level of the upper deck, so that a hole for a spare tiller could be cut into it and the head of the rudder thus protected by the counter of the stern.

The forward edge of the rudder was completely straight, except for the holes cut in it so the pintles could be fitted. On some seventeenth century ships the bottom forward corner of the rudder was removed, to make room for a skeg, a triangular projection from the aftermost part of the keel. This was intended to protect the rudder if the ship went aground. Sir Henry Mainwaring disapproved of them, because 'they are apt to snap off, and so endanger the stern post; next, in a harbour or river where

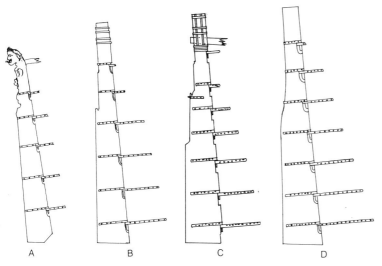

Changes in the shape of the rudder.
A. From the Phillips print of about 1690. As was normal for a large seventeenth century ship, the corner of the foot is cut away for a skeg, and the head is curved and decorated.
B. A rudder with two hancings, as fitted on the Anson *of 1781. The head is bound up with metal straps, and is completely straight.*
C. The rudder fitted to the Victory *in the 1800s. It has three hancings, and a considerable amount of ironwork at its head.*
D. The 'round' rudder fitted to the Caledonia *in 1808.*

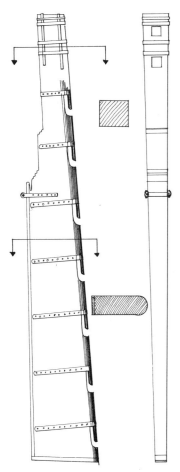

The basic shape of a rudder, c1780. The fore edge is rounded up to the level of the top of the sternpost. Though the head shown here is square, they could also be hexagonal.

ride many ships, they are apt to catch another ships cable betwixt that and the rudder.'[5] They were relatively rare by the middle of the century, though they appear in Edward Dummer's draught of the 1680s, and the Phillips print of the 1690s. They do not seem to have been used in the eighteenth century, though they can be seen on a few ships of the early nineteenth.

The stern rudder did pose a problem. Ships were normally trimmed to have their sterns lower in the water than the bows, thus the foot of the rudder was often the lowest part of the whole ship. The rudder would not be particularly vulnerable if the ship went aground on a steep bank, as the bows would strike first, but if the ship scraped over the top of an underwater obstruction, the rudder might be the only part to hit it. In the later years of the eighteenth century the problem was partially solved, because extra false keels were fitted and the rudder was not extended downwards to this level. In the early nineteenth century, the bottom edge of the rudder was angled upwards slightly, so that it no longer formed a straight line with the keel, but was approximately parallel to the waterline of the ship when she was trimmed by the stern.

The after edge of the rudder was also straight, up to the level of the waterline. It was not quite parallel to the fore edge, but angled so that the rudder became slightly narrower towards its upper part. Just above the waterline, the width of the rudder was reduced much more dramatically, by means of a hancing of rather complex shape. In the seventeenth century the rudder was radically reduced to about half its width in this way. A second hancing was first used from the 1670s, though it was well into the next century before it became universal. The introduction of the first hancing meant that just above the waterline the rudder was reduced to about two-thirds of its greatest width. The second hancing above that reduced it by another third. From about the middle of the eighteenth century, a third hancing began to come into use, so that the rudder was reduced in three stages. The first hancing was now situated just below the waterline.

The rudder continued to reduce in width and increase in thickness right up to its head. Thus, though in cross-section it was long and thin at its foot, it became square, or nearly so, at its head so that there could be a tenon or two, for fitting the tiller. Large fore and aft width was not necessary above the waterline. In the eighteenth century the rudder head was as straight as the rest of the fore edge, and as plain. In the previous century, it was curved slightly backwards, and was often heavily decorated, usually with a carved lion's head. In the eighteenth century this would have been superfluous, as the head of the rudder was concealed inside the structure of the stern.

The 'round rudder' was first tested around 1795, and became common in the 1800s. It dispensed with the hancings of the old system, and the rudder above the waterline was now tapered by means of regular curves. On most ships the area extending from just below the waterline was shaped as a single concave curve. On other 'round rudders' the shape below the waterline was more complex, and the after edge of the lower part was no longer straight.

In cross-section, the rudder was rectangular, except for its forward edge, which was rounded off to facilitate its movement. Early in the nineteenth century, it became customary to round off the after edge of the sternpost as well, so that the rounding of the rudder could be correspondingly reduced. The corners of the head of the rudder were often trimmed off, so that in cross-section it was almost a regular octagon.

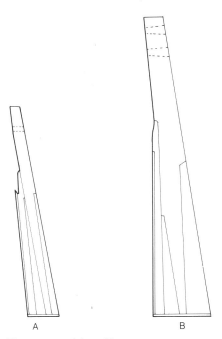

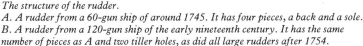

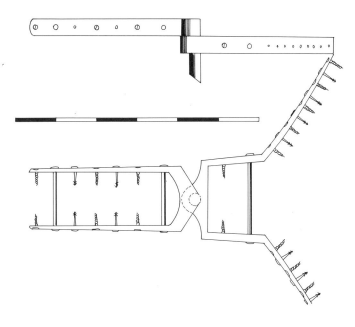

The structure of the rudder.
A. A rudder from a 60-gun ship of around 1745. It has four pieces, a back and a sole.
B. A rudder from a 120-gun ship of the early nineteenth century. It has the same number of pieces as A and two tiller holes, as did all large rudders after 1754.

A system proposed for fitting gudgeons and pintles to a 90-gun ship, c1780. Though the idea of using bolts and nails was experimental, the shape of the gudgeons and pintles was perfectly standard. Based on a drawing in the PRO.

The Structure of the Rudder

According to one source, in the early part of the eighteenth century it was possible to build the rudder of a First Rate from a single piece of wood.[6] If true then, it was certainly no longer common by the middle of the century, by which time even Fourth Rates had their rudders made from several pieces. Normally the rudder was made from four main parts, joined together by tables and coaks before 1800, and by dowels in the early nineteenth century. The 'main piece' was of course the largest part, and formed the centre. This was made of oak. In most cases it appears to have extended the whole length of the rudder, though this was variable. The timber fayed to the main piece to form the fore edge was often of elm, as it could provide a very straight piece of timber. The after parts were quite often of fir. In addition to these pieces of timber which made up the main structure of the rudder, narrow strips were often applied to the lower and after edges. These were known as the sole and the back, and served to protect the main structure from damage.

Fitting the Rudder

The rudder was attached to the sternpost by several hinges. In 1625, according to Mainwaring, there were four to six of these. By the early 1800s, a large First Rate had seven hinges, a 74 of the 1780s had six, and a frigate of the same date had four or five.

The hinges came in two parts: the gudgeons (called the 'googins' by William Falconer in 1769) which were attached to the hull of the ship, and the pintles, which were fitted to the rudder. The gudgeon had a ring, through which the pintle was placed. From the ring led two arms, with holes for bolts. Each arm was shaped to follow the contours of the hull at the level at which it was to be fitted. A bolt was passed through the first hole, through the sternpost, and through the corresponding hole on the opposite arm, where it was clenched. The other arm had bolts which passed through the side of the hull, rather than the sternpost. This meant that a bolt was needed on each arm of the gudgeon, and they were each clenched inside the hull. In the 1780s, a system of alternating bolts and screws was tried, but it is not known if it later came into general use.

The pintle (originally 'pintail') was built round a pin, which was inserted into the ring of the gudgeon, when the rudder came to be fitted. Above the pin itself was a head, of larger diameter than the pin, to prevent it from passing all the way through the ring. Like the gudgeon, the pintle had two arms, one for each side of the rudder. As on the gudgeon, the first bolt passed all the way through the rudder and was clenched in the other side. The number of holes depended on the width of the rudder at that level. Usually the arm was carried back as far as possible, almost to the after edge of the rudder, with holes positioned regularly along its length.

The two assemblies, the hull with its gudgeons and the rudder with its pintles, were prepared separately and brought together only when the rudder was finally fitted to the hull. This system meant the rudder could be replaced easily, but great care was required in the fitting of the gudgeons and pintles, to ensure that they were evenly spaced on both assemblies. If they were not, there was a danger that undue strain would be placed on some components, and little on others. The lower pintle was longer than the others, in the eighteenth century at least. This probably helped to locate the rudder when it was being fitted.

For each pintle, a recess called a score was cut in the fore edge of the rudder. The top of the pintle was level with the top of this recess. The score extended downwards below the lower end of the pintle, so that the total length of the recess was equal to the

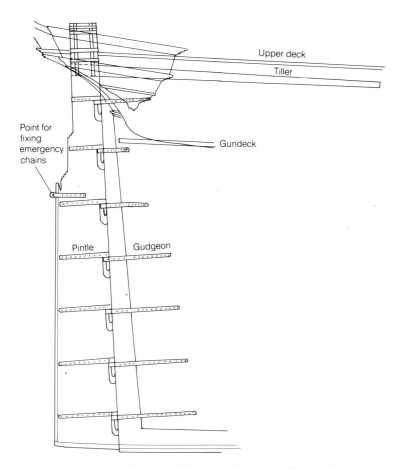

The rudder of a 74-gun ship, c1780. The spacing of the ironwork is clearly shown.

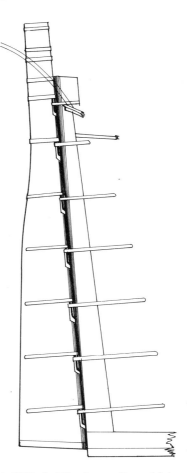

A rudder of the early 1800s. It differs from earlier models in several respects: the bottoms of the scores are squared-off rather than rounded; rings have been placed between the gudgeons and the pintles; the after edge of the sternpost has been partly rounded, though it tapers away towards its foot; the rudder's foot does not extend below the main keel, and it is angled upwards from the line of the keel, to protect it from grounding.

length of the lowest and longest pintle, plus the thickness of the ring of the gudgeon, with a little extra to allow room for insertion. After fitting, the rudder was held in place by means of a chock known as a woodlock. This was placed under the first pintle above the waterline, and kept the rudder rigidly in position. In the third quarter of the eighteenth century the forward face of the rudder was covered in lead, to prevent wear on the wood. This was superseded when copper sheathing came into use.

Other Ironwork

In the eighteenth century, after the head of the rudder became straight and square, and was carried up through the upper deck to provide space for a spare tiller, the head of the rudder was bound up with several metal straps. These were placed both vertically and horizontally, and gave extra strength in this crucial area, preventing the different parts from which the rudder was made from separating under pressure.

Another iron fitting, known as the spectacle frame, was fitted just above the waterline, usually at the level of one of the hancings, to act as an emergency steering chain. It consisted of a pair

of rings, one on each side of the rear face of the rudder. These were linked by a bar of iron, which also extended round the sides of the rudder, and was bolted firmly in position. Chains were fitted to these rings, to give some control over the rudder in the event of damage to its head. They also prevented the rudder from being completely lost, should an accident break the gudgeons and pintles. Ringbolts were fitted on the wing transom, just under the stern galleries, to hold the other ends of the chains when not in use.

According to William Falconer, writing in 1769, scientists of the time had deduced that the best angle for operating a rudder was 54 degrees, but Falconer believed from practical experience that an angle of about 35 degrees would be better.[7] Modern science would tend to substantiate Falconer's opinion, for a greater angle would merely retard the motion of the ship, without doing much to increase the turning motion. However, for much of the period covered by this book the question of angle was irrelevant, for other factors prevented the rudder from turning very far.

Chapter 2. Tiller and Whipstaff

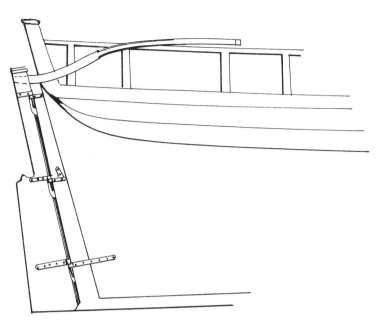

Smaller vessels used the tiller without whipstaff or wheel for much longer than larger vessels. This drawing is from the draught of the William, *a gun-vessel of 1794, and shows a tiller which would not have been unusual on a small vessel of the previous century.*

The Tiller

In order to move a rudder from side to side, some system is necessary to provide leverage, and in most cases the tiller has been found to be the most convenient. Ideally the tiller should be as long as possible, to give the greatest leverage. In a small boat the need to save space is the limiting factor and in a full-sized sailing ship the tiller can be taken forward only as far as the mizzen mast. On a warship with more than one complete deck, including a frigate on which the lower deck was unarmed, the tiller was fitted just below the upper deck, or the middle deck on a three-decker. This meant that it took up no space on the flat of the deck, though it prevented hammocks from being slung under the deck above. On smaller ships, Sixth Rates and less, the tiller was operated on the after part of the main deck, as there was often no room for it elsewhere.

The seventeenth century tiller appears to have had a slight curve near its aftermost end, to accommodate it to the curve of the rudder head. In the eighteenth century when the rudder head became completely straight, so did the tiller. The tiller was square in cross-section, and was fitted tightly into a square hole cut in the rudder head. Its maximum thickness was where it entered the hole in the rudder. It was tapered slightly to fit into the hole, and it also tapered towards its forward end until, at its extremity, it was about half its maximum thickness.

The Helm Port Transom

In the seventeenth century the head of the rudder was outside the main structure of the ship, and it was the tiller which penetrated the hull, through a hole known as the helm port transom. To enable the tiller to be moved, the helm port transom was cut in the vertical plane, though the hull was in fact curved at this point. A hole of considerable width would have been needed to allow free movement of the tiller; this was not provided. From contemporary models and paintings, it can be seen that the hole was quite narrow, which must have restricted the tiller's motion considerably. If vertical timbers were placed on each side of the hole, as seems likely, the movement of the tiller would probably have been restricted to less than 20 degrees.

In the last years of the seventeenth century, it became customary to fit the counter at a greater angle to the vertical, so that the structure now covered the rudder head. Thus the latter was protected from the effects of shot and the sea. It also meant that the rudder head, rather than the tiller, now penetrated the hull. As a result, the space needed to allow a wide angle of movement was reduced, for the rudder head was quite narrow, and unlike the tiller it rotated about its own axis. This change was of great significance. It probably heralded the introduction of the steering wheel, for several models[1] show the new type of counter, without the steering wheel.

The helm port transom was a source of weakness in a ship. A following sea could break against the stern, forcing water into the hull. There was no easy way of closing this port without restricting the movement of the rudder, but the eighteenth century system was an improvement for it interfered much less with the rudder's movement and the hole was a little further above the surface of the water.

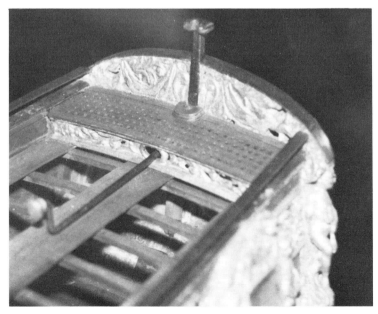

The tiller of a royal yacht of around 1690. The narrow aperture through which it emerges is very typical of models of the time. It illustrates how little tiller movement was possible in the late seventeenth century.

A model of a 90-gun ship of the 1690s, showing the narrow aperture for the tiller. Author's photograph, courtesy of NMM.

A slightly later model, showing the new shape of the counter, and how it covered the head of the rudder. Author's photograph, courtesy of Science Museum.

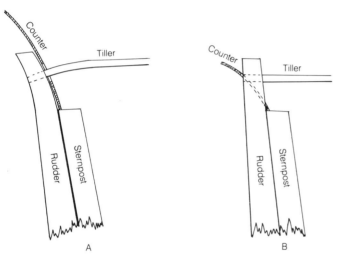

The change in the counter's shape, showing how it affected the rudder's head. A. The old shape. B. The new shape.

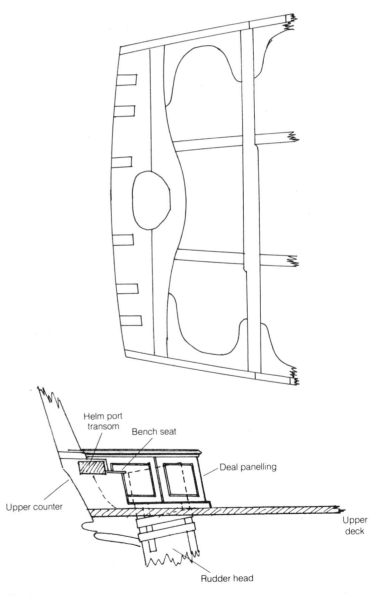

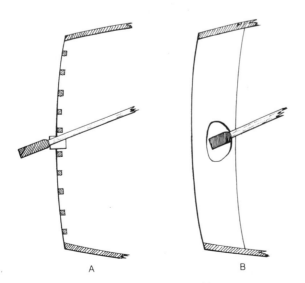

The result of the changes. On B, where the rudder head comes through the counter, there is much less restriction on the movement of the rudder.

The shape of the helm port transom, on the Dorsetshire *of 1757. The rudder head has been extended up to the wardroom, and is covered with deal panelling.*

The Whipstaff

The whipstaff, or 'whip' as it was sometimes called, was the standard means of steering a large or medium sized vessel in the seventeenth century. In 1625 it was described as follows: 'The whip is that staff which the steersman doth hold in his hand whereby he governs the helm and doth port it over from one side to another. It hath a ring at one end which is put over the end of the helm [ie the tiller] and so comes through the rowle up into the steerage.'[2]

Apart from this, there is little written evidence about how the whipstaff was fitted to English ships. However, the Phillips print of the 1690s shows it quite clearly. An iron neck, known as the gooseneck, is fitted to the end of the tiller. The whipstaff itself is shown vertical, in its neutral position, with the helm amidships. The whipstaff is a simple pole, rather flimsy looking for the work it had to do. It passed through the roll, or 'rowle', which was defined as 'that round piece of wood or iron wherein the whip doth go, and is made to turn about that it may carry over the whip from side to side with more ease.'[3] The rowle was placed in a fore and aft direction at the level of the upper deck, or the middle deck of a three-decker. The lower end of the whipstaff had a metal ring, which was placed round the end of the gooseneck, to which it was held by a hook or head.

The whipstaff had three main advantages. First, it allowed extra leverage on the tiller, depending on the length of the staff above the rowle. Second, it meant that the helmsman's vision was raised by at least two decks, so that, on a two-decker at least, he could have a limited view of the sails. The tiller remained under the upper deck, but the helmsman could stand above that deck, and if he was raised a little by a platform, and given a small structure on the quarterdeck through which he could see, his viewpoint would be above that deck as well. In theory this was also possible on a three-decker, for a longer whipstaff would have allowed the helmsman to be on the upper deck, but there is no clear evidence that this was ever done, and the Phillips print implies the opposite. Perhaps the long whipstaff had too many disadvantages, for it would have required an enormous hole to be cut in the upper deck to allow reasonable movement.

The third advantage of the whipstaff was that it cleared more space on the deck. If the tiller had simply been operated by hand, as on many small vessels to this day, its sweep would have taken up considerable deck space. It would have to have been fitted 2 or 3ft above the deck, and a considerable amount of space on either the lower deck or the one above would have been wasted. With the whipstaff, on the other hand, the tiller could be fitted under rather than above a deck, and the deck space saved. This was not an important consideration on an overcrowded warship.

However, the whipstaff had many disadvantages. The most obvious was that it enabled only very limited movement of the tiller. If the staff was actually fixed in the rowle, as has usually been assumed, the tiller's movement must have been very limited indeed – probably less than 10 degrees. This would have caused another problem, for if the whipstaff was put at its most 'extreme' angle, it would have tended to lift the tiller out of position. The fitting of the tiller made no allowance for such a movement, and the available evidence suggests that the gooseneck was not intended to pivot. The tiller was normally fitted close to the underside of the deck beams, and there was no room for it to move upwards. Moreover, there is evidence that in the 1690s, when the whipstaff was still in use, efforts were made to prevent the tiller from moving up and down.

Part of the Phillips print of the 1690s, which gives the clearest view of an English whipstaff. It also shows the curve of the tiller, the decoration on the rudder head, the rowle, and the gooseneck. NMM.

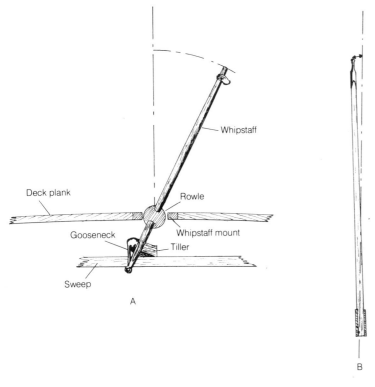

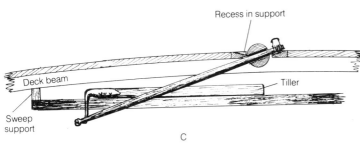

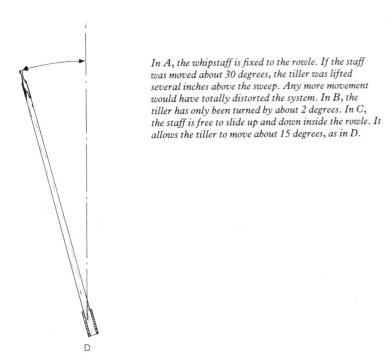

In A, the whipstaff is fixed to the rowle. If the staff was moved about 30 degrees, the tiller was lifted several inches above the sweep. Any more movement would have totally distorted the system. In B, the tiller has only been turned by about 2 degrees. In C, the staff is free to slide up and down inside the rowle. It allows the tiller to move about 15 degrees, as in D.

It is clear that the whipstaff which was fitted to French ships in the early years of the eighteenth century was not fixed in the rowle, but was able to slide up and down through it.[4] It would seem logical that English ships were fitted in a similar way. This is largely confirmed by Mainwaring's comment that a sucking movement was when 'a ship doth draw down the helm and doth, as it were, suck the whipstaff out of his hand at the helm'.[5] Moreover, some models show grooves cut in the mount on each side of the staff, which were obviously intended to accommodate the staff when it was put hard over.[6]

The ability of the whipstaff to slide meant the tiller could have more movement. The tiller in the Phillips print would have been able to move about 15 degrees before the end disappeared down the rowle, and it is possible that the whipstaves fitted to other ships were longer, so the helmsman could see through the quarter-deck. Nevertheless, the problem was not entirely solved. Pushing the staff through the rowle would soon cause a loss of mechanical advantage, and the helmsman would be less able to exert force on the tiller at extreme angles, just when the pressure of the water on the rudder was greatest. The tiller could only have been operated at these angles on very small ships, or at low speed. It was at low speed that the rudder needed to be moved most and the water pressure on it was least, so this facility could have had its uses even on large ships.

Another disadvantage of the whipstaff was that it did not allow many men to operate it at once. According to Mainwaring, it was not used at all on ships of over 500 tons. 'By reason of the weight of the rudder and the water which lies upon it in foul weather they are not able to govern the helm with a whip, because conveniently there can stand but one man at a whip.'[7] Again Mainwaring is contradicted by the evidence of the Phillips print, which shows a three-decker, of at least 1200 tons, with a whipstaff. Moreover, contracts of the 1690s demand that a whipstaff be fitted to ships of 80 guns, and these were far larger than 500 tons.[8] Possibly whipstaffs were not fitted to such ships at the beginning of the century, but this was not the case by the end.

However, there must have been many occasions when the whipstaff was put under great strain. Perhaps, despite what Mainwaring says, more than one man could have operated it, by one standing on each side. Yet greater pressure could have been applied by fixing a tackle from the top of the staff to the side of the ship. It is more likely that the whipstaff was disengaged, and a tackle fixed between the end of the tiller and the side of the ship. This would have required an elaborate command procedure, with orders being shouted from the quarterdeck to the men on the tiller lines below. Such a procedure would have been necessary in any case on a three-decked ship, even with the whipstaff in use. Such a method seems to have been the only one possible on those great ships which, according to Mainwaring, did not carry a whipstaff. The system of construction suggests that there would have been no difficulty in removing the end of the gooseneck from the ring of the whipstaff, when necessary.

The Companion

In 1815 a companion was defined as a 'framing formed with glass at the upper part or sides'.[9] Then it was fitted to give light to the captain's cabin, but for the years covered by this book it refers to a structure put on the quarterdeck, above the whipstaff, to give the helmsman a view of the sail – very useful if he was steering

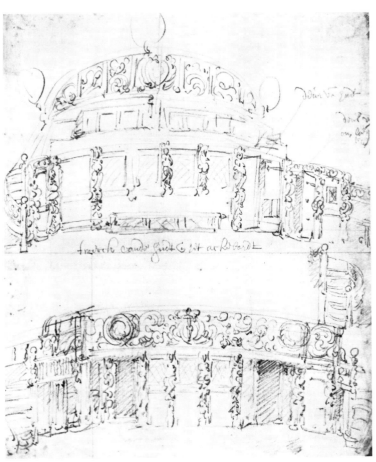

This drawing by Van de Velde *shows the companion used by the helmsman on one of the 70-gun ships of 1677.* NMM.

The lower window in the bulkhead of the poop, on this model of the Boyne *of 1692, is for the helmsman. Like all such structures, it is behind the mizzen mast where the view must have been very restricted.* Author's photograph, courtesy of NMM.

close-hauled. It does not appear to have been used much on English ships in the earlier part of the seventeenth century, and it is not mentioned in any of the nautical dictionaries by Smith, Boteler or Mainwaring, all compiled in the 1620s. Another work of the same period refers to the 'steerage room' on the upper deck, 'where they stand to steer the ship by the help of the whipstaff moving to and fro at liberty in the rowles'.[10] The binnacle for the compass was fixed before the whipstaff, but there is no mention of any view through the quarterdeck above.

The companion can be seen on some late seventeenth century models and drawings, for example in a sketch by Van de Velde of one of the two-decker 70s of 1677, and on the model of the *Boyne* of 1692. In the latter it is not a separate structure, but is included within the compartment under the poop. A later version of this can be seen on a deck plan of a ship built in 1712. The implication is that the companion became more common in later years, but it was not universal even then. The fact that a binnacle was fitted on the upper deck, as well as the quarterdeck, suggests that the helmsman could control the situation when sailing off the wind, in the open sea. When sailing close to the wind, or in confined waters, the quartermaster or pilot would often have to shout orders down to the helmsmen.

Support for the Tiller

It is sometimes suggested that the sweep, a piece of timber which supported the tiller from either above or below, was linked to the development of the steering wheel. In fact some support for the tiller would have been necessary with the whipstaff, for as the tiller was pushed out to one side, much of the force used must have tended to push the tiller downwards. If the tiller had any tendency to bend, it would have become increasingly difficult to push it past a certain point. The earliest form of support was a straight bar, placed under the tiller about two-thirds of the way along its length. This can be seen on the Swedish *Vasa* of 1628. By the 1690s, according to the Phillips print, the bar had been moved up to the end of the tiller, where it would obviously give much more effective support against the pressure of the whipstaff. It is not clearly shown in the print, but it can be assumed that the bar was curved, otherwise the tiller would have fallen off as soon as it moved too far from its central position. From this time the tiller support was known as a sweep, because it was part of the radius of a circle, as drawn out by the movement of the tiller.

The bar or sweep under the tiller could not always be completely effective over the full range of movement, for it too had to be supported. Unless it was to be propped up from below, which would again restrict the space on deck, it could only be supported at its ends, by being bolted to the deck beams above. If the sweep was too long, there was a danger that it would sag in the middle and lose some of its efficiency. This problem was solved near the end of the seventeenth century, by placing the sweep above the tiller instead of below. In this position it could be bolted to the deck beams above, in as many places as proved necessary. A small cleat was fixed to the upper side of the tiller, to hold it up to the sweep. This system is described in a contract of 1693: 'To fit it with a full-grown tiller of oak, without knots; a gooseneck of iron for the whipstaff, and an elm cleat butted and forelocked on the tiller to swing the same upon a sweep of 3 inch oak plank fastened to the middle deck beams for that purpose.'[11] Clearly, the sweep

17

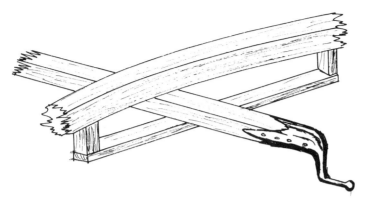

The old type of sweep which illustrates how the movement of the tiller must have been somewhat restricted.

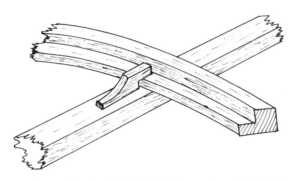

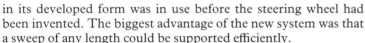

The later type of sweep, introduced in the 1690s. Because it was bolted to the upper deck beams, it was much more rigid than the old type.

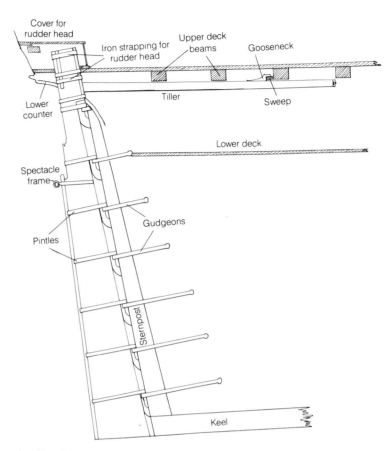

A rudder of the 1750s, showing the tiller, the gooseneck, the sweep, and many other features.

in its developed form was in use before the steering wheel had been invented. The biggest advantage of the new system was that a sweep of any length could be supported efficiently.

By the end of the seventeenth century, the British Navy had just ended a long war with France. It was more gruelling than any of its previous wars against the Dutch, in that it was fought in the more turbulent waters of the English Channel and the Atlantic, further away from home bases, in a great range of weather, and

often against fast privateers. Perhaps it was this experience which caused three important changes in the system of steering in the years between 1690 and 1710. The first was the extension of the counter of the stern, which allowed much freer movement of the rudder. The second was the new type of sweep, fitted above the tiller, which had the same effect. The third and most dramatic was probably a consequence of the other two – the invention of the steering wheel.

Chapter 3. The Steering Wheel

Early Development

We have already seen that the tiller's freedom of movement was increased around 1700, something of which captains must have been very conscious. Especially on the large three-deckers, they must have used the tiller tackle often, when the state of wind and sea meant more strength was needed than the whipstaff could provide. At some stage, someone thought of leading the tiller lines up to the quarterdeck, and fitting them to a windlass, so that they could be operated by a helmsman on deck. This first stage in

the development of the wheel can be seen on a model at Greenwich, conventionally dated 1703 (see left-hand photograph on page 19).

The next stage, which followed soon afterwards, was to turn the barrel of the windlass round to a fore and aft direction, and to fit it with spokes and a rim, so that pressure could be applied at any angle, and by several men if necessary. A rope was led from the end of the tiller to a block at the side of the ship, back to the centre line of the ship, through another block, and up through as many decks as necessary to reach the barrel of the wheel above. Several turns were taken round the barrel, and the rope was nailed to it at one point. The rope was then led down again, through a similar set of blocks on the other side, and back to the end of the tiller. Any turn on the wheel would turn the tiller, and therefore the rudder, to one side.

An early eighteenth century model showing the earliest known version of the steering wheel – a windlass set athwartships. NMM.

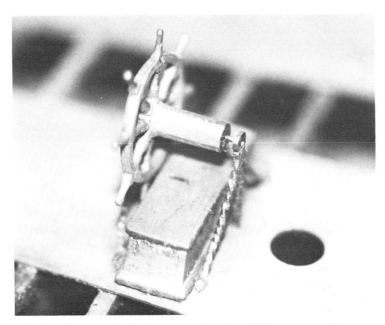

The oldest known model of a fully developed steering wheel, on another model at the National Maritime Museum. Author's photograph, courtesy of NMM.

The Date of the Wheel

It has often been remarked that the wheel came surprisingly late in the development of the ship, and that the inefficient whipstaff was retained for a long time. But, as we have seen, it had only just been discovered, or rediscovered, how to operate the tiller through a wide angle, and the wheel followed this development remarkably quickly. Though the invention of the wheel is rightly credited to the British Navy, no trace of any order to introduce it has ever been found, despite extensive searches in the archives. This suggests that it was developed by sea officers and the artisans in the dockyards, rather than by the central administration.

Much of our evidence about the early wheel comes from two models in the National Maritime Museum at Greenwich.[1] The earliest of these, already mentioned, shows a windlass with its barrel running athwartships. The other (above, right) shows a ship fitted with a fully developed steering wheel, but still with the rowle for the whipstaff fitted below. Both these models are considered to date from about 1703, though the evidence for this is based almost entirely on their decorations. It is conventionally believed that decoration was greatly restricted by an order of 1703, and that ships built after that year were much plainer. Both these models have dimensions which suggest a later date than 1703, but decorations which, according to this theory, can only have come from before that year. Therefore they are dated as '1702' and 'circa 1703'.

All these theories are based on rather flimsy premises. Many orders were issued to restrict carved works in the late years of the seventeenth century, and the early years of the eighteenth. Most were almost completely ignored by the master shipwrights, and there is no reason to believe that the orders of 1703 alone were effective. It is more likely that the orders had a cumulative effect over the years, and it is rather dangerous to single out 1703 for exclusive mention. Moreover, it is believed that the second of these models, the one with the fully developed wheel, was made for or by the Master Shipwright of Plymouth, and was not an official Navy Board model. To decorate his home, he might well have requested a model with carvings which were no longer fitted to real ships. The other model is also very unconventional in style, and does not have the look of a true Navy Board model. Nevertheless, both models do date from the early years of the eighteenth century, as one bears the cypher of Queen Anne, who reigned from 1702 to 1714, and the other has a partly obscured date which reads '170–'.

More precise dates can be found from other sources. It is clear from her contract that the *Russell*, an 80-gun ship begun in 1707, was intended to carry a whipstaff.[2] On the other hand a plan of the *Ossory*, a 90-gun ship launched in 1711 shows a 'steering rowle' in exactly the right position for a steering wheel. Another ship of the same date, the 50-gun *Gloucester*, had a companion for the whipstaff.[3] All this evidence tends to suggest that the wheel was invented a little later than usually believed, nearer to 1710 than to 1703, and that it was applied first to larger ships. This is no surprise, for larger ships suffered worst from the disadvantages of the whipstaff, its bad location and relative weakness. No First and Second Rates were used between 1697 and 1702 because they were rarely employed in peacetime. On the other hand, they saw heavy service in the early years of the War of Spanish Succession, which began in 1702. It was probably during these years that the wheel was developed, on active service. Its use spread fairly rapidly after 1711, and it seems to have been a standard fitting on warships by 1715.

Early Improvements

The early wheel was situated directly above the end of the tiller, and behind the mizzen mast. This of course was inclined to restrict the helmsman's view, and during the 1730s there was a tendency to move the wheel forward of the mast. This presumably involved a slightly more sophisticated system of rigging the tiller ropes.

The original wheel was fitted in front of a cylindrical barrel. In heavy weather two men could operate it with plenty or space, but more would tend to get in one another's way. Some ships had a double wheel by about 1740. An extra wheel was fitted at the rear of the barrel, allowing four men to pull at it when necessary. By the 1740s it was being fitted to most ships of the Third Rate and above. In the 1750s, it was fitted to the new classes of Fifth Rate frigates, and it was later fitted to some Sixth Rates, though many of the smaller vessels retained the single wheel.

The wheel was held in position by two brackets which rose vertically from the deck. On two-deckers, after the quarterdeck was extended forward of the mizzen, the foremost bracket extended up to the beams of the poop deck above, which it helped to support. When a single wheel was still fitted on a two-decker, it was put on the after side of the barrel. On frigates and smaller vessels there was no poop, and the wheel was in a very exposed position on the quarterdeck.

Pollard's System

The problem with the early wheel was that the system did not allow equal tightening and slackening of both sides of the tiller rope. As the rope was hauled in on one side, the angle between it and the centre line of the ship altered. The rope on the other side was affected in a different way, and it became either too tight or too slack, according to the position of the blocks. The latter could be repositioned to minimise the problem but it could not be prevented altogether. Using blocks alone, it was not possible to keep both sides of the tiller rope tight in all conditions.

It has been suggested that the wheel could not be introduced until a system had been developed to overcome this,[4] but this is not the case. Many deck plans of the early eighteenth century, such as that believed to be the *Torbay* (ex-*Neptune*) of 1730, show the tiller ropes rigged through blocks on a very simple principle. The problem was tackled merely by leaving some slack in the ropes. Indeed, the French retained the whipstaff in addition to the wheel for several years, precisely because it could make the tiller react immediately, whereas the wheel had to take up some slack first.

This was tolerated for 60 or 70 years, until 1771, when Pollard, the Master Boatbuilder at Portsmouth Dockyard, suggested a new system. 'The present method of steering His Majesty's ships', he wrote, was 'attended with many inconveniences and fatal accidents that have happened and are generally known to have been by the unavoidable slack rope when the tiller is near its greatest angle, by which the men are often thrown from the steering wheel, the tiller in danger of being broke, the rudder head and pintles work loose, the tiller ropes are in the way of working the guns, and are in danger of being shot away.'[5]

Pollard made a model of his new system, which consisted of 'sweeps and rowles', and it was tested aboard the *Centaur*, under Captain Bentinck, in August 1771. Bentinck reported, 'I have the highest satisfaction of doing justice to that most ingenious contrivance . . . it answers every purpose that can possibly be desired of it.'[6]

Pollard's method was to place the sweep as far forward as possible, and to lead the tiller ropes along its forward edge. That edge was fitted with small rollers, which allowed the free movement of the tiller rope. Apart from this the lead of the ropes through a block at the side of the ship, back to the centre line, and

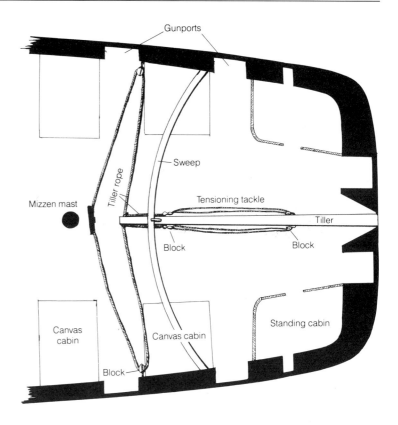

A mid-eighteenth century steering arrangement, from a draught in the Mulgrave Collection, possibly of the Neptune *of 1730. Note the slackness in the tiller ropes, and the fact that they do not go forward of the mizzen mast.*

up to the wheel, was unaltered. Pollard's invention appears to have been successful, and it was soon adopted for general use, by order of the Navy Board. It can be seen on the drawing of the *Bedford* of 1775, and aboard the *Victory* at Portsmouth.

The Tiller Lines

Rope made from hemp has a natural tendency to stretch, and even in the old system there had to be some means of combating this, before the slack became excessive. It was of course even more important in the Pollard system, where tautness was paramount. In both cases, the end of the tiller rope was not fixed to the end of the tiller. Instead, it was passed through a loop there, and led aft a short distance along the side of the tiller. There, it was attached to a block and tackle arrangement, which was in turn hooked into an eyebolt near the aftermost end of the tiller. By tightening on the tackle, the slack on the tiller rope could be taken up as required.

A longer term solution was to make the tiller ropes from a material which stretched less. Rawhide was suitable for this, and its use was made standard by an order of 1815.[7] It was used experimentally for some years before then, and it is believed that the *Victory* had rawhide tiller ropes at Trafalgar in 1805. They were also fitted to the *Medusa* during a visit to South America in 1807, and six years later they were recommended for general adoption.[8]

The forward end of the Victory's *tiller, showing how the tiller lines are led through eyes and then onto the sweep.* Author's photograph, courtesy of HMS *Victory.*

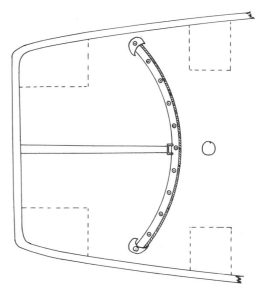

A drawing of the Pollard system taken from a rather crude draught of the Bedford *of 1775. The gooseneck on the tiller appears to be double-ended. The small circles on the sweep presumably represent the rollers. The rope is shown forward of the sweep, though of course it should be in contact with the rollers. The cabins in the gunroom are indicated by dashed lines.*

Behind the Victory's *sweep showing the gooseneck, and how it engages the sweep.* Author's photograph, courtesy of HMS *Victory.*

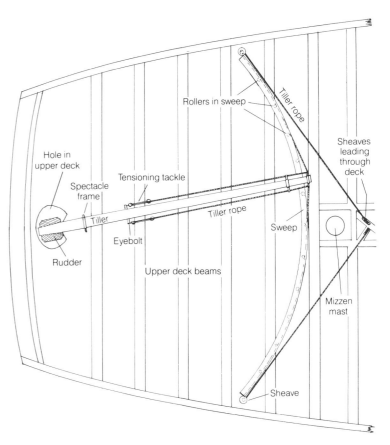

The method of rigging the tiller ropes, c1790, shown from below. The drawing is based on plans in Rees' Naval Architecture *of 1819. The spectacle frame near the after end of the tiller may be part of a system for locking the tiller to the rudder.*

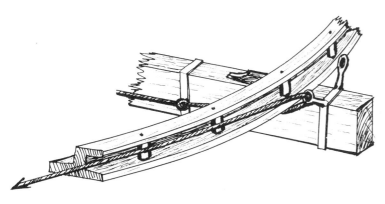

The Pollard system, showing the rollers fitted into the sweep.

The tiller ropes of the Victory, *which are led through blocks in the middle deck, and up to the wheel.* Author's photograph, courtesy of HMS *Victory.*

The Shape of the Wheel

Ideally the wheel had to be as big as possible, to allow maximum leverage. In practice its height was limited by the need to fit it under the poop deck on larger ships. Furthermore, the spoke which was parallel to the deck had to be about 3ft off the deck so downward pressure could easily be exerted on it. The typical wheel, then, had an outside diameter of a little over 5ft. This meant it could fit under the poop deck, if necessary, with a few inches of clearance above and below.

The centre of the wheel was formed by a metal spindle around which the whole system rotated. Each end of this spindle fitted into a wooden bracket which lifted the wheel above the deck. When the wheel was under the quarterdeck, the bracket usually extended upwards to meet the beams of the deck above. The brackets were decorated with carvings on the outward faces, and were roughly hour-glass shaped.

The barrel was wood, and fitted round the spindle. Its purpose was to give extra diameter, so that the tiller rope could be wound round it, usually five or seven times; it was nailed to the barrel in the middle. The British barrel was normally cylindrical, until the later eighteenth century when there was a move away from this because it was discovered that a barrel which had a greater diameter at its ends than in its centre could help in compensating for the slack in the tiller ropes. Such barrels were sometimes cut with

The Victory's *wheel showing how the tiller ropes are wound around the barrel. One end of the line is led through a hole near the forward end of the wheel, the other through a hole near the after end.* Author's photograph, courtesy of HMS *Victory.*

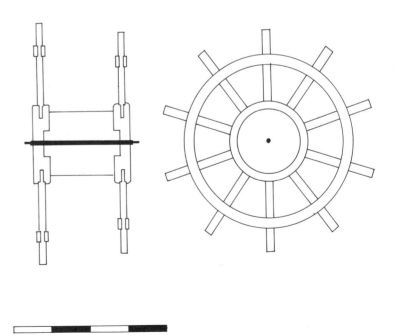

This wheel is said to be from the 74-gun Arrogant *of 1760. Though it gives no indication of any decoration, it does provide much information about the proportions and structure of the wheel.*

grooves to hold the ropes in position. It is known that they had been fitted to Danish ships as early as 1796, and to British ships by the 1820s.[9] It is not clear whether any were used before 1815.

The hub of the wheel was fitted at one end of the barrel, or at both ends when the double wheel was used. It had a slightly larger diameter than the barrel, to help stop the ropes sliding out of position. It was tenoned to receive the spokes of the wheel. Most wheels had ten spokes, so that they were fitted at an angle of 36 degrees to one another. A few smaller wheels had eight spokes. The rim of the wheel was fitted at about two-thirds, or more, of the distance between the outside of the barrel and the end of the spokes. It was important in giving the wheel strength, for without it each spoke would have borne its load independently, and therefore been much weaker. The extension of the spoke outside the rim gave a little extra leverage, and was an essential grip for the helmsman, who stood beside the wheel, rather than behind it. It also allowed him to apply much greater pressure than on a modern, car-type steering wheel with no spokes outside the rim.

The carving of the spokes began very early in the history of the wheel, and assumed a form familiar even today. Each spoke was evidently turned in a lathe. The carvings inside the rim were purely decorative, but the shape of the spoke outside the rim gave a more comfortable and efficient grip for the helmsman. The hub and the barrel were not usually decorated, and the rim only a little, with ridges carved in its inner and outer edges.

Steering on Smaller Vessels

On some vessels, small Sixth Rates and many sloops, there was no upper deck, and no room to fit the tiller under the quarterdeck. It was therefore above the quarterdeck, exposed to the sea and gunfire, and took up a large amount of space on the deck. The wheel was fitted just forward of the end of the tiller, and a simple system of tiller lines was used, even in the early nineteenth century.

The very smallest vessels – yachts, advice boats, cutters, gunboats, small brigs and schooners – continued to use the tiller without the wheel. Often there was some attempt to protect the head of the rudder. On some vessels the rudder led up through the deck, and under a small quarterdeck. The end of the tiller projected forward of this tiny deck. On other vessels the head of the rudder was merely covered with a small box built on the deck, with the tiller projecting forward from it. On the very smallest vessels, the tiller was curved upwards. This allowed the rudder head to be at deck level, but carried the tiller up to a position where it could be more easily held by the helmsman. On slightly larger vessels, the tiller was straighter and stronger, and rose upwards at a slight angle.

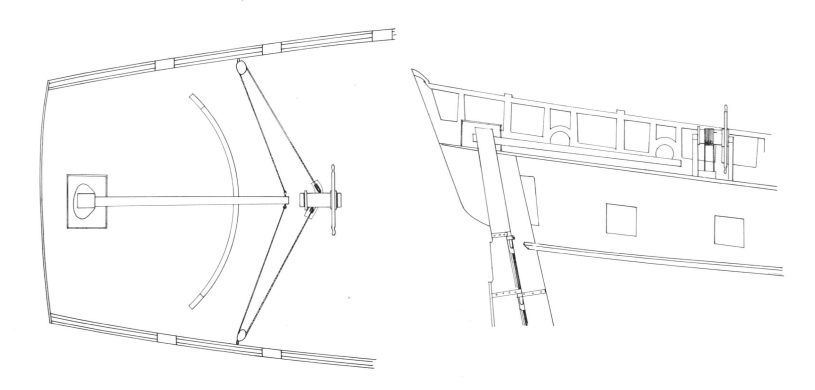

The steering system of a small late eighteenth century vessel. The rudder head is covered by a light structure, but no other parts of the system are protected, and there is no attempt to compensate for the unequal tensions on the ropes on each side.

Chapter 4. Navigational Fittings

Navigational Instruments

The state, like other shipowners of the time, did little to provide its ships with navigational equipment. Ships' officers, in particular the master, were expected to provide their own. According to Admiralty instructions, the master was, 'under the command of the captain, to have charge of navigating the ship'. To execute this responsibility, he was 'to provide himself with such charts, nautical books, and instruments as are necessary for astronomical observations and all other purposes of navigation.'[1] In the late eighteenth century, the official production of charts was expanded, and by 1809 sets of charts were made up in boxes for different areas, and issued to ships.[2] Like most artisans of the age, the master was responsible for providing most of his own tools and equipment.

The other officers – captains, lieutenants, mates and midshipmen – were also expected to take an interest, and to have some navigational skill and equipment. Thus in 1627 Captain John Smith recommended that a seaman ought to provide himself with 'compasses, so many paire and sorts as you will; an astrolabe quadrant, a crosse-staffe, a back staffe, an astrolabe, a nocturnal.'[3] In 1733 a 'volunteer', or naval cadet, was equipped with a quadrant, a plain scale, a pair of compasses with three points, a large pair of compasses, a slate and four pencils, a 'marriners compass rectified', and a 'prospect glass' or telescope.[4] But there were some items that had to be provided by the government. They were too expensive, large, or vital to the running of the ship, or needed checking too often to be left to the whims of individual officers.

The compass was by far the most important of these items. Great feats of navigation were performed by Phoenicians, Vikings, Celts and other peoples without it, using celestial navigation alone, but considerable skill was needed, the skies were not always clear enough to navigate by, and the risks were great. The compass, first known to have been used in the twelfth century, reduced risks, and opened up a new range of possibilities.

The Construction of the Compass

The essence of the compass was the needle, a piece of iron or steel which was magnetised by means of a lode-stone, so that, given free movement in the horizontal plane and the absence of interference from other sources, it would always point towards magnetic north. The shape of the needle varied over the years. Early ones, common up to about the middle of the eighteenth century, were made from two pieces of wire, bent in the middle and joined at the ends. These were replaced by a straight iron bar, made of tempered steel. The rest of the system was designed to keep the needle level, and give it the free movement it needed.

The needle was pivoted on a cone or pedestal. It was placed inside a 'box', which was in fact round and shaped like a bowl. This was made of brass because any ferrous metal would greatly reduce the accuracy of the compass. The compass card, or fly, was a circular piece of paper, graduated with the points of the compass.

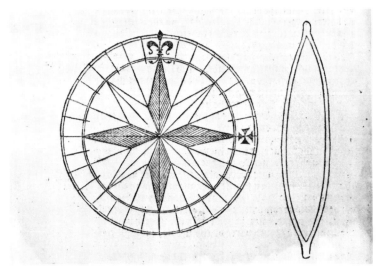

A compass card and a needle of 1545. NMM.

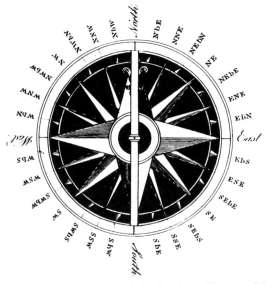

An early nineteenth century compass card, showing the needle on top of the card.

A typical compass, showing the brass bowl, wooden case, and the system of gimballing. Author's photograph, courtesy of NMM.

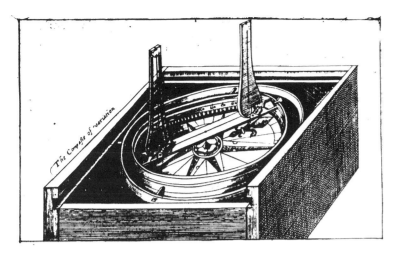

A compass of 1597, with the sighting ring fitted.

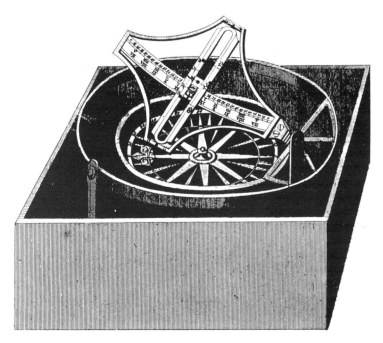

An azimuth compass, with its attachments for taking sights on stars and measuring variation.

It was often highly decorated, especially the arrow which pointed to the north. It could be highly coloured, but those used for night sailing were black and white, to heighten the contrast. It was primarily marked in the 'cardinal' notation, being divided into 32 points, and sometimes half and quarter points. Degrees were more useful for celestial navigation, and in later years these were marked in smaller figures round the edge, outside the cardinal markings. In 1814 it was recommended that degrees should be removed from steering compasses, as 'no seaman can steer by a degree'.[5] The principle of variation was partially understood, and at the beginning of the seventeenth century the compass card was offset to compensate for it. By about 1635 it was known that variation altered with both time and place, and the attempt to compensate for it within the compass was gradually abandoned. The card was now fitted to indicate magnetic north, and the navigator had to make the correction for true north as part of his calculations. Normally the needle was fitted under the card. Some drawings of the middle and late eighteenth century show the new bar type of needle fitted above the card, but this was possibly just an artist's convention. A circle of glass was fitted to the box above the card, to protect the latter from wind and rain.

The whole bowl and its contents were gimballed, so that the compass would remain level despite the movement of the ship. The bowl was placed inside a brass ring, and pivoted on one axis within it. This ring was put inside a wooden box, and within that it was pivoted on an axis perpendicular to the first axis.

Types of Compass

The compass was a very important, and rather delicate instrument, so a ship which intended to spend several months at sea independent of shore bases needed to carry several. In 1688 a typical First Rate ship was issued with 12, and in 1795 with up to 8.[6] The compass had to serve several purposes. Its most vital use was for steering. At least two, and sometimes four, were placed near the helmsman or the pilot, so that the ship could be kept on an intended course, or, when sailing close to the wind, the quartermaster could report to the navigator what course he had been able to make.

Another use of the compass was to measure the bearing of a particular object, a seamark, landmark, or celestial body. The compass used for this was probably similar to the steering compass. It was possible for the navigator to take one out of the binnacle and place it where he had a clear view of the object concerned. When used in this way, the compass was fitted with an azimuth ring which was placed round the top of the bowl of the compass, and fitted neatly inside it, so that it could rotate. From it rose two vertical pieces of brass, with holes for the observer to look through, and a piece of cat-gut stretched down the centre of the larger aperture. The two holes were lined up with the object concerned, so that its bearing could be read off from the compass card.

No separate azimuth compasses were listed in 1688, so it is likely that one of the 12 ordinary compasses was used for taking bearings. One is listed in 1795, alongside seven ordinary compasses, and an 'improved' steering compass invented by Adams.[7] It is unlikely that only one compass was available for taking bearings, so it seems possible that this azimuth compass was of a specialised type, for the sole purpose of measuring variation, and testing the accuracy of the other compasses, by taking readings from stars.

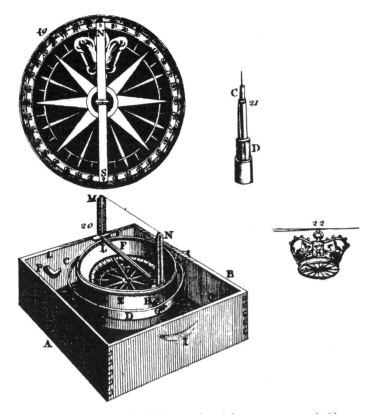

These drawings, from Burney's Dictionary *of 1815 show a compass card with degrees marked round the outside (top left); the pin on which the compass needle pivots (top right); a compass fitted with a sighting ring (bottom left); a hanging compass, with typical crown-shaped head (bottom right).*

Another type was the hanging compass. This was used, especially in captains' and admirals' cabins, to give a convenient reading of the ship's course. As its name implies, it was suspended, from a deck beam. Its upper parts were usually crown-shaped. Its card had to be printed in reverse, so it could not be used on the other compasses. In 1750 it was said that hanging compasses were issued to flag officers to hang in the great cabin.[8] Captains presumably had less need of them as their cabins were much closer to the steering compass, but they had the option of providing them from their own funds.

The Binnacle

The steering compass had to be placed within easy sight of the helmsman or pilot, and therefore on the open deck. It had to be protected from wind and rain and other hazards, and capable of being lit at night. The binnacle, which first appeared in the fifteenth century, served these purposes. In the seventeenth century it was more commonly known as the bittacle, which more

A typical mid-eighteenth century binnacle, from Falconer's Dictionary, *1769.*

This model of a frigate of about 1780 is one of the few to show the binnacle in place. Author's photograph, courtesy of NMM.

closely indicated the name's origin in the Italian word 'abitacolo', and the French 'habitacle', meaning small building.

By the seventeenth century the binnacle was a wooden box, divided into three compartments. The one in the middle was fitted to hold a lantern, and the ones either side each to hold a compass. The side of the middle compartment which faced the helmsman was solid, so that he would not be dazzled by direct light. Each compass was placed low in its compartment, so that the helmsman could look down on it. Two compasses were fitted, because the helmsman might steer from either side of the wheel. It was known that the presence of ferrous metals in the vicinity of the compass could cause deviation, so iron nails were not used in the construction of the binnacle. On the other hand, the effect of placing two compasses so close together was not fully appreciated, and this must have caused some inaccuracies. Above the compasses, the binnacle had drawers which held other navigational aids, such as log lines, lead lines, and hour glasses.

Ships fitted with a whipstaff usually had two binnacles, one on the upper deck for the helmsman and another on the quarterdeck,

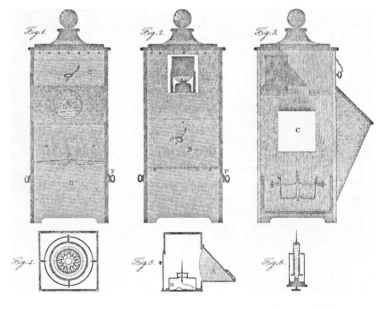

Details of the construction of the binnacle, from Burney's Dictionary, *1815.*

within sight of the sails, for the quartermaster or pilot. Up to three binnacles were carried in the middle of the eighteenth century, but by an order of 1779 this was reduced to two, 'unless demanded by flag officers'.[9] It is not clear where the extra ones were placed; possibly they were kept below as spares.

Helm Indicators

The movement of the tiller was directly linked to that of the rudder, so there was no difficulty in knowing which way the latter was pointing. Similarly, the whipstaff moved to left or right to exactly the same degree as the rudder. The wheel, on the other hand, had a much more complex relationship with the rudder. It would take several turns of the wheel to take the rudder to its maximum angle, so it was not easy for an observer to tell what position it was in. The helmsman, of course, was expected to operate by feel, and did not need to see the rudder. The officer of the watch or the pilot, however, might need to know in order to assess the ship's likely manoeuvrability in a particular situation, or to measure the amount of weather helm needed, in order to decide whether or not to trim the sails. The helm indicator was intended to show him.

The first helm indicators in the British Navy appear to have been copied from the French 74-gun ship the *Invincible*, captured in 1747.[10] The indicator was placed in front of the foremost beam of the poop, directly above the wheel's forward bracket. A graduated scale covered about two-thirds of the length of the beam. It was probably linked to the tiller, by means of lines leading down through the deck. These moved a pointer back and forward, showing the number of degrees the rudder was from the central position. Such an indicator can be seen on a few models, such as that of the *Royal George* of 1756. By December 1757, Captain Rodney was complaining that the new 74, the *Dublin*, had not been fitted with one, and 'mistakes having often happened from the officers not knowing how the helm was', and he asked for one to be fitted.[11] Another type, known as the steering index, was developed in the early years of the nineteenth century. It consisted of a dial placed on the forward side of the wheel bracket, with an arrow which rotated and pointed to the wheel's position. At first it was used, by an order of 1808, for ships where the beam of the poop was unsuitable for the fitting of the older type of indicator. There is no mention of what was done aboard frigates and smaller vessels, which had no poop.[12]

A model of the Royal George *of 1756, showing a helm indicator.* Author's photograph, courtesy of NMM.

Log Lines

The speed of a ship was measured by casting overboard a piece of wood attached to a long line. The piece of wood was known as the log, and the line as the log line. The amount of line which ran out over a fixed period of time was measured, and a speed calculation made from this. The line was knotted at regular intervals, so that the distance could be measured easily, hence the expression 'knots' to measure the speed of a ship. The log itself was shaped like a sector of a circle, with two straight edges and one curved. It was about 5 or 6in long, and $\frac{1}{2}$in thick. Pieces of lead were fixed to its rounded edge, to weigh it down and make it hang perpendicular. Two lines were fitted to it, arranged so that it could be tripped up when being hauled in, which helped reduce water resistance. It was essential that the log was clear of the turbulence created by the ship's wake before the measurement began, and part of the line was allowed to run out before the calculation started. The log line was put on a large reel, which was held by a seaman and allowed to rotate freely so that the line was unhindered. Twelve lines were carried by a First Rate in 1688, and up to 30 by a large ship on foreign service in 1795. Obviously this item was often lost and broken, so many spares were needed.

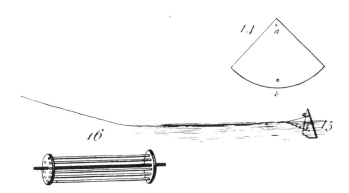

Parts of the log, from Falconer's Dictionary. *14 is the log itself, 15 is the log in the water, showing the lines attached, and 16 is the reel.*

Lead Lines

In the days when charts were rare and inaccurate, and mathematical navigation was beyond the ability of many, a knowledge of the bottom of the sea was essential to the navigator and the pilot. The shape of the contours of the sea floor could give the experienced seaman a good idea where he was, but the nature of the bottom, whether of sand, mud, shingle or rock, could often give the navigator just as much information, especially in the relatively shallow waters around the British Isles. It could also give him some advance warning of danger.

The depth was measured by a piece of lead attached to a line. The lead was conical in shape, and hollow. It was partly filled with tallow, so that it would pick up a sample of the bottom. Two types of lead were used, depending on the depth to be sounded. The ordinary, or hand lead, weighed about 7lbs, was about a foot long, and was attached to a line 20 fathoms long. The deep-sea line was much heavier, and attached to a much longer line. It weighed from 14 to 30lbs, and had a line of up to 200 fathoms. The lead was cast by a seaman standing in the channels, which overhung the sea on each side of the ship. The hand line could be

This watercolour of the Deal Castle *of 1756, gives an unusually realistic view of the deck of a small ship. The steering wheel and binnacle can be seen, as can the hen-coops, a swivel gun on the gunwale, and the awning.* NMM.

used when the ship was in motion, but to use the deep-sea line she had to heave to, for the movement of the ship while the lead was sinking would give an inaccurate reading over such a long period. In 1688, a First Rate carried six deep-sea lines. In 1795, a First Rate fitted for foreign service would carry five deep-sea leads, ten hand leads, six deep-sea lines, and a reel to allow the deep-sea line to run out. All lead lines were marked in a standard system, with different marks to indicate particular depths. For example, a piece of black leather meant three fathoms, a white rag, five fathoms, while further pieces of black leather indicated ten and thirteen fathoms.

A seaman in the chains, casting the lead.

Glasses

Time-keeping was very important at sea. In the longer term, it could help give a useful indication of the ship's position but from day to day and hour to hour, it aided the smooth running of the ship, as watches were changed, readings were taken and entered in the log, and the ship's routine took place. In the absence of any more accurate instruments, the sand glass served as the short-term timekeeper.

Several types of glass were used for different lengths of measurement. The watch glass ran for four hours, the length of a watch and the half-watch glass for two hours, the length of a dog watch. Each watch was divided into tricks of half an hour, after which look-outs and helmsmen were changed round, and glasses were issued which ran for this period. Smaller glasses, of half-minute, minute, and four-minute duration, were used to measure the time as the log line was run out, with the glass with the shortest duration being necessary for higher speeds.

Chronometers

Sand glasses had many inaccuracies, and were of little use for long-term time measurement. Conventional clocks and watches were not much better, as they were subject to cumulative errors, especially in varied conditions of temperature and humidity, and due to the movement and wear which was encountered aboard ship.

The chronometer, as developed by John Harrison in the course of the eighteenth century, was the answer to these problems. It was specially designed to compensate for all these inaccuracies, and allowed the seaman to calculate his longitude accurately without extensive and difficult calculations. Harrison's chronometer was first tested aboard the *Centurion* in 1736, and the captain's report was favourable, but it took another 40 years for his work to be fully appreciated. Thereafter the chronometer was accepted by the Navy, but it was a very expensive item. Unless the captain was able to provide his own, it was issued only for long foreign voyages, and only on the captain's application. It was not a standard fitting on all ships.

A sand glass recovered from the Invincible, *lost in 1758.* Author's photograph.

PART II

Anchors and Capstans

Chapter 5. Anchors

How the Anchor Worked

The type of anchor used in the seventeenth and eighteenth centuries had changed very little from that of classical times. It consisted of four parts: the shank, which was long and thin, and lay horizontal when the anchor was on the sea-bed, and vertical when it was being hauled up; the arms, which extended outwards and upwards from either side of one end of the shank, and were fitted with spade-like flukes; the stock, which extended from the other end of the shank, in a plane at right angles to the arms; and the ring, which was fitted to the end of the shank just above the stock, and was used to fasten the anchor cable. The shank, arms and flukes were made of iron, forged together into a single piece. The ring was also iron, but was fitted separately. The stock was usually made of two pieces of wood, held together by iron hoops.

The principle of the anchor was simple. On reaching the sea-bed, the stock would lie flat on the bottom, and one of the arms would dig itself into the ground, its broad and thin palm or fluke resisting any attempt to move it. The efficiency of the anchor depended on several factors. The anchor might slip in soft mud and on rock it might not hold at all. The cable attached to it had to be long enough so that the pull on the ring was horizontal rather than vertical. Otherwise, the shank would be lifted, and the fluke would tend to lose its grip. The anchor had to be big enough to hold the ship against wind and tide, but not so big that it would be impossible for the crew to handle, or the ship to carry.

The Shape and Proportion of Anchors

The proportions of anchors changed very little between 1600 and 1815. In 1625 Mainwaring wrote that the shank should be three times as long as one of the flukes, and this proportion was still common in 1809. He suggested that the stock be proportional to the length of the shank: in 1815 it was equal to the length of the shank plus half the diameter of the ring. In 1717, as in 1809, the length of the fluke was half the length of the arm. The breadth of the palm was a little less than half the length of the arm and equal to the diameter of the ring. The anchor itself was identified by its weight, which was proportional to the cube of the length of the shank. A ship's anchors were proportional to her tonnage. Mainwaring suggested in 1625 that a ship's largest anchor should be a five-hundredth of her tonnage. In 1809 this still prevailed for larger ships, but smaller vessels had proportionally smaller anchors.[1]

The anchor's ring was fitted through a hole in the end of the shank. It was covered in rope, known as puddening, to protect the cable from wear and tear. The stock was made from two pieces of wood, held together by four hoops. In the late eighteenth century a gap was left between them, so that if the wood shrank the hoops could be hammered closer to the centre, to retain the stock's shape and strength. The top surface of the stock was flat, but the other surfaces tapered towards the ends. Before 1780 the ends of the stocks were square. After this date it was stipulated that they be rounded off, to reduce damage to the copper sheathing when the anchor was being hauled up.

The upper part of the shank was square in cross-section, and had two raised lips, called nuts, to help keep the stock in position. Below the stock, the shank was rounded. The shank gradually increased in thickness towards its lower end. The thickness of the shank was measured at the trend, a point one-third of the shank's length from the lower end. At the lowest point, known as the throat, the arms joined the shank. For nearly all the years between 1600 and 1815 the angle-crown anchor, in which the arms were set at an angle of 60 degrees to the shank, was common but in the early nineteenth century this was superseded by the round-crown anchor in which the arms formed the arc of a circle. The palms were roughly triangular in shape, though most had their sides curved outwards. The arms were reduced in thickness towards their ends. In 1809 it was found that some anchors broke at the small of the arm, where it joined the palm, and thus it was ordered that this part be thickened in future anchors.[2] The extremities of the arms, beyond the ends of the palms, were known as the bills. There was a hollow in the lower edge of the bill which gave it a sharper point. The point of an anchor, where the two arms and the shank met, was known as the crown.

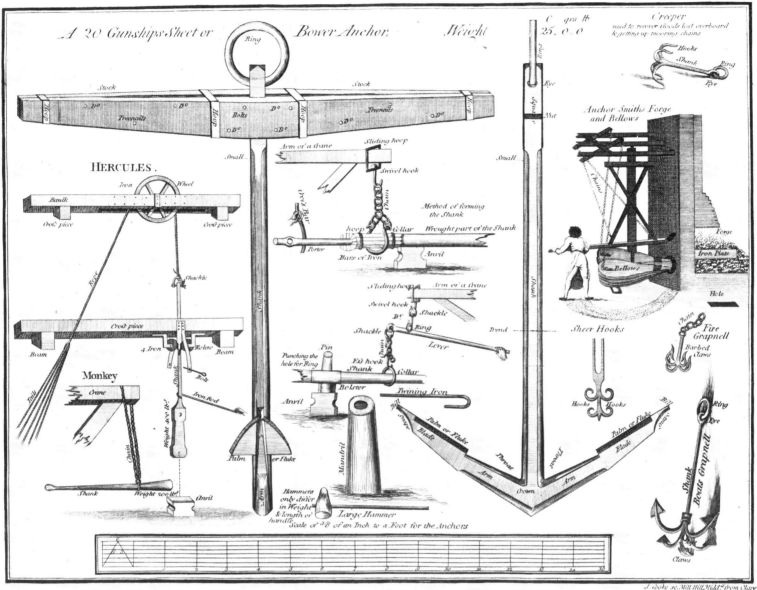

A plate showing details of the construction of anchors, 1797. Science Museum.

Drawing showing the basic principle of the anchor, and why a horizontal pull was necessary. An anchor buoy is attached to one of the anchor's arms.

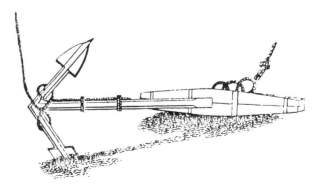

An anchor about to bury itself in the sea-bed, showing how the buoy rope was attached.

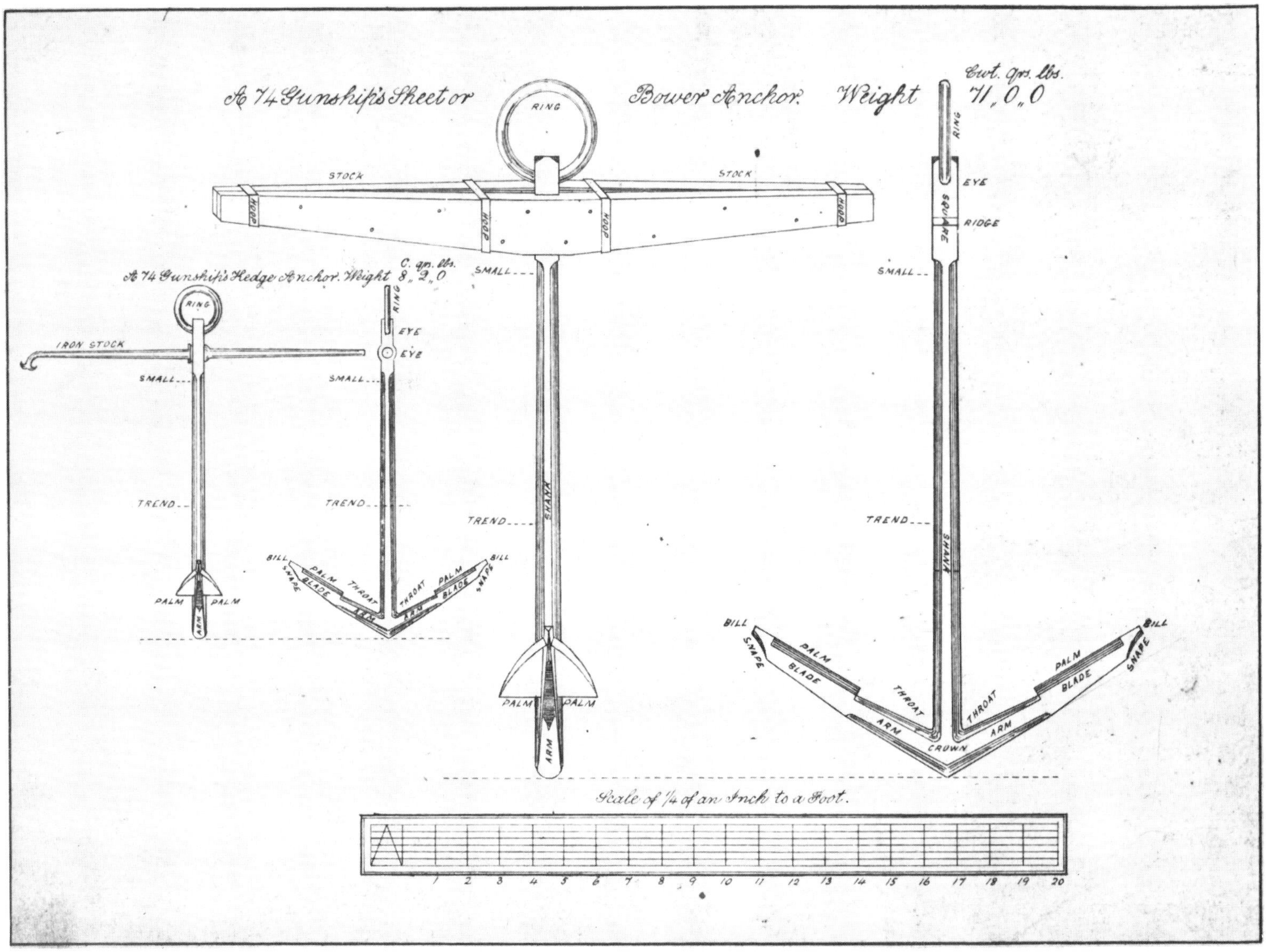

Anchors of a 74-gun ship, c1800. NMM. *The proportions given are:*

Weight of anchor	8cwt	17cwt	71cwt
Length of the shank	9ft 6in	12ft 6in	18ft 6in
Length of the arms	3ft 2in	4ft 2in	6ft $1\frac{1}{2}$in
Breadth of the palms	1ft 5in	1ft $9\frac{1}{4}$in	3ft $1\frac{1}{2}$in
Thickness of the palms	$1\frac{1}{8}$in	$1\frac{3}{8}$in	$3\frac{1}{4}$in
Size of the trend	$4\frac{1}{4}$in	$5\frac{1}{4}$in	$9\frac{1}{4}$in
Size of the small round	$3\frac{3}{4}$in	$4\frac{3}{4}$in	$8\frac{1}{8}$in
Outer diameter of the ring	1ft 5in	1ft $9\frac{1}{4}$in	3ft $1\frac{1}{2}$in
Thickness of the ring	$1\frac{7}{8}$in	$2\frac{3}{8}$in	$4\frac{1}{16}$in

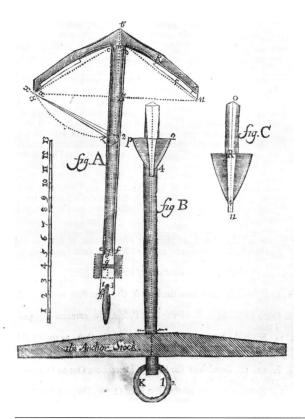

Early eighteenth century anchors, from Sutherland's Shipbuilding Unveiled.
NMM.
Fig A.
Length of the shank, mh   *Length of the bill, 4n*
Bigness of the great end, cd   *Clutching of the arm, em*
Bigness of the small end, ef   *Inside meeting, zxc*
Length of the square, gh   *Outside meeting, x2c*
Length of the nut, gh   *Middle meeting, xyc.*
Bigness of the nut, square, g   *Fig B.*
Diameter of the ring's hole, 1,3   *Diameter of the ring, inside, clear, kl*
Length of the crown, mb   *Bigness of the ring, 12*
Length of the fluke, R4   *Breadth of the fluke, pq*
Thickness of the fluke, 65   *Rounding of the fluke, 24*
Square of the arm at the fluke, R   *Fig C.*
    Length of the arm, cx or on

Tonnage of the six sizes	1677 tons	1488 tons	969 tons	625 tons	364 tons	225 tons
Weight of the biggest anchor [in cwt. qrs. lbs.]	71.2.0	64.0.0	45.0.0	30.0.0	18.3.6	11.2.1
Cube root of the weight	$4\frac{7}{100}$	4	$3\frac{53}{100}$	$3\frac{1}{10}$	$2\frac{66}{100}$	$2\frac{26}{100}$
Length of the shank as aforesaid [in ft. in.]	18.6	18.2	16.1	14.2	12.2	10.8
Bigness of the great end of ditto	$0.11\frac{1}{2}$	$0.11\frac{1}{10}$	$0.10\frac{1}{10}$	$0.8\frac{8}{10}$	$0.7\frac{11}{20}$	$0.6\frac{14}{20}$
ditto at the small end	$0.8\frac{13}{10}$	$0.8\frac{5}{10}$	$0.7\frac{1}{8}$	$0.6\frac{6}{10}$	$0.5\frac{13}{20}$	$0.4\frac{7}{10}$
Length of the square	2.11	$2.10\frac{4}{10}$	$2.6\frac{4}{10}$	2.3	1.11	1.8
Length to the nut	1.11	$1.10\frac{6}{10}$	$1.8\frac{8}{10}$	$1.5\frac{6}{10}$	$1.3\frac{1}{10}$	$1.1\frac{4}{10}$
Bigness of the nut square	$0.2\frac{3}{10}$	$0.2\frac{26}{100}$	0.2	$0.1\frac{76}{100}$	$0.1\frac{51}{100}$	$0.1\frac{34}{100}$
Diameter of the rings inside, clear	$2.1\frac{1}{2}$	2.1	1.10	$1.7\frac{6}{10}$	1.3	1.2
Bigness of the ring	0.4	$0.3\frac{94}{100}$	$0.3\frac{48}{100}$	$0.3\frac{6}{100}$	0.3	$0.2\frac{71}{100}$
Diameter of the hole for the ring	$0.4\frac{6}{10}$	$0.4\frac{5}{10}$	$0.3\frac{98}{100}$	$0.3\frac{5}{10}$	0.3	$0.2\frac{66}{100}$
Length of the crown	1.2	$1.1\frac{7}{10}$	$0.11\frac{1}{10}$	$0.9\frac{3}{4}$	$0.8\frac{7}{10}$	$0.7\frac{7}{10}$
Length of the arm	7.0	6.9	6.1	$5.0\frac{7}{20}$	$4.0\frac{6}{10}$	$4.0\frac{1}{20}$
Breadth of the fluke	2.8	$2.7\frac{5}{10}$	$2.3\frac{8}{10}$	$2.0\frac{4}{10}$	1.9	1.6
Length of ditto	3.9	$3.8\frac{1}{3}$	$3.3\frac{2}{10}$	$2.10\frac{4}{10}$	$2.5\frac{5}{10}$	2.2
Thickness of ditto	$0.2\frac{9}{10}$	$0.2\frac{85}{100}$	$0.2\frac{51}{100}$	$0.2\frac{22}{100}$	$0.1\frac{9}{10}$	$0.1\frac{68}{100}$
Square at the arm of the fluke	0.7	$0.6\frac{9}{10}$	$0.6\frac{1}{10}$	$0.5\frac{7}{10}$	$0.4\frac{6}{10}$	$0.4\frac{1}{20}$
Length of the bill	$0.10\frac{1}{2}$	$0.10\frac{3}{10}$	$0.9\frac{1}{10}$	0.8	$0.6\frac{9}{10}$	$0.6\frac{1}{10}$
Rounding of the fluke	$0.1\frac{16}{100}$	$0.1\frac{14}{100}$	$0.1\frac{1}{10}$	$0.0\frac{89}{100}$	$0.0\frac{76}{100}$	$0.0\frac{66}{100}$
Clutches of the arm	3.6	$3.5\frac{1}{3}$	$3.0\frac{4}{10}$	2.6	$2.4\frac{1}{2}$	$2.1\frac{2}{10}$
Inside meeting	6.6					
Outside meeting	6.6					
Middle meeting	6.6					

How Anchors Were Made

A bower or sheet anchor was by far the largest metal object carried by a ship, and it was expensive in terms of materials and labour. One of the larger anchors of the early nineteenth century cost £470, and took 20 men 30 days to make.[3] A full complement of anchors for a First Rate in 1809 cost £1750. The larger anchors were usually made in the royal dockyards; in the early eighteenth century Deptford Dockyard predominated in this kind of work. In 1748 it had a master smith, 12 foremen smiths, and 88 hammermen.[4] This was the largest single group of skilled workers in the yard, except for the shipwrights. It soon became apparent that Deptford could not keep up with the demand created by large scale shipbuilding programmes, and in the second half of the century the forges at the other yards were greatly expanded.

Smaller anchors were made by private forges, which usually had standing contracts to supply them as demanded over a fixed period. The work was not always profitable, and the Navy Board drove a hard bargain. At the beginning of the eighteenth century one of the leading ironmasters, Sir Ambrose Crowley, found that when his contract expired he was left with several anchors which were too large for any but naval use – they were eventually bought by the Navy, but on unfavourable terms.[5] In 1703 three ironmasters, Davis, Smith and Bradfield, declined to accept orders from the Navy Board on the grounds that 'they had better prices of the merchants than are now given by the navy'.[6]

The stock and arms of an anchor were made up of many small strips of metal, forged into a single piece. Small bars, including scrap iron, were cut and bent into suitable shapes, put together, and heated in a furnace until they were white hot. They were then hammered into a solid mass, by a team of men under a master smith or foreman, who directed the movement of the anchor while the others operated the hammers. Various types of hammer were used. For a small anchor, ordinary sledge-hammers would suffice. For bigger anchors, mechanical devices known as trip hammers were needed. An instrument known as a 'hercules' was used in the late eighteenth century. This lifted up a weight of 400lbs and dropped it on the appropriate part of the shank or arm.[7] Because anchors were forged rather than cast, they had great strength along the direction of their shanks and arms. Nevertheless there were problems, especially with the largest ones, when the metal at the centre of the core was not so fully treated as that at the outside. In 1700 it was found that a 40cwt anchor 'appeared so very ill wrought that the bars were whole and entire in the middle, and only cased over with a shell of iron'.[8]

After the metal had been hammered into a single mass, so that no gaps between the component parts of metal could be detected, the anchor was fitted with a metal ring and wooden stock. It was marked with a broad arrow, and its weight and the initials of its maker.

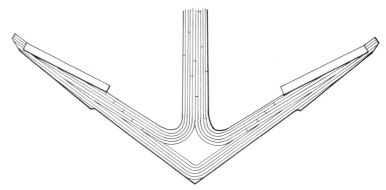

Proposed method of joining strips of metal together to form an anchor, c1780, from a drawing in the Public Record Office.

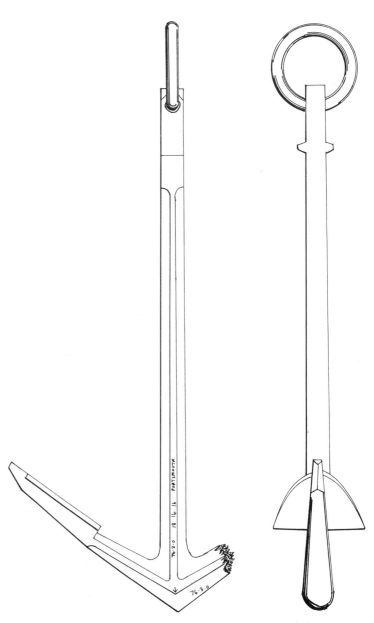

The puddening of the anchor ring, from D'Arcy Lever's Young Sea Officer's Sheet Anchor *of 1811.*

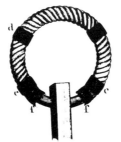

An anchor of the early 1800s, showing how it was to be marked with the maker's name and its weight. NMM.

Types of Anchor

By tradition the largest anchor carried by a ship was the sheet anchor. It was treated with an almost religious reverence, as 'that which the seamen call their last hope, and is never used but in great extremity ... This is the true "anchora spei", for it is their last refuge'.[9] In the seventeenth century it really was bigger and better than the other anchors but in the eighteenth it was usually the same size as the others, though reserved for emergencies. The anchors for ordinary use were the bowers. As the name implies, they were kept ready in the bows of the ship, so that they could be used instantly if needed. In the seventeenth century the 'best bower' was rather heavier than the 'second bower'. The best bower was carried on the port side, for use in a storm. Seamen knew that in the northern hemisphere a wind would shift in an anti-clockwise direction in a depression, so it was best to have the most effective anchor on the port side.[10] Spare anchors were also carried. The number changed during different periods, tending to decline in later years.

Though the sheet and bower anchors varied slightly in size from ship to ship, their size in relation to each other was standard, the sheet being at most about 25 per cent bigger than the best bower, and so on. At the other end of the scale was the much smaller stream anchor, which was for short-term use in light weather, to hold the vessel against a weak current. The kedge anchor was even smaller. It could be lashed under the ship's launch or long boat, and rowed out ahead, so that it could be hauled in to give the ship headway in calm weather or in a confined space where there was no room to tack. After 1805, anchors of less than 15cwt (including most kedge anchors) were to have metal stocks, which could be pulled out and lashed against the shank when not in use. It is of course possible that metal stocks were used on many anchors before this date.[11]

The grapnel was an anchor used by the ship's boats. It had four arms at right angles to one another, so a stock was not needed.

The Size and Number of Anchors Carried

As late as 1769, Falconer claimed that 'every ship has, or ought to have, three principal anchors': the sheet, the best bower, and the second bower.[12] In fact ships of the previous century had carried rather more. In 1640 the *Sovereign of the Seas* had four, but she was rather unusual for her time.[13] By 1656 most ships of the Fourth Rate and above had five main anchors, and the *Sovereign* had six.[14] For most of the eighteenth century First and Second Rates had five main anchors, until an order of 1779 stipulated they carry only four.[15] From the 1680s onwards two-decker ships normally had four anchors; small Sixth Rates and unrated vessels usually had only three.[16]

The weight of anchors tended to increase in the middle years of the seventeenth century. The *Sovereign*'s large anchors ranged from 36 to 55cwt in 1640, from 43 to 60cwt in 1656, and from 58 to 69½cwt in 1686. The *George* had anchors from 25 to 28cwt in 1640, and from 32 to 36cwt in 1686.[17] After 1686, the size of anchors did not increase greatly, except in proportion to the ships themselves.

The four main anchors carried by a typical ship retained their different names and roles for most of the eighteenth century. On a 70-gun ship of 1709, the sheet anchor weighed 52cwt, the best bower 51cwt, the small bower 48cwt, and the spare anchor 47cwt.

By 1780, the sheet anchor was no longer the largest. On the *Bedford* of 1775, the sheet anchor weighed less than the best bower, and the second bower was the lightest of all.[18] In 1784 the Admiralty found 'The true establishment of anchors not being known at some of the yards'. A new list was prepared, and was to be used for fitting ships in future. According to this, the four main anchors were to be of identical weight, though of course there must have been some variation in practice.[19]

Smaller anchors usually included only the stream and the kedge, but First and Second Rates sometimes had an even smaller anchor, which in 1686 was called simply the 'small anchor'. In that year, the stream weighed about one-third of the weight of the best bower; a century later, it was about a quarter. The kedge weighed a little more than a third of the stream in 1686, and half the stream by 1709. The small anchor, when carried, was about half the weight of the kedge.[20]

A grapnel was carried by each boat in proportion to its size and function. For example, a Third Rate of 1677 had a 32ft longboat with an 80lb grapnel, while a 31ft pinnace on a similar ship had one of 56lbs. This disparity is explained by the fact that the pinnace was used in sheltered waters, and the longboat at sea.[21]

A boat's grapnel, from Burney's Dictionary.

Round-crown Anchors

The standard British pattern of anchor, with the two arms meeting at an angle was superseded in France and Holland in the late eighteenth century by one in which the arms formed the arc of a circle. This tended to make the join stronger, and to add slightly to the holding power of the anchor. In 1800 Richard Pering, Master Smith at Plymouth, had proposed some improvements, but was not encouraged by the Navy Board. 'The adopting of it at present would occasion so many applications for a change of anchors for the fleet, that we think it better to defer until a peace may afford a better opportunity of determining its merits.'[22] Despite several cases of anchors breaking around 1809, it was many years before Pering's anchor was manufactured and tested.

It was an improvement in several ways. It was constructed of 'wide flat bar iron' rather than loose bars, which had been used previously. The scarfs joining the arms to the shank and to one another were longer, and stronger. Pering applied the principle of the arch, but made it round rather than angled. His first anchor was made in April 1813, and examples were tested aboard the *Menelaus*, *Vengeur*, *York*, and *Impregnable*. They were considered successful, but very few were produced before the end of the Napoleonic Wars. By September 1815, only 25 had been made and 14 issued.[23]

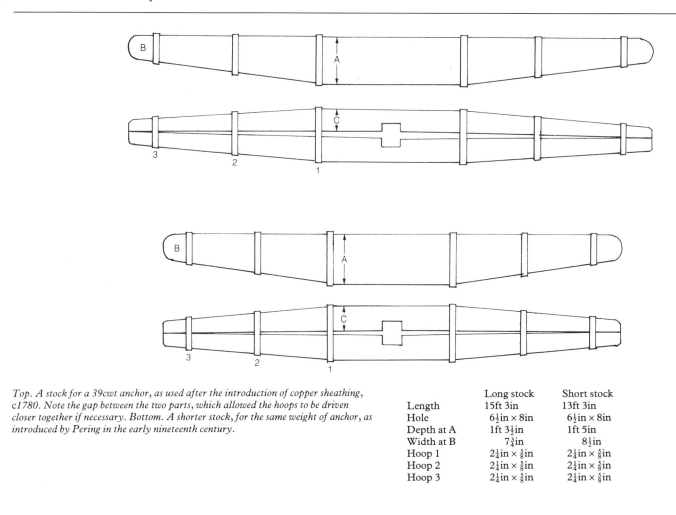

Top. *A stock for a 39cwt anchor, as used after the introduction of copper sheathing, c1780. Note the gap between the two parts, which allowed the hoops to be driven closer together if necessary. Bottom. A shorter stock, for the same weight of anchor, as introduced by Pering in the early nineteenth century.*

	Long stock	Short stock
Length	15ft 3in	13ft 3in
Hole	6½in × 8in	6½in × 8in
Depth at A	1ft 3½in	1ft 5in
Width at B	7¾in	8½in
Hoop 1	2¼in × ⅝in	2¼in × ⅝in
Hoop 2	2¼in × ⅝in	2¼in × ⅝in
Hoop 3	2¼in × ⅝in	2¼in × ⅝in

Chapter 6. Capstans

Principles

Despite the large crews carried by warships, seamen in the age of sail used muscle power as little as possible, preferring to employ wind, tide, and gravity when they had the opportunity. But there were many tasks which required the lifting of heavy weights. The seaman was ingenious in using ropes and blocks to reduce his work, but there was still the need for a machine to lift the very heaviest weights. Guns, yards, stores, and especially anchors, often weighed several tons, and sometimes had to be lifted against the effects of natural forces.

The windlass was the oldest means of lifting such loads. It had a rotating barrel which was set in the horizontal plane, usually across the foredeck of the vessel. Numerous holes were cut along its length and round its circumference. Seamen put bars into the appropriate holes as they rotated to the top of the windlass, and then pulled backwards and downwards on the bar to apply strong pressure. One of the advantages of the windlass was that if it was long enough, a fairly large number of men could operate it at once. Much of the pressure was applied downwards which was an efficient use of effort. On the other hand, the number of men who could operate it was limited by the length of the barrel, which in

turn was restricted by the width of the ship. An individual could only apply his force over about a quarter of the barrel's circumference at a given time. Also, placing the bars into the holes on a moving barrel required considerable skill, which was not always available among the hastily assembled crew of a warship.

The capstan's barrel was in the vertical plane. This meant that the bars could be kept in place all the time the capstan was in use, so that each man pushed through a full circle, rather than just a quarter of one. Up to eight men could push on each bar, and up to 12 bars could be fitted, so that nearly a hundred men could push on a fairly simple capstan, and space could be found for even more if necessary. The effect was restricted by the fact that each man was pushing horizontally rather than pulling downward, as on a windlass. But the capstan's advantages were clear. It employed more men, more efficiently, and required less skill than the windlass.

Standard capstans were built around a solid wooden barrel. Except on very small ships, this extended the full distance between two decks, and a few feet above the uppermost deck, to allow the bars to be fitted at a suitable height. The capstan was securely fitted to both decks, giving it much greater strength than if it had been fitted to only one. The barrel was free to rotate about its own axis. Flat pieces of timber called whelps projected from the circumference of the barrel. These were intended to increase the diameter slightly to make it more suitable for the cable

A typical windlass, on a late seventeenth century yacht. Only six men could use the bars at a time, and possibly fewer if space was needed to wind on the cables. Author's photograph.

A crab capstan on a model of about 1650. Note how the capstan bars are all at different heights. Author's photograph, courtesy of NMM.

which was wound round it and to increase the friction and thus hold the cable more securely. The whelps were shaped to prevent the cable from riding up too far, where it would interfere with the men at the bars.

The bars were removeable, so that the capstan took up little space when it was not in use. Their height was such that the men could bend over and push with their chests, though this was not always possible with the early capstans. The bars fitted into holes at the head of the capstan. At its lower end, just above the deck, were the pawls. These were pieces of metal which pivoted on the deck, and were used to prevent the capstan from surging backwards when the pressure on the cable was uneven.

The Early Capstan

According to Sir Walter Raleigh, the capstan was first used for weighing anchor in the reign of Queen Elizabeth I, in the second half of the sixteenth century, though there is evidence that it was in use by 1546.[1] Certainly it was well established aboard English warships by the beginning of the seventeenth century. The original type, later to be known as a crab, had no separate head to hold the capstan bars. Four square horizontal holes were merely cut through the upper part of the barrel, at 45 degrees to one another. A long bar was put through each, so that it protruded an equal amount on each side. Obviously it was not possible to put all the bars at the same height, for they would have met in the middle, thus some were a little higher, and others lower than the optimum height. It was not possible to have more than four bars, as this would increase the range of heights even further, and weaken the barrel.

This type of capstan was sufficient for the relatively small ships of the early seventeenth century. Up to eight men could push on each bar, according to the size of the ship. Two capstans could perhaps be used in tandem in certain circumstances, so that up to 128 men could apply force at once. Since large parties were also needed for stowing the cable, preparing the sails, and catting the anchor, only about a third of the crew would be available to operate the capstan while weighing anchor. In 1666 the English fleet had only nine ships with a crew of more than 400 men, and as yet there had been no need for a more powerful capstan. From 1666 to 1680, 37 ships with a crew of more than 460 were ordered.[2] The larger ships needed a slightly more effective method of raising their anchors and performing other heavy tasks.

The Drumhead Capstan

The well-known model of the 100-gun ship *Prince*, and Anthony Deane's *Doctrine of Naval Architecture*, both date from 1670, and both show the old type of capstan very clearly.[3] The First Rate *Britannia*, completed in 1682, is shown in prints as carrying the new type, called the drumhead capstan. Thus the new type can be dated with reasonable certainty to the 1670s; by 1686 Sir Samuel Morland was claiming that he had invented it some years back. The difference from the old crab was simply that the bars were no longer put directly into the barrel of the capstan. Instead, a large thick circular piece of wood, called a

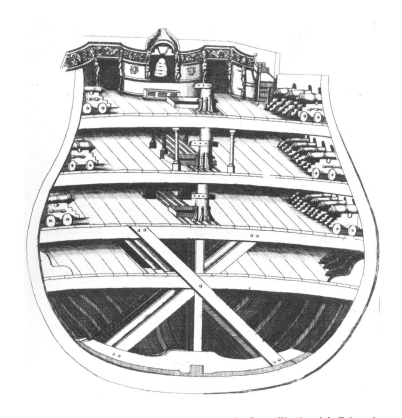

The earliest evidence of the drumhead capstan, on the Coronelli print of the Britannia *of 1682. The triple-headed capstan, however, is highly unusual, and may be an inaccuracy.* NMM.

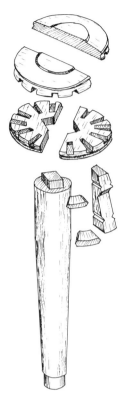

The construction of a capstan, showing the four parts of the head, the whelps, the wedges, and the barrel.

drumhead, was tenoned into the top of the barrel, to give a greater circumference. Holes were cut in it for bars, but these no longer extended all the way through the capstan. Instead there was a separate bar for each side, thus more bars could be fitted, and they could all be at the same height. The greater circumference given by the drumhead meant that the end of each bar could be fitted well into it, and pushed in far enough to prevent it from falling out accidentally; previously all the bars had met in the middle. The bars were tapered so that they would be wedged in reasonably tight, and so the holes cut in the drum could narrow towards the centre, causing less weakness in the structure.

The new capstan had great advantages. More men could operate it at once, for up to 12 bars could now be fitted (equivalent to six in the old system of double-ended bars) and each bar could be placed at the ideal height for an average man to push against it.

The Single Capstan

The simplest form of capstan was confined to flush-decked vessels, those with only a single deck, and no, or very small, quarter-deck or forecastle. They had no room to fit a capstan which would extend over two decks, so it had to be fixed securely in only one deck. Such capstans were used in the late seventeenth century, for example on some royal yachts, but they must have been rare, for most small ships had a windlass. They became more common in the late eighteenth century because a large number of cutters, schooners, gunboats and brigs were built. The barrels of these short capstans rotated round a stout iron spindle, which had a strong iron plate at its bottom, firmly bolted to the deck.

In the more common type of single capstan, the barrel was long enough to extend between two decks, though whelps and bars were fitted only to the upper part, above the uppermost deck. Such capstans were found on many ships, particularly before the middle of the eighteenth century. On large two-deckers and some three-deckers they were the secondary capstans. They were fitted between the upper and lower decks of most small ships, so that they operated on the upper deck, thus keeping the hawse holes as high as possible.

The barrel of this type of capstan tapered considerably after it had passed through the uppermost deck. Single capstans, like double ones, were either of the crab or drumhead type, according to the period in which they were built.

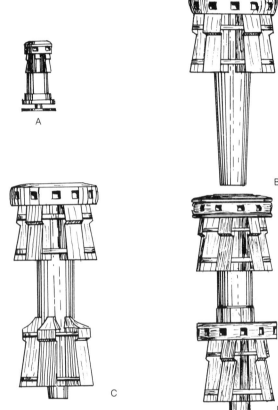

Types of capstan.
A. The short single capstan. This model was fitted to a late seventeenth-century yacht. The plate at the bottom held the capstan to the deck. The whelps are raised some way above the deck, possibly so the cable was lifted clear of obstruction. Such capstans were relatively rare.
B. The single capstan. Note how the lower part tapers.
C. The early eighteenth century double capstan. It has whelps on the lower part, but no head for bars.
D. The double capstan with a trundlehead. This is a relatively late model, which had the same number of holes in the trundlehead as the main drumhead.

The Double Capstan

The double capstan differed from the single capstan in that the lower part of the barrel did not taper, and was fitted with whelps like those on the upper part. It could thus operate on the deck below. For instance, on a typical two-decker, men could work at the capstan bars on the upper deck, while the cable was wound round the whelps on the lower deck. The obvious advantage of

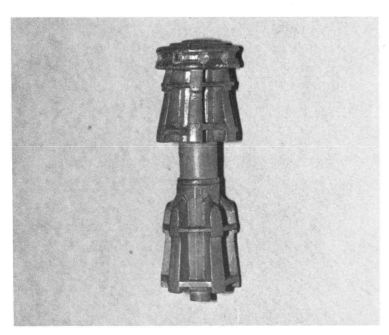

A model of a double capstan, c1700. It has two sets of whelps, but only one drumhead. Author's photograph, courtesy of Liverpool Maritime Museum.

this was that the men would not need to step over the cable as it was brought to the capstan. The whelps on the upper deck were retained, for they could be useful for other tasks such as raising the yards, when it was better to operate from the upper deck.

The Trundlehead

The original double capstan offered no means of fitting bars at lower deck level. When ropes were led to the upper half of the capstan, it was still necessary for the seamen to step over the part that was led to the capstan. This was eventually remedied by fitting a second drumhead, known as the trundlehead, above the second set of whelps. This had two advantages. The rope could be put round the upper whelps, and the bars fitted to the trundlehead, or, if the raising of the anchor required extra effort, bars could be fitted to both the trundlehead and the main drumhead, to allow more men to push.

A print of the *Britannia* of 1682 shows her with an unusual triple capstan, extending through the lower, middle and upper decks, with whelps and a drumhead on each. This is the last evidence of trundleheads for some considerable time. Their next appearance is on a draught of a capstan intended to be fitted to the *Lancaster*, almost certainly the 80-gun ship of 1722.[4] It is clear that such heads were rare then, but by the 1740s they appear on many draughts, and seem to have become standard. The trundlehead is mentioned in the establishment of 1719, but solely as a means of using pawls suspended from the deck above, and at that stage there was evidently no intention of fitting bars to it.[5]

In most cases in the eighteenth century, far fewer holes for bars were cut in the trundlehead than in the main drumhead, suggesting that it was intended mainly for lifting relatively light weights, such as yards. The typical trundlehead of this period had four or six holes, while an upper head had 12. In the early years of the nineteenth century, the trundlehead usually had two less holes

than the upper head. In the late eighteenth century, the lower barrel usually had five whelps, while the upper had six. This was because the lower barrel was used mainly for the thicker ropes, such as the messenger for the anchor cable. It was believed that the greater distance between the whelps would allow the rope to turn round them better, and would create more friction.

Triple capstans are also mentioned in the 1719 establishment, for First and Second Rates. These were called 'triple jeer' capstans, and had bars only at their head, with three rows of whelps on the lower, middle and upper decks. A rare illustration of such a capstan can be seen on a print of about 1710.[6]

The Construction of Capstans

The barrel was the centre of all capstans, being 'the main ... piece to which all other parts are fixed'.[7] Its length varied according to the type of capstan. That of the short single capstan was of course much smaller than any other as it did not have to extend between two decks. Its height above the uppermost deck also varied. The crab, which needed more vertical room for its bars, was about 5ft above the deck, the drumhead about 3ft. The barrel was cut to have as many sides as there were bars. Thus a typical eighteenth century barrel would be 12-sided in its cross-section in its upper part and ten-sided in its lower. These sides were called squares, and determined the size of several other parts. On a single capstan, the part of the barrel below the deck tapered to about half, or slightly more, of its diameter above. In the seventeenth century the diameter of the lower barrel of a double capstan was about seven-eighths of that of the lower, and it was even narrower at the partners, where it passed through the deck. By the mid-eighteenth century, the difference in diameter between the upper and the lower barrels had been reduced, and by the end of the century they were equal in size.

The lowest end of the barrel was fitted into the step. This was a thick piece of timber bolted firmly to the deck beams, which was intended to bear much of the strain imposed during the operation of the capstan. The step had a hole cut in its centre, to receive the spindle, which projected from the bottom of the barrel, and formed the pivot round which the capstan rotated. In the seventeenth century the spindle appears to have been made of wood; by the mid-eighteenth, it was 'shod with iron'.[8] By about 1795, it was made of iron, and held to the barrel by an iron hoop. It normally projected about 6in below the lowest part of the barrel.

The partners of the capstan were situated on the deck above the step, and fulfilled a similar purpose. They too were made from stout pieces of timber, and were firmly bolted to the deck beams as they played an important part in bracing the capstan against the strains imposed on it. The barrel was considerably narrower at this point to help keep it in position. The partners could be removed to enable the capstan to be taken out. By the early nineteenth century, an iron hoop was placed inside the hole in the partners, to reduce friction between them and the barrel.

The barrel was fitted with one whelp for every two squares of its cross-section, thus a 12-sided barrel had six whelps, and the ten-sided part below had five. Each whelp fitted onto one of the squares of the barrel, and at its lower end it was of the same thickness as the width of the square. The whelp was divided into two parts. The lower part, called the surge, was about two-thirds of the total height. It tapered in a curve until the depth of the whelp had been reduced by about a third. That part was intended to

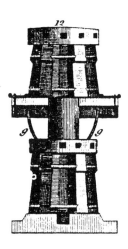

A double capstan from Falconer's Dictionary. *showing the drop pawl (no 9) fitted to the lower capstan and a beam of the deck above.*

A model showing the new type of pawl, c1795. Author's photograph, courtesy of Buckland Abbey, Devon.

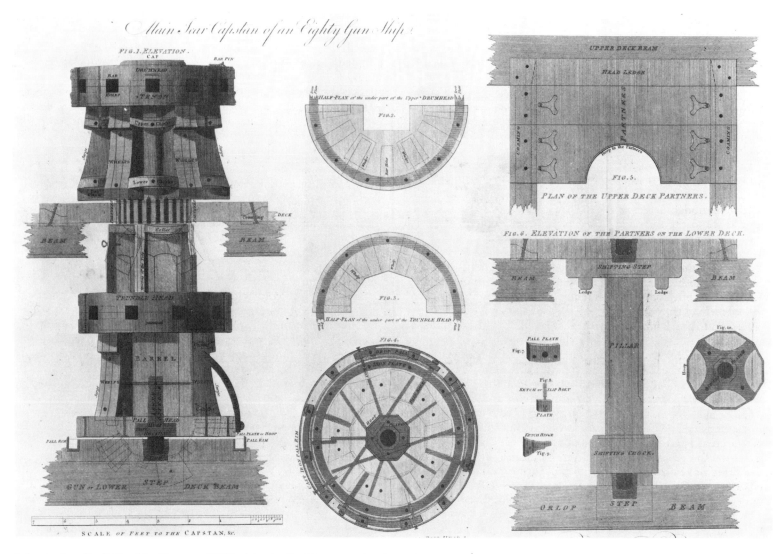

A drawing from Steel's Naval Architecture *of 1805, giving details of the construction of an early nineteenth century capstan. NMM.*

hold the cable, while the part above, the head, jutted out and prevented it from rising too far, thus hindering the men on the bars.

The chocks were pieces placed between the whelps, to hold them rigidly in position. There was an upper and a lower row of these, which in combination with the whelps gave the whole assembly a roughly circular cross-section at the level at which the chocks were fitted.

The bar holes on the old crab capstan were four-fifths of the width of the square. When the drumhead was fitted, the end of the barrel was cut to a square tenon, with a depth equal to half that of the drumhead. The head itself was made in four parts. The top half was composed of two semi-circles, with the recesses for the bar holes cut out. The bottom was made in a similar way, with a square hole for the tenon of the barrel. The bottom and the top were joined together, care being taken to ensure that the join of the top half was at right angles to that of the bottom. The top part of the drumhead often had some slight decoration, with perhaps a raised circle halfway inside its rim, or some other minor variation from a plain flat surface.

By the late eighteenth century an iron hoop was fitted under the head and bolted to it, to give extra strength. Holes were sometimes drilled vertically through the head and the bar hole, and pins put through them to hold the bar in place.

The construction of the trundlehead was similar to that of the drumhead, except that the barrel was not tenoned, and the head was merely cut to the shape, usually ten-sided, of the barrel at that point. Both the drum and the trundlehead rested on the tops of the whelps, and were bolted to them, as well as to the barrel.

Pawls were used to prevent the capstan from surging backwards under intense pressure. For most of the period, they were usually fitted to the deck beside the capstan. Normally there were two, one to hold the capstan in each direction as needed. The pawl itself was a straight iron bar, pivoted on the deck so that one end could be inserted between the whelps to stop the movement of the capstan. In the early nineteenth century pawls were only fitted to the main, not the fore capstans of most ships, though the evidence of models suggests that they were fitted to fore capstans throughout most of the previous century.

Another type of pawl, in use around the middle of the eighteenth century, hung down from the deck above and had its loose end dropped onto the head of the capstan. Presumably recesses were cut in the head to engage the pawl, but it is not clear how much these drop pawls were actually used. Their main advantages were that they took up no space on deck, and could be dropped into position when needed. Possibly they could have been used in a ratchet arrangement.

A third type was introduced in the late eighteenth century, probably by an order of 1795, after being tested on the 50-gun ship *Salisbury* in 1787.[9] An extra circle of timber, called the pawl head, was fitted to the lowest part of the capstan, round the barrel and under the whelps. Four pawls were fitted to the pawl head, two to operate in each direction. When in use they would drop into a circular iron trough placed round the step, called the pawl rim. Inside the pawl rim were stops to catch the pawls as necessary. When not in use, the pawls were held by pins fitted in the pawl head.

On larger ships of the eighteenth century, a second removeable step was fitted between the orlop deck and the lower deck. It was held in place by a shifting step under the lower deck, a shifting chock above the orlop deck, and a step fitted to the orlop deck beams.

The Siting of Capstans

The number and size of capstans carried by a ship of a given type do not seem to have been covered by any particular regulations, though the positions of the partners normally had to be taken into account in the design of the ship. The main deciding factor was convenience. Obviously big ships carried more, bigger capstans than small ships. The number carried was usually equal to the number of full gundecks. In order for there to be room for long bars, the head of the capstan had to be where the hull was broad and unobstructed by permanent features such as the steering wheel. There was a tendency to keep the capstan away from the officers' cabins. Preferably one capstan head was placed in the open, where it could be used for raising yards and hoisting in guns. It was essential that at least one had its whelps on the deck where the cable was hauled in, and its position was governed by the position of the hawse holes. Though there were few formal rules dictated by high authority – custom, practice, and necessity combined to create some informal rules which were followed, as is evident from the study of models and draughts of ships.

Single-deckers

The smallest vessels – gunboats, schooners, and cutters – often did not have enough deck space for a capstan, and used a windlass situated in the bows. Slightly larger vessels used the short single capstan without the lower barrel, and placed it amidships, where there was most room. Sixth Rates carried a double capstan from early in the eighteenth century. At first it was put in the waist, and then aft of the mainmast. The drumhead was on the upper

A model of a mid-eighteenth century double capstan. The old type of pawl, with a straight piece of metal on a pivot, can be seen on the upper level. Typically, the trundlehead has only a few bar holes. Author's photograph, courtesy of NMM.

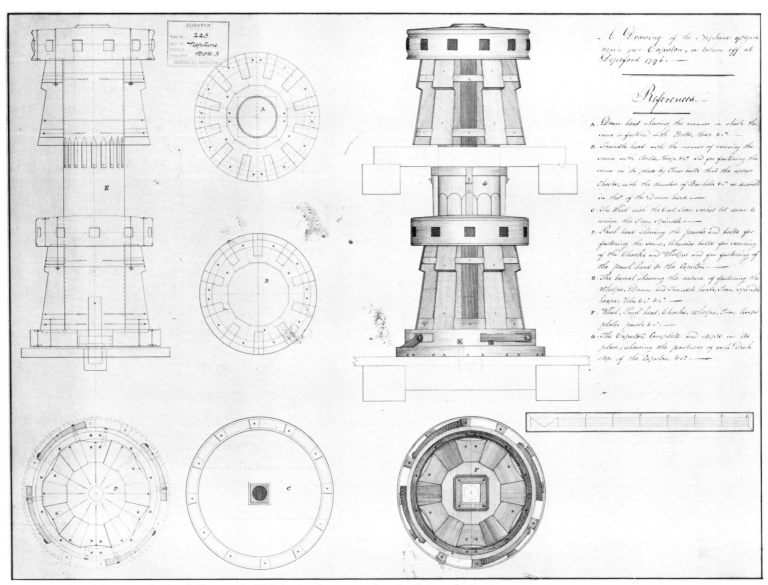

Detailed drawings of the capstan fitted to the Neptune in 1796, showing the new type of pawl, which was fitted to the capstan rather than to the deck. NMM.

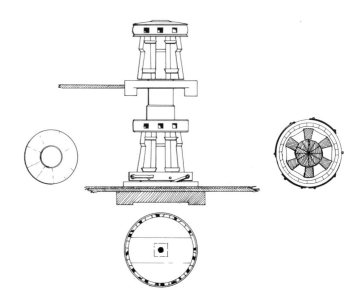

A drawing of a capstan for a 36-gun ship, c1800. Again, it shows the new type of pawl.

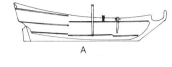

A

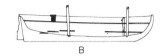

B

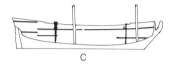

C

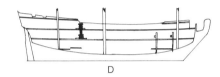

D

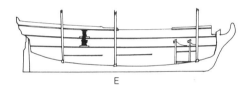

E

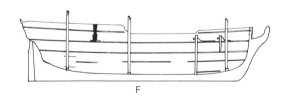

F

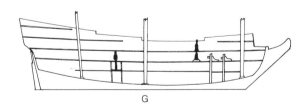

G

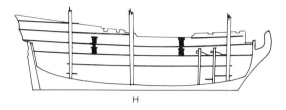

H

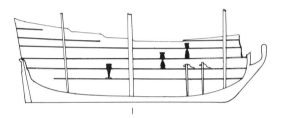

I

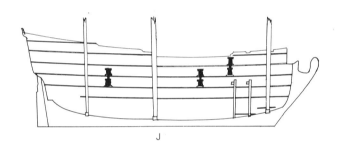

J

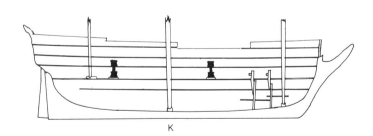

K

The number and location of capstans on different types of ship.

A. A yacht, c1680, with a short single capstan.

B. A short single capstan on a gunboat of 1801.

C. A single capstan on a brig sloop of 1740.

D. A double capstan on a Sixth Rate of 1740.

E. An early frigate of the Southampton class, with the capstan still on the upper and lower decks.

F. A later frigate, with the capstan in its new position on the quarterdeck and the upper deck.

G. A seventeenth century two-decker, from Deane's Doctrine of 1670. It has a single capstan aft, and a double one amidships.

H. A two-decker of 1746, one of the first to have a double capstan fore and aft. This remained common for two-deckers.

I. A late seventeenth century three-decker, from the Phillips print of around 1690. Each of the three capstans is a different size.

J. The Royal George, a mid-eighteenth century three-decker. It has two double capstans as on a two-decker, plus an additional, smaller one, which must have been used for hoisting weights such as spars and guns.

K. An early nineteenth century three-decker. The lighter capstan has been abandoned, and the capstan layout is now similar to that of a two-decker, except that the heads of both capstans are covered by decks.

deck, and the lower whelps were on the lower deck, which carried few or no guns, but which had the hawse holes for the cables.

In the 1750s the 'true frigate' was introduced. This had only one full deck of guns, though it still had a lower deck, now completely unarmed and largely below the waterline. In the first generation of frigates, such as the *Southampton* class, the capstan arrangement was the same as on old Sixth Rates, with the hawse holes on the lower deck, and the capstan aft of the mainmast. Soon afterwards, it became common to fit the hawse holes just above the upper deck, raising them clear of the waterline. This meant the capstans too had to be moved up, so the drumhead was on the quarterdeck and the step was on the upper deck. Because the quarterdeck extended over only the aftermost part of the ship, it was no longer possible to fit the capstan in the waist. The new position was facilitated by the fact that tumblehome had been reduced over the years, and the upper decks of a ship were no longer as narrow as they had been in past years. Nevertheless, the capstan was now left in a rather exposed position, where it could well suffer from damage in action. The move of the capstan to the after position was also made easier by the use of the messenger rather than the viol to raise the anchor, a point which will be considered later.

Two-deckers

Two-deckers nearly always had two capstans, called the main and the jeer, or the fore jeer. In the seventeenth century the main capstan was single, and was on the lower deck, about halfway between the main- and the mizzen masts. The fore jeer capstan was double, and had its head on the upper deck, and its step on the lower deck. It was placed in the waist between the fore- and the mainmast. Its head was in the open, so that it could be used for lifting spars and guns. It could also be used to haul in the cable, by means of its whelps on the lower deck. This was done with a rope known as the viol, which was attached to the cable and led through a large block attached to the mainmast. By the end of the century the main capstan was evidently misnamed, for there was little need for it except as a spare, as both its main tasks could be performed better with the fore jeer capstan.

The main capstan remained single until the 1740s, perhaps

because an upper head would have obstructed the area where the officers had their meals. It was only after the great cabin was moved up to the quarterdeck that a double capstan was fitted aft. As the Navy Board stated in 1744, 'the fixing of the main capstan on the upper deck of all two-decked ships will afford many advantages to the service; and when the main capstan is so fitted, there will be seldom occasion for the use of the jeer, which may be unshipped and stowed below decks to make room for the stowing of the longboat out of the way of the guns.' Largely as a consequence of this, the viol was replaced by a messenger, and the viol was needed only as a spare. The main capstan had been larger than the jeer, but it was proposed that the 'main and jeer capstans may be made exactly alike, so that in case of an accident to either, the other may serve instead of it'.[10]

Three-deckers

According to the longitudinal sections of First Rates produced in the late seventeenth century by Dummer, Phillips and others, three-deckers were fitted with three capstans, all with different characteristics. The main capstan was, like that of a two-decker, single, and situated on the lower deck. The fore or jeer capstan was placed on the middle and upper deck, where it could have lifted yards and guns, but would have been no help with the anchor cables. Sometimes in the first quarter of the eighteenth century this was a triple capstan. The middle capstan, sometimes called the warping capstan, was on the lower and middle deck, and could be used for anchors in the same way as the jeer capstan of a two-decker, with men at the bars on the middle deck and the cable round the whelps on the lower deck.

By the middle of the eighteenth century, three-deckers had followed two-deckers in that the main capstan was now double, and equal in size to the jeer capstan. A three-decker also had a small jeer capstan on the upper and middle deck in the waist, where it was in the open. By the beginning of the nineteenth century the small capstan was no longer fitted, and a three-decker no longer had any capstan fitted in the open. To raise the yards, they must have used a rather complicated system of blocks to lead the ropes to the capstans on the decks below.

Chapter 7. Cables and Accessories

Cables

A cable was simply a piece of three-strand hemp rope, and was distinguished from other ropes only by its great thickness. Its sole purpose was to hold the ship to its anchor on the sea-bed. A cable was 120 fathoms in length; this was adopted as a standard measurement on land as well as sea. There were a few exceptions to this on smaller ships. In 1809 it was ordered that brigs and smaller vessels should carry bower cables of only 80 fathoms.[1]

According to Henry Bond, writing in 1642, 'your sheet cable is commonly so many half inches as your ships is breadth in feet at the midship beam',[2] but in fact most ships had cables slightly thinner than this. The *Sovereign*, with a beam of $46\frac{1}{2}$ft, had cables of 20in in 1640, 21in in 1656, and 22in in 1686. A Third Rate of 1686 had a cable of $18\frac{1}{2}$in, and a beam of just under 40ft, while a standard 74-gun ship of the late eighteenth century had a beam of about $46\frac{1}{2}$ft and cables of 22in.[3]

A ship carried considerably more cables than anchors, for two main reasons. First, the cable was subject to much wear as it moved about the sea bottom, or was dragged up through the hawse holes of a ship. Spares had to be carried if the ship was not to be excessively dependent on the dockyards. Second, cables could be joined together for use in deep water. According to Falconer, 'it is necessary to splice at least two cables together, in

The Victory's *anchor cable and the main hatchway specially cut away to allow it to run down to the orlop. The grating was removed when the cable was hauled in.* Author's photograph, courtesy of HMS *Victory.*

order to double the length when the ship is obliged to anchor in deep water. For although it is not common to anchor in a greater depth than 40 fathoms, yet if there is only one cable, and the ship rides in a storm and tempestuous sea, the anchor will of necessity sustain the whole weight and jerking of the ship, in a direction too nearly perpendicular'.[4] This implies that the cable in use should be three times the depth of the water in normal circumstances and more in dangerous conditions.

In the seventeenth century the main cables varied a little in circumference, in much the same way as the anchors varied in weight. Each cable was, in theory at least, allocated to an individual anchor. Thus in 1686 a standard 70-gun ship had two cables of $18\frac{1}{2}$in for the sheet anchor, one of the same dimensions for the spare anchor, three more for the best bower, and one cable of 18in for the second bower. Most medium-sized ships of the period had a total of eight large cables which meant in practice there were two cables per anchor. The largest ships, of the First and Second Rates, had nine. The number carried tended to be reduced over the years, and by an order of 1779, Second Rates were to have eight cables instead of nine. Two years later it was ordered that ships of 80 guns should have only seven cables instead of eight, and frigates of 32 or 36 guns should have six instead of seven, but if they were fitted for foreign voyages they were to have one more.[5]

Smaller cables were carried for the stream and kedge anchors. In 1795 a 100-gun ship had a single cable of 15in, while a 74-gun ship had one of 13in.[6] These were evidently intended for the stream anchor; those for the kedge were to be found among the hawsers and cablets.

Hawsers and Cablets

Hawsers and cablets were types of small cable, used for various purposes, such as warping the ship, putting springs to the cable, and as mooring lines on those occasions when the ship came alongside. A cablet was defined by some authorities as a cable of under 9in,[7] but according to the list of 1686, cablets and hawsers were not distinguished by size, for hawsers ranged from 8 to $3\frac{1}{2}$in, and cablets from 9 to 4in. Presumably the difference was in the lay of the rope, for a hawser was made up of three strands, and a cablet of nine. In 1686, a Third Rate was issued with four hawsers and three cablets. In 1795, a 100-gun ship had five cablets, ranging from 9 to $4\frac{1}{2}$in.[8]

Stowage of the Cables

In 1670 the cables of a First Rate weighed from 36 to 45 tons, and those of a Third Rate from 15 to 18 tons. The seven 22in cables of a 74-gun ship of 1795 had a volume of more than 1300ft³.[9] Clearly a large amount of space was needed in which to stow them. The cables were wet when brought up so it was desirable to have them low in the ship, where they could drain into the bilges. On the other hand, they had to be ready for use when necessary and could not, for example, be stowed under the barrels of provisions in the hold. On two- and three-decked ships, they were therefore stowed on the orlop deck. They were laid in enormous coils, some on each side of the row of masts, capstan steps, sail rooms, pump well and hatchways which ran down the centre line of the ship. The area they occupied was about two-fifths of the total length of the ship. On a 74-gun ship of about 1800 it measured 70ft long, 6ft high, and at least 12ft wide on each side.[10] After about 1755, this part of the orlop was not planked in the usual fashion. Instead of planks which ran over the tops of the deck beams, those of the cable tier were made in short lengths, and each was fitted between two beams, into recesses cut for the purpose in the top corners of the beams. The short planks were removeable, and this system allowed water from the cables to drain into the hold, and thus find its way to the well, where it could be pumped out. Stanchions and light bulkheads were erected to keep the cables in position, and in particular away from the sail rooms, where wet cables might damage the sails.

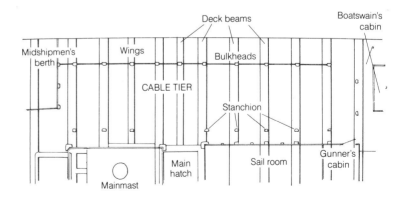

The area for stowing the cable on a 74-gun ship of about 1815. Stanchions and bulkheads kept the cable within certain limits, and prevented it from coming into contact with the sail room when wet.

The larger frigates kept their cables in the orlop, like two-deckers. Sixth Rates had no separate orlop deck amidships so they carried their cables on top of the barrels in the hold, which must have been inconvenient at times. Smaller vessels stowed them where they could, sometimes directly on the bottom of the hold.

Fixing the Cable to the Anchor

The cable was removed from the anchor if the ship was not close to any hazard which might necessitate its use. This allowed the hawse hole to be plugged to prevent the entry of water in a heavy sea. When the anchor was likely to be needed, the cable was bent through its ring and looped over itself. The loop was then seized with several bends of twine. Thus a form of noose was made which tightened round the ring as the pull on the cable increased.

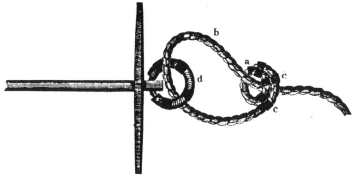

The type of loop used to bend the cable to the anchor, from D'Arcy Lever's Sheet Anchor, *1819.*

Hawse Holes

The cables entered the hull through the hawse holes. Normally there were four of these, in the foremost part of the hull, where the curve of the bows meant that they would face forward rather than to the side. The timbers in this area, known as hawse pieces, were fitted parallel to the keel rather than perpendicular to it. On most ships there were four holes, two on each side, of which one was for the main anchor. Usually they were all on one level, but on some seventeenth century ships, such as those shown in Deane's *Doctrine* the outermost pair was higher than the inner one.

The position of the hawse holes determined that of the capstans, bitts, and other anchor gear. The hawse holes were not situated on the orlop deck where the cables were stowed as they would have been too near the waterline, where sea could have entered the ship too easily. On full two-deckers they were situated just above the lower deck and the cable was brought in at that level. On early eighteenth century Sixth Rates, where the lower deck was only partly armed, they were nevertheless placed at lower deck level, perilously close to the waterline. On the 'true frigates' of the mid-eighteenth century the lower deck was even lower, and after the first generation of these vessels the hawse holes were positioned just above the upper deck. On smaller ships there was little choice, and the hawse holes were at the level of the main deck. In most cases hawse holes were positioned slightly above the level of the deck concerned, to give a suitable lead to the

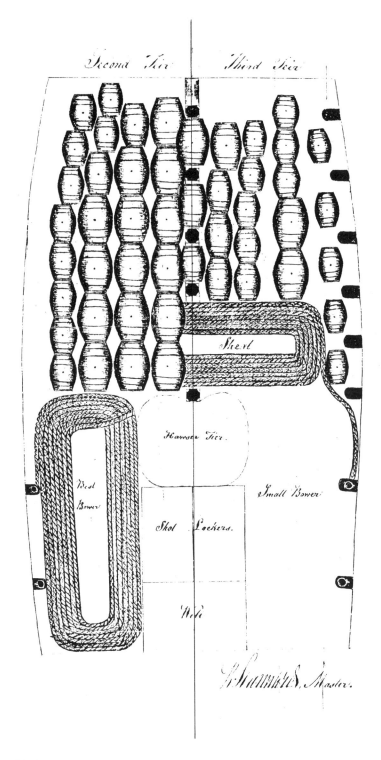

The hold of a Sixth Rate in 1815, showing how the cables were stowed on top of the barrels of provisions. NMM.

capstan. In some cases, such as on the early Sixth Rates, this would have brought them too near the waterline so they were placed just below the level of the deck above.

Hawse holes had to be rather bigger than the cables intended to pass through them. A 74-gun ship of 1795 used a cable of 22in circumference and 7in diameter, so her hawse holes were 15in in diameter.[11] By an order of 1799, a 100-gun ship, for example, had a hawse hole of 19in for a cable of just under 8in in diameter, and other ships had holes in proportion to their cables.[12] After 1811 when chain cable was first being tested, hawse holes had to be lined with iron. There is some evidence that this may have been done for many years before that.

Mangers

Naturally the hawse holes had a tendency to let water in in a heavy sea. They could be blocked by means of hawse bags, canvas bags filled with oakum, which could be stuffed in around the cable. These were not totally waterproof, and had to be removed when the cable was being hauled in. To limit the spread of water, the manger was erected on the deck just aft of the hawse holes. It was removeable, being supported at its corners by stanchions known as cants. The spaces between the cants were filled with planks 3 or 4in thick, rabbetted together. The manger was situated as far aft as possible without interfering with the gunports, and typically it was just under 4ft high.

The Viol

As ships grew larger so too did their cables, until they were too large and heavy to wind round the capstan. This had not yet happened by 1625 when Mainwaring and other contemporary writers mentioned a rope called a viol, which was for use only 'when the anchor is in such stiff ground that we cannot weigh it, or else that the sea goes so high that the main capstan cannot purchase in the cable.'[13] Clearly the main capstan was used in normal circumstances, and the cable was led to it. Mainwaring's description is a little unclear, but it seems to imply that the viol was used to enable the jeer capstan to be used in tandem with the main capstan.

As the century progressed, ships greatly increased in size, and the jeer capstan, which was a double capstan, became more important than the main capstan. It is not clear precisely when the change came about, but it seems likely that by the 1670s it was normal to use the viol for raising the anchor, rather than lead the cable directly to the capstan.

A viol was considerably thinner than the cable with which it was used; it was about 60 per cent of its circumference in the mid-eighteenth century. It had an eye splice in each end, which were seized together to make a loop. When in use, part of the viol was held temporarily to the cable by means of ropes called nippers, and it was then led to a very large block, known as a viol block, which was attached to the mainmast. It was then led forward to the jeer capstan, and turned round it several times. After that it was led further towards the bow and attached to the cable again.

The complicated lead of the viol, through the viol block, was necessary because the jeer capstan was too close to the hawse

holes and the bitts, for the nippers to be fitted properly. The viol block meant there was some extra space, and it pulled the cable as far aft as the main hatch, where it was passed below to be stowed on the orlop deck or in the hold.

The viol block was very large – 4ft long on a late eighteenth century First Rate.[14] It was open at one end, so that the viol could be put in and taken out without taking off its seizings. It, and the ropes which held it to the mainmast, had to bear the whole strain of the cable, which must have been a source of weakness. There were cases where the ship was put in serious danger by the breaking of the block or its strapping. This is one of the reasons why the viol began to be replaced in the early 1740s by the messenger.

The Messenger

The messenger was similar to the viol in most respects. Its thickness in proportion to the cable was similar, its ends were seized together in the same way, and it served almost the same purpose. The only significant difference was that it was somewhat longer, because it was led, not to a block at the mainmast, but direct to the main capstan, which was further away from the hawse holes than the mainmast. The messenger began to come into use in the 1730s and '40s, when the main capstan became double. In 1738 the Surveyor of the Navy wrote that 'all 70- and 60-gun ships, whose great cabins is on the quarterdeck [and could therefore be fitted with double main capstans] should have two messengers near the size of their viols, and on all occasions make use of their main capstans. This would soon find their viols of very little service, or however make their viols last much longer than they can do with all the unnecessary strains they heave with their jeer capstans.'[15]

An order of 1744 stipulated that all ships were to have a messenger in lieu of one of their viols.[16] In the 1790s, only sloops of 200 tons or less, and smaller vessels, had no messenger or viol. Frigates of 36 guns or less had only one messenger which presumably was not used often, or they would have been given at least one spare. All larger ships had two messengers, but frigates, of whatever size, had no viol, for they had no fore capstan on which to use it. Larger ships, of 44 guns or more, had one viol which presumably could be used in addition to the messenger, so that the two capstans could pull together. The messengers of a 74-gun ship were 13in in diameter and 60 fathoms long; her viol was of the same diameter, and 44 fathoms long. A 100-gun ship's

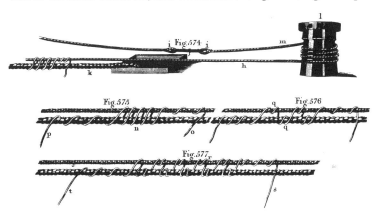

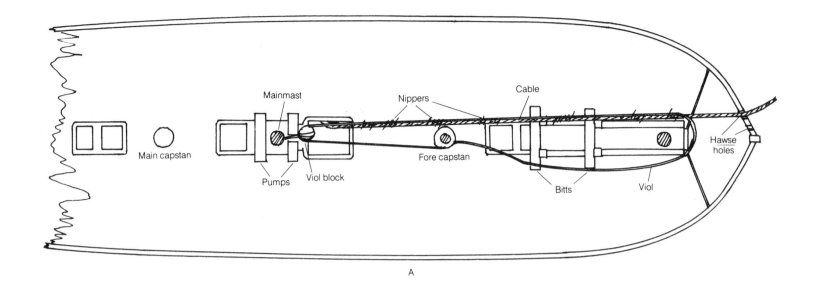

A

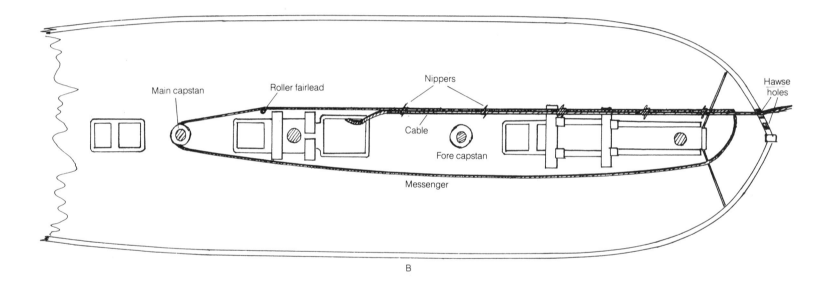

B

Raising the anchor, using A. the viol and B. the messenger.

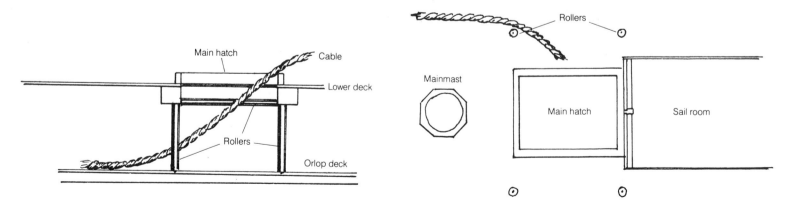

A proposal for fitting rollers to help guide the cable into its tier on the orlop deck, 1814.

Raising the anchor, c1815. As was common on many ships, the capstan is manned mainly by marines. Only the top drumhead is being used in this case. Both the vertical and the horizontal rollers are shown. On the forecastle a party stands by to cat and fish the anchor, while a larger party works in the hold to stow the cable.

viols were of 14in diameter, the messengers being 65 fathoms long, and the viol 46.[17] By about 1805, the viol had fallen into disuse, and was not even carried by the largest ships.[18]

Towards the end of the eighteenth century, some gear was fitted to make the operation of the messenger easier. By an order of 1792, vertical rollers were placed near the ends of the messenger's travel, to help it on its way. Two were situated in the bows, near the hawse holes, one on each side, and two more between the main capstan and the main hatch. In some cases horizontal rollers seem to have been hung from the deck beams above to allow the slack side of the messenger to travel back through them.[19]

Chain Cable

Chain cables had long been used for static moorings, in harbours and rivers, but they were not regarded as suitable for use at sea, where they would have to take much greater strain, and be hauled in and out regularly. In 1811 Lieutenant Samuel Browne approached the Admiralty with a suggestion for an improved type of chain cable, and this was tested on several ships, mostly at the Downs and the Nore, over the next few years. In 1813 chain was tested against hemp at Portsmouth, and Browne was promoted captain for his efforts. But there were some difficulties. The cable of the sloop *Phipps* broke in 1812. Browne made some further improvements, and the *Crescent* was issued with 'an anchor with a chain cable of 150 fathoms and sufficient strength ... at least equal to two anchors with the same scope of hempen cable, particularly in deep water'. But nearly all the tests were still made in harbour or in sheltered anchorages. In January 1814 chain cables had still not been used aboard a sea-going ship, despite Browne's urging. As a standard fitting, they belong to the period after 1815.[20]

Chapter 8. Anchor Tackle

The Bitts

When a ship was riding at anchor, most of the strain of holding her cables was taken up by the bitts. The bitt pins were stout vertical pieces of timber. All but the smallest vessels had four of these, arranged side by side in pairs, with their uppermost parts on the same deck as the hawse holes. Each pin passed through at least two decks, and was bolted securely to the beams of each. The base of each pin was rooted deep in the hold, and fixed by its lowest end to one of the timbers of the frame. The upper end protruded several feet above the deck where the cables were taken in. This part of the pin was parallel sided, below it tapered gradually until its lower end was about half the size at the top.

Each pin was reinforced by a strong inverted knee, known as a standard. This was fitted on the deck where the cables were taken in, and braced the pin against the strain from the anchor. Between each pair of bitts, on the after side, was fitted the cross-piece. This was another stout piece of timber, which joined the two bitts, and protruded several feet on each side of them. When the cable was in use, it was turned round the ends of the bitt pin and the cross-piece, in the same way as a smaller rope would be turned round a cleat or a staghorn. The cross-piece also tended to spread the load between the pins.

The Stoppers

Obviously a turn round the bitts was not sufficient to hold the cable completely securely, though it greatly absorbed the shocks caused by a heavy sea or a strong wind. The cable was led aft of

The bitts of a 70-gun ship of the 1730s. The upper parts of the pins, the cross-pieces, and the standards can be seen. Author's photograph, courtesy of NMM.

the bitts, and further secured by means of a stopper. This was a short piece of rope with a knot in one end. It was spliced to an eyebolt just aft of the bitt pin. A lanyard, of thinner rope, was attached to the other end of the stopper and also tied round the cable. Two or more eyebolts for stoppers were placed aft of each bitt pin. Each stopper was about the same thickness as the viol or messenger, so that those of a Third Rate of 1677 were 10in in diameter; the lanyards were 3½ or 3in in diameter.[1]

Occasionally a cable would be let out secured by the stoppers alone, without a turn round the bitts, but this was 'not safe riding in a stress'. When a ship was being prepared to anchor in a known depth of water, a suitable amount of cable was laid out on the deck, and the stoppers attached at the appropriate point. The

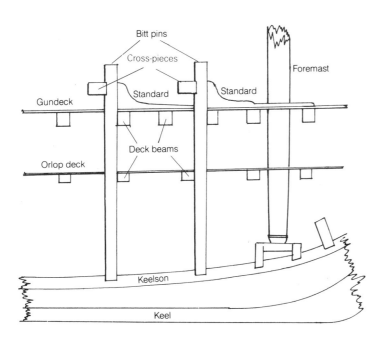

The bitts of a 64-gun ship of 1781.

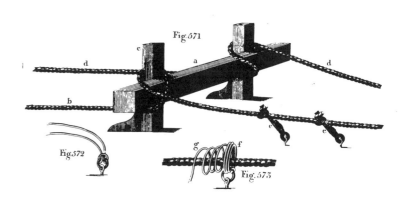

The bitts, illustrating the methods of taking a turn round them with the cable, and the use of the stoppers. Figs 572 and 573 show ring ropes, which could be used as short-term stoppers when running out the cable. From D'Arcy Lever's Sheet Anchor.

The cathead of a late eighteenth century frigate showing how it is bolted under the forecastle beams. Author's photograph, courtesy of NMM.

anchor was then let go, and ran out until restrained by the stoppers.

The Cathead

A cathead was a strong piece of timber, approximately square in cross-section. In most cases it was fitted so that its lowest side rested on the forecastle deck, and it projected out from each side of the forward corner of the forecastle, at an angle of about 45 degrees to the ship. It was inclined upwards by about ten degrees. The cathead was similar to a crane, holding the anchor clear of the ship's side when it was being raised out of the water, or

The cathead of a ship of the line, the knee behind it, and the cat block and cat rope. Author's photograph.

lowered. It had two, three or four slots cut side by side near its outermost end. These were used to fit sheaves, which were part of a block and tackle system for raising the anchor up the side of the ship. The cathead played no part in lifting the anchor from the bottom of the sea; it only came into use after the top of the anchor had broken surface.

The cathead had to be well supported for this task. Inside the hull it had an arm, of equal thickness to the head itself, which was bolted to the deck beams of the forecastle. On larger ships this arm ran across the foremost part of the forecastle deck, but on smaller ones it often passed diagonally under the deck. In either case, it was securely bolted to the deck beams. Outside the hull, the cathead was supported from underneath by a knee, which was often joined to the decorative rails of the beakhead. On some ships the cathead was also braced from behind by another knee.

The cathead usually had some form of decoration. It derived its name from the lion's face which was often carved on its outermost end, a custom which persisted well into the eighteenth century. In the seventeenth century, especially on large ships, the cathead was often carved all over. In the eighteenth century the amount of carving gradually declined and the cathead became much plainer, with simple panels cut in its sides, and sometimes a bas-relief carving on its outer end.

Cat Tackle

The structure of the cathead was very strong, and unlike the fish davit which had a rope led from the mast to brace it it did not need to be supported from above. From the outer end of the cathead hung the cat block, which had the same number of sheaves as the cathead, and was suspended from it by the cat rope, which was led through alternate sheaves on the block and head, and back to the forecastle deck. This gave sufficient purchase to raise the anchor. The cat block was large, 26in long on a late eighteenth century Third Rate, and iron-bound to give it extra strength.

Suspended under the cat block was the cat hook. This was intended to catch the ring of the anchor as it appeared from the water, and hold it until it had been raised high enough. Lanyards, sometimes known as cat-backs, were attached to the block and led

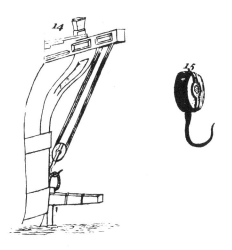

The cat tackle and the cat hook, from Falconer's Dictionary.

The Sovereign of the Seas. *A seaman is standing on the stock of the anchor, presumably in order to engage the cat hook. Two other anchors are held in place by stoppers and shank painters.* NMM.

into the ship. They helped to guide the hook onto the ring. If this failed, a seaman had to climb down onto the anchor stock, or one of the ship's boats was lowered. Possibly this was common in the early seventeenth century; the well known engraving of the *Sovereign of the Seas* (above) shows a seaman standing on the anchor stock to move the cat hook onto the anchor ring.

The Davit or Spanshackle

After the anchor had been raised from the water, with its ring uppermost and its shank vertical, it was necessary to raise the other end and lay its shank horizontal, so that the whole anchor could be placed where it was least likely to move about and damage the hull. A separate beam, known as the fish davit, was

used to lift the crown end of the anchor. It was not nearly as strong as the cathead because it never had to lift more than half the weight of the anchor. Until 1780 ships carried only one davit, which could be moved to either side as necessary. It was as long as the ship was broad, and $\frac{1}{2}$in wide per foot of its length. Its inboard end was put through a very large shackle, known as the spanshackle. Until about 1750 one of these was fitted, on the centre line of the ship, aft of the foremast. Later two were fitted, one on each side of the ship, still close to the centre line. Each spanshackle was fixed to a forecastle beam, known as the spanshackle beam, which was often stronger than the others.

The other end of the davit was hung over the side, passing through the fore shrouds. Many ships had a special location for it, and either a part of the forecastle rail was cut away, or a block of wood was fixed to the rail to protect it. The fish hook, which was

A model of the Sovereign of the Seas *showing the fish davit, the lining and billboard.* Author's photograph.

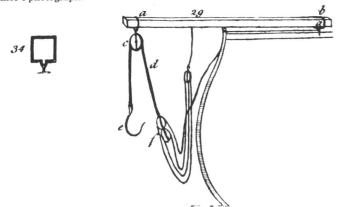

The fish davit, with its tackle rigged. No. 34 is a spanshackle ring. From Falconer's Dictionary.

new type of davit was much shorter, as it did not have to extend from the middle of the deck. It was three-tenths of the ship's beam in length. Its innermost end was mitre-shaped, so that it would fit into the angle between the channel and the side of the ship. It was square in cross-section for a little of its length, and then octagonal. Near its outer end, a necking was cut to hold the fish tackle. When fitted, it projected from the hull at right angles to the centre line of the ship, and was angled about 45 degrees upwards. It was held in position by three ropes called guys, leading from ringbolts just inboard from the necking. One led upwards to the foremast, one forward to the end of the cathead, and a third led aft and was fixed to the after part of the channel. The tackle and pendant which actually raised the anchor were the same as those used before 1780.

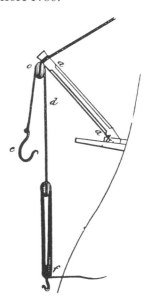

Early nineteenth century fish davit, with its tackle, from Burney's Dictionary.

Lining and Bolsters

Though the cathead was intended to keep the anchor clear of the side of the ship while it was lifted out of the water, it still tended to swing inwards while it was being pulled up by the fish tackle. The flukes and bills of an anchor could do considerable damage to a wooden hull so some protection was needed. This was provided by the bolster and lining. The arm of the anchor was normally stowed against the fore channel so this determined the height and position of the lining. The lining proper began at about the middle of the channel wale, where the chain plates were fixed. While the anchor was being fished its ring would be suspended just under the cathead, and its crown would describe the arc of a circle as it was pulled up, thus the forward edge of the lining was circular, but of a slightly smaller radius than that drawn out by the anchor, to allow for any movement caused by the pitching and rolling of the ship. Up to the middle of the eighteenth century, the after edge of the lining was circular on most ships, after which it was straight, and descended vertically down the side of the hull. The lining was usually wider in the eighteenth century than in the nineteenth.

The lining normally extended down from the top of the main wale. It is rarely described in works on naval architecture, but it

used to hold the shank of the anchor, was much bigger than the cat hook, which only had to hold the ring. The fish hook was secured to the fish tackle pendant, which passed through a large block under the outer end of the davit. The other end of the pendant was led through a system of blocks and tackle, known as the fish tackle, which was used to give mechanical advantage when hauling up the crown of the anchor. A small rope, a cat-fish-back, was attached to the fish block, and used to guide it on to the shank, in the same way as the cat-back was used with the ring.

The Fixed Davit

From about 1780, the moveable fish davit was replaced by more permanent structures, one on each side of the ship. The

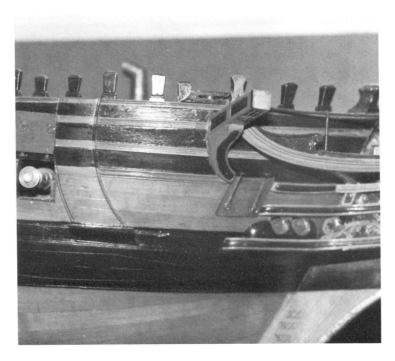

The anchor lining of a sloop. On this size of ship there was no need to protect the channels with a billboard. Author's photograph, courtesy of NMM.

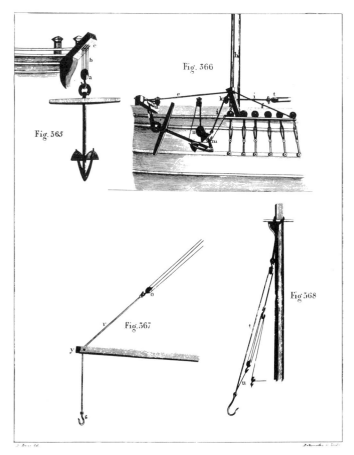

Various pieces of anchor tackle, from D'Arcy Lever's Sheet Anchor. *Fig 365 shows the anchor catted; Fig 366 shows it fished, with the later type of davit in use; Fig 367 shows how the older type of davit was supported, and Fig 368 shows the method of fishing the anchor on a small vessel which has no fish davit.*

seems to have been very simple in construction. It merely consisted of a number of planks bolted to the planks of the ship's side. For a 74-gun ship of the 1780s, 3in plank is specified.[2]

On large ships, a rather different structure was needed above the level of the channel wale. The channels and the chain plates protruded some way from the side of the ship, and they too had to be protected. This was done by the billboard, so called because it was designed to protect the ship from the bill of the anchor. It appears to have been supported by two stanchions, angled outwards from the channel wale and joined to the channel just under its outer edge. On these stanchions were placed planks running in a fore and aft direction, to keep the anchor off the chain plates. On smaller ships, especially brigs, schooners and cutters, which had less than three masts, the foremast was not near enough the bows for the channels to be close to the anchor, and so there was lining, but no need for a billboard.

The bolster was introduced around the middle of the eighteenth century. It was a thicker, more permanent timber, some of which was decoratively carved, fitted along the middle of the channel wale where the lining joined the billboard. It was intended to support the stanchions of the billboard, but it must have tended to obstruct the free movement of the anchor as it was hauled up and down, because it projected beyond the lining. Its other purpose was to provide a platform for the man sent down to help in fishing the anchor. For this reason, it projected forward of the lining and billboard by 10 to 24in.

Stowing the Anchors

The two bower anchors were usually kept at the level of the fore channels, with their shanks vertical and their stocks forward. The height of the channels varied over the years. In two- or three-deckers they were raised from the level of the middle or upper deck to that of the forecastle as a result of several orders in the course of the eighteenth century. The cat and fish tackle were suitable for raising the anchors, but unsuitable for releasing them because it was difficult to disengage a heavy object from a hook. In order to be ready for use, the ring of the anchor was held to the cathead by means of a stopper. This was a rope with a wall-knot in one end. The other end was passed through a cleat on the after side of the cathead, through the anchor ring, and back to the cathead, where it was made fast. When the hook was removed from the ring, the anchor was ready for release.

It is possible that the stopper was not in use in the early part of the seventeenth century, and it is not mentioned by Mainwaring. The well-known print of the *Sovereign* (on page 52) shows a man standing on the anchor stock, either about to release the cat hook from the anchor ring, or having just engaged it. If the former were the case, then it would suggest that the stopper was not in use, but in the same print two other anchors are shown stowed, using ropes which look very similar in principle to the stopper, though it is not clear if they were used in the same way. Certainly the stopper was in use within the next twenty years, and it appears on the rigging lists of 1656.[3]

The fish pendant also had to be removed when the anchor was stowed, especially when the davit had to be moved in order to stow the anchor on the other side of the ship. To hold the anchor in position, a rope known as the shank painter was passed under the shank, and both ends were secured to the timberheads on the rail of the forecastle. The fish hook could then be removed.

The anchors stowed, on a 70-gun ship of the 1730s. The stream anchor is lashed to the sheet anchor, and an anchor buoy is tied to the shrouds. The cable would normally be removed from the anchor when the ship was at sea. NMM.

Another rope was put round the upper arm of the stock, to hold it square and prevent the anchor from rotating. The hull was protected from the upper fluke of the anchor by a wooden fender, known as a shoe. This had a hole in its outer face, to hold one of the points of the fluke. It was hung over the side of the ship by a rope, and it was able to travel up and down with the anchor as it moved with the motion of the ship. By about 1800, an anchor chock was fitted. This was a more permanent version of the shoe, recessed to take the fluke, and bolted to the side of the hull.

The other main anchors were stowed along the channels, aft of the bowers. Presumably shank painters and stoppers were used in a similar way, though of course there was no cathead to attach the stopper to. Smaller anchors had no fish tackle, and the fluke was hauled up to the gunwale and secured there.

Anchor Buoys

When an anchor became stuck fast in the ground, a pull near its crown would dislodge it more effectively than one on the ring. If it was known that the ground was difficult, this problem could be anticipated and a line attached to the crown. The other end of the line, which would be pulled to dislodge the anchor, was attached to a buoy. This marked the position of the anchor, so that in a crowded anchorage other ships could avoid hitting it. When the ground was rocky, buoys could also be attached to the cable away from the anchor itself, to lift it over the most difficult areas.

Can buoys were conical in shape and were used mainly to mark navigational hazards, so were not carried aboard ship. The usual anchor buoy was called a nun buoy. It was thickest in the middle, and tapered to a point at each end. It was constructed from hoops and wooden staves, rather like a barrel. Then it was parcelled, by covering it with strips of canvas in a spiral fashion like a bandage,

and then served by winding twine round it. A complicated system of slings and hoops was fitted to hold the buoy ropes at each end, and to make it easier to pick up with a boat hook. A ship of the 1680s carried six of these buoys. When not in use, they were kept lashed to the fore shrouds near the appropriate anchors.[4]

Smaller buoys were made from solid wood. A ship of the 1680s would have carried four of these. They were shaped either like a cylinder, or like a nun buoy and were generally used for boat work. In 1805 it was suggested that ships on foreign service should have nun buoys made of iron rather than wood, but only 41 of these had been manufactured by 1813.[5]

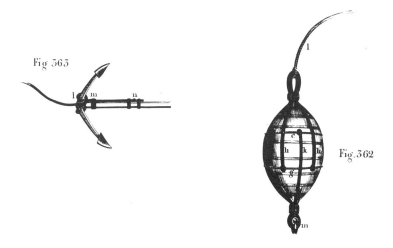

An anchor buoy, from D'Arcy Lever's Sheet Anchor, *showing the rope slings attached to it. Fig 363 illustrates a method of attaching the buoy rope to the anchor.*

PART III

Underwater Protection

Chapter 9. Graving and Paying

The Problem of Hull Decay

One of the many myths about sailing ships is that they had long lives with a minimum of maintenance. From examples like the *Royal William*, which lasted from 1719 to 1813, and the *Victory*, which was 40 years old at the time of Trafalgar, it has been deduced that longevity was the norm. In fact neither of these vessels is at all typical; the *Royal William* saw very little service in the early part of her career, and the *Victory* had very extensive repairs amounting to several times the cost of her original building.[1] The average ship of the early 1700s was said to last 14 years, and there were many which were broken up after shorter lives.[2]

Several factors determined the longevity of a ship. The quality of the timber, the length of its seasoning, and the type of service in which the ship was engaged, were all of critical importance. Good maintenance, regular cleaning, renewal of decayed timbers, and protection of the hull did much to increase the life span.

There were two main problems that threatened the underwater hull of a wooden ship: weed, which encumbered the bottom, drastically reduced speed, and to a certain extent damaged the timbers, and shipworm, either *teredo navalis* or gribble, which ate its way along the planks, and could reduce a vessel to a leaking fragile wreck within months, if allowed to get into the hull. These two problems dogged shipbuilders for many centuries. Sometimes they were treated separately, sometimes together. Both attracted the attention of scientists and inventors, and many experiments were tried over the years, before a satisfactory solution was found in the last quarter of the eighteenth century.

Until then, the two problems were usually treated separately. Ships were protected against the worm by sheathing and were graved to guard them against weed. Usually ships which were sheathed by the conventional method had also to be graved, to protect the sheathing against weed.

Weed could make an enormous difference to a ship's performance. One of the main reasons why French ships were regarded as superior in sailing was that they spent much more time in their home bases and were thus cleaned more frequently than British ships, which spent long periods on patrol and blockade. To protect against weed, ships' bottoms were covered with various substances, intended to create a surface which would repel it. These never proved very efficient, so regular cleaning was necessary if ships were to keep up their speed. The intervals between cleaning varied according to the service in which the ships were engaged. All contemporary accounts say that ships laid up in harbour should be cleaned and graved at least once every three years. It was a characteristic of a bad naval administration that this was not done. The Commission of Enquiry of 1618, and the Special Commission of 1684, both complained that their predecessors had failed to keep up this rate of maintenance.[3] Ships intended for speed had to be cleaned much more frequently. An Act of Parliament of 1708, which laid down means by which the Admiralty was to combat French privateers,[4] stipulated fast ships be cleaned three times a year.

The need to clean ships had far reaching effects on naval development. The most important provision of a naval base, apart from a secure harbour, was an area where ships could be cleaned and graved, either by careening, as in some of the smaller overseas yards, or by putting the ship into a dry-dock, as was done in the main yards, with all large ships. Such docks were among the most expensive and important of the government's possessions and they were crucial to the development of naval resources and strategy.

Caulking

Strictly speaking, caulking was part of the building, rather than the fitting of a ship. All the ship's planking was caulked, above and under water, inside and outside in order to seal the joins between the planks and make them watertight. Oakum was made from strands of old rope, and forced between the seams. It was then covered with pitch or resin to keep it watertight. This was done before the ship was launched, by skilled workers known as caulkers. Sometimes the underwater caulking had to be renewed in dry-dock, or when the ship was careened.

After caulking, if the ship was not to be sheathed the bottom was graved with either 'black stuff', 'white stuff', or 'brown stuff'. Tallowing was a slightly different process, which could be used on its own, or in combination with either caulking or graving.

A model of the famous Centurion *of 1732, showing white stuff.* NMM.

White Stuff

The application of white stuff was one of the oldest methods of covering the hull. In the seventeenth century it consisted of train oil, obtained from whales, seals or fish; rosin, from pine trees; and brimstone, or sulphur, which was believed to form a slightly poisonous mixture which prevented the weed from flourishing. In 1702, a Fourth Rate needed 7cwt of rosin, 18 gallons of oil, and 84lbs of brimstone.[5]

White stuff was very common during most of the seventeenth century, but towards the end of the century black stuff, which cost half as much, came into use. It tended to be used for ships in home waters, while white stuff, which most people still regarded as superior, was reserved for the more demanding waters of the Caribbean and the Mediterranean, where bases were fewer and worms more prevalent. Early in the eighteenth century, white stuff fell into complete disuse for a time. The materials, especially rosin which came from the Baltic, were difficult to obtain because of war. In 1705, Captain Passenger recommended the reintroduction of white stuff for foreign voyages, but although this was 'formerly the use of the navy', the Navy Board ruled against it. Prices had trebled or quadrupled 'by reason of the war with some of those nations from whence some of them used to come'. In any case, the dockyard officials believed that 'black stuff could be laid on and keep clean as long; they all gave their opinion in favour of black stuff (save only that white stuff is handsomer to the eye.)'. However, white stuff was still believed to be 'better on foreign voyages', in that 'the sulphurous taste prevents the worms eating so fast as they would through pitch'.[6]

Already there was some attempt to encourage supply from the colonies in North America, as a substitute for the unreliable source in the Baltic. In 1702 Captain Crow of the *Shrewsbury* tested a mixture which used New England turpentine instead of rosin. He 'observed that it lay very smooth on the side, looked very white, and stuck very fast to the plank, more than ever observed on any graving in England', and that 'it lay very fast on

the plank without cracking or breaking off, which is very usual to other graving.'[7] The turpentine cost slightly more than rosin, so the new white stuff was still more than twice the cost of the black stuff. Though the government showed some interest in this, as it wished to promote supplies from the colonies, it did little about it. In 1716 it was found that both pitch and turpentine were being produced in New England with the help of a system of premiums, but 'the latter of which is not used in the navy'.[8] On the other hand, turpentine was among the stores sent to Port Mahon in the 1740s, though it is not clear what it was used for.[9]

In 1735, white stuff was recommended for the ships laid up at Chatham, where shipworm had recently made an appearance, 'as white graving is found by experience to be much more durable and a greater security against the worm than black graving, and the difference of the charge may not be more than £7 for a 70-gun ship.'[10] Already by this date it was back in common use for ships at sea, though only a minority, about a quarter to a third, of the ships fitted out in the 1720s and '30s were coated with it. When ships were sheathed with wood, white stuff was usually put over the sheathing, to give extra protection.[11]

By the 1740s, dockyard records fail to distinguish what type of composition was used on the bottom of ships, so it is not easy to tell how common white stuff was by the middle of the century. It is not clear from Falconer, writing in 1769, what substances were used, but he does refer to black paying, just under the lower wale, 'forming an agreeable variety with the white bottom beneath', implying that white stuff was common.[12] Its use survived until 1777, when it was replaced by a new substance.[13]

Black Stuff

Black stuff was a mixture of tar and pitch. Tar was obtained from pine trees, particularly in Scandinavia, and had various uses in fitting out a ship, for instance caulking the seams and covering the standing rigging. Tar was boiled to produce pitch, a much more solid substance. Black stuff was a mixture of two parts of pitch to one of tar, which gave a substance which was viscous enough to penetrate the seams and the grain of the wood, but hard enough to withstand the rigours of sea service. Unlike white stuff, it was applied hot, so that it could be 'laid on smoother than white, so that a ship must needs sail faster'.[14]

Black stuff seems to have come into use slowly in the course of the seventeenth century. The lexicographers of the 1620s, Smith, Mainwaring and Boteler, describe the use of oil, rosin and brimstone, but make no mention of black stuff. A document of 1654 refers to 'stuff, viz. rosin, oil and brimstone,' implying that this was the only kind of stuff in use.[15] But in the same year the dockyard officers were ordered to sheath a ship and then to 'pay her sheathing all over with black hard stuff', and then to tallow her.[16] It was mentioned again in 1670 when the Act setting up the Company of Milled Lead compared the new material with 'pitch, tar, rosin, brimstone, or any graving hitherto used',[17] though there is no other evidence that it was used in the 1670s. In 1677 there is reference to 'tar prepared by a late stranger who offered the same to His Majesty as an effectual prevention to the worm, by paying the plank with it, without other sheathing',[18] but this sounds like one of the inventions intended to defeat shipworm, rather than a part of the mainstream development of graving materials.

By 1690 black stuff seems to have become established, as a regular alternative to white stuff. A commissioner's notebook of

Paintings and models invariably show the bottoms of ships payed with white stuff, but black stuff, though not very picturesque, was far more common. This painting by Charles Brooking is of a 64-gun ship of the 1740s on the stocks at Deptford. NMM.

1691 describes 'the laying on of pitch or other mixed stuff of rosin, tallow and co.', and refers to graving, which was 'to pay them all over under the water with pitch and other mixed matter, with rosin and co.'[19] By 1702, black stuff had almost entirely superseded white stuff, and it remained predominant for many years.

The great advantage of black stuff was its cheapness. In 1702 it cost £3/12/0 to pay a Fourth Rate with black stuff, and £7/4/9 with white stuff,[20] and it should be emphasised that this was before the price rise caused by the disruption of supplies from the Baltic. Black stuff was said to give a smoother surface on the bottom. In general it was regarded as less effective against the worm, though it is not clear if there was any real evidence for this. It was occasionally used for paying sheathed ships, though white stuff was rather more common for this. In 1741, for example, the *Norwich* was sheathed and payed with black stuff.[21]

Brown Stuff

In 1737 a new compound was invented, probably by Lee, the Master Caulker at Portsmouth. It consisted simply of brimstone mixed with the pitch and tar of black stuff, so that it had some of the advantages of both compounds. It was known as brown stuff, and became common in the 1740s, though it did not entirely

A ship being careened. This was done to smaller ships when dockyard facilities were not available.

replace white stuff.[22] In 1777, when the American War caused further rises in the price of rosin and turpentine, a new system was introduced. The ship's bottom was to be payed with brown stuff up to 3ft below the load waterline, and 'the remainder with tallow and lime, with a shallow skirting with tallow and white lead'. This practice did not last long, for within a few years ships were being sheathed with copper.

Tallowing

A mixture of tallow and soap was used for coating the underwater hull by the early years of the seventeenth century, and it was described by Smith, Mainwaring and Boteler. Its greatest advantage was that it formed a very smooth surface, and thus contributed to the speed of the ship. Furthermore, it came from animal fat, and so could be obtained without resorting to foreign suppliers. Its main disadvantage was that it wore off rather quickly. For this reason, in 1657 a captain complained of 'the foulness of his frigate, not having been tallowed these three months'.[23] Tallow was particularly suitable for small ships, which needed speed, and could be cleaned and tallowed on a beach, unlike a larger ships which had to use a dry-dock. It was by far the most common method of protection in the 1640s and '50s, when large numbers of vessels were fitted out against Royalist privateers and gunrunners. Such vessels were small, fast, and operated from home bases. Some larger ships were also tallowed. In 1658 the *Naseby*, the second largest ship in the fleet, was so treated, and in the same year there was an order that ships of the Third and Fourth Rate were to be put into repair 'so that they may be in a posture, tallowing excepted, to be put to sea in any emergency.'[24]

Many accounts suggest that tallowing was used mainly as an alternative to graving with black or white stuff, but sometimes it was used on top of a graving. In 1654 tallow was applied over the black stuff of a sheathed ship.[25] The *Naseby*, too, was to be graved and then tallowed. Smaller ships, on the other hand, seem to have relied exclusively on tallowing.

Tallowing declined in the later years of the seventeenth century, as the wars with the Dutch necessitated warships with durability rather than speed. By 1679 even the royal yachts, always renowned for their fast sailing, were to be graved and not tallowed. It was said that if they were only tallowed, 'the tallow doth so soon wear off and leave the plank bare, that it is very chargeable to keep them tallowed, and commanders are rather desirous to have them graved than tallowed, unless they may be tallowed upon their graving.'[26] Tallowing was revived somewhat in the early years of the eighteenth century, as the campaign against the French privateers demanded fast cruising ships. In 1706, for example, it was used for a squadron cruising off Dunkirk, one of the main bases for the privateers. In the 1740s it was used on ships which operated close to home bases. 'Caulked her bottom, sides and decks, and tallowed her', is a common entry in the reports of work performed in Portsmouth Dockyard in that period. It is clear that in these cases tallowing was applied without any graving. Out of 24 ships in Portsmouth in 1741, six were tallowed, two of which were also graved.[27] In 1759 it was ordered that where, 'by the shortness of the cruise, the tallow remains on the bottom with a good body', it was only necessary to 'wash down the said bottom dry, and amend the same where it is bare, with new tallow as before'.[28]

Inventions

Few subjects, except perhaps pumps, attracted as many inventors as the treatment of the ship's underwater hull. As well as those who experimented with various forms of sheathing, there were many who produced compounds which they believed would protect the bottom of ships from various hazards. One such was Charles Ardesoif, whose composition was tested in the 1690s, and again in 1705. The Navy Board discovered that it cost three times as much as normal black stuff and had no great advantages, so lost interest.[29] Gaschen and Hammond produced another mixture in 1721, 'for preventing the worm from eating ships bottoms'.

Pieces of elm and fir were treated with it, and nailed to the bottom of a ship going to the West Indies. On her return in 1724, they were found to be 'so much worm eaten that some of them dropped from the bottoms.'[30] Numerous other ideas were sent to the Navy Board. In 1697, one Geddy produced a composition for use against the worm, and in 1699 Bezin proposed another. In the late 1760s and early 1770s alone, compositions by Boulton, Hunt, Constable, Crawford and Murdock were tried out, usually by nailing a few sheets of plank to the side of a ship. Others were never actually tested, probably because their inventors lacked either persistence or influence.[31] None of these hopefuls provided a solution to the problem, which was not found until the 1780s.

Chapter 10. Wood and Lead Sheathing

The Method of Wood Sheathing

Wood sheathing was first used in Elizabethan times, its invention claimed by John Hawkins. For a time it seems to have been used on all English warships, but by the early 1600s it was only used for those going to areas where they might be exposed to the worm, and for those with special problems. Essentially, sheathing consisted of a layer of tar and hair, covered with a layer of thin wood. The tar and hair was what kept the worm away from the main structure of the hull. 'Some hold opinion that the tar killeth the worm; others that the worm passing through the sheathing, and seeking a way through, the hair and tar so choke him that he is choked therewith.'[1] Other materials, such as loose ends of cloth and pieces of old cloth known as thrum, were often added to make the mixture more repellent. In the eighteenth century, a layer of paper rags was also put under the tar and hair, to help keep the worm out. The paper was thick and brown, and at least 45lbs per ream in weight. This method was not used in the 1650s, but was well established by the 1720s.[2] In 1770, a dockyard was ordered to take care to have 'the thick paper laid smooth and fair and well fastened to the plank, that it may continue as long as possible to guard the bottom from the worm after the sheathing may be eat through.'[3]

In the late sixteenth century, $\frac{1}{2}$in deal board was recommended for sheathing. By 1654 this measurement had increased to $\frac{3}{4}$in, which was still standard in 1728.[4] Around 1600, elm was preferred to oak, 'for it riveth not, it endureth better underwater and yieldeth better to the ship's side.'[5] Later fir became more common. It was agreed that the board had to be thin: 'It is to be observed that the thinner the outboard boards may be, so much the better is; for the worm will sooner pierce through it and come to the tar and hair that is laid between the new and old planks; the which they can by no means endure, and thereupon will forsake the ship.'[6] Furthermore, the thinness of the plank made it easier to bend to the shape of the hull. Large quantities were needed; a 74 of the 1770s used 18,200ft, and in 1761 it was ordered that at least 150,000ft should be kept in stock in the dockyards, for emergency use.

The nails which held the board in place were driven very close together, about $\frac{3}{8}$in apart in 1728. In 1654 it was said that 3in nails were long enough, and that they should weigh 24 or 26lbs per hundredweight. By 1728 this had been considerably reduced, and $1\frac{1}{4}$in nails were stipulated, so that they should not penetrate the inner plank too far.[7] Again, enormous quantities were necessary. In 1654, 150,000 nails were required for sheathing the *Dover*, and in the 1770s a 74-gun ship needed more than a ton and a half.

One criticism of wood sheathing was that it formed a rough surface on the hull, reducing the speed of the ship. In the eighteenth century this was partly solved by planing the boards after they had been fitted. This was tried on the *Sorlings* in 1711, and was adopted as standard practice in 1726.[8] Another problem was that the sheathing was often eaten by the worm, or rubbed off through contact with boats, rocks, or piers. One answer to this was to 'fill' the sheathing. Filling brads or nails were placed over the brown paper, so that this layer would remain even if the wood sheathing was removed. This method was standardised by orders in 1728. Though these were cancelled in 1730, in the 1770s there is again mention of the use of filling nails as an alternative method of protection.[9]

Despite the complications of 'filling', wood sheathing could be done quite quickly. In 1708 it was claimed that a ship could be sheathed in 24 hours, 'which, upon emergency, may be of consequence'.[10]

The Purpose of Sheathing

The main purpose of wood sheathing was to protect the hull from shipworm. There was also a secondary aim, which was to

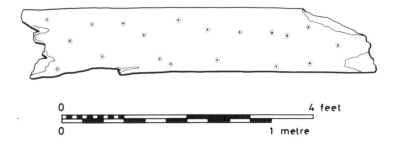

A section of the sheathing board recovered from the wreck of the Dartmouth, *lost in 1690.*

strengthen a weakened hull. In 1698 the *Resolution* was found to be leaking after a rebuild, and it was proposed to sheath her simply to prevent leaks. The Admiralty objected to this: 'in regard we do not think it proper to sheath ships of her nature, unless for a foreign voyage.'[11] But this did not remain policy for long. In 1707 the *Essex* was to be sheathed to prevent her from leaking, 'in regard of the scarcity of plank in the navy at this time'.[12] In 1721 the *Newcastle* was to be un-sheathed, and it was ordered 'not to sheath her again, if she can be made a tight ship without it.'[13] In 1726 the *Royal Oak* was to be sheathed because her bottom was already worm-eaten, and the dockyard officers reported that they 'cannot promise her being a tight ship without sheathing'.[14]

The Effectiveness of Sheathing

According to an informed opinion of about 1780, wood sheathing was very inefficient. 'Some ships under wooden sheathing, after 18 months' service in the West Indies, obliged to have every plank stripped and shifted in a six months repair.'[15] A more optimistic seventeenth century view was that it could last for up to seven years.[16] An examination of records of the maintenance work done to ships in the 1720s suggests the longevity of sheathing lay on average between these two extremes. Most ships seem to have needed their sheathing renewed after about three years, though there were cases where it was kept on for ten years.[17] It was sometimes very effective in keeping out the worm. The *Enterprise* was surveyed in 1724, and it was found that 'the sheathing is much worm eaten, but having taken the worst off in several places, don't find the plank touched; the false keel is eaten to pieces, and the main keel only at the end of the skeg.' In other words the sheathing had done its job, and sacrificed itself to the worm. The main structure of the ship had hardly been touched.[18]

Even if the sheathing worked as planned, some felt that the very act of nailing it to the timbers did almost as much damage as the worm itself, as reflected in the following: 'The plank at the sheathings, being pulled off, is not much better for service ... than had the worm eat the same, since the nails will as effectually split and tear the plank to pieces as the worm will eat it.'[19] 'It is no extraordinary thing to find ships which have been sheathed to be leaky, because that the exactest caulking of such ships which have been so wounded comes often short of the numerous small perforations which nails make.'[20]

For sheathing to be successful it had to be kept tight, and repaired quickly if damaged, because once the worm penetrated it could breed quickly, and eat its way along the planks. Facilities for repair were not easy to come by on foreign stations, where they were most needed, and as a result many ships were badly damaged. Even if the worm had penetrated all was not lost, for treatments to 'kill the worm'[21] were applied in the 1720s and 1730s. Planks which had been heavily eaten could be replaced, but again extensive maintenance facilities were required. Few ships were actually lost because of the worm, but the expense of protecting them against it was very great.

Paying over the Sheathing

Sheathing protected against the worm, but other remedies were needed to reduce the growth of weed, which was as common in the tropics as anywhere else. White stuff was generally favoured for this, because it was 'the most durable', and 'the sulphurous taste thereof may prevent the worms eating so fast as they would through pitch.'[22] In the 1700s the use of white stuff was rare, but it was revived later. In 1741, seven of the ships in Portsmouth harbour were sheathed. Two of these were tallowed, one graved with black stuff, two with white stuff, and two had not yet been graved.[23] This of course was not a fully representative sample because most of the sheathed ships would have been sent to the West Indies, which was then the main theatre of war.

Girdling

Like sheathing, girdling consisted essentially of nailing planks to the outside of the hull, over the main planking. The planks used for girdling, however, were much thicker, and served a different purpose. Whereas in sheathing they were intended to protect the hull or seal it against leaks, in girdling they were intended to enlarge it. Girdling was necessary because crude design techniques often resulted in failure. Many builders did not have the mathematical skill to calculate the displacement of a hull before it was launched. Moreover, in the seventeenth century there was often a tendency to cram a hull with more guns, men, and stores than it had been designed for. This was particularly common in the third quarter of the seventeenth century, when the demands placed on warships tended to increase quite quickly. Girdling added much more to the breadth than the length of a hull, which tended to increase stability, a quality lacking in many ships of the period. There was a particular tendency to overload the biggest ships, the three-deckers, and as a result many of the most famous ships of Charles II's Navy needed girdling. The *London* and *Henry* of 1656, the *Royal Katherine* of 1664, the *St Michael* of 1669, the *Prince* of 1670, the *Royal Charles* of 1673, and the *Britannia* of 1682 all had stability problems, or lay too low in the water, and needed girdling. In contrast, very few ships below the Third Rate were treated in this way.

The plank used for girdling had to be much thicker than that used for sheathing. According to one account from the 1690s, it would be 'as occasion requires ... from four to eight and ten inches thick on each side of the ship, in the parts that lie about the water's edge in the midships'.[24] The *Prince* of 1670 had $6\frac{1}{2}$in girdling, and it was proposed in 1674 that this should be replaced by 7in timber, but this was not considered worthwhile. Earlier, oak had sometimes been used for girdling, but fir was used for the *Henry* in 1654 and thereafter became the most common material. Fir was considerably lighter than oak, and it was suggested that to replace the fir on the *Prince* with oak would add 50 tons to her weight. Fir was a third of the cost of oak, could be acquired in greater lengths, and was easier to fasten, for it could be fixed with spike nails rather than bolts.[25] Girdling normally started below the lower wales of the ship, and extended to several feet below the waterline, where it was faired in with the original lines of the ship, hence the need for different thicknesses of timber.

Girdling tended to fall out of favour after 1690. In 1694 it was proposed to girdle the *Royal William* with 'a girdling containing 12 strakes, 14 inches broad and 8 inches thick ... wrought in proportion from the midships fore and aft.' The Navy Board opposed this, pointing out 'the uncertainty of any benefit in the practice of it, from many remote accidents; the certain destruction all such doubling makes upon the body tis wrought upon ...

and the danger of ill-stopping leaks where the girdling is disabled; the chargeableness thereof; and that all arguments for girdling are for making ships greater rather than better.' They also suggested that, taking the weight of the extra timber into account, girdling added very little to the buoyancy of a ship. There followed an acrimonious correspondence with the Admiralty, who eventually insisted that the ship be girdled.[26] Very few ships were girdled after the *Royal William*.

The Introduction of Lead Sheathing

There was nothing new about lead sheathing. Archaeologists have shown that it was used by the Romans, and in the late sixteenth century it was favoured by the Spanish and Portuguese.[27] The English were not impressed by it, for 'besides the cost and weight, although they use the thinnest sheet lead I have seen in any place, yet it is nothing durable, but subject to many casualties.'[28] In the 1660s Sir Phillip Howard invented a method of making sheet lead by rolling, rather than casting. This produced a thinner sheet, more regular in its thickness. By 1669 he had shown it to Sir Anthony Deane, then Master Shipwright at Portsmouth and a close friend of Samuel Pepys. Deane was encouraging. He saw many uses for the sheet, and predicted that it 'would not do amiss for sheathing, if nails can be found to last.'[29] In the following year Howard formed a company to manufacture and trade in the new product, and it was protected by Act of Parliament. It was soon recognised that there was an opportunity for a great market for lead sheathing if the Navy, and other shipowners, could be convinced of its value.

Some members of Parliament had already pointed out the disadvantages of lead. 'Its excess in charge above the current method, its rough lying on a ship's sides to the prejudice of their sailing, its liableness to galling from the cables, and cracking when brought aground; its tediousness in bringing on or off; aptness to foul, and difficulty in cleaning; lastly, its undurableness and doubtful efficacy in what was chiefly expected of it against the worm.'[30] This was not enough to deter the Navy Board, and early in 1671 it was persuaded to allow the lead sheathing of the *Phoenix*, recently built by Deane at Portsmouth. Deane used $5\frac{1}{2}$ tons of lead sheet, and $6\frac{3}{4}$cwt of lead nails in the process.[31]

The experiment was regarded as a success. The *Phoenix* was examined at Sheerness in 1673, after two voyages to the Mediterranean, and was found to be in good condition. A further report of 1674 stated that 'the sheathing of the said ship is firm and good, not at all damnified by the ranging of the cables along the side, or by rubbing on the ground, or otherwise.'[32] By the end of 1673, lead sheathing seemed ready to replace wood as the standard means of protection for ships on foreign voyages. The Admiralty decided that 'His majesty's ships may for the time to come be sheathed in no other manner than that of lead, without especial order given for that same from the board; These are to authorise to cause this, His Majesty's pleasure, to be duly complied with.'[33] The *Henrietta* had already been sheathed, and 20 more ships were

fitted over the next five years. The largest was the Third Rate *Harwich* which was as big as any ship normally sent to a foreign station. One Second Rate, the *St Michael*, was also considered for sheathing in 1675, but by that time opinion had begun to swing against milled lead, and its defects had begun to show themselves in a very spectacular manner.[34]

The Disadvantages of Lead

In April 1675 Sir John Narborough, in command of a squadron sent to the Mediterranean to protect shipping from the Barbary corsairs, was almost cast away in his flagship the *Henrietta*. 'My rudder was washed from my stern, the irons on the sternpost broke, and those on the rudder broke and drew from the wood, so that I was forced to get my rudder inboard to save it, and drove in the sea three days with the rudder lying on the deck.'[35] The problem, it was soon discovered, was that the gudgeons and pintles of the rudder had decayed rapidly, far more so than could be expected by normal wear. Soon other ships showed signs of the same decay. The *Phoenix*, reported of favourably in 1673, got into difficulties in the following year. 'We were coming home in a storm of wind, reeving our fore course when our rudder snapped off, the water's edge being worm eaten quite through, the lower part tore away all the eyes of the braces under water excepting one, and so sunk, the upper part hung fast, which I hung overboard, and took off, unto which I hung fastened planks to make a rudder as well as I could.'[36] Soon reports began to come in from all the lead sheathed ships that their rudder irons were dangerously weak.

The problem, not fully understood at the time, was that iron and lead in water caused an electrolytic reaction which resulted in rapid decay. The Company of Milled Lead attempted to explain it by claiming that the rudder irons had not been properly fitted before the ships sailed, but this was a spurious argument. Later, it provided its own rudder irons, covered with sheet lead, to alleviate the problem. By this time the very bolts of the hull were being affected by electrolysis in some ships. This phenomenon took some time to become apparent, because a coating of tar had been placed under the lead, as in normal sheathing, and this had delayed the penetration of the water. In 1678 it was found that the *Henrietta*'s 'inch bolts were eaten to the thickness of a straw, the braces and stirrups of the false keel eaten to nothing, and so it was likewise in the *Antelope*, occasioned by the copper nails, lead and salt making a kind of copperas that eats the ironwork very much in a short time, which will not be found so on ships that are sheathed with board.'[37] Already the Admiralty had ordered that the Navy Board 'do not for the time to come sheath any of His Majesty's greater ships with lead, till a more certain knowledge can be had of the true ground of the said evil.'[38] Over the next few years Deane and his allies attempted to find ways round the problem, but to no avail. No more ships were sheathed with lead after 1679, and the problems of shipworm remained unsolved.

Chapter 11. Copper Sheathing

Early Proposals

Copper had long been used in small quantities in place of lead which was usually used to cover parts of the anchor lining and to line parts of the sternpost and rear face of the rudder, for example. It was first proposed for sheathing in 1708, by Charles Perry and others. The Navy Board rejected it on grounds of expense, the amount of time and labour involved, and the belief that it would be very difficult to repair if damaged. Its use was not to be suggested again for over half a century.[1]

In the late 1750s some experiments were made in the use of copper on ships' keels and false keels. It seems that the *Invincible*, lost off Portsmouth in early 1758, had her false keel coppered.[2] Late in 1759 copper plates, 2ft × 4ft and weighing 20oz per square foot, were sent to the yards to be fitted to the bottoms and sides of the main keels of several ships. Copper was also to be fitted to the bearding of the rudder and the back of the sternpost, and the false keel was to be 'filled' with copper and iron nails driven close together. Ships fitted in this way included the *Norfolk*, *Panther*, *Medway* and *America*.[3]

First Experiments

In 1761 the Admiralty, horrified by the bad condition of the ships which had recently returned from the West Indies 'remarkably eat by the worm', decided to try a radical experiment on the 32-gun frigate *Alarm*. Her bottom was to be covered with 'soft stuff', which comprised hair, yarn and brown paper, over which very thin copper, weighing 12oz to the square foot, was to be nailed. The Navy Board ordered 'the greatest care be taken that the surface thereof be set smooth, easy, and close to the ship's bottom, and that the joints and edges of each plate are wrought with a lap over each, of $\frac{3}{4}$ or $\frac{7}{8}$ of an inch ... well fastened with copper nails throughout the whole.' The sheathing was to extend up to 1ft below the waterline, and a strake of elm, 3in thick, was to lap over the upper edge of the copper. Above that, conventional sheathing was to be fitted.[4]

The *Alarm* was surveyed in 1763, and the report was generally favourable, though there had been a recurrence of an ancient problem. The Navy Board was 'greatly surprised to perceive the effect the copper had upon the iron where the two metals touched; but it was most remarkable at the rudder and in the fastenings of the false keel.'[5] Two more ships, the *Dolphin* and *Tamar*, were coppered in 1764. The former was sent on a voyage of circumnavigation. In 1766 the *Alarm* was surveyed again, and more flaws were found. 'The copper sheathing with respect to preserving the ship's bottom from the worms, and from fouling, has fully answered expectation, but that it has not succeeded equally well in other respects, the verdigris produced from the copper being found to have very pernicious effects upon the iron-work underwater, some of the bolts being so much wasted as to render many of them of very little service.' The *Alarm*'s copper was to be taken off and not replaced. The *Tamar* showed evidence of similar problems, and it was recommended that the copper of both the *Dolphin* and *Tamar* be removed.[6]

In 1767, the Admiralty reverted to the experiments of a century ago, and tried lead sheathing again. This was fitted to a surprisingly large ship, the 74-gun *Marlborough*, and in 1769 it was ordered that it should be tried on another 74, the *Egmont*. However, in early 1770 before this had been done the *Marlborough* was surveyed. The surveyors examined the condition of her bottom and found 'the lead all off, except a small part on the knee of the head and the rudder'.[7] Lead was less malleable than copper, and apparently could not survive the demanding conditions of the time. It was ordered that both the *Marlborough* and the *Egmont* be sheathed in the conventional manner.

A few more ships were coppered in 1769, including the *Aurora*, *Stag* and the *Hawke* sloop.[8] This time some attempts had been made to solve the problem of decay in the hull bolts, for the *Hawke* had bolts made from a cuprous alloy. She was to return from a five-year cruise in relatively good condition.

War with America began in 1775, and fast frigates were needed to combat the American privateers. Moreover, the supplies which had been carefully cultivated in North America, of rosin, tar and turpentine, were now cut off. Seven ships, one 32, one 24, four 20s and a sloop, were coppered during 1776. Early in 1777 it was ordered that eight vessels about to be built should have cuprous bolts fitted below the waterline, and then be coppered.[9] This experiment was not a success. The bolts were not strong enough to hold the hull together securely, as a suitable alloy had not yet been developed, and they could only be fitted to ships which were building. In a war which was rapidly escalating, there could be no question of re-bolting the whole fleet in this way. In general the Navy Board pinned its hope on keeping the copper away from the iron, by placing various substances between them. But one problem had now been solved. The iron braces and pintles of the rudder were replaced by ones made of 'mixed metal', an alloy including copper. There were no more reports of decay in these parts.[10]

Coppering the Fleet

By 1778, the trend towards coppering had gained some momentum. Captains were becoming familiar with its dramatic effects on speed and on the preservation of the hull, and were beginning to ask for their own ships to be coppered, but its general application would be an enormous step. To fit a 74-gun ship in copper would cost £1500, in contrast to wood which cost £262.[11] In the days when naval administrators tended to be cautious, and Parliament expected them to be frugal, it would have taken a considerable impulse to initiate such a programme. Much of the impetus came from the war situation. France declared war in 1778, Spain in 1779, and the Netherlands in 1780. For the first time, the Navy was expected to face its three greatest rivals, combined and undefeated. It was heavily outnumbered, but coppering could add to its strength by reducing the need for maintenance so that ships could spend longer at sea, as well as making them faster. One captain wrote that the sheathing on his ship 'answered beyond my hopes as her superiority in sailing is hardly credible'.[12]

Charles Middleton, Controller of the Navy, provided much of the impetus for coppering. He collected reports, lobbied his superiors in the Admiralty, and even explained the advantages of

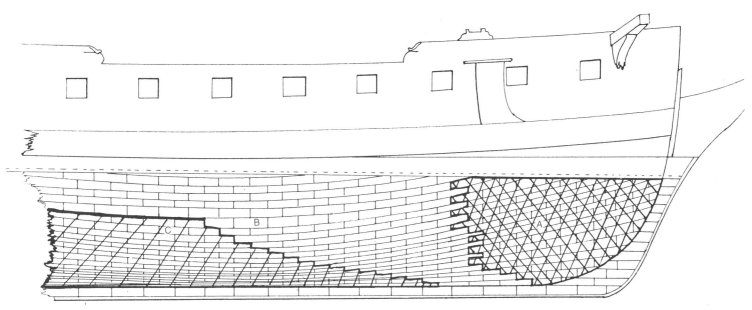

Coppering a 32-gun frigate, by an order of November 1779. A. Thick copper, 32oz per square foot. B. Medium copper, 28oz per square foot. C. Thin copper, 22oz per square foot. Note that the area immediately below the waterline is still sheathed with wood.

the new system to the King. Perhaps his role was not so crucial as he would claim, for he had a tendency towards self-publicity, and the First Lord of the Admiralty himself was not averse to change. But the importance of the decision to go ahead with coppering the whole fleet cannot be overstated.

The programme began in earnest in May 1779, when it was ordered that all ships of 32 guns and less should be coppered next time they were in dock. In July this was extended to 44-gun ships, and in April 1780 to cutters. The coppering of ships of the line began early in 1779, with two 74s, the *Invincible* and *Russell*. Because a fleet made up of both coppered and un-coppered ships would be difficult to keep together, it was decided that the whole battlefleet should be coppered. By 1781, 82 ships of the line, more than half the fleet, had been coppered. So had 14 50-gun ships, 115 frigates, and 182 sloops and cutters.[13] By the end of the war in 1783, it was accepted that all ships should be coppered, though by that time the decay of the underwater bolts was beginning to cause problems again.

Under the Copper

Numerous remedies were tried to prevent the interaction between the iron bolts and the copper. By 1775 the inside of the sheets were painted with white lead, and by 1779 they were to be painted three times, ensuring that there was no gap in the paint to allow contact between the two. Paper was to be placed between the hull and the copper. In early 1779 cartridge paper was specified, substituted later in the year by brown paper. In 1780 a compound invented by one Dawson was tried, and by the middle of the year it was established as the main means of coating the inside of the copper sheets (though it had only been tried out for three months, and it is difficult to see how this could prove its long term effectiveness). The traditional coating of tar was still applied under the copper and brown paper, and efforts were made to see that the hull bolts were driven well into the wood, the space thus

created being well filled with tar, so that the iron would be as far as possible from the copper.[14]

It was enough to maintain the fleet together in the short term, but even before the end of the war grave difficulties were being experienced. In a storm at the end of 1782, four ships of the line were lost; this was largely attributed to the corrosion of hull bolts.[15] Surveys showed serious decay on many ships, and by 1783 the whole policy of coppering was in serious doubt.

Coppering Techniques

From early on, the standard sheet of copper was 4ft long and 14in wide. The plates used for the *Alarm* in 1761 were very thin, weighing only 12oz per square foot. They wore away far too quickly, and much thicker plates were used from then on. By 1779 three thicknesses of sheet were available, weighing 32, 28 or 22oz per square foot, and these were to remain standard. They were distributed about the ship according to the wear they were likely to encounter. The thickest were in the bows, the medium ones just behind the bows, and the rest of the ship was covered in the thinnest type.

The coppering roughly followed the run of the planking, so that it curved downwards towards midships. The lowest strake was put on first, and each plank was to overlap its neighbour by about $\frac{3}{4}$in.[16] On the first ships to be coppered, one sheet seems to have been placed directly above the corresponding one on the strake below; by 1779 this had been changed, and the strakes were staggered, as in brickwork.

Early copper sheathing stopped a foot or more below the waterline, and the area above was covered with conventional wooden sheathing. This was presumably because it was likely to be worn away by boats and anchors rubbing against the side. Wood was assumed to be less vulnerable to such wear, and it was easier to repair with the resources on board ship. Such a system was used on the *Alarm*, and also the *Dolphin*. It was still regarded

The coppering of a model, showing the arrangement of the sheets, and the positions of the nails. Author's photograph, courtesy of NMM.

as standard late in 1779, though it cannot have been used much later than this, for the *Bedford* did not have any sheathing boards in May 1779, nor did any of the ships coppered at Deptford in 1781. Contemporary models of coppered ships are rare, but those that exist show the copper ending below the waterline. In 1783, it was ordered that the copper should end 16in above the waterline.[17]

The false keel presented some difficulties. It was vulnerable to damage in any grounding, and could not be repaired easily in a dockyard, for the whole ship rested on it. In 1779 it was to be covered with prepared paper, but after 1780 it was to be filled with small nails, both copper and iron, as this was a more robust protection than copper sheets. The main hull was protected by the copper between the main keel and the false keel, so that in a sense the latter could be sacrificed.

The nails used to sheath the *Alarm* were 3in long. Later, various sizes of nail were used, but they were specified by weight rather than length. In 1779 nails with countersunk heads were used as an experiment, and these were found to be 'superior in every way'.[18] The top of the sheathing, where it reached the waterline, was covered by a batten of 3in² elm. This was placed over the edge of the copper, so that there would still be some protection if the wood was eaten away. In 1781, it was ordered that the batten should be fitted properly, following complaints that this was not always so.[19]

The gudgeons, or braces, and pintles of the rudder had long presented a problem due to their deterioration. By 1768 it was appreciated that they would have to be made from a cuprous alloy, so this was done. It was beyond the capabilities of the yards to make them, and exact models of the braces and pintles of each

The coppering on the bow and stern of a model of the 74-gun ship Bellona *of 1760. It is said, though without any irrefutable evidence, that this model was used to demonstrate the principle of sheathing to the King in 1779.* Author's photographs, courtesy of NMM.

ship had to be sent to the contractor, William Forbes of Deptford. These models were not always accurate enough and in 1781 it was ordered that the braces and pintles be made thinner rather than thicker, as the metal tended to expand in casting. Another order of that year stipulated they should also be covered with copper sheets to protect them further but this practice is not evident on any models or drawings.[20]

The Success of Copper

One great advantage of copper sheathing was that it did not have to be imported. As the American Colonies were lost, and the Baltic proved as unreliable as ever, the old materials of rosin, tar and turpentine became more expensive and difficult to obtain. Copper was expensive too, but its supply could be guaranteed. Initially it came from mines in North Wales, and later from Cornwall.

It is possible that copper was first seen as a direct substitute for wood sheathing, in that it merely covered the coating of tar and hair that did the actual work of keeping out the worm. The coating of tar, paper, and other substances was still placed between the sheathing and the hull, but now its function was to protect the copper from the iron, except when the sheathing had been removed by accident when it also had to keep out the worm. In general the copper worked because it formed a tight, impenetrable seal. If this was breached by damage or due to faulty workmanship, then the worm could get in. A case in point was the 74-gun ship *Alfred*. A year after damaging her copper in a collision with a frigate, it was reported that 'The accident last year to the *Alfred*, by running on board the *Nymphe*, has given such scope for the worm, that her bows are quite destroyed; several plank had not half an inch left sound.'[21] Orders from the Navy Board aimed to ensure that the sheets of copper were nailed on as securely as possible. At some stage the system of nailing was changed. Originally nails had been placed only round the edges of the copper. Later they were placed across the surface as well, to guarantee a tight seal.

The most immediate advantage of copper was its protection against weeds and barnacles. In contact with the water it formed a slightly poisonous surface, which deterred weed far more efficiently than any of the old compounds. One side effect of this was that the copper gradually decayed; this was why thicker sheets were used after the earliest experiments. The introduction of copper sheathing was one of the great successes of the eighteenth century naval administration. The expression 'copper bottomed' began to take on its present meaning, and Sandwich, First Lord of the Admiralty, wrote, 'copper bottoms need fear nothing'.[22]

Replacing the Hull Bolts

Unfortunately Sandwich was a little too optimistic. The greatest danger to a copper bottom was still the decay of the bolts which held the hull together. The solution to this problem, which

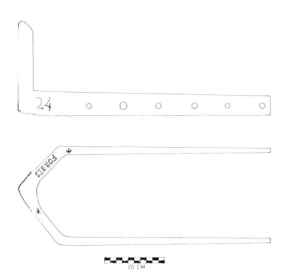

A rudder iron recovered from the wreck of the Pandora, *lost in 1791. It is marked with the number of guns carried by the ship and the name of Forbes, the Admiralty's main contractor for copper.*

was to replace the iron bolts with those made from an alloy, was known as early as 1768, but two factors prevented its immediate application: the cost, and the difficulty of finding an alloy which would not react with copper, but would be nearly as strong as iron.

The cost of replacing the copper bolts would be enormous. The Navy had 471 ships and vessels at the end of the war in 1783. Each one would have to be put in dock, unsheathed, and have every iron bolt drawn out and replaced by an alloy one. For a ship of 32 guns, about the middle of the range in size, a set of copper bolts was estimated to cost £622, whereas iron ones would cost only £161.[23] This did not even take into account the labour of taking the old bolts out and replacing them. However, time was available after the end of the war. All the ships would eventually have to be docked, and on many of them the bolts were already decaying. It was reasonable to spend a few hundred pounds on each ship, if only to preserve the work that had been done already.

By 1783 a suitable alloy had been found, which was made of copper and zinc, and was drawn though grooved rollers to harden it. It was developed by Forbes, Westwood, and Collins, and was a notable example of the new scientific and industrial spirit which was prominent in Britain in the age of industrial revolution. In December 1783 the Navy Board was asking 'whether in order to remove every objection that can arise from ignorance or prejudice against copper sheathing ... it may not be most prudent in the end to use compound metal bolts.'[24] In August 1786 it was decided to re-bolt all ships as fast as possible. This took a few years, and thereafter no major changes were needed in the system of coppering, which further proved its worth in the long wars with France which were to follow.

PART IV

Pumps

Chapter 12. Pumps and Drainage

Drainage of the Decks

Wooden ships were never entirely watertight. However carefully the joins between the planks were caulked, they were strained and forced apart by the movement of the ship, and soon let in water. More came from above, from rain, spray, and the breaking of waves against the hull. Water could infiltrate all parts of a vessel, so that in a storm there was not a dry place anywhere. Vital areas had to be protected, and the water removed before it overwhelmed and sank the ship. The water which came in from underneath the vessel, and a proportion of that which came in from above, reached the lowest part of the ship, where it was eventually removed by the pumps. Most of the water which found its way to the higher decks could be ignored, as it would drain over the side of the ship.

The system of drainage was an integral part of the ship. All the decks were cambered, to allow water to run to the sides. The orlop deck had much less camber than the others, because it was underwater. As a general rule, the higher the deck, the greater the camber. By modern standards the degree of camber on each deck might seem excessive, but it must be remembered that the ship would usually be heeled to one side or the other when under way. Moreover, a large camber may have been useful in arresting the recoil of the guns.

The hatchways, ladderways, gratings, and partners of the masts and capstans, were placed in a line down the centre of the deck. They were protected from water by coamings, raised several inches above the deck. Unless the level of water on the deck was very high, none would penetrate the coamings. The water was kept off the planking and timbers of the sides of the ship by waterways. These were not sunken gutters, as one would expect to find on a modern ship, but thick planks. They formed the join between the internal planking of the side and the planking of the deck and protruded a few inches above the deck planking.

Scuppers were placed at intervals along the waterways. They were lead pipes which each had a flat plate on the inboard end, to prevent them from being slowly pushed overboard by the pressure of the water. Large ships had about six or seven scuppers on each deck, smaller ones slightly fewer. Some scuppers had a flat plate at the outboard end, and ran through the flat of the deck itself. Others had an angled plate, and ran partly through the waterway and through the deck. The scuppers of a 74-gun ship of the 1780s had an internal diameter of 4in.[1] Seventeenth and eighteenth century scuppers seem to have been straight, but some of those used in the early years of the nineteenth century were curved, and systems were devised for opening and cleaning them.[2] Scupper leathers were fitted on the outside of the hull. They were hinged against the hull in such a way that water could flow out, but none could enter. By the mid-eighteenth century, a more sophisticated version was in use, which had a form of leather spout which made the water run clear of the side of the hull.

Naturally the more exposed decks – the forecastle, poop, quarterdeck and upper deck – were the most vulnerable to rain-

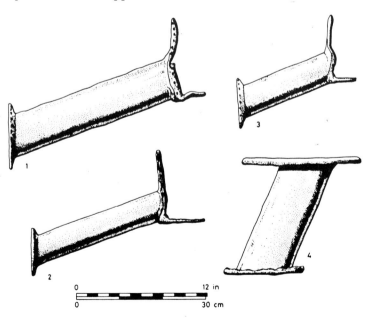

Lead scupper linings of different shapes, recovered from the wreck of the Dartmouth *of 1655. Number 4 is a pissdale pipe.*

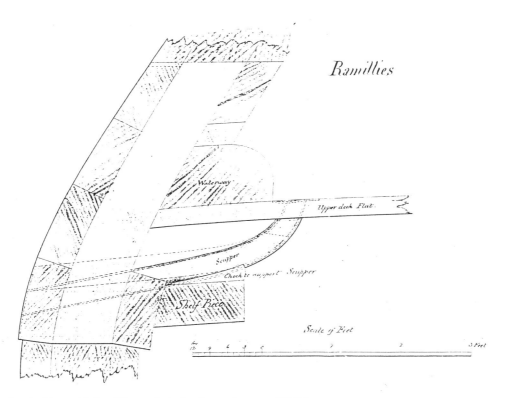

The type of scupper fitted to the 74-gun ship Ramillies, *early in the nineteenth century*. NMM.

water and spray, but the middle and lower decks had to be protected too, as some rainwater would fall through the gratings. The gunports sometimes had to be opened for action in rough weather, but even when closed a certain amount of water came through them. On the lower deck, water also came in through the hawse holes, which could not always be stopped up efficiently. This was partly controlled by the manger, which separated the formost part of that deck from the rest. It had its own scuppers which were evidently intended to make the water drain into the main part of the deck in a controlled manner.

Drainage of the Hold

Water which found its way to the bottom of the ship, whether by leaking through the sides or by draining down from the decks above, had to be removed by the pumps. First it had to be collected together near the pump intake. Dutch ships had flat bottoms, so needed pumps placed well away from the centre line. British ships had much rounder bottoms, thus always had their main pumps situated close to the centre line. The lowest part of the ship was in midships, close to the heel of the mainmast, and arrangements were made so that the water would drain to that area. The very smallest vessels sometimes had a pump some way aft of the mainmast, because ships were usually trimmed at the stern, and water could be collected more efficiently in the aftermost part.

Many ships had holes, known as limber holes, drilled fore and aft through the lowest timbers of the frame, through which water which found its way between the timbers could drain. These are described in all the marine dictionaries. 'Limber holes are little square holes cut in the bottom of all the ground timbers next to the keel, right over the keel, about 3 or 4 inches square. The use whereof is to let the water pass to the well of the pump, which would else lie betwixt the timbers.'[3] There is reason to doubt that these holes were cut in British warships by the later seventeenth century. First, contracts for ships, fully detailed in all other respects, make no mention of them. Second, the spaces between the timbers at the lowest part of the hull were very small indeed. A typical contract of the 1690s[4] ordered 'The navel timbers to fill up the rooms' suggesting that there was to be no gap at all between the timbers at this level. Later, builders were allowed to leave some space if suitable timber was not available, but according to framing plans and models the gaps remained very narrow, and cannot have held a large quantity of water. Third, the pump itself must have had very little effect below the level of the top of the floor timbers. Though recesses were cut in the timbers to accommodate the lowest part of the pump, the chain pump did not actually take effect until some way above its lowest part (see page 68).

Instead, a drainage channel was created above the top of the floor timbers and first futtocks. On each side of the keelson one strake of internal planking was omitted, and this served as a gutter for the water. It was covered over by limber boards, short lengths of planking placed diagonally between the inner edge of the first strake of planking and the top corner of the keelson. The limber boards had small spaces between them to allow water to enter from the sides, but they kept the channel free from shingle ballast from the hold, and any other objects which might block the passage.

The Principles of the Chain Pump

The chain pump was of very ancient origin. It had been used by the Romans, and many other peoples, for agricultural drainage, and it has some claim to being the oldest form of pump ever used. It was introduced to English ships in Elizabethan times, probably as part of the Hawkins reforms in the 1580s.[5] Thereafter it remained the standard pump for all British warships above the Sixth Rate.

The chain itself was a loop, and was fitted with burrs, or saucers, every few feet. It passed through a tube leading from the hold of the ship to the lowest gundeck. The burrs had leathers, and fitted snuggly in the tube, so that their upward motion drew up the water. The chain was turned round a wheel fitted on the gundeck, which was equipped with winches for the men who actually provided the motive power. The water was discharged into a horizontal tube, called a dale, which directed it out to the side of the ship, where it drained into the scuppers and out of the ship. After lifting the water, the chain passed over the wheel, down another tube, round a small wheel in the hold at the bottom of its travel, and back again through the first tube.

It has been estimated that the chain pump was only about 50 per cent efficient, but it could be used to raise a large volume of water very quickly. The rotary motion of the winches, as opposed to the lever motion of a suction pump, allowed a large number of men to operate the machine at once, and this was a definite advantage on a ship with a large crew. On the other hand, the rotary action was hard on the men. 'Few officers of any experience must not have known the difficulty with which men are almost drove to return to the pumps of leaking ships, when obliged to keep them constantly going. It strains their loins, affects the muscular parts of their arms like violent rheumatic pains, and galls their hands.' It was therefore suggested by some that a horizontal motion, as on a capstan, would be easier.[6] However, the chain pump relied largely on speed of movement for its effect, especially if the leathers were worn; that of a capstan would have been much slower.

Other disadvantages of the chain pump were that the chain tended to break in times of stress, which could be disastrous in a leaking ship in a storm, and that the leathers had to be renewed every 20 days, even with normal wear.[7] To counteract these defects, ships carried at least two pumps, spare chains, complete with burrs, and plenty of spare leathers. Another disadvantage of the chain pump was that it did not eject water under pressure, so it was little use in fire-fighting.

Parts of the Chain Pump

The tube was bored from a solid piece of wood, usually elm in the seventeenth century. In 1717 it was ordered that it be bored from oak, and have 5in internal diameter in the chamber, and 5½in diameter above that. On the outside, it was usually square in cross-section, though round ones were introduced at the beginning of the eighteenth century and eventually these came to predominate. The length of the tube related to the size of the ship. In 1686, the largest pumps of a First Rate were 31ft long, while those of a Fifth Rate were 16ft.[8] Until 1717 the chain itself was made up of S-shaped links. After that, conventional welded links were used until the third quarter of the century.[9]

The burrs were fitted every few feet along the chain. Usually they were saucer-shaped, and had a round piece of leather attached to them to form a reasonably tight seal within the tube. Some sources imply that there was one saucer per leather, but it seems more likely that the leather was sandwiched between two saucers.[10] Other shapes of burr, for example cup-shaped or spherical, can be seen on some chain pumps, but not on ships' pumps which invariably had saucers and leathers. It is not clear how tight the leathers had to be. If very tight, they would hold the water well, but slow down the movement of the pump, if too loose, the converse would occur. In general, speed of movement seems to have been preferred to tightness of fit.

At the bottom end of the pump, the chain passed round a simple roller. This must have been a point of weakness in the system, as the burrs passed over it, causing very uneven movement. But there is no sign of any complaints about it, and only one drawing, in Falconer's *Dictionary*, shows a pump which seems to be fitted to correct this fault. In this case the lower wheel is recessed to take the burrs as they pass round it. The burrs of the conventional system were flattened as they passed over the roller, because of the flexibility inherent in the chain; but this was not to be the case with the new pumps introduced in the 1770s.

The bottom part of the pump was known as the chamber. In the 1680s this consisted of two plates, one on each side, through which the spindle for the roller passed. Under the chamber lay the sole, which formed the base of the pump. All these parts were made of iron, except the roller, which was brass. In 1717 the chamber was to be 4 or 5ft long.[11]

The pump did not begin to operate until the burr entered the tube. Usually this occurred at the level of the roller, and space had to be provided under the roller to allow the burrs to turn round it. In most cases the roller was fitted at the level of the top of the floor timber, with a recess cut in the timber to allow room for the burrs and chain to pass under the roller. Though the timber's recess was cut to half or two-thirds of its depth, very little water could be drawn off at such a low level, hence it seems unlikely that limber holes were needed, and water was taken only from above the level of the floor timber. Generally the pump was fitted between two timbers, so that each was cut out through half its width.

At the upper end of the pump was the wheel. This seems to have been turned from elm. Round its rim were sprockets, which were Y-shaped pieces of iron, with the upper arms curving outwards. The base of the Y was hammered into the wheel, and the arms were designed to hold the burrs as they came round. This feature of the design was much criticised. It was claimed that the sprockets could not hold the burrs efficiently, but often surged back under the weight of water.[12]

An axletree, or axle, passed through a square hole in the centre of the wheel, and was fixed in place by wedges. The windlass, or winch handle, was fitted to the end of this when the pump was in use. Until about 1730, the winch handle used for this seems to have been a simple L shape, which would have allowed room for only about three or four men to operate it at once. Later it was extended considerably, and shaped like a crankshaft, with several sections. It was supported at its outer end and in the middle by pillars and bitts, and it rotated through brass cleats known as rhodens. By this system, far more men could operate a pump. In 1768, 26 men were used on the pump of a 74-gun ship, and it is estimated that a pair of the *Victory*'s pumps could employ about 30. Because regular relief was necessary, a large proportion of the ship's company would have been used in an emergency. By the

Seventeenth century chain pumps, from the Phillips print of the 1690s. There is no sign of a cistern. The weatherboarding of the well is shown, as is the method of fitting the windlass handle. Drawings by Dummer and Coronelli show similar pumps, but less clearly. NMM.

1750s, two pumps on the same side of a ship could be linked by a shaft between the axles, so that they could be operated in tandem.

The dale carried the water from the head of the pump to the side of the ship. The part of it which joined the pump was always square in cross-section. The rest of it was usually round in cross-section, except for a few which were square throughout their length. It tapered towards its outer end, and at the side of the ship it was supported by a light framework, and discharged into the scuppers. Some models show it penetrating the side of the ship, but neither models nor draughts of ships show any holes to make this possible. In the seventeenth century it seems that only one dale was provided for each pair of pumps, as only one pump would be operated at a time. Later, one was provided for each pump.[13]

Originally the pump discharged directly into the dale, but by around 1700 the cistern had been introduced. This was simply a wooden box, caulked round its edges, which was placed round the head of the pump, and had holes cut in it for the dale and the tubes. It allowed a certain amount of water to be stored, and helped regulate the flow into the dales. It also enabled two pumps on opposite sides of the ship to operate together, for a common cistern often linked them. A piece of wood could be placed down the centre of the cistern, to separate the two if necessary. Sometimes the pump's tube ended at the bottom of the cistern, but in other cases it went some way above it, probably to prevent the water from running back down again if the pump was temporarily stopped. The cistern was raised a few inches above the deck,

either by legs known as chocks, or by the extension of its inner and outer sides downwards.

In later years the double cistern went out of fashion, perhaps because it restricted access to the mast. From about the middle of the eighteenth century pumps fitted forward of the mainmast had separate cisterns, with a space between them. Evidently these could be linked when necessary by conduits. By this time the dale was fitted into place by means of a U-shaped recess in the outer face of the cistern. The conduits were put in place in a similar way.

On its return journey back to the chamber, the chain passed through another tube known as the back casing. It is possible that this was not used in the seventeenth century, as it was not absolutely necessary, but with the introduction of the cistern some means had to be found of stopping the water running out again, through the return hole. The back casing therefore had to extend some way up into the cistern. In the 1700s it did not extend all the way down to the chamber, stopping about a third of the way from the bottom, probably to allow room for maintenance. It is likely it remained like this until the old type of pump began to be replaced in the 1770s.

The hood was a semi-circular cover which fitted over the wheel, to protect it from damage, and perhaps to prevent water from splashing about the decks. It is first seen around 1730, though it is not shown on all models.

The Number and Position of the Chain Pumps

Shipbuilding contracts make little mention of pumps, though they sometimes specify the positions to be left clear for them on the decks. It can be assumed that pumps were made by the dockyards or by private contractors, and were fitted after the ship was completed. The pumps were placed in an area known as the well, round the mainmast. This extended through the orlop deck down to the hold, and the floor of the ship. It was rectangular, and sealed off from the rest of the ship by weatherboarding, which was fitted with doors so the pump could be reached.

In the early seventeenth century most ships had two pumps, side by side on the lower deck, aft of the mainmast. Three-deckers had four by the third quarter of the seventeenth century, two aft and two forward of the mainmast. After about 1740 ships of 70 guns and more were also given another extra pair, as were all ships of the line later on.[14]

It was essential that the wheel of the pump was placed in the athwartships plane, as this allowed the winch handles to run fore and aft, so that they could be extended almost indefinitely. It also made it somewhat easier for the wheel to discharge directly into the dale, before the advent of the cistern. The head of the pump had to be placed on the lower gundeck because this was the first deck above the waterline. Pairs of pumps were always fitted side by side, so that the one on the lee side could do most of the work, especially in the seventeenth century when there was no direct connection between the two. If the ship had a substantial heel, as was likely in a storm, then the water had to be discharged over the lee side, for to put it over the other side would involve pushing it upwards.

Though the conventional chain pump predominated for many years, it was never without its critics. It was not used on the smallest vessels, and there were many who suggested its improvement, or replacement, on the larger ships.

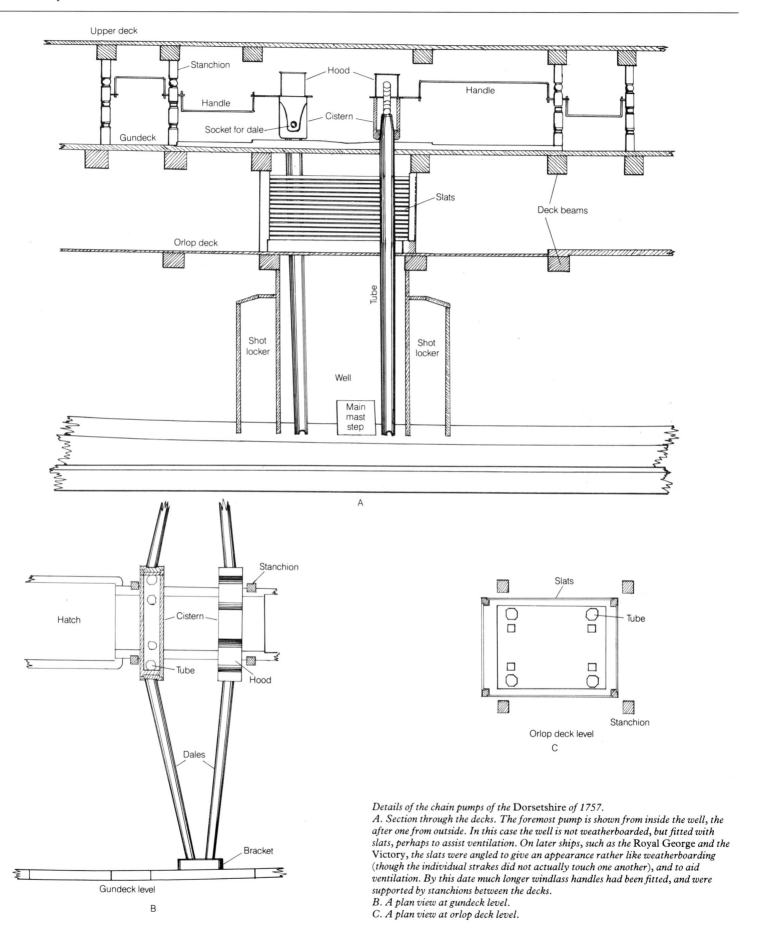

Upper deck

Stanchion

Hood

Handle

Handle

Cistern

Gundeck

Socket for dale

Slats

Deck beams

Orlop deck

Tube

Shot locker

Shot locker

Well

Main mast step

A

Stanchion

Hatch

Cistern

Tube

Hood

Dales

Bracket

Gundeck level

B

Slats

Tube

Stanchion

Orlop deck level

C

Details of the chain pumps of the **Dorsetshire** *of 1757.*
A. Section through the decks. The foremost pump is shown from inside the well, the after one from outside. In this case the well is not weatherboarded, but fitted with slats, perhaps to assist ventilation. On later ships, such as the **Royal George** *and the* **Victory**, *the slats were angled to give an appearance rather like weatherboarding (though the individual strakes did not actually touch one another), and to aid ventilation. By this date much longer windlass handles had been fitted, and were supported by stanchions between the decks.*
B. A plan view at gundeck level.
C. A plan view at orlop deck level.

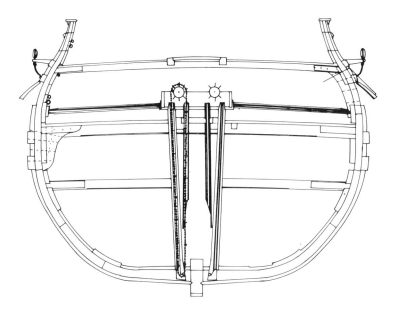

The early eighteenth century chain pump, on a midship section of the Resolution *of 1708. This is one of the first examples of a chain pump with a cistern. The shortness of the back casing can also be seen.*

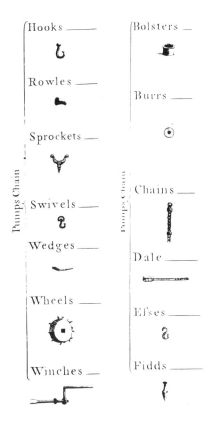

Pumps Chain

Hooks _____	Bolsters _____
Rowles _____	Burrs _____
Sprockets _____	
Swivels _____	Chains _____
Wedges _____	Dale _____
Wheels _____	Efses _____
Winches _____	Fidds _____

Parts of the chain pump, from Blanckley's Naval Expositor *of 1750. Many of the items shown in this illustration would have been for repairs only, but it also shows the shape of the sprockets and how they were fitted to the wheel, the windlass handle and how it fits to the axle, how the burrs fit on the chain, and a square section dale.*

Left. A rather simplified model of the pumps on a 70-gun ship of around 1730. It is one of the first sources to show the hood in use. It also displays the slot in the side of the cistern for fitting the dale, and the short windlass handles which were then in use. Author's photograph, courtesy of NMM.

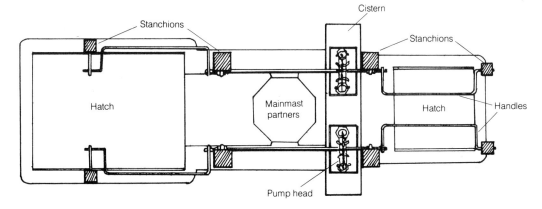

The plan of a pump on the gundeck of an early 74-gun ship. This vessel is unusual because it only had one pair of pumps, unlike most ships of its size, which by the 1750s had two pairs. It also clearly shows how the handles were fitted.

Chapter 13. The Improved Chain Pump, and the Brake Pump

Inventions

By the third quarter of the eighteenth century, the chain pump was beginning to attract considerable attention from inventors, and the Navy Board received several proposals every year for improving it. By the end of the century one inventor complained that 'the many trifling applications made to the public boards for encouragement by individuals of all descriptions make it difficult to procure attention to any.'[1] The chain pump attracted attention because it was one of the few mechanical devices aboard ship with which a land-based engineer was familiar. It had many applications in agriculture, mining, and civil engineering, and the most succesful improvement to it came directly from the construction industry. It was very simple in principle, and could be understood by the amateur scientists and engineers of the day. All felt a patriotic duty to help the Navy, and were lured by the potential of profit from a device which might end up being fitted aboard several hundred ships.

The first suggestions for improvement came in the 1690s, when Robert Ledingham produced a machine which would 'not only prevent the ascending of that poisonous stench from the bilge water, but also afford a means of cleaning and purifying the same'. It could do three times as much work as the old pump, while 'still reserving the use of the chain pumps'.[2] By the 1750s, the Navy Board was testing one or two proposals a year. In 1750 one by Adam Cooper was rejected; at the end of the year one by Francis Millay and Co was tested and found wanting. In 1751, the proposals of Thomas Templar were rejected, though it was to be 1754 before this machine was finally abandoned. In 1753 Tuite, Donaldson, and Spivey produced a pump which they claimed could discharge 113 tons of water an hour. This plan gained some support from the Assistant Surveyor of the Navy, but it was finally rejected in 1755. In the 1800s, the process of testing continued: Roberts in 1805, Blake and Stole, Grynne the mathematics master at Christ's Hospital, and Joseph Seaton in 1807, and Noble in 1808, all produced inventions with limited success.[3]

The Coles–Bentinck Pump

William Coles was an engineer and pump maker. His new machine was largely inspired by a pump used for building the new Blackfriars Bridge in London. In co-operation with Captain John Bentinck of the Royal Navy, he presented it to the Admiralty in 1768, and it was tested aboard the *Seaford* in August, against a more conventional pump. At first the Navy Board was not impressed and Slade, the Surveyor of the Navy, suggested that it was no improvement on the older model. A further test was made aboard the *Swiftsure* in July 1769, with more success. It was concluded that the old pump was still better in that 'it will bring up considerably more water at a stroke', and that the chain on the

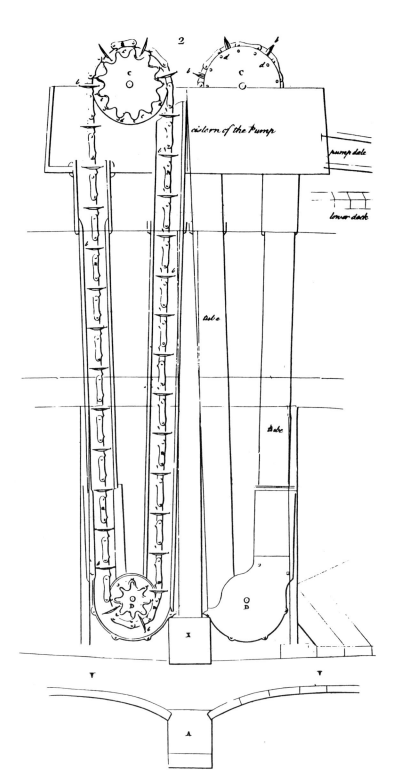

A mid-eighteenth century chain pump, from Falconer's Dictionary. *Though it has some features in common with the Coles pump there are also many differences, most notably, the wheels. The lower wheel is much bigger than normal, and has recesses to receive the burrs. Though this would have greatly enhanced the smoothness of the pump's movement, it would also have created a large area at the bottom of the pump where it would not be effective. Either this is an early version of the Coles pump, or it is one of the many other inventions of the period.*

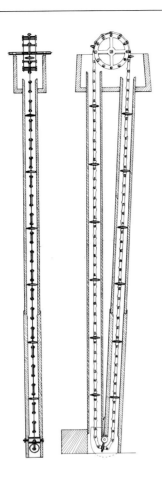

A sectional view of the Coles pump, as eventually adopted.

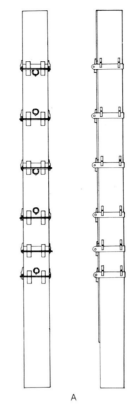

Details of the Coles pump.
A. The tube, showing the removeable sections.

B. A perspective view of part of the tube, showing the arrangement of pins and wedges which made it possible to remove one of the panels for repair.

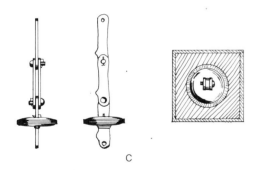

C. Details of the chain and the saucers, illustrating how they fitted in the tube.

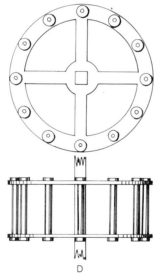

D. The wheel.

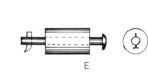

E. The return roller, at the foot of the pump, showing the cotter pin which held it in place.

new one was difficult to repair in case of breakage. On the other hand, the Coles pump 'works so very easy to the people, and without any surges, that it will . . . in that respect, have the advantage of the chain pump.'[4]

At another test in 1770, it was complained that the 'standard' pump provided by the Navy Board was in fact a specially improved model. 'The additional sprockets on the wheel are all secured with bolts through each, also a small additional burr on the upper part of the leathers, and the whole pump in general is fitted in a more complete manner than they are on board His Majesty's ships to which we belong', wrote the carpenters who were ordered to witness the trial. Nevertheless, the new pump was favoured by the eleven captains present. 'The new invented pump was worked with greater ease, and the people appeared much less fatigued, and in all respects it greatly has the preference.' It could be operated with less men, and it could lift nearly twice as much water in a given time than the old one. The Navy Board agreed to recommend its general adoption. Soon afterwards, the trial model was used to help fight a fire in Portsmouth Dockyard, and its success in this influenced the final decision.[5]

An Admiralty order of October 1770 specified that it should be carried by all ships large enough to carry a chain pump.[6]

The Advantages of the Coles–Bentinck Pump

The most important feature of the new pump was the chain itself, and the wheel round which it passed. Whereas the old pump had used ordinary chain, the Coles pump used something rather like modern bicycle chain, with links made from cast iron. Each 'centre link' was oval in shape, with a flange on its inner edge, and a hole at each end. Between the centre links were the 'paired links', rather irregular in shape, but also with a hole at each end. They were held to the centre links by link pins, which in turn were retained by cotter pins. Two links, side by side, alternated with a single centre link, along the length of the chain.

The wheel of the old pump, made of solid wood and fitted with sprockets, was replaced with a new type. Two cast iron wheels were placed side by side on the axle, a few inches apart, and joined by bolts placed at intervals near their rims. Each link of chain had a triangular flange on its inner edge, and these were intended to be caught by the bolts of the wheel as it came round. Like the old pump, the leathers and saucers were fitted to some of the centre links, at regular intervals but unlike it, the burrs were held constantly at right angles to the chain. This had some disadvantages. During the trials of 1769, 'a broom by some accident

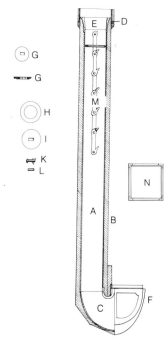

The type of metal chamber introduced in 1802, and produced by Collins, Noble and Broughton.
A. Metal chamber.
B. Oak case.
C. Metal circular bottom, and brass frame.
D. Cast iron hoop.
E. Metal conical piece with square at the top.
F. Oak cheek.
G. Metal saucers.
H. Leather ring.
I. Plan of the top saucer.
K. Metal bolt with copper forelock for joining the length of chain.
L. Metal bolt for riveting the links together.
M. Lengths of metal chain.
N. Top view of square top.

The pumps fitted on a model of a frigate of the 1780s, showing the handles. In this case cisterns do not seem to have been fitted. Author's photograph, courtesy of Science Museum.

One of the Victory's *pumps, showing how the metal chamber was joined to the wooden tube.* Author's photograph, courtesy of HMS *Victory.*

Part of the Victory's *windlass handle.* Author's photograph.

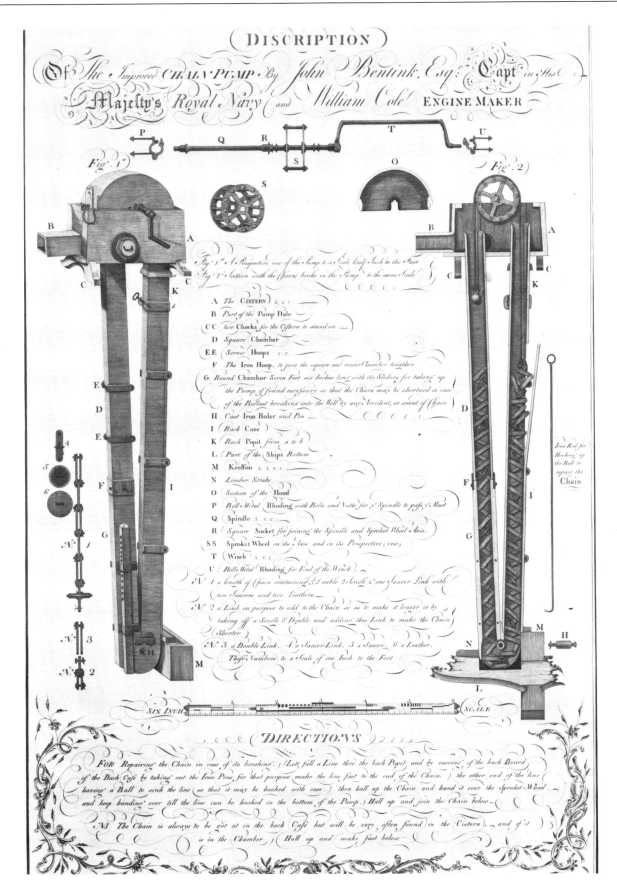

The 'pump print' which was issued to ships' carpenters. It contains instructions on how to deal with breakages in the Coles pump, and details of its construction. NMM.

was left in the well, and was brought up in the old chain pump . . . Had the accident happened to the new pump, we presume it could not have been brought up, but must either have broke the chain . . . or entirely stopped the working of the pump, on account of the burr being cast on the plate, and therefore at right angles to the plate. The burrs on the old pump when any obstruction of the like kind happens is put into an oblique situation, and gives room between the burr and the cylinder for it to be brought up with the water.'[7] Later pumps seem to have had the burr placed over the chain, rather than cast as part of it; perhaps this allowed more flexibility.

Another complaint was that the new pump brought up less water per revolution than the old. This was attributed to the fact that the chain itself took up more space within the system. But the main advantage of the new pump was that it was less likely to surge. The projections on the links were held quite efficiently by the bolts on the wheel, better than the sprockets on the old system held the burrs.

Improvements to the New Pump

By early 1773, Coles was forced to admit that some of his pumps were not entirely satisfactory, and that the chain was liable to 'many capital defects'.[8] It was ordered that the old pumps be re-issued, 'taking care that the lower part of the chamber be $5\frac{1}{2}$ inches diameter, one third part of the length of the pump from the bottom, of 6 inches bore, in order to take off the friction between the burrs and the upper part of the chamber, and that two burrs may always be in the lower part of the chamber, to prevent the escape of the water downward out of the lower part of the pump.'[9]

By early 1774, Coles had modified his pumps to the Admiralty's satisfaction. Evidently there were some alterations to the manufacture of the chain for it was ordered that chain from old Coles pumps be used for dockyard service.[10] It was probably at this time that the pump gained another new feature. The tube of the old pump had been bored from a solid piece of wood, and it is probable that the first Coles pumps were the same in this respect. Later pumps had an opening panel for most of the length of both the tube and the back casing. This made access to a broken chain much easier, for the new type of chain, unlike the old, could not easily be reached by hooking it from above. In later years further precautions were taken against breakages. From 1781, a print of the pump, with full instructions on how to recover the chain, was issued to the carpenter of every ship which had one fitted, and carpenters were recommended to practice this. Another improvement came in the 1800s, when the links of the chain were made of brass rather than iron.

The Brake Pump or Hand Pump

The chain pump, despite its many advantages, was not suitable for smaller ships. It worked best only when a large number of men were operating it and these had to be replaced at short intervals because they became tired. Merchant ships, like the smallest warships, had much smaller crews than other warships, and few of them carried chain pumps. Instead they had a brake, or hand pump.

The brake pump operated simply, on the principle of suction. A tube, usually bored from elm (thus the pump was sometimes called the elm tree pump) led from the lower deck to the hold of the ship, in the well. Inside the tube were an upper and a lower 'box'. These were cylindrical in shape, and fitted tightly inside the tube, with the help of leather coverings. Each was bored through its centre, and above the hole a leather flap was fitted which could hinge upwards but not downwards. The lower box remained stationary during the working of the pump, and merely prevented water escaping. The upper box moved up and down the tube, sucking water after it. On the down stroke the flap opened and allowed the water to pass through. A staple, rather like the handle of a bucket, was fitted over the top of the box. To this handle a 'spear' was fixed, which was a 'long rod of iron with an eye at the upper end, which hooks to the brake and to the lower end of which the box is fitted.'[11] The 'brake' was the handle of the pump, and was simply a lever which pivoted above the top of the tube. Because of the lever action, only two or three men could operate each pump at a time, which was the main reason why it was not the standard pump on larger ships. By an order of 1743, hand pumps were to have 'brass chambers fitted to them, of good hard metal, of about $\frac{1}{4}$ of an inch thick, and 22 inches long; 5 inches bore in the clear, and to be about 30 pounds in weight, the lower edge of the chamber to be cyphered off withinside to prevent the lower box catching; the inside to be very smooth.'[12]

In the late seventeenth century the brake pump was carried by Sixth Rates and smaller vessels such as sloops and yachts. It can be seen on models of these ships, because the 'lower' deck was in fact the only complete deck above the waterline, and is visible from outside the ship. By 1800, Sixth Rates had generally expanded in size and number of crew, and carried two chain pumps, as did sloops. Brigs, fireships, cutters and bomb vessels were the only ships to carry hand pumps as their main pumps. Fireships had five, bomb vessels three, and brigs and cutters two.[13]

Improvements to the Brake Pump

After 1779, Coles supplied brake pumps as well as chain pumps to the Admiralty, but it is not clear if they were any different from

The heads of the brake pumps, on a sloop of the 1780s. Author's photograph, courtesy of NMM.

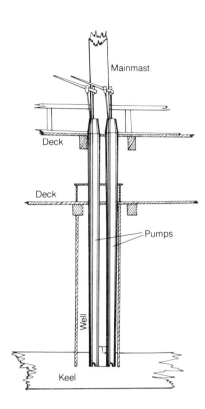

Suction pumps as fitted to the Experiment, *a transport purchased in 1765.*

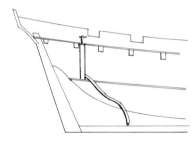

A hand pump as fitted to a cutter of the 1780s, to clear the after part of the ship. It has a pulling motion, rather than the usual lever action.

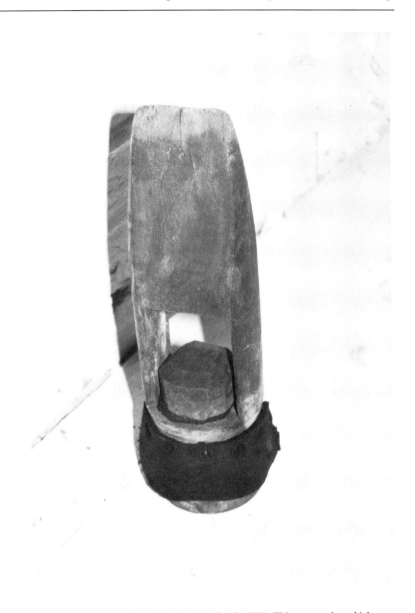

A pump box recovered from the Invincible, *lost in 1758. This may not be a ship's pump, but one brought on board from the dockyard while the ship was in danger.* Author's photograph.

the old type. There was a small change in 1789, when it was ordered that the brakes were to be fitted with quadrants, presumably to guide their movement.[14] Hand pumps attracted nearly as many inventors as chain pumps, and in 1795 Noble's pumps were fitted to many ships for a time. In 1803 Coles' improved brake pump was introduced. This seems to have had many more metal parts than the old ones. Its brake had an extension downwards through the deck, so that more men could operate it if necessary. It was evidently not a success, and was withdrawn in 1806. In 1804 elm still being used for the tubes of hand pumps; in 1807 pitch pine was allowed as a substitute.

A slightly different type of brake pump was fitted to cutters after about 1785. Instead of the usual lever action, it was operated by a simple pulling motion, perhaps because this took up less space on such a small vessel. It was placed near the stern, well away from the pump's usual position near the mainmast, because

'cutters draughts of water are so much by the stern, that when the pumps draw water out of the well, some water lays in their runs, which causes so great a stench that it is proper to have a pump fitted in their run.'[15]

Additional Brake Pumps

Sometimes ships with chain pumps carried extra hand pumps in the well. Ships of 70 guns and upwards evidently carried two by 1743, and according to an order of that year, they were to be placed 'in the well from the upper deck, and the ships of lesser classes allowed likewise two brake pumps, to be fixed in the well, to assist their chain pumps on occasion'.[16] This order seems to have lapsed in the 1750s, when the larger ships began to carry four chain pumps instead of two.

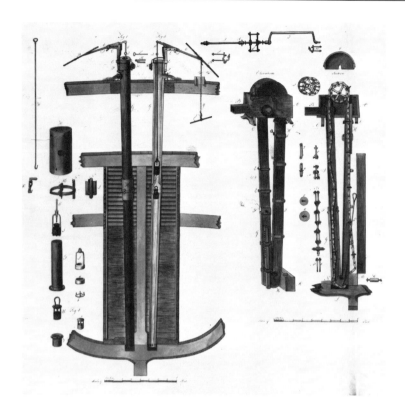

Drawings of a Coles hand pump of the 1780s. NMM.

A system of suction pumps and inlet tubes developed in 1807. NMM.

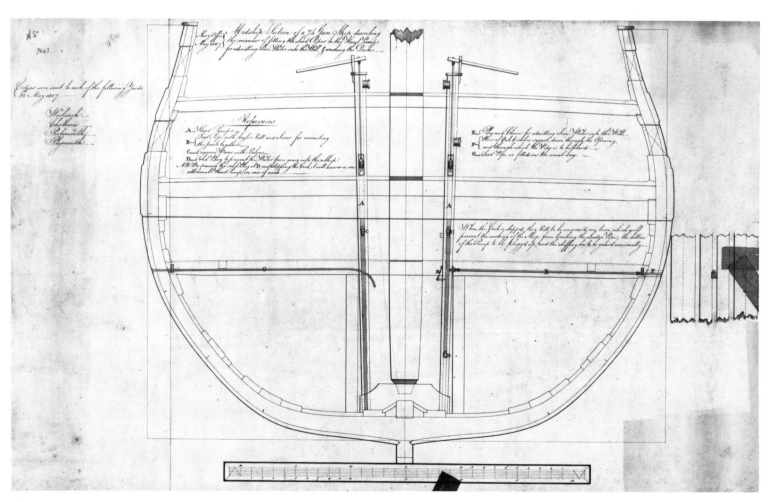

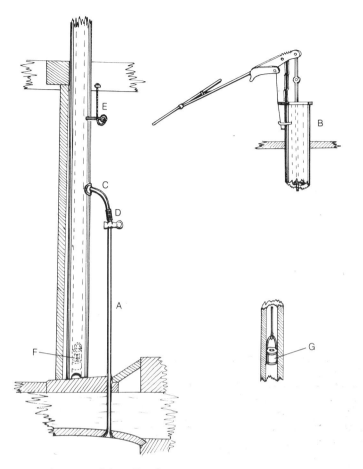

Some improvements introduced to the hand pump in 1803.
A. A lead pipe, 7 or 8ft long, with a stop-cock and hose, connected to the pump by a haunch.
B. A pump which received the water from the lead pipe A, and could be used occasionally to assist the other pumps in freeing the ship of water.
C. The hose and haunch with a screen for connecting the hose and pipe at D. A long hose could be fitted to C for washing the ship's decks in lieu of the short pumps and cistern.
D. A plug and chain for letting out the water contained between the pump box F and the piston G, for letting clean water into the well.

Pumps for Washing Decks

Until well into the eighteenth century, ships had either carried small hand pumps which were put temporarily over the side to draw up water for washing their decks, or hung buckets over the sides. These two methods were inconvenient, in that 'whilst they are in chase it is a hindrance to their sailing'. In 1743 the dock-yards were ordered to 'cause a leaden pump to be fixed in the heads of His Majesty's ships of 40 guns and upwards, as you may have time and opportunity for doing the same.'[17] In 1757 Captain Rodney of the *Dublin* asked for one, as 'the hand pump allowed for that purpose is not only troublesome to get over the side, but is very inconvenient in a cruising ship'. The custom had evidently fallen into disuse by 1771, when it was suggested that the *London* and *Victory* should have 'lead pumps ... fitted in the head, for watering their decks.'[18] The Admiralty vetoed this, and ordered the yards 'to cause no lead pumps to be fitted in the heads of His Majesty's ships'.[19]

A new system of supplying water for washing decks was introduced in 1770. The dockyards were ordered to 'fix a cistern in the well on board all three- and two-decked ships building, repairing and refitting, taking care that the cock is sufficiently large for the supply of water'.[20] A copper pipe was fitted on each side of the ship, about 3ft below the waterline, and led down to the cistern. When the ship was heeling under sail, at least one of the cocks would always be available. It was during repairs to such a pipe in 1782 that the First Rate *Royal George* was accidentally capsized and sunk.

The chain pump could only bring water to the level of the lower deck, so it was not an efficient means of supplying water to the upper and middle decks of larger ships. Despite its success at Portsmouth in 1770, it was of little use in fire-fighting. However, from the 1780s chain pumps were given some limited fire-fighting capacity. They were fitted with a removeable plate on each side, to which a hose could be attached. But this was not enough, and from 1807 the 'wash deck' pump was added. Two of these were fitted in the wells of two-deckers and above.[21] They were suction pumps, with outlets on the lower and upper decks, and middle deck if applicable. They were linked to the inflow pipes in the sides of the hull, so that water could be pumped direct without going through the cistern, though the latter was available if needed. Many different arrangements for deck-washing pumps were tried over the years, so it is often difficult to know which one, if any, was standard.

PART V

Guns

Chapter 14. The Supply of Guns

The Board of Ordnance

Ships' guns, along with their carriages, powder, shot and numerous other items which fell under the heading 'gunners stores', differed from the other articles aboard a naval ship, in that they were not under the direct control of the Admiralty and its subordinate, the Navy Board. Instead they were contracted for, tested, supplied and administered by the Board of Ordnance, a body similar in many respects to the modern Ministry of Supply or Ministry of Munitions.

The origins of the Ordnance Board can be traced back to late medieval times, but it developed in terms of both independence and permanence during the Tudor age. By the middle of the sixteenth century it was similar in status and composition to the Navy Board, as a government department headed by a committee of administrators, accountants and technicians, providing the government with the means to wage war. Unlike the Navy Board, it was not directly subject to Admiralty control. Its duties were to supply both the Army and the Navy with guns and all their associated equipment, to build and repair fortifications, and, in the case of the Army, to supply many other goods.[1]

The rationale behind this arrangement was that the same guns could often be used for either fortress or sea service. This was possible because guns were not the permanent fixtures they were to become in the late nineteenth century, and could be removed from ships with relative ease, and the Army's and the Navy's guns were usually cast in the same foundries, by the same manufacturers. Nevertheless it led to many difficulties over the years. There were disputes about the supply of guns; over which department was responsible for certain tasks, such as removing guns from ships being laid up; and over finance, as for example when the Admiralty failed to pass on money which had been voted by Parliament for naval ordnance.[2] Such arguments often had to be settled by a higher body, the Privy Council, and indeed the most important regulations, such as the various establishments of guns, were often enforced by Order in Council, to make them binding on both departments. The Ordnance Board, like the Navy Board, was often accused of inefficiency, neglect and corruption, though it was probably no worse than the average government body of the time.

The Ordnance Department was headed by the master general. The post was often held by men of considerable standing in society, such as Lord Dartmouth, the Duke of Schomberg, and the First Duke of Marlborough. But the master general took little interest in the running of the department, and was not much more than a figurehead. The Board of Ordnance itself, which did the real work, was composed of the principal officers, who included the lieutenant general, the treasurer, the surveyor general, the clerk of the ordnance, the storekeeper and the clerk of deliveries. Between them they provided enough technical and administrative skill to supervise the state's supply of weapons, but they had no naval representative. Few of the Board's members had any sea experience, so inevitably they relied on the Admiralty and Navy Board for advice. This factor did help create some healthy friction between the different departments.

The Ordnance Board itself did not make many guns. Though expensive and prestigious brass guns were sometimes cast in the Tower of London, and later all in the arsenal at Woolwich, the great majority of guns, especially the iron ones which were produced in vast numbers by the middle of the seventeenth century, were cast by private companies and individuals, to specifications drawn up by the Board of Ordnance. The Board tested them, stored them when necessary, and issued them to ships, fortresses and the train of artillery. By the early eighteenth century the Tower of London was still controlled by the Board of Ordnance but it was becoming a museum of ancient and interesting guns, rather than a centre of modern enterprise. The Royal Arsenal at Woolwich became the Board's most important site. It included a foundry for brass cannon (opened in 1716), extensive store houses, proving grounds, and facilities for making, testing and storing powder and shot. For the more immediate service of the royal dockyards, smaller depots were built at Upnor, near Chatham, at Priddy's Hard in Portsmouth Harbour, at Sheerness, and latterly at the Morice Yard, adjacent to Plymouth Dockyard. These issued guns and stores to ships, and housed them ashore when the ships were taken out of commission and laid up 'in ordinary'.

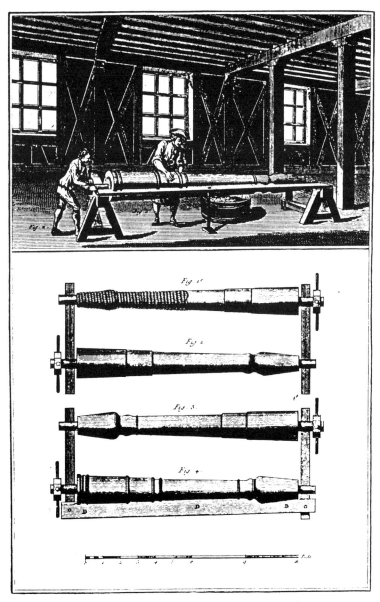

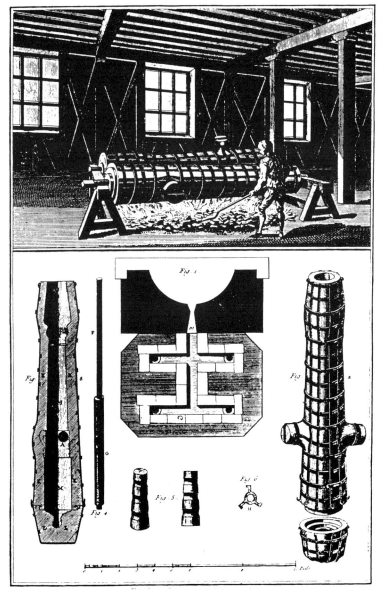

Making the mould for a gun. In the top picture the mould is being turned against the strickle-board to give it its final shape. This illustration dates from the mid-eighteenth century.

Drying the mould (above) and its final shape (below).

The Gunfounders

The casting of guns, especially those of iron, was done by contractors. In early years the industry was based near London, with foundries at Houndsditch, Vauxhall, and Chelsea, but by the middle of the sixteenth century the main centre had become Sussex and the Weald of Kent. This area was close to the supplies of iron ore, and the forests provided charcoal for the furnaces. It was close to Woolwich and to the main dockyards on the Thames and at Portsmouth, but many of the furnaces were some distance from navigable waterways, and the finished product often had to travel by expensive and difficult land transport for part of the journey. By the early seventeenth century, English ordnance was regarded as superior to that of the rest of Europe, and measures were taken to prevent its export to potential enemies. It was said 'The ordnance of England have been sold for £12 a ton; in Amsterdam for

£40, in France for £60, and in Spain for £80 all in one year. For it is to be noted that the English ordnance is of another nature to that ordnance made in Biscay, which break and shiver into many pieces, to the destruction of men on board the ship.'[3] This superiority was to increase in the next century, with the developments of the Industrial Revolution.

For most of the seventeenth century the industry was dominated by the Browne family, whose members successively held the office of royal gunfounder. John Browne, who died in 1652, made notable contributions to the techniques of gunfounding, and was rewarded for discovering a more effective way of making iron ordnance. In the 1650s the industry expanded greatly, due to the need to supply guns for the wars against the Dutch. Though many other contractors came into the trade, they generally worked in co-operation with the Brownes. Dyke of Frant, Courthorpe of Ashburnham, Bedgebery or Horsemonden, Foley

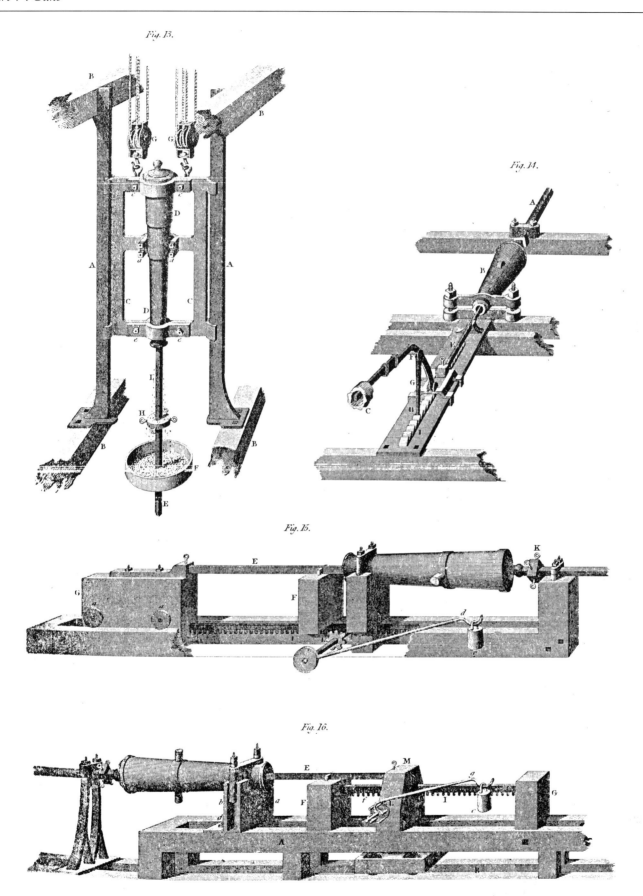

Fig. 13.

Fig. 14.

Fig. 15.

Fig. 16.

Various methods of boring out the gun, c1800.

of London, Baker of Mayfield and many others supplemented the efforts of the Browne furnaces at Buckland, Spelmonden and Horsemonden.[4] The Browne organisation was a very large one, and from 1664 to 1678 it was paid more than £136,000 by the government. It attracted investment from outside the industry, especially from the London livery companies. Eventually it collapsed because of bad debts from Charles II's government, but the Weald was to remain a centre for ironfounding for another seventy years.[5] The Fuller family of Heathfield was a major supplier in the first half of the eighteenth century, producing some of the largest guns up to the 1750s.[6]

However, by the middle of the eighteenth century the forests of the Weald had been heavily depleted, by the demands of construction and shipbuilding as much as by ironfounding. Moreover, the latest founding techniques, invented by Abraham Darby around 1710, used coke made from coal rather than charcoal made from wood. As the Kent coalfield had not yet been opened, the iron industry tended to move northwards, in particular to Birmingham, Nottinghamshire, Sheffield, Leeds and central Scotland. The most famous foundry of the new era was the Carron Ironworks, founded in 1759 near Falkirk. As well as inventing the carronade, the Carron Company cast ordinary guns, and supplied many to the Navy. Another large contractor was the firm of Samuel Walker and Co, which was founded at Sheffield in 1741, moved to Rotherham, and began to supply the Ordnance Board in 1771. By 1781 Walker was supplying 1200 tons of guns a year, and by 1812 had a capital of £300,000.[7] Other suppliers of this period included Gordon and Harley, Wiggin and Graham, Sturges, and Danson.

The new iron industry was of course much further from the main centres of naval activity, but foundries were generally situated close to rivers, or the new canals, and the Carron Company, like some other firms, developed its own fleet of ships for supplying the southern English dockyards.

Gunfounding Techniques

The earliest guns were made rather like barrels. Strips of metal were placed together round a core, and bound together by hoops. This system was used for very large guns called bombards, such as 'Mons Meg' in Edinburgh Castle. Later it was also used for much smaller guns, called breech-loaders, which were often fitted on the upper works of Tudor ships, including the *Mary Rose*. Some of these guns, called port-pieces and fowlers, were still found on ships in the first half of the seventeenth century, but they were weak and inefficient, and only survived because gunpowder was not yet very powerful. They became extinct about the middle of the seventeenth century. Another type, called the leather gun, was made in Sweden from sheet copper rolled round a core, strengthened with rings, and finally covered with leather. There is no evidence that these were ever used at sea.

The naval gun of the great age of sail was muzzle-loading. It was basically a tube closed at one end, with trunnions protruding near its middle to allow it to be fitted to a carriage, a cascable at its rear to hold the breeching rope, and a touch hole to ignite the powder. This type of gun was cast in one piece, either in iron or in a metal which was commonly called brass, but was in fact more like bronze.

The gunfounder began his work by making a full-sized model of the weapon to be produced. He wound strips of hay or rope

Above, a sixteenth century horizontal gun borer. Below, the head of the gun being cut off.

round a tapering wooden core to build it up to a suitable thickness. This was covered with a mixture of clay, hair and horsedung, or loam. While this was still wet the model was turned against a piece of wood called the strickle-board, which gave the model its final shape, including reinforcing rings, taper, and extra thickness at the muzzle. Moulds for the trunnions were nailed to this, as were those for the decorations, if any. The whole construction was then covered in a layer of clay, which was dried and formed the mould for the gun. The rearmost part of the gun, the breech and cascable, was shaped by a separate mould, but the two parts were brought together for the actual casting. The bore of the gun was formed by a core, which was inserted down the mould as close to the centre line as possible. Near its lower end it was held in place by a metal tripod, which would eventually form part of the completed gun. The whole mould was strongly reinforced by iron rings round the outside, and the molten metal was poured in at the muzzle end. After the metal had cooled and hardened the mould was broken, and the completed gun was taken out. As it was necessary to leave room to pour in the metal, a large extra piece, called the gun-head, was formed at the muzzle. This was sawn off and melted down for other uses.

Because the mould had to be broken after each gun, no two weapons were ever identical. This was one of the main reasons why guns, even from the same foundries, often differed considerably in weight. In 1665, for example, guns from a single batch of 9ft demi-cannon varied from 44 to 52cwt, those of 8½ft from 43 to 47cwt, and culverins of 10ft varied from 40 to 46cwt. These differences caused the Ordnance Board some concern. In 1705, for example, seven 24-pounders produced by a Mr Gott were rejected 'on account of their being heavier considerably than they should be by their contract'.[8] Even more serious was the fact that the bore was not always inserted correctly, or was inaccurately formed, so that the gun would not aim properly.

Throughout the eighteenth century attempts were made to remedy these faults, and the system of gunfounding was generally improved. By 1716 full-size drawings of the guns were being sent to the founders, so that they were made to a common pattern, rather than that decided upon by the individual founders.[9] There is evidence that from the 1730s brass 'rammers' were sent out from the Ordnance Office, to form the cores. To ensure that the bore was even more accurate, it later became the custom to drill out the cores after moulding. In 1776, after a series of failures of guns produced by the Carron Company, it was decided that in the future all guns should be bored directly from the solid.[10] Since about 1750 it had been normal to use sand instead of clay for the mould, placing it inside an iron jacket or flask. The old type of model, built up round a wooden core, was sometimes replaced with one made of copper, which gave greater accuracy. As a result of these changes, guns delivered at the end of the eighteenth century seldom varied from their specification by more than a hundredweight or so. A survey of guns taken out of ships between 1803 and 1806 shows that 32-pounders of relatively recent construction ranged between 55cwt and just over 57cwt in weight.[11]

Despite increasing standards of accuracy in the eighteenth century, there were some practical limitations to improvement. Thomas Blomefield, the Inspector of Artillery from 1780, did more than any other individual to raise standards of gun construction, but even he conceded that, regarding naval guns, 'The nature of that service renders it unnecessary to insist upon the most scrupulous executions in every part of their construction. Was not some latitude allowed, the number rejected would render it impossible for the contractors to furnish them on the same terms.'[12]

After delivery to the Ordnance, the gun had to be proved before the manufacturer was paid. The most important part of the test was to fill the gun with twice its normal charge of powder, and explode it. If the gun survived this it was carefully examined for cracks, and filled with water under pressure to see if it leaked. This was a tense moment for the founder, who was not paid if the gun failed. 'There is very little difference standing between 50 and 60 pound in a blast of gunpowder and the cut of a card'.[13] By the eighteenth century other tests were made and guns could be rejected because their weight did not match the specification, or because they were not bored accurately enough.

The ironfounding industry, in which gunfounding played a major part, was one of the main developments of the Industrial Revolution in the eighteenth and nineteenth centuries. It is estimated that in 1795 it was using 26,000 tons of iron a year – about a quarter of total British production.[14] Gunfounding had expanded enormously in the previous 200 years, for by 1795 it had to supply a fleet of 600 ships and vessels, compared with 42 in the late Elizabethan Navy. Even the fleet of 1795 was outnumbered by that of 1812, which had over 1000 vessels.[15]

Chapter 15. Materials: Brass and Iron

Elizabethan Brass

In medieval times iron guns were the most common, but they were forged rather than cast, being made up of metal plates bound together by hoops, by a blacksmith rather than a founder. Larger guns, from the fourteenth century onwards, were more likely to be cast, in a metal commonly known as brass. In fact it was more akin to bronze, comprising 85 to 90 per cent copper, with proportions of tin, lead, zinc, and sometimes other metals. Until the third quarter of the sixteenth century most ships' guns were made of forged iron. The *Mary Rose*, for example, was listed as carrying 126 guns, of which only 15 were brass.[1] But the iron guns were mostly very small, and the total included 50 'hand gonnes', 20 'hayle shott' weapons, and various slings, fowlers and port-pieces which were intended to clear the men from the enemy's decks, rather than damage the ships themselves. The most powerful guns, of the cannon and culverin types, and hail-shot pieces, were of cast metal.

In the sixteenth century iron was not regarded as a suitable material for casting guns, mainly because of its tendency to harden before all of it could be poured into the mould. Cast-iron guns were either of small calibre, too heavy for their calibre, or dangerously unreliable. They were suitable for merchant ships, which seldom fired their guns, but not for the King's Navy. Henry VIII built up his fleet cheaply and rapidly by the large scale production of iron guns, but they were not considered suitable for long term use.

Around 1569 it was decided to equip Queen Elizabeth's Navy entirely with cast brass guns. In fact this decision was not as radical as it first might appear, for already 264 out of 312 guns on board ship were brass.[2] Moreover, many of the guns required could be taken from the royal fortresses, and the Navy was given priority for brass guns, a policy which was to last well into the next century. Nevertheless, the policy was expensive, for brass guns were very costly, and a queen like Elizabeth, always careful with her money, would not have undertaken it lightly. In 1570 iron ordnance cost £10 to £12 per ton and brass, £40 to £60.[3] The difference in cost tended to increase over the years. By 1600 the price of iron had fallen slightly.[4] By 1670 brass cost £150 per ton, iron £18.[5] But brass, in addition to its strength, had several other advantages over cast iron. It did not rust, and today's underwater archaeologists have recovered brass cannon virtually undamaged after centuries under the sea, whilst those of iron are almost unrecognisable.

Brass was a better investment than the ships themselves, which decayed at such a rate that they had to be rebuilt or replaced every 15 years or so. Brass was subject to a certain amount of wear and tear in service, but unlike iron it could be recast without losing any of its strength. Of course these advantages were irrelevant if the ships themselves were sunk or captured, but the Elizabethan Navy, despite its reputation for daring, did not take unnecessary risks. In 16 years of war with the Spanish only two ships were lost – one sunk, and one, the *Revenge*, was taken by the enemy.[6]

One disadvantage of brass was that after firing a large number of shots in continuous action, it became so hot that it lost some of its strength. This did not become apparent until much later, because Elizabeth's fleet did not engage in the close action of the Nelson period, and did not fight so intensely. It set out against the Spanish Armada with about 25 shots per gun in its lockers. By the 1760s, British ships carried 60 or 70 shots per gun.[7] The Elizabethan rate of fire was very slow, as loading methods were inefficient. Eventually the fleet of 1588 ran out of ammunition, but only after a week of almost constant contact with the enemy as they sailed up the English Channel.

Brass, then, was suitable for the English Navy of the late sixteenth century, and the attempt to equip the Navy with it was largely successful. When Elizabeth died in 1603, 93 per cent of its guns were brass.[8]

Experiments with Iron

The successor to Elizabeth, King James I, made peace with Spain and allowed his fleet to fall into neglect for some years. It was revived in the latter part of his reign, and further under his son, Charles I, who extended the tax of ship-money to build up his fleet. The number of ships did not greatly increase between 1603 and 1633, rising only from 42 to 50, but the number of guns carried rose from 989 to 1430, because the new ships were rather bigger than the old ones.[9] The number of guns required was even greater in 1637, after Charles completed his largest ship, the *Sovereign of the Seas*, with 102 guns.

Right at the beginning of Charles' reign, in 1625, it was realised that if the fleet was to expand any further, it would be necessary to find a cheaper way of providing it with guns. A set of brass guns could add about a third again to the cost of a new ship, if there were none in store. Furthermore, complained one of the secretaries of state, 'Our pieces grow every day more weighty and dear, and yet of less proof'.[10] The Commissioners of the Navy, 'having been directed to see what could be done towards reforming the abuse of the overweight of iron ordnance', had 'consulted various gunfounders'. The only one to show any interest was John Browne, the royal founder, who claimed he could cast iron ordnance 'to be servicable, and to endure the King's proof, yet to be as light as brass ordnance'.[11] In March 1626 he delivered six iron pieces (two culverins, two demi-culverins and two sakers) which were proved successfully. In the following month it was recommended he receive a reward of £200.[12]

There were still many objections to iron. It was believed that 'because of lightness it would deliver shot uncertainly',[13] that brass could be recast while iron could not (to which Browne replied that new iron guns could be produced for the cost of melting down and casting brass), and above all that iron guns simply did not have the prestige and appearance of brass. In 1628 Charles' fleet, returning from an unsuccessful expedition to La Rochelle, was still equipped almost entirely with brass. Of the King's own ships only the 'Whelps', small vessels built for patrol and reconnaissance duties, carried iron guns, and even these had a few brass sakers. The hired merchant ships and the prizes, on the other hand, were entirely equipped with iron – a fair representation of what was standard at the time.[14]

By 1636, the fleet had expanded further and iron guns had spread to the decks of some of the larger ships. The *Unicorn*, *Garland* and *Happy Entrance* of the Second Rate, and the *Adventure*, *Mary Rose* and *Assurance* of the Third Rate, all carried some iron guns, but only the 'Whelps' were mainly equipped with iron. According to a list of that year, out of 24 ships only 10 had any iron guns at all.[15] It appears that iron was used to make good the deficiencies in guns as the fleet slowly expanded, but there were still enough stocks of brass guns to make large-scale iron founding

unnecessary. There were experiments with 'fine metal', a form of iron, though it is not clear how this differed from the standard metal. Browne provided 18 guns of this sort between 1618 and 1625, and the same type was still being ordered in the 1650s.[16]

The very largest ships were still given brass guns whatever the cost. The *Sovereign of the Seas* cost £40,833 to build, rig, store and decorate. Her 102 brass guns were estimated to cost a further £24,753. It was certainly not intended that iron guns should arm the largest ships, and it was to be another forty years before this policy was challenged.

The Age of Transition

When the English Civil War broke out in 1642, virtually all the fleet, along with its ordnance and stores, fell into the hands of Parliament. Great battlefleets were not immediately required, but small patrol vessels were, and many of these were captured or hired, rather than built specially for the Navy. They often came into the fleet complete with iron guns, and so the Parliamentary Navy became familiar with iron. There is no sign that large numbers of guns were cast for ships during the Civil War, as supplies from the merchant fleet were adequate.

After the war, and the King's execution in 1649, the leaders of the new English Republic found no peace. During their 11 years in power, in addition to English Royalists, they fought the Irish, the Scots, the French, the Dutch and the Spanish. From the beginning of 1649 the Admiralty Commissioners ordered many 'frigates' of two, and later three decks. The largest new ship, the *Naseby*, carried around 80 guns, while the two-deckers of the *Speaker* class, built in some numbers during these years, carried about 60. A few ships were captured, but the great majority were built in English yards, and therefore had to be provided with guns. By 1660 the fleet had risen to a total of 157 ships and vessels, carrying 4390 guns.[17] This of course created an unprecedented demand for new weapons, and it would have been too costly to make more than a few from brass. Guns were ordered from the iron founders in large quantities: 259 in August 1652, 1500 (enough to equip the whole fleet of 1633) in February 1653, and 1450 in July 1653.[18]

Experiments were made in casting the largest pieces from iron. As early as 1627, iron demi-cannon drakes had been cast and issued to the fleet, but drakes should not be regarded as equivalent to normal guns of the same calibre.[19] In 1657 twelve iron cannon-of-seven were delivered for the new First Rate *London*. Besides the usual proofs, they were to be tried in service and it was 'said that if the said guns were not well liked of after six months experience, to take than [back] again'.[20] Despite the fact they were reasonably successful, in 1664 George Browne was still sceptical about the feasibility of casting such large guns in iron, and asked to be allowed to make them in brass.[21]

There was still a residual belief in brass guns, especially for the largest pieces and the biggest ships. Completely new brass guns were rare, though in January 1653, for example, some unserviceable brass guns were ordered to be cast into new.[22] But care was taken that the largest ships, especially the flagships, were issued with as much brass as possible. The forts were scoured for pieces, and those of Ireland and Scotland, recently subdued by Cromwell's armies, provided a new supply. Ships designated as flagships often had their guns exchanged with those from less

The Charles *Yacht of 1675. Such vessels continued to carry brass guns even after other small ships were usually equipped with iron.* Science Museum.

important vessels. Thus in 1652 the *Fairfax*, intended to carry the flag of the Vice Admiral of the Red, was to exchange 20 iron guns for brass ones out of the *Happy Entrance*, 'which is a vessel less nimble and serviceable'.[23]

By 1660, when the Republic collapsed and the monarchy was restored in the person of Charles II, the fleet was largely armed with iron guns. An analysis of 50 ships put into reserve in 1660 and 1661 shows that about three-quarters of their guns were iron. Such brass as remained was usually to be found among the larger guns, such as the demi-cannon and the cannon-of-seven, or among the older types, the culverins, demi-culverins and sakers. An exception was the 12-pounder, but these were almost certainly captured from the Dutch, and thus did not represent English practice.[24]

The early governments of Charles II did little to change policy in this respect. Brass guns were still used for First and Second Rate ships, as for example in 1663, when spare guns at Woolwich and the Tower were to be used for two new ships, the *Royal Oak* and *Royal Katherine*, both Second Rates.[25] New brass guns were still occasionally produced, as in 1666 when Browne was ordered to cast 40 new cannon-of-seven from old copper, and in 1670 when it was 'desired that a competent number of brass chase guns be cast for the first rate frigates to be set forth in the spring'.[26]

Again, old materials were to be used, and it is rare to find any new copper being acquired, though in 1664 200 tons were to be bought in Sweden.[27]

In his fleet list of 1670, Sir Anthony Deane made the distribution of brass and iron guns look very straightforward: all First and Second Rates had brass guns as did the royal yachts, and all other ships had iron guns.[28] But nothing in the Restoration Navy was ever as clear cut as this, and many medium-sized ships had mixed armaments. The policy of issuing brass to flagships, however small, was continued, and in 1663 the *Rainbow*, intended to be Sir Thomas Allin's flagship was to be given brass guns removed from other ships.[29] In 1665 the *Henry*, also fitting for a flagship, was issued with four brass guns, to be put on the coach and quarterdeck where they would be closest to the Admiral. It seems that this policy of putting brass guns where they would be seen by the Admiral occurred more than once, for in 1672 the *Fairfax*, flagship of Sir John Narborough, was reported to carry 72 guns, well above her standard complement of 60. These included 22 of brass, which comprised 'four brass saker on the forecastle, 14 brass saker on the quarterdeck and coach and after cabins, two brass twelve pounders in the great cabin, two saker drake cutts of brass on the poop'.[30]

The Decline of Brass

The difference in price between brass and iron ordnance increased over the years. In 1625 John Browne estimated that brass would cost £8 per hundredweight, and iron only £2. In 1670 Deane allowed £7/10/0 for brass, and 18s for iron.[31] It is clear that half a century of development in the iron industry had worked very much to iron's advantage. Such a distinction in price was not likely to escape the attention of Charles II's government, always hard-pressed for money, and supported only reluctantly and inadequately by Parliamentary grants.

Matters came to a head in 1677, when Parliament voted £600,000 for 30 new ships, including one First Rate, nine Second Rates, and 20 Third Rates. Despite the oratory made by Samuel Pepys, Secretary to the Admiralty, the grant was barely adequate to cover the building of such large ships, and equipping them with rigging, stores and guns. The problem was compounded by the King, who insisted that the ships be even larger than intended by Parliament, promising that any extra money needed would come from his own funds.

Pepys, left to administer the programme, made various calculations about the expense. To equip all 30 ships with brass guns would cost about £450,000, leaving only £150,000 to build them. To build only 20 ships and equip them with brass guns would cost £624,910, and would satisfy neither Parliament nor the officials of the Treasury. He also considered the possibility of using 'neyled', or annealed iron. This was considerably more expensive than ordinary iron, for example, the guns of a Third Rate would rise in cost from £5880 to £12,740.[32] The superior iron was, according to some accounts, 'as commended as brass guns', but it was never produced in large quantities. In 1702 it was written 'there are several iron guns which are nealed and turned, only I never found them to exceed other iron guns, only they were free from honeycombs [and] they were truly bored and the metal equal on all sides.'[33]

In fact all 30 ships of 1677 were to be fitted with iron ordnance, for the shortage of cash ruled out the possibility of giving even the First Rate, the *Britannia*, brass guns. Eventually, as the largest ship of the fleet, she was to acquire a set of brass guns taken from other ships. But the precedent had been broken, and after 1677 it was no longer customary to keep enough brass ordnance to equip all the largest ships.

By 1698 the fleet had expanded yet again to 323 ships, and brass guns had become very rare. According to an inventory taken in that year, only 11 ships had any brass at all. Three of the seven First Rates, the *Britannia*, *Royal William* and *London*, were the only ships to carry an all brass armament. Two more First Rates, the *Victory* and the *Sovereign*, had no brass at all, while only four of the 12 Second Rates had any brass guns. Two Third Rates, the *Resolution* and the *Stirling Castle*, also carried a few brass guns. The latter ship had four 6-pounders, originally of Dutch manufacture.[34] She was lost on the Goodwin Sands in the Great Storm of 1703, and one of her guns was recovered in 1979,

The royal coat of arms on a mid-eighteenth century brass gun.

still bearing the serial number recorded in the 1698 inventory.[35]

The use of brass declined further in the eighteenth century. In 1716 it was stated that the only ships with brass guns were three First Rates. In 1782 it was recorded that only one ship, the First Rate *Royal George* of 1756, still carried brass guns.[36] Nelson's *Victory* had been completed in 1765, and she was now the largest and most prestigious ship in the Navy, but it seems that she was never allotted brass guns. The *Royal George* sank at Spithead in 1782, and she took with her the last brass guns carried by a major British sailing warship. In fact she was not carrying a full set. Her lower deck 42-pounders had originally been captured French 36-pounders (equivalent to 39 English pounds) and they had been bored up to 42 English pounds. During her final refit they had been taken out, and exchanged for conventional 32-pounders of iron.[37] On her middle deck she still retained brass 24-pounders, made at the Royal Brass Foundry at Woolwich in 1743. Some of them were later recovered from the wreck, and can be seen in the Tower of London and Southsea Castle.

Cast iron had many disadvantages as a material for guns. It was weaker than wrought iron, though because of the primitive engineering techniques of the time it was impossible to build up a gun of the latter material which was not liable to leakages or bursting. Other metals were far too expensive for mass production, and steel was too brittle. The expanding British iron industry, on the other hand, was able to cope with the growing needs of the Navy. The great majority of naval guns, and all those used after 1782, were therefore made of cast iron.

Chapter 16. The Shape of Guns

Parts of the Gun

The smooth-bore muzzle-loading gun was in essence a tube of cast metal, closed at one end and open at the other, with a small hole at the closed end to ignite the powder, and a projection on each side to hold the gun on its carriage.

The centre of the tube was known as the 'bore'. Most guns had a straight bore with parallel sides, and were described as 'home bored' or 'full bored'. Others were 'taper bored', or 'drakes' (see pages 90–92). The part of the bore nearest the closed end of the gun, where the powder and shot were placed ready for firing, was known as the 'chamber'. In the late seventeenth century some guns had spherical chambers, so that they could carry a larger charge of powder, but it does not seem that these were used at sea.[1] The early breech-loading guns of the sixteenth century had separate chambers, which could be loaded away from the rest of the gun. Some guns also had chambers which were smaller in diameter than the rest of the bore, but these were difficult to load, and were not common at sea. The chamber was of the same diameter as the bore in the vast majority of naval guns. The exceptions were drakes, where of course the taper would make the chamber slightly narrower, and carronades.

The closed end of the gun, around the chamber, was known as the 'breech'. This was the thickest part of the weapon, as it had to withstand the full force of the explosion of the powder. The very widest part, just behind the chamber, was the 'base ring'. The gun was measured from this ring; the part behind was not included in the length.

Forward of the base ring, the gun was divided into three main parts, the 'first reinforce', 'second reinforce' and 'chase'. The gun tapered gradually within each of these sections, and rather more so at the junctions between them, so that at the neck, or narrowest point, just behind the muzzle, it was perhaps three-fifths of the diameter at the base ring. In the area of the muzzle, forward of the neck, the gun widened considerably.

The first reinforce was two-sevenths of the length of the gun, and the second reinforce about one-seventh plus the diameter of the bore. The chase was therefore four-sevenths of the gun's length minus one bore. The boundaries of these parts were marked by sudden reductions in the thickness of the metal, but also by rings known as the 'first reinforce ring', and the 'second reinforce ring'. These rings, which were moulded as part of the gun, were flat and mostly undecorated. Forward of the base ring, the second reinforce ring, and sometimes the first reinforce ring, were ogees, rings which were shaped like double curves in cross-section, convex at the back and in front. These rings served no practical function, but were reminiscent of the days when wrought iron guns were held together by hoops, like a barrel.

There were several other rings round the gun barrel. An area known as the vent field, part of the first reinforce, lay immediately in front of the base ring, and behind the vent astragal and fillets. The astragal was a moulding of semi-circular section; the fillets were narrow bands on each side of the astragal. The vent field was so called because the 'vent', or 'touch hole', was positioned centrally on top of this part of the gun. This was a small hole bored through the gun, and was used to ignite the powder. Usually it was angled forward about 10 or 11 degrees, and it was one-twentieth of the bore in diameter. The hole was usually slightly wider at its upper end, to make it easier to ignite. On later guns the area around the vent, on the upper part of the weapon, was considerably thickened by a rectangular casting.

Sometimes there was another astragal, known as the 'chase astragal', forward of the second reinforce ring. The 'muzzle astragal' was well forward on the chase, just before the barrel widened out to form the muzzle. These astragals had flat rings, known as fillets, on each side.

The gun widened considerably near the muzzle; the widest part was known as the 'swell of the muzzle'. Forward of the widest part it narrowed quite sharply, and there were two or three 'muzzle mouldings', or 'muzzle rings', which were usually semi-circular or ogee in section. The flat part on the extreme front of the muzzle was known as the 'face' of the piece.

The 'cascable' was originally the ball at the rear of the piece, to which the breech rope was fixed. Later the term came to mean the whole area behind the base ring, and the ball became known as the 'button'. Behind the base ring, the gun tapered rapidly by means of several ogees and fillets to the 'neck of the cascable', its narrowest point; after that it widened into the button. On the new guns introduced by Blomefield around 1790, the ogees and fillets behind the base ring were dispensed with, and the diameter was reduced by a simple curve. A ring was added above the button, to help hold the breech rope.

'Trunnions' projected from the side of the barrel, forward of the centre of gravity, so that the piece pivoted about them, and rested on its breech. In the seventeenth century trunnions tapered sharply; in the eighteenth century they were cylindrical. The trunnions were round in cross-section, so that the gun could be elevated and depressed. The centre of the trunnions was level with the lowest part of the bore, so they were rooted in the thicker metal under the gun, though some believed a better balanced gun would be produced by raising them up to the centre line.[2]

Dolphins were only fitted on brass guns. They were lifting handles, positioned on the upper part of the barrel between the trunnions. Usually they were heavily decorated, often in the form of the sea creature after which they were named. Most guns had two, some had four, with lifting rings, and a few had only one.

Decoration on Guns

Brass guns, in accordance with their greater status and prestige, were much more heavily decorated than iron guns. Few, however, had the very elaborate ornaments some ceremonial and fortress guns had. Most had decorated dolphins and carried two coats of arms, one on the first reinforce and one on the chase. These represented the sovereign, and the master general of the ordnance. Iron guns, on the other hand, usually had a badge on the second reinforce, between the trunnions. The 'Tudor rose', a rose surmounted by a crown, was not in fact very common in Tudor times, but it was used under Charles I, Charles II, and Queen Anne. Under the Georges, after 1714, the monogram 'GR', surmounted by a crown was standard. Sometimes it was enclosed within a belt or wreath, later it stood alone. Other

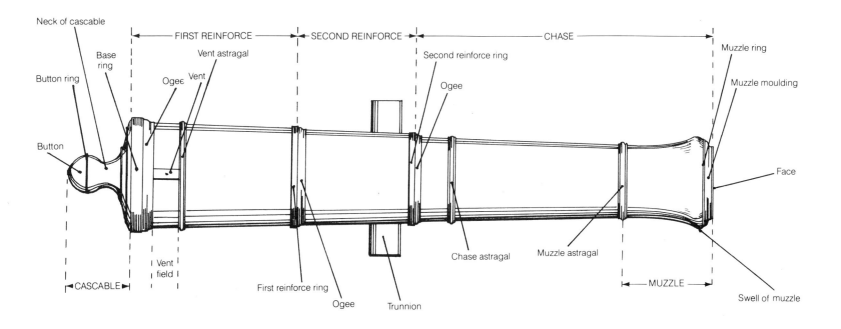

Neck of cascable
Base ring
Button ring
Button
Ogee
Vent astragal
Vent
FIRST REINFORCE
SECOND REINFORCE
CHASE
Second reinforce ring
Ogee
Muzzle ring
Muzzle moulding
Face
CASCABLE
Vent field
First reinforce ring
Ogee
Trunnion
Chase astragal
Muzzle astragal
Muzzle
Swell of muzzle

Parts of a gun, c1750.

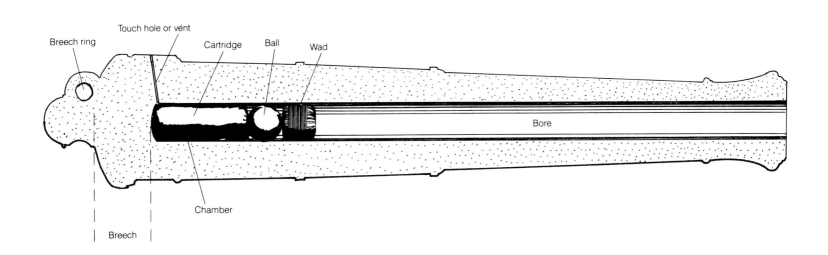

Breech ring
Touch hole or vent
Cartridge
Ball
Wad
Bore
Chamber
Breech

Section of a gun, c1800.

The relatively small cascable of a gun of c1670. Author's photograph, courtesy of Science Museum.

The cascable of a Blomefield pattern 32-pounder, showing the loop. Author's photograph, courtesy of NMM.

The dolphins on a brass gun.

decoration was in the form of the rings, astagals, fillets, and ogees which were cast as part of the gun.

Decoration was cast as an integral part of most guns. In the 1660s, however, Charles II attempted to erase the memory of those who had executed his father and usurped his power. It was ordered that 'the gravers be contracted with to grave 'CR' and crown upon all the iron guns, and Colonel Legge's [the master general of the ordnance] name upon all the new brass guns.'[3] The practice of engraving guns in this manner seems to have been standard in the early eighteenth century, and the records of the Royal Brass Foundry at Woolwich show that hundreds of pieces of new iron ordnance were engraved there in the 1720s and '30s.[4]

By the 1780s, the contractor was expected to cast the decorations as part of the gun, and until 1795 it appears that the metal left over in the casting process often had to be trimmed off the guns at Woolwich. In that year it was ordered that in future the badges of new iron guns were not to be chipped. The contractors were to mould them as neatly as possible, and they were not to project as far as they had done in the past. In the same year copies of a new cipher were sent to the manufacturers, with orders that it was not to project more than $\frac{1}{5}$in.[5]

Drakes

'Drake' is one of the most confusing terms to be encountered, largely because its meaning changed at least once in the course of the seventeenth century. It is thought that drakes were first used by Prince Maurice of Nassau at the siege of Bergen-op-Zoom in 1622, that they were very light weapons for their calibre and mainly fired grape-shot.[6] The name may originate from the Dutch 'draak', or the German 'drache', meaning dragon, and is related to the English word 'firedrake'. Drakes were first brought to England in 1625, by Sir Edward Cecil.[7]

The English had started to make their own drakes by 1627, and by the end of the following year Browne, the Royal Gunfounder, had produced 216.[8] It is clear that they were mainly intended for naval use, and until 1630 all drakes were reserved for the King's service, because it was feared that such a powerful new weapon, if used on merchant ships, would soon fall into the hands of enemies or pirates, and be used against the King's Navy.[9] Browne argued successfully against this prohibition, and thereafter they were allowed on merchant ships.

Drakes, as originally conceived by the Dutch were certainly lighter than other pieces. Great emphasis was placed on the fact that they could be used on the upper decks of ships where only very light guns had previously been carried. It was said that 'this new invention made demi-cannon and whole culverin in the stead of demi-culverins hard fortified.'[10] Reference was made to their 'lightness and smallness', and also to the fact that 'by reason of

Typical insignia on iron guns.
A. Elizabethan rose and crown, c1580.
B. The crest of the 'Commonwealth' gun.
C. Rose and crown, Charles II, c1666.
D. George I's monogram, 1714–27.
E. George II's monogram, 1727–60.
F. George III's monogram, 1760–1820.

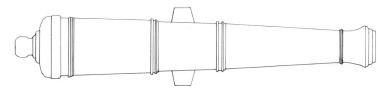

Known as the 'Commonwealth' gun, this is the only known example of a gun bearing the arms of the English Republic – largely because the Republican arms were systematically removed from guns after the Restoration. It is a culverin drake, 8ft long, and is believed to have been cast in 1652. It was recovered from a ship lost in the battle of Scheveningen in 1653.

the thinness of their metal they are soon overheated.'[11] It was said that 'they are fit for the upper decks, even to the poop and fore-castle'.[12] Large calibre drakes could be carried on the very smallest ships, and in 1636 the 'Whelps', of around 120 tons, were fitted with demi-cannon drakes, a calibre which in later years would be carried only by the largest ships of the line.[13]

It is clear that drakes were light for their length and calibre. The brass demi-culverin drakes ordered for several new ships in 1637 were to weigh 17cwt, whilst ordinary culverins weighed 30cwt.[14] This lightness was largely achieved by making the metal round the bore thinner than normal, and so after the introduction of drakes ordinary guns were referred to as 'fortified'. Drakes were expected to withstand a lighter charge of powder, and therefore have a shorter range. 'But another question is that if upon lying at anchor or upon a calm the enemy, with their fortified ordnance, shooting more powder than our pieces will, reach our ships with our shot when ours will not reach theirs.' The range of the new weapon was expected to be only 11 or 12 score (yards?) 'which is conceived by most seamen to be far enough at sea'.[15]

Probably the original drakes were shorter than other pieces of the same calibre. Certainly ease of loading and rapidity of fire were claimed among their advantages, and it was said that a drake could fire 'two or three shots to one fired by a piece of great ordnance', and that it needed only two men, compared to four or five for a fortified piece. It was the shortness of the gun which made

this possible. Not only would it have been easier to ram home the powder and shot, but the gun would have less distance to run out, and this, combined with its lightness, would have increased the rate of fire which could be achieved with such a small crew.

However, the list of ordnance proposed for the *Sovereign of the Seas* in 1637 raises many questions.[16] First, all her guns except 14 chase pieces were intended to be drakes, and this contradicts the belief, expressed a few years earlier, that drakes should be reserved for the upper decks, for fear that an enemy could keep his distance and defeat the ship by long-range gunnery. A large ship like the *Sovereign* was well known to be slow and un-manoeuvrable, and if she carried mainly short-range guns no enemy would have to fight, unless they wished to initiate action. Second, some of her so-called drakes were extremely long. Four of her demi-cannon were to be 12ft 6in long – longer than any other gun known to have been carried at that time. On the other hand, they were very light for their length and calibre. The 12½ft guns weighed only 53cwt, scarcely more than a normal 10ft gun. Her culverin drakes of 8½ft were to weigh 28cwt, whereas a standard culverin of that length weighed 33cwt in 1626, and one of 1653 was to weigh 36cwt.[17]

It seems that by this time, ten years after their introduction to England, the concept of drakes had been somewhat devalued. Shortness was no longer regarded as an essential characteristic of a drake, and a new term, cutt, had recently been introduced for a very short gun. Moreover, the *Sovereign* was an exceptional ship, both in size and in the number of guns carried. King Charles had increased her armament from 90 to 102 guns, against the advice of the builders. Perhaps he had tried to reduce the extra weight by using lighter guns. There was a certain absurdity in some of them. A 12½ft demi-cannon could only have been efficient if a large enough charge of powder was employed to make full use of its length, but because the breech was thinner than normal, this would have destroyed the gun. It seems that the guns intended for the *Sovereign* were a result of the desire for royal grandeur, rather than tactical usefulness. They cannot be seen as representative of drakes. However, lightness remained a characteristic of drakes for some years yet. Culverin drakes delivered into the arsenals in 1648–49 weighed 17 tons 19cwt, and a demi-culverin drake of 7ft weighed 15 to 16cwt.[18]

Another characteristic associated with drakes is that they were taper-bored, that is, the bore was greater at the muzzle than at the chamber. Though there is no primary evidence that this was the case with the original guns, they were intended mainly to fire grape-shot to scour the decks of the enemy, and a taper bore would spread such shot. A taper bore would make loading easier, but on the other hand, was dangerous with round shot. Several contemporary writers drew attention to the fact that if a badly shaped ball stuck part of the way down the bore, the whole gun would explode when the powder was detonated.[19]

In later years, there can be no doubt that drakes had tapered bores. In 1653 Admiral Blake wrote 'whether the cannon contracted for the fleet be made drakes or home bored, it is our advice that, provided they be made of the same weight, and yet allow the same metal as you do for whole bored guns, drake bored will be of much use, other wise make them whole bored'.[20] Apparently his advice was heeded. For example, of the guns ordered in July 1653, 8½ft culverins, whether drakes or fortified, were to weigh 36cwt, and 8ft demi-culverins, whether drakes or fortified, were to weigh 24cwt.[21] It seems by this time the taper bore was the only remaining distinction between drakes and ordinary artillery.

This is confirmed by later orders, for example of November 1664, in which guns are referred to as drakes as opposed to 'full bored'.[22] A few years later Pepys was to complain (probably with his usual exaggeration) of 'the Dutch out-shooting us and thereby cutting our rigging and sails before we could come near enough to them to wrong them with our guns, their guns being found to be home-bored, while ours were all out-bored, led us to make all our guns home-bored.'[23] He was presumably referring to the Second Anglo-Dutch War of 1664–67. Certainly there is no sign that any new drakes were ordered after about 1666, but the type was used right until the end of the century. Nearly 1300 drakes were in service or in store in 1685.[24] The list of 1698 contained many, though by this time they were referred to as 'taper-bored'.[25] The new guns establishment of 1703 made no provision for them, and it can be assumed that they died out in the early years of the eighteenth century.

Cutts

As well as drakes and fortified guns, there was a third subdivision among late seventeenth century guns. Cutts were, as their name implies, guns which were shorter than normal for their calibre and type. It is not clear how they originated. It has often been assumed that they were produced when the muzzles of ordinary guns were accidentally damaged, and were therefore cut down and used in a different form. There is little primary evidence for this. Guns cut in this way would be immediately recognisable because they would have no swelling at the muzzle, and the trunnions would be too far forward. No surviving guns have such a shape. The most unambiguous evidence comes from a list of 1689, in which guns are categorised as: 'fortified', 'drakes', 'to be proved', '*muzzle to be cut*', and 'unserviceable'.[27] Although only nine out of 309 guns were so listed, this does not preclude the possibility that many had already been cut in this manner. However, the list appears very late in the history of cutts, and it is odd

that there should be no earlier mention of cutting guns in this way. They had already been in service for more than 50 years, and more than 500 were in stock in 1685.[28]

The earliest mention of cuts is in the fleet list of 1636. They were carried by only two ships.[29] The *St Andrew* had two demi-culverin, and the *Triumph* had one. According to the proposed armament of 1637, the *Sovereign* was intended to carry four: two 'culverin drake cuts' on the bulkhead abaft the forecastle, and two 'demi-culverin drake cuts' on the quarterdeck. All were very short guns, of 5½ft, and the demi-culverins were to weigh 8cwt, less than half the weight of a normal 9ft demi-culverin drake. This suggests that they were originally manufactured as cuts rather than from damaged guns, for the latter would not have been a simple matter of cutting off the muzzle. Because most of the weight of a gun was behind the trunnions it would have been impossible to reduce the weight of a gun by 50 per cent without cutting it behind the trunnions, which is most unlikely. A reduction in the length of the gun from 9 to 5½ft would not have been nearly enough and would have produced a very odd weapon, with the trunnions almost at the muzzle. It would have been very difficult to elevate, and completely unbalanced. It is not impossible that the very small number of cuts in service in 1636 were the result of accidents in casting, and that this inspired the use of the term cutt. However, it is without doubt that in later years cuts were originally manufactured as such.

The Ordnance Board records of 1648 show that many cuts were delivered from the founders from that year onwards. Many more were contracted for in the 1650s and 1660s. A typical demi-culverin cut was 6ft long, and weighed 14 to 15cwt. A normal demi-culverin was from 8 to 10ft long, and weighed 24 to 31cwt. Saker cuts were 5½ to 6ft long, and weighed 9 to 11cwt.[30]

It is not clear when the cutt went out of use. There was no mention of them in the 1677 establishment, which suggests that this type was out of favour, though not out of stock. They probably became obsolete in the early part of the eighteenth century.

Chapter 17. The Proportions of Guns

Systems of Proportions

Formal rules for the proportions of guns developed quite late in their history. In the seventeenth century, contracts specified weights and lengths, but left the rest up to the skill and discretion of the gunfounder. Presumably practice and experience produced some informal rules, but it is not always easy to find out what they were, for gunfounders, like other craftsmen of the age, did not reveal their trade secrets except to their apprentices. Books on gunnery give us some clues, but these were written for and by the users, rather than the makers of guns. Information on the proportions of guns is scant, and not always to be trusted.

In 1670, after the defeats of the Second Dutch War, there was an attempt to draw up a new establishment of gun sizes, but it is

Borgard's proportions, 1716. Dimensions of the parts of an iron 6-pounder cannon, 6ft long.

Length		Calibre	Inches
AT	Total length	25 15/16	96.00
AG	Fore part	12 31/32	48.00
GN	Middle part	5 3/16	19.20
NT	Hind part	7 25/32	28.80
AD	Head with astragal	3 7/16	12.75
AR	Cylinder or bore	24 15/16	92.30
RT	Resistance	1	3.70
TX	Cascable, whole length	2	7.40
WX	Neck and button	1 19/64	4.81
LT	Trunnions centre from base ring	11 1/8	41.14
IK	Do length	1	3.70

Mouldings breadth with frieze

AB	Muzzle	5/16	1.12
CDEFPQ	Astragal	13/64	0.75
GH	Second reinforce ring	41/64	2.37
NO	First reinforce ring	41/64	2.37
ST	Base ring	23/32	2.62
TV	First cascable with stave	25/64	1.43
VW	Second cascable with stave	17/64	1.00
QS	Plain frieze	1	3.70
PG	Second reinforce ring Do	3/4	2.77

Length		Calibre	Inches
Thickness of metal			
lm	Over the vent	$1\frac{1}{4}$	4.62
no	Behind the first reinforce	$1\frac{3}{16}$	4.39
rs	Before	$1\frac{1}{16}$	3.93
tv	Behind the second reinforce	1	3.70
yz	Before	$\frac{7}{8}$	3.24
34	Muzzle	$\frac{1}{2}$	1.85
Mouldings greatest height above the metal			
ik	Base ring	$\frac{7}{32}$	0.80
pq	First reinforce ring	$\frac{3}{32}$	0.37
wx	Second reinforce ring	$\frac{3}{32}$	0.37
1–2	Head	$\frac{31}{64}$	1.80
Semi-diameter of the ...			
gh	First cascable stave	$1\frac{7}{32}$	4.50
ef	Second cascable stave	$\frac{23}{32}$	2.65
cd	Neck	$\frac{1}{2}$	1.85
ab	Button	$\frac{39}{64}$	2.24
LM	Trunnion	$\frac{1}{2}$	1.85

Table for surveying iron cannon		
Length		Inches
AT	Total length	96.00
AG	Fore part	48.00
GN	Middle part	19.20
NT	Hind part	28.80
AD	Head with astragal	12.75
AR	Cylinder or bore	92.30
RT	Resistance	3.70
TX	Cascable's whole length	7.40
WX	Neck and button	4.81
MT	From behind the trunnion to the base ring	41.14
tv	Trunnion	3.70

Mouldings breadth with frieze		
AB	Muzzle	1.12
CDEFPQ	Astragals	0.75
NO	First reinforce ring	2.37
GH	Second reinforce ring	2.37
ST	Base rings	2.62
TV	First cascable with stave	1.43
VW	Second cascable with stave	1.00
QS	Plain frieze	3.70
FG	Second reinforce ring Do	2.77

Diameter		
8–9	Bore	3.70
7–10	Muzzle stave	7.80
5–6	Head	11.12
3–4	Behind the head astragal	8.12
1–2	Before the second reinforce ring	10.17
yz	Over the second reinforce ring	11.87
wx	Behind the second reinforce ring	11.10
KM	Trunnion	3.70
rs	Before the first reinforce ring	11.56
pq	Over the first reinforce ring	13.25
no	Behind the first reinforce ring	12.49
lm	Vent	12.95
ik	Base ring	14.57
gh	First cascable staves	9.00
ef	Second cascable staves	5.30
cd	Button neck	3.70
ab	Button	4.48

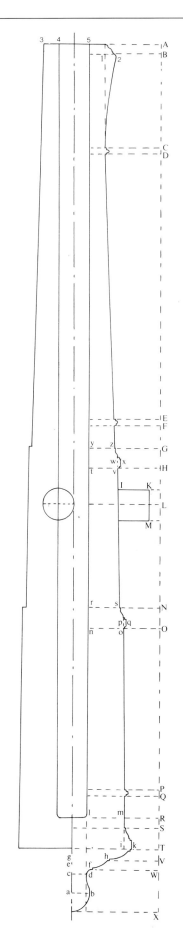

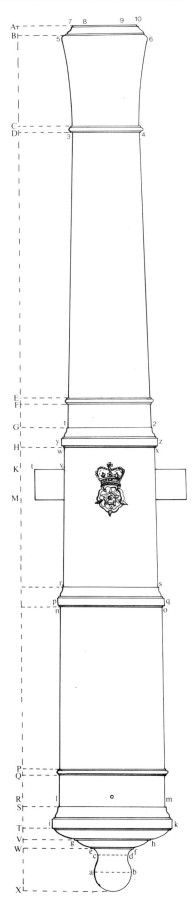

not clear how far this actually specified the actual sizes of the different parts of guns, and how successful it was in imposing uniformity.[1] The system was regulated much more closely in the early eighteenth century, by Albert Borgard. He was a Dane who became Chief Firemaster of the Royal Arsenal in 1712, and the first Colonel Commandant of the Royal Artillery in 1722. It is not apparent how far his 'Table for surveying iron cannon in their several parts'[2] was intended to be used for other guns besides the 6-pounder shown, but it seems likely that they had general application.

Borgard's rules, drawn up in 1716, were succeeded in 1725 by those of John Armstrong, Surveyor General. Armstrong had little experience of cannon design when he took up his office, and it took several years of experimentation to get the formula right.[3] Most of our information on Armstrong's rules come from printed sources, but they were in use for the greatest part of the eighteenth century. One work, published in 1819, claimed that they were 'still retained by us', but it is certain that they had been superseded by 1793, at the latest.[4]

In 1753 some attempt was made to modify the rules, in order to introduce a slightly lighter type of weapon, perhaps based on the Robins proposals of 1747. Falconer's *Marine Dictionary* lists the new guns, and there is a drawing of one in the Danish Archives. But there is no clear evidence that they were ever used. There is no list of guns issued to the fleet in the late eighteenth century, but those for later years show no signs of the lighter guns. In any case, according to Abraham Rees this establishment was succeeded in 1764, by one which was not very different from the old one of 1725.[5]

Captain Thomas Blomefield of the Royal Artillery was appointed to the new and relatively junior post of Inspector of Artillery in 1780. Over the next few years he reorganised the whole department, and introduced new rules for the proving and making of guns, as well as conducting numerous other experiments. In 1786 he began to look seriously at the design of the guns being made, and made some experiments, in co-operation with Samuel Walker, an ironfounder. Blomefield's overall plan was to strengthen the breeches of guns, mainly to enable them to withstand the new cylinder powders being introduced. The ogees and decorations which had embellished the older guns were largely abolished, and replaced by a simple curved breech. Extra thickness was given to the sides of the gun in this area. Blomefield also added a ring to the top of the cascable button, to help hold the breech rope in place. All this added weight, but this was compensated for by making the chase of the gun rather thinner. Initially Blomefield believed that it would be possible to reduce the total weight of each gun, but the gun which was eventually evolved was of the same weight as the old model.[6]

At first Walker found many difficulties in casting the new guns. The neck, behind the muzzle, was too thin, and did not allow the molten metal to flow freely into the lower parts during casting. The ring was also difficult to cast by the usual methods. Blomefield and Walker persisted, and in the years after 1786, guns of various calibres were made and tested at the Royal Arsenal. It is not clear exactly when the gun passed out from the experimental stage, but from about 1790 the draughts sent out to the gunfounders, besides Walker, were for guns of the new pattern. In November 1794 two 32-pounders of the old pattern burst under proof, by the 'separation of the breech from their bodies'.[7] It was now considered that the old guns were too weak to withstand the new powder, and no more were to be received from the founders. Thus the Blomefield gun became standard pattern, in time to serve as the main naval weapon of the French Revolutionary and Napoleonic Wars.

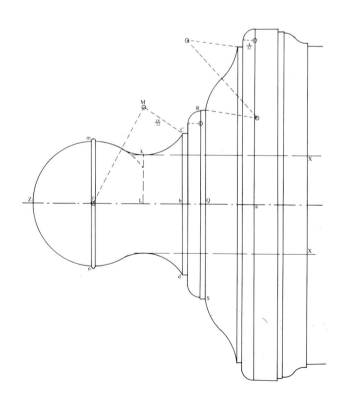

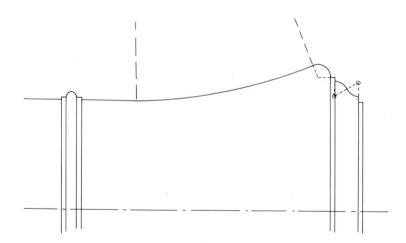

Method of drawing the muzzle and cascable of a 24-pounder, c1770. From NMM GUN/10.

$Za = 2\frac{9}{32}$ calibres
$db = \frac{24}{32}$
$fL = \frac{16}{32}$
$fn = LQ = \frac{20}{32}$
$ab = \frac{24}{32}$
$bc = \frac{24}{32}$
$Rs = 1\frac{30}{32}$ or $SQ = \frac{31}{32}$
Notes. X---X represents the bore, extended backwards.

Bore

The bore of a gun was determined by the size of the ball it was intended to fire, and in any muzzle-loading weapon the bore had to be slightly larger than the ball to allow it to be pushed into the barrel. Moreover, allowance always had to be made for inaccuracies in casting, which might make a ball jam on the way out, causing the gun to explode. From early times it seems to have been accepted that one-twentieth should be added to the bore to allow for 'windage'. By the late eighteenth century, after casting techniques had been considerably improved, it was being questioned whether this amount of windage was too great. 'The present proportion of British artillery might at the time it was established be very judiciously determined, since it is certain ... that pieces of artillery were formerly very inaccurately bored, and consequently a large allowance was necessary. At present no such reason subsists, as the construction of guns are much more strictly attended to, and no shot ought to be received which are not nearly round, and of the proper diameter.'[8] Despite this, and the introduction of new standards in the accuracy of casting brought about by the carronade, improvements were slow and slight. A 32-pounder of the second quarter of the nineteenth century had a windage of 0.233in on a bore of 6.412in, about one twenty-eighth of the bore.[9]

Length

Early guns varied considerably in length according to their bores, largely because they were designed for different purposes. Cannon perriers were intended for close-range work, and had correspondingly short barrels. Culverins, which made up the great bulk of the English fleet's guns in the sixteenth and seventeenth centuries, were usually very long, especially in the late sixteenth century. There is much controversy about why these pieces were made so long. It has been suggested that it was because when casting in bronze the tin content sank to the bottom, making the breech much stronger than the muzzle. There are many unresolved contradictions about this theory.[10] On the whole it is easier to believe that they were intended to give longer range, however inaccurately. The gunpowder used in the sixteenth century was slow burning, and unless the barrel was long enough some of it would still be burning when the ball reached the end of it.

Eighteenth century scientists and gunners would have preferred a more uniform length for guns, proportioned directly to the calibre. Benjamin Robins suggested the 32-pounder as an ideal, and that the other guns should be proportional to it in weight and therefore in length.[11] Captain Thomas Lawson of the Royal Artillery hinted that guns could be proportioned to the 24-pounder. But there was a major difficulty, as Lawson recognised. 'In the land service, the different natures have a fixed proportion assigned to them, but here, guns carrying the same ball are frequently cast of various lengths, in order to accommodate the rate of the ship designed for, and the local situation on board. From the necessity of this variety in the lengths of ships' guns, very few of them are properly proportioned to the magnitude of their shots, which all pieces of ordnance should be regulated by. As for instance, a 24-pounder being nearly 21 diameters of its shot in length, or 9½ feet; a 6-pounder, to be proportioned to it, should not exceed six feet, whereas many of them extend as far as nine, or 31 diameters of the shot. By this mode of comparison (supposing the 24-pounder of a proper length) it will be found that guns in general are much larger that is necessary, with regard to the

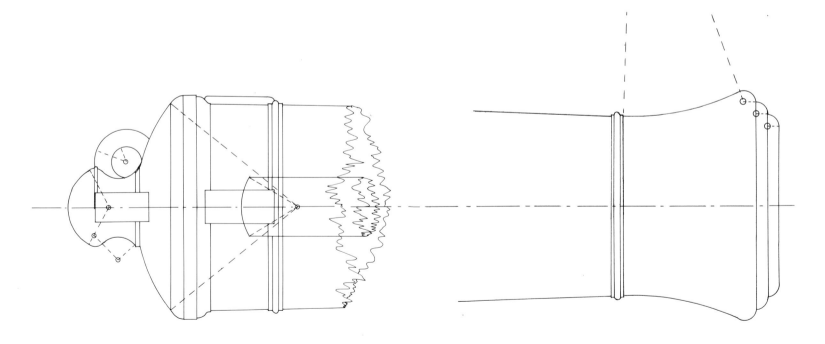

Method of drawing the muzzle and cascable of a Blomefield pattern 12-pounder, 1791. From **NMM** *GUN 10.*

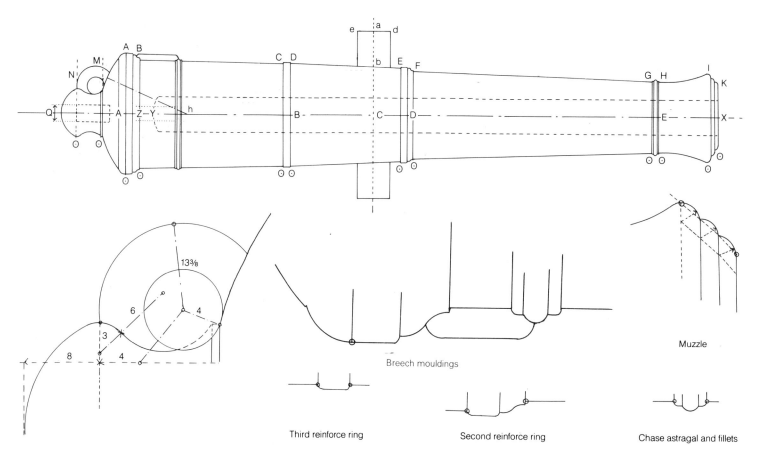

13⅜

Third reinforce ring

Breech mouldings

Second reinforce ring

Muzzle

Chase astragal and fillets

Details of a 32-pounder Blomefield pattern gun, 1796. See p266 for dimensions.

ranging of their shots. Therefore, the closer this proportion is can be adhered to, the more advantageous it will be in serving the guns, and with less strain on the ships.'[12] In the 1720s it was said, 'It is certain that from a six-pounder upwards, the nearer they are to ten feet the better'.[13]

Guns had to be long enough to penetrate the ship's side, and allow the muzzle to clear the port lid and any rigging which might be in the way, for ships were made of wood, their rigging of rope – both of which were highly inflammable. Fire was recognised as the greatest disaster a ship could face, worse than storm, disease, or enemy attack. The discharge of a piece of ordnance produced a large flash from the barrel, and it was important that this be carried well clear of the ship. Many guns were, admittedly, longer than necessary merely to carry them through the hull, but about a third of them were in the way of the shrouds and the channels. Since uniform armaments were usually considered desirable, gunners were reluctant to fit shorter guns away from the rigging, and preferred an unbroken line of guns of similar calibre and length. The smaller calibres of gun, on the other hand, were fitted to the forecastle, poop, and quarterdeck, where they would, to a certain extent, fire over, rather than through, the ship's side. Even where they fired through the side, at that level the structure was thinner, the tumblehome less, and the shrouds closer to the ship's side. Therefore it was often possible to make the lighter guns, of six or nine pounds, shorter than the others, particularly in the eighteenth century.

Because of these factors, guns of the main armament (those of

the lower, upper and middle gundecks), were longer than many land gunners would have liked. Even where very short guns were used in large numbers, after 1780, they were nearly always confined to the quarterdecks, poops and forecastles, where length was much less necessary.

On the other hand, few guns were more than 11ft long because they needed room to recoil on the deck, and they could not be allowed too close to the centre line, where they would encounter masts, capstans, gratings and various other fittings. The muzzle had to come far enough inboard to allow reloading, but the rear of the carriage had to be kept clear of the fittings at the centre of the ship. These practical considerations imposed a severe limitation on the length of ship's guns.

The gun's length was measured from its widest point, at the base ring, to the muzzle. Though this was probably the easiest way to measure it, it was not the most useful. It was not directly related to the length of the bore, which would give a more accurate indication of the performance of a gun. Nor did it provide the gun's total length, which included the cascable behind the base ring, which would give a better indication of the space the gun would occupy on deck.

The Cascable

In the late eighteenth century it was generally accepted that the full length of the cascable, from the base ring to the end of the button, should be a little over two calibres, and Muller, published in 1768, suggested $2\frac{1}{4}$ calibres.[14] The size of the button and cascable had to be increased over the years. Those of the seventeenth century had been rather smaller, though the rules, if any, by which they were proportioned are not known. In the eighteenth century the neck of the cascable, between the button and the breech, was equal to the bore in diameter, while the button itself was, of course, slightly wider. The eighteenth century button was always spherical, but that of the seventeenth century often had a rather less regular shape. Some came to a point via a series of decorations, and others had flattened ends.

Thickness of Metal

The thickness of metal at the breech was obviously crucial to the strength of the gun. In the mid-seventeenth century it was rather less than the diameter of the bore for 'lessened or slender fortified' culverins, and equal to the diameter of the bore for ordinary culverins. Cannons were less strong, and only on those 'double fortified or reinforced' was the thickness of metal at the breech equal to that at the bore. On ordinary cannon it was seven-eighths of the diameter.

By the eighteenth century, guns had generally become stronger and heavier. According to Borgard's proportions, the thickness of metal 'over the vent' was to be $1\frac{1}{4}$ times the calibre. By Armstrong's rules of a few years later, the thickness was to be slightly more, at $1\frac{1}{7}$ of the calibre. The gun was tapered in several stages to the neck of the piece, just behind the muzzle, where it was at its thinnest point forward of the base ring. At the neck the metal was half, or slightly less, its thickness at the breech.

The Trunnions

In the seventeenth century the trunnions tapered as they extended away from the barrel. By 1716 they were cylindrical, and equal in length and diameter to the bore. The trunnions were placed three-sevenths of the length of the gun away from the breech ring so that the gun could pivot backwards to rest on its breech. They were fitted below the centre line of the gun, with their centres on a level with the lowest part of the bore. This was criticised by some, who believed that there would be less strain if the trunnions were placed level with the gun's centre line.

Chapter 18. Types of Gun

Categories

Until the early years of the eighteenth century, English guns were identified by their traditional names, rather than their weights or calibres. Though this old terminology was complex, in essence the classification was simple. There were four main categories, based mainly on the proportion of calibre to length. The shortest were the mortars, $1\frac{1}{2}$ calibres long. They were intended to fire heavy balls on a high trajectory, and they were not in the strictest sense naval weapons at all, because they were not normally used in ship-to-ship engagements. They were fitted only to a special class of vessel, known as a bomb ketch or mortar vessel, and they were used to fire into enemy fortresses or towns. They must be treated separately from other naval weapons.

The next category was the perrier, which was six to eight calibres long. In naval service the most numerous of this type was the cannon perrier. Perriers were comparatively rare, but there were a few on most of the largest ships in the first half of the seventeenth century. Though some were breech-loading, it seems that the naval ones were muzzle-loading, as there is no mention in the ordnance lists of the separate chambers which would have been necessary for breech-loading. As the name implies, the perrier was originally intended to fire stone shot. This would splinter on impact, and do a large amount of damage to the enemy, but it was expensive and difficult to manufacture, and by 1600 it had largely been replaced by iron shot. There were also smaller forms of the perrier: port-pieces, slings and fowlers. All guns of this type had become obsolete by the middle of the seventeenth century.

Though the cannon proper, or 'cannon of battery', eventually became a widely used naval gun, it was rather rare until about 1650. This class included the cannon-of-seven, or 42-pounder,

which was the heaviest broadside gun carried, and the demi-cannon, or 32-pounder, which was to become the standard weapon of ships of the line in the second half of the eighteenth century. It was originally 18 to 28 calibres long. Even longer was the culverin, 32 to 34 calibres long in its original form. This class included the culverin proper, the demi-culverin, the saker, falcon, minion, robinet, falconet and base. It covered a wide range of calibres, for the whole culverin had a bore of up to $5\frac{1}{2}$in, while the base culverin had one of only $1\frac{1}{2}$in. Nevertheless it did not overlap with the cannon, for the demi-cannon had a bore of at least $6\frac{1}{2}$in.[1]

This range of guns left many gaps, especially towards the higher end of the scale. There was no gun, for example, which lay between the 32 pounds of the demi-cannon and the 18 pounds of the culverin, or between the culverin and the demi-culverin, which fired a ball of 9 pounds. These gaps began to be filled in the third quarter of the seventeenth century, by guns of 24, 12, 8, 6 and 3 pounds. It was rather fortuitous that none of these guns had to be manufactured in England, except for some 24-pounders in the 1660s.[2] Instead they were captured from the Dutch, during the three wars fought between 1652 and 1674. As early as June 1653, the 'Generals at Sea', Blake and Monck, wrote to the Admiralty that 'we have several Dutch pieces carrying a bullet of 8 and 12 pounds, others of 24 pounds weight, and have little shot fit for them, and therefore we desire you will write to the Officers of the Ordnance that a considerable quantity thereof may be expidited to us.'[3] In 1691 John Seller referred to guns of 24, 12, 8, 6 and 3 pounds as 'Dutch pieces',[4] and as late as 1702 Captain Povey wrote that 'all countries but England name their guns by the weight of shot; which I think very proper'.[5]

The Cannon-of-seven, or 42-pounder

The cannon-of-seven was the largest broadside gun used by the sailing navy, except for the very big carronades introduced at

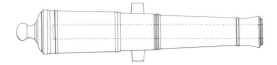

A 9ft 6in long 42-pounder of 1673. This was one of the 'nealed and turned' guns produced around that time.

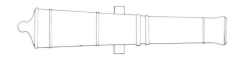

An iron 32-pounder from the Edgar, lost in 1711.

the end of the eighteenth century. Within the cannon category it was quite small, for in 1627 the 'canon royall' had a bore of 8½in, and could fire a ball of 66 pounds, while the ordinary cannon used a 60-pound ball[6] – but these pieces were never used at sea. The *Sovereign of the Seas* of 1637 was evidently the first ship to use the cannon-of-seven in large numbers, and she was intended to carry a full battery, albeit drakes, on the lower deck. After this date the use of 42-pounders was eventually extended to the lower decks of all First Rates. In 1666 it was even used by some Second Rates, but only for a short time.[7] It was to remain the standard heavy gun for First Rates until 1778, when Admiral Keppel applied to have those on his flagship, the *Victory*, replaced with 32-pounders, believing that the heavier gun had a lower rate of fire because of the weight of the ball.[8] However, the other First Rates continued to carry 42-pounders until in 1790 it was ordered that they should be replaced at the first opportunity. Even so, some ships were not re-equipped for a considerable time, and the *Royal George* and *Britannia* carried 42-pounders until 1807.[9]

Being the largest gun, the 42-pounder was the last to be made of iron rather than brass. Nevertheless, this happened surprisingly early in its career, for iron ones were being cast by 1657.[10] Brass was to remain the standard material for another twenty years, but by the beginning of the next century the iron gun was more common. The gun came in only two lengths, 10ft and 9ft 6in. Its weight remained relatively constant over the years. Iron guns of 9ft 6in and 65cwt were proposed in 1677, and this was still the standard weight for this type in 1800. The brass guns actually carried in 1698 were rather lighter, ranging from 54 to 62cwt.[11] In 1753 a much lighter iron gun of 55cwt was proposed, but it is doubtful if any were ever made.

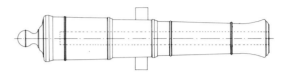

A typical Armstrong pattern 32-pounder, 9ft 6in long. This type was in use from 1725–90. Based on proportions given in Muller's Treatise on Artillery, 1768.

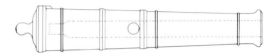

A type of lighter 32-pounder proposed in 1753. It is unusual because its chamber is narrower than its bore, and it has trunnions at the level of the centre of the bore. There are drawings of such weapons in Falconer's Marine Dictionary, and in the Danish Archives, but there is no evidence that they were made or used in any quantity.

The Demi-cannon, or 32-pounder

Early demi-cannon were quite long, up to 12ft in the late sixteenth century, but such pieces were rarely used on ships. The demi-cannon was used in small numbers on the largest ships of the first half of the seventeenth century. The *Sovereign* of 1637 introduced a new practice by carrying a larger number of demi-cannon. Its use was greatly extended in the 1650s, when it became the standard lower deck gun for the largest Third Rates. By this time it was quite short. Those ordered in 1653 were to be 8ft 6in long, and those of 1655 were to be 8 to 9ft long, and to weigh from 53 to 55cwt.[12] They then became slightly longer. Those ordered for the 1677 establishment were to be 9ft 6in, and by 1703 there were two types, of 9ft 6in and 10ft, weighing 53 and 55cwt respectively.[13] Thereafter there was little change, except for a slight tendency to increase in weight. In 1782 a 10ft gun weighed 58cwt, and a 9ft 6in gun weighed 55cwt.[14]

The 32-pounder was introduced on the lower decks of Third

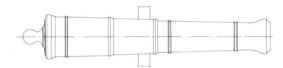

A 9ft 6in 32-pounder of c1770, from NMM GUN/10.

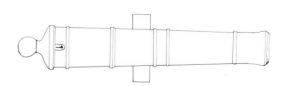

An iron 32-pounder from the Royal George, lost in 1782. It is 9ft 6in long.

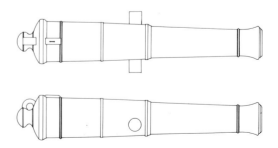

A standard Blomefield pattern 32-pounder, c1793.

Rates in the 1650s. Its use was extended throughout the 1660s and '70s, as more of the larger type of Third Rate, carrying 60 to 70 guns, were built. It was also carried on the new type of three-decker Second Rate, developed in the 1670s. It already looked set to become the principal weapon of the line of battle, but it began to decline in 1685, when there was a general tendency to reduce the weight of guns carried. Third Rates continued to carry this type until 1703, when it was replaced by the 24-pounder. It was partly restored in 1716, when it became the standard lower deck gun for all ships of 80 guns or more.

The 32-pounder's real heyday began after 1740, when it became recognised as the ideal gun for the ship of the line, the heaviest that could be handled efficiently in action. In 1733 there was an attempt to fit it to the lower decks of the old 70-gun ships, removing six guns in the process and re-classifying them as 64s. This was deferred, but carried out on new ships in 1743. Larger ships were built by the 1745 establishment, and the 70-gun ship was revived, carrying the 32-pounder. It also became the main weapon of the new 74s which were built in large numbers after 1755. Around this time there was an attempt to extend it to a new class of 64-gun ships, but this was short-lived. After 1778 it began to replace the 42-pounder on the lower decks of First Rates. By 1800 nearly all ships of the line, excluding a few old 64s and those First Rates which had not yet been re-equipped, carried the 32-pounder.

Early demi-cannon were of brass, but it is doubtful if this was so after 1655, when the gun became popular.

The Cannon Perrier

This was the largest gun of the perrier type. Originally it was breech-loading, with a separate chamber, and fired, as its name implies, stone shot. The later ones were muzzle-loading and fired iron shot. In 1590 it was described as weighing 3000 pounds, carrying a ball of $24\frac{1}{2}$ pounds with a calibre of 6in.[15] In the first half of the seventeenth century a few were carried on each of the largest ships. In 1631, for example, all the great ships had two.[16] It seems to have become obsolete about 1635.

The 24-pounder

The 24-pounder was the largest of the Dutch guns captured after 1652, and it was mentioned by Blake and Monck in 1653. In fact few Dutch ships of this period carried such a large gun, and not many of them were captured during the First Dutch War in 1652–54. Only 16 were available for the Navy in 1664, and only one ship, the *Matthias* (a Dutch prize) was fitted with them.[17] Evidently the need for such a gun was already apparent, and at least 46 were cast in England during 1666.[18] The Dutch had increased the gun power of their fleet since 1654, and in the Second Dutch War (1664–67) many more ships carrying 24-pounders were captured, so there was no need for further domestic production.

In 1666 only three ships, all Fourth Rates of 50 to 54 guns, carried 24-pounders, and one of these, the *Matthias*, was lost the following year.[19] In the 1677 establishment their use was greatly extended. They were to be carried by the small Third Rates, of 60 to 64 guns, and the large Fourth Rates of 54 guns. Both these classes, however, were out of favour between 1660 and 1690, so

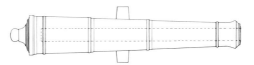

An early 24-pounder, 9ft long, recovered from the Matthias, *lost in 1666. Though it bears a rose and crown crest it is not clear whether it is an English gun, for few English 24-pounders had been made by this date; it may have been a captured Dutch gun given a new crest.*

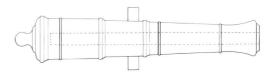

A Borgard pattern 24-pounder, 9ft 6in long, c1716.

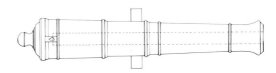

A 24-pounder, 9ft 6in long, c1745.

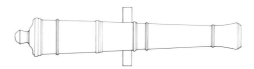

A light 24-pounder from the Maidstone *of 1744, lost in 1747.*

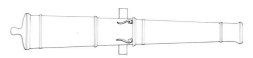

A brass 24-pounder recovered from the Royal George, *lost in 1782. It was probably made in 1743, and was 9ft 6in long.*

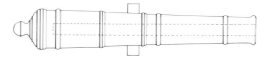

A 24-pounder c1775, based on the drawings in Robertson's Treatise of Mathematical Instruments.

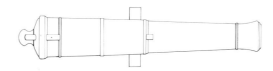

A Blomefield 24-pounder, 9ft 6in long, c1800.

few new ones were constructed, and thus there was no need to manufacture any 24-pounders. In 1685, 347 24-pounders were available to the Navy, and 346 of these were allocated to ships.[20] They were to be carried by approximately the same ships as the 1677 establishment had stipulated, the small Third Rates and large Fourth Rates.

The 24-pounder began to gain in popularity after 1690, when it was chosen for the lower decks of ten new 60-gun ships. Around this time it made its first appearance as a secondary weapon, as the middle deck gun of the First Rate *Britannia*. It became yet more common in 1703, when it was nominated as the lower deck gun of all Third Rates, in place of the 32-pounder. In 1716 it was to be used for the lower decks of all ships of 60 and 70 guns, and as the middle deck gun of First Rates. After that it tended to decline, being replaced by 32-pounders on many ships after 1743. However, it remained as the main armament of 64-gun ships, and as the second largest gun carried by First Rates, as well as two-decker 80s and the very largest 74s.

There were only three lengths of 24-pounder: 10ft, 9ft 6in, and 9ft. Like most types of gun they tended to increase in weight over the years: the 10ft gun from 45cwt in 1679 to 51cwt in 1716, and 52cwt in 1800. The 9ft gun grew rather more, from a minimum of 38cwt in 1679 to 47cwt in 1761 and 1800.[21] This gun was always made of iron except, presumably, for a few brass 24-pounders manufactured for the middle decks of First Rates.

The Culverin, or 18-pounder

Along with its junior partner the demi-culverin, the culverin was the most common gun in the fleet until the early eighteenth century. It made up 25 per cent of the Navy's guns in 1603, 16 per cent in 1660–61, and 16 per cent in 1685.[22] Until the 1650s it was the main armament of most of the large ships, which carried bigger guns only in small numbers. It was largely replaced in this role by the demi-cannon, but it still had many uses, as the middle deck gun on most three-deckers, upper deck gun on the largest Third Rates, and main armament on most Fourth Rates. It was gradually eased out of some of these roles, being replaced by the 24-pounder on the middle deck of 100-gun ships in 1716, and by the demi-culverin on the upper decks of 70-gun ships in 1703. It regained its place on the upper decks of the new 64s in 1743, and on the 70s of 1745. Ten years later it became important as the upper deck armament of most 74s. From 1780 it entered a totally new role, as the main armament of the large 38-gun frigates, and from 1790 it was extended to a new class of 32-gun frigates.

The seventeenth century culverin was made in a great variety of lengths. Some, presumably cutts, were as short as 8ft in 1653, and others were as long as 11ft in 1698. The great majority were between 8ft 6in and 10ft long, and weighed between 30 and 47cwt. In the eighteenth century two lengths became standard. The 9ft 6in gun weighed 41 or 42cwt, and the 9ft gun between 39 and 42cwt. After 1780 a much smaller gun, weighing 37 to 38cwt, was produced for the gundecks of frigates.

Early seventeenth century culverins were of course made of brass. These were slowly replaced by iron guns after 1625. In 1660 about 30 per cent of them were still brass. It is doubtful if any brass ones were still in naval service after 1716, because they no longer formed part of the armament of First Rates.

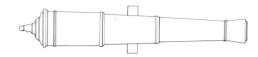

A brass culverin of 1590.

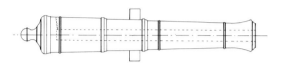

A 9ft Armstrong pattern 18-pounder. This type was used from 1725 to 1790.

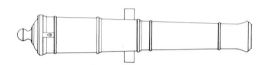

An 18-pounder, c1745, from a drawing in the Danish Archives.

The 12-pounder

This type, like the 24-pounder, was originally captured from the Dutch. In the 1650s it was much more common in the Dutch fleet than the 18-pounder, and much larger numbers were captured in the First Dutch War. There is no evidence that any were manufactured in England in the seventeenth century, but 462 were in British possession in 1664.[23] This was rather more than were needed, for the gun establishment of that year demanded only 202, leaving 260 in store. Some 12-pounders were used as the upper deck gun of some of the larger Third Rates in 1666, but otherwise they were confined to Dutch prizes. In 1677 the 12-pounder was to be used on the upper decks of 20 new 70-gun ships, and on a few of the old Third Rates. Nearly a thousand were in stock in 1685, far more than any of the other Dutch guns. In order that existing stocks should not remain idle its use was extended to the upper decks of some First, Second and Fourth Rates.

In the eighteenth century it was used for miscellaneous purposes. From 1703 to 1716 it was fitted on the middle decks of 80-gun ships, and on the lower decks of Fourth Rates of 50 guns. Its use on the upper decks of three-deckers was extended, so that it was carried by all First and Second Rates. From the 1750s it gained some importance as the main armament of the new 32- and 36-gun frigates, until these began to be replaced with larger ships in the 1780s and '90s.

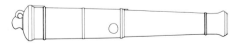

An 8ft 6in long Blomefield 12-pounder of 33cwt, c1800.

The original 12-pounders were relatively long, between 9 and 10ft. The 8ft 6in gun was introduced in 1743 for the upper decks of 50-gun ships. The frigate guns, first used in the 1750s, were even shorter; they were 7ft 6in long and weighed 28½cwt. An even shorter gun, of 7ft, is mentioned in the early nineteenth century.[24] The 12-pounder was nearly always made of iron, though some of the guns fitted to First Rates in the first half of the eighteenth century may have been brass.

The Demi-culverin

This was the favourite gun of the Elizabethan Navy. Nearly 300 were in service in 1603, almost 30 per cent of the fleet's armament.[25] Its predominance increased slightly throughout the first half of the seventeenth century, and it made up about 34 per cent of the Navy's guns in 1660. By 1685 it had declined in relative terms, for it made up about 20 per cent of the guns available, and 18 per cent of those actually needed. For the first three-quarters of the century it was almost universal, and there were few ships of any size which did not carry it somewhere – on the lower decks of Fourth and Fifth Rates, and the upper decks of First, Second and Third Rates. In 1666 only 16 ships above the Sixth Rate did not have any, and most of these were Dutch prizes. Its decline began in 1677, when none were allocated to any of the 30 new ships, and some of the older ships were given 12-pounders instead. It was evidently out of favour by 1685, when 1820 were on hand, but only 1385 were allotted to ships.

The 9-pounder was retained throughout the first half of the eighteenth century – on the upper decks of ships of 90, 100, and sometimes 50 or 60 guns, as well as the main deck armament for ships of 30 guns (though very few of the latter class were actually built at that time). It was largely replaced by the 12-pounder on the upper decks of three-deckers after 1743. On the other hand, it was now used as the main armament of ships of 24 guns, and the secondary armament for those of 44. It took on a new lease of life in the 1750s, when it was adopted as the forecastle and quarter-deck armament for new 64- and 74-gun ships, and as the main armament for small frigates of 28-guns and less. It continued in these roles until the end of the century, when it was largely replaced by the carronade.

The demi-culverin was probably used in its 'cutt' form more than any other weapon. The list of 1685 shows it as the most numerous type of cutt; the culverin cutt was evidently not used in any great quantity. Therefore it is not surprising to find that the length of demi-culverins ranged from 5 to 10½ft. Guns shorter than 6ft, or longer than 10ft, were rare, but in the seventeenth century there was every other possible size. At least nine sizes were in use in 1679, and at least seven in 1698.[26] Because of this great variety it is not easy to tell where the distinction between cutts and normal guns began. Naturally their weight varied, even more than their length. In 1679 a 5ft gun weighed 11cwt, and a 10ft gun could weigh as much as 36cwt.[27]

A demi-culverin of the 1570s. This gun, in Pevensey Castle, is unusual because it is made of iron. About 12in is missing from the muzzle, and has been replaced by a ring.

There was some attempt to impose order on this chaos in the eighteenth century, and the 1703 establishment stipulated there should be only two types, of 9 and 8ft. But the 9-pounder, like the other medium-sized guns, was used for many purposes, and was needed in different sizes. By 1761, after its revival, it was used in five different lengths, ranging from the 7ft, 23cwt weapon for the main armament of Sixth Rates, to the 9ft, 26cwt gun which was used on the upper decks of 80-gun ships. By 1782 another size had been added, and the 9ft 6in gun reintroduced.[28]

The demi-culverin was similar to the culverin in that it was made of brass until 1625, but slowly replaced by iron thereafter. In 1660 about 20 per cent of demi-culverins were still made of brass.[29]

An iron demi-culverin of 1680, from the Dartmouth, *wrecked in 1690.*

A 9-pounder of 1716, in the Tower of London. This gun is very similar to the one described in Borgard's instructions.

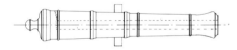

An Armstrong pattern 9-pounder, 7ft 6in long, used between 1725 and 1790.

The 8-pounder

This was another Dutch gun, introduced through capture in the three Dutch Wars. Unlike other captures, it found little favour with the Navy, for it did not fill an obvious gap in the range of sizes, and was too like the demi-culverin to be useful except as a stop-gap. There were 254 8-pounders available in 1664, but only 166 of these were to be used, on the Dutch prizes. In 1685, 424 were in store or aboard ship, but only 282 were needed. They were used as the upper deck armament of some of the smaller Fourth Rates, and a few of the Fifth Rates. Some 8-pounders evidently survived into the eighteenth century, and in the 1720s it was proposed to use them on the upper decks of

A brass 8-pounder of 1623. This was a Dutch gun, made in Enkhuisen, and captured in the Dutch Wars.

80-gun ships, because of the shortage of 6-pounders.[30] The Navy never really wanted the 8-pounder, and there is no evidence than any were ever manufactured in Britain. It varied from 7 to 8ft in length, and from 19 to 21cwt in weight.

The 6-pounder

This too was a Dutch gun, but much more successful than the 8-pounder. Though it was not much different in calibre from the large saker of $5\frac{1}{4}$lbs, it had the advantage of using a round-figured weight of shot. It thus gained acceptance in the early part of the seventeenth century, when British guns came to be known by their weight of shot rather than their traditional names.

In 1664, 440 6-pounder guns were available but only 170 were to be used. It was still not in great demand in 1685, when only 382 out of 558 were needed, mostly for the upper decks of Fourth and Fifth Rates. The 1703 establishment first brought the 6-pounder into prominence, when it ordered that they be placed on the quarterdecks and forecastles of all ships of 40 guns or more, and on the upper decks of 80-gun ships, and Fifth and Sixth Rates. Few, if any, had been manufactured in Britain by this time, and it is not surprising that the Ordnance Board was not able to give many ships their established armament, being forced to substitute either sakers of 8-pounders.[31] This situation continued throughout the 1720s, for the 1716 establishment stipulated as many 6-pounders as that of 1703, though evidently little had been done to increase the supply of them. After 1743 the 6-pounder was no longer used on the main decks of any new ships, but it was still to be carried on the quarterdecks and forecastles of most. In the 1750s it was replaced by the 9-pounder on the new 74s, but it was fitted on the upper works of the new 32- and 36-gun frigates. It tended to decline in the 1790s, when it was largely replaced by 9-pounders and carronades.

The 6-pounder was used in a variety of sizes throughout its career. The 1703 establishment demanded six different lengths, from 6ft to 9ft 6ins. Little had changed by 1782, when seven different. lengths varying from 6ft to 9ft were listed.[32] In that year the smallest 6-pounder weighed 16cwt, and the largest 24cwt.

A Dutch brass 6-pounder of 1643 which was recovered from the wreck of the Stirling Castle. *It is listed as being fitted to her in 1698.*

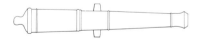

A 6-pounder from the Dartmouth, *c1680.*

The Saker

This was a gun of the culverin type. In the late sixteenth century it was made in three different calibres: 7 pounds, 6 pounds,

A saker of 1601.

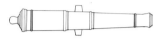

A saker drake from the Dartmouth.

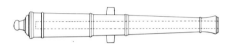

A late seventeenth-century saker.

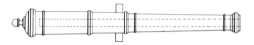

Another saker, probably from the late seventeenth century.

and $4\frac{3}{4}$ pounds.[33] By the early seventeenth century its calibre had been standardised as $5\frac{1}{4}$ pounds. It was the third most common gun in the Navy of 1603, after the culverin and demi-culverin. In the first half of the seventeenth century most large ships had a small number of sakers, presumably for firing over the bulwarks of the quarterdeck or forecastle. Many smaller ships used it for their upper deck armament. These old ships were given extra guns in the 1640s and '50s, many of which were sakers. By 1666 it was almost as universal as the demi-culverin, and only 30 ships above the Third Rate had no sakers. However, it was used only in small numbers on each ship. Second Rates mostly had two or four, and only two Third Rates had more than ten each, for they carried them on their upper works, and often on the poop. The smaller Fourth Rates and the Fifth Rates carried rather more, on their upper decks. But there began to be less call for this type. In 1664, 944 were available but only 302 were needed. Saker cutts were in much greater demand, 212 were needed, but only 71 were available. It is doubtful if any more ordinary sakers were produced after this date. In 1684, 854 were in store or in use, a slight decline on the 1664 figure which can probably be accounted for by natural wastage. There were 234 saker cutts available, which suggests that some had been manufactured. The saker was still used as the main quarterdeck and forecastle gun on most ships.

The saker's decline began very early in the eighteenth century. The 1703 establishment had no use for it, though it did actually continue in service for 20 years or more, to make up for deficient stocks of 6-pounders. But its peculiar calibre did not fit into any eighteenth-century scheme, and it had probably disappeared by 1730. Even so, the life-span of individual guns was remarkably long; though there is no evidence that any ordinary sakers were made after 1660, some saker cutts were certainly delivered in the 1660s.[34]

Because so many cutts were produced, there were many different lengths of saker, varying from 4ft 6in to 10ft. Cutts were presumably of 7ft or less, and weighed between 7 and 19cwt. Ordinary sakers were 8ft or more, and ranged from 16 to 30cwt.

The Minion, or 4-pounder

This gun was of the culverin type. Various weights of shot were used in its early career, until the 1620s when shot of 4 pounds or slightly less became standard. It was used on as many ships as the saker, but in even smaller numbers, because it was fitted on the poop. By 1664 it had fallen completely out of favour in its standard form. Though there were 341 of these guns in stock, none were to be used for the fleet. However, cutts were in some demand: 66 were wanted, but only 32 were available. These were to be used entirely on Dutch prizes, as an alternative to 3-pounders. The minion was still unpopular in 1685. There were 245 on hand, and only 218 required. Like the saker, it continued in use in the early part of the eighteenth century as a substitute for other guns, in this case the 3-pounder. In its original form it probably died out around 1715.

It had a minor revival later, in the form of the 4-pounder. This gun was used only in a few subsidiary roles. In theory it was allocated to the quarterdecks of 30-gun ships between 1716 and 1743, but none of these ships were actually built until later. It was also used on 24-gun ships of the same period. Later it was carried on at least one non-standard ship, Cook's *Endeavour* of 1768. It continues to appear on lists of guns in 1800, though it does not seem to have been much used by that time.

Minions varied from 4 to 7ft in length, and from 4 to 9cwt. Their successors, the 4-pounders, were 5ft 6in or 6ft long, and weighed 11 or 12cwt, respectively.

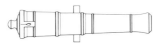

A 4-pounder, 5ft 6in long, c1770.

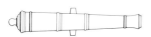

A 3-pounder from the Dartmouth.

The 3-pounder

The 3-pounder was the smallest of the Dutch guns. In 1664 it was apparently not listed separately from the minion, so it is not clear how many were available. By 1685, 324 were needed and 422 were available. It was used on the poops of many of the larger

ships, and on the quarterdecks of some of the smaller ones. According to the establishment of 1703 it was to be carried on the poops of 70- and 80-gun ships, but the larger ships, the 90s and 100s, were to have 6-pounders instead. Poop deck armament fell out of favour in the early part of the eighteenth century, and the 1716 establishment found no use for the 3-pounder. After 1743 it was revived to some extent, being used for the quarterdecks of small frigates, and for sloops and cutters. The eighteenth century 3-pounder was between 4ft 6in and 6ft long, and weighed between 4 and 9cwt. After 1743 the gun was invariably 4ft 6in long, and weighed 7cwt.

A brass minion of 1685.

Murderers, Fowlers and Port-pieces

These were smaller versions of the cannon perrier. They were breech-loading and fired either stone or grape-shot, for clearing the men from an enemy's decks. Originally they were made of cast iron, but the few which survived into the seventeenth century were mostly cast in bronze. They were carried in small numbers, two or four per ship. They were largely obsolete by 1635, having been replaced by drakes, though at least one murderer was in use in 1647.[35]

The murderer was the largest of this type, but specifications are few, and vague. The brass port-piece weighed about 9cwt, plus about 1½cwt for the chamber, and the fowler weighed about 5cwt, plus 1cwt for the chamber.

Falcons, Falconets and Robinets

These were the smallest guns of the culverin type. The falcon carried a ball of 2½ to 3 pounds, and weighed from 650 to 800 pounds. The falconet weighed from 400 to 500 pounds, and fired a ball of 1¼ to 1½ pounds. It was about 6ft in length. The robinet was the smallest of all, and fired a ball of less than 1 pound. It weighed 300 pounds, and was about 5ft long. All these guns were carried in very small numbers in the early years of the seventeenth century, often singly or in pairs. They had gone out of use by about 1635, except for isolated examples.

A brass falcon of 1580, 5ft 5in long.

Swivel Guns

In a sense these were descended from slings, which were small breech-loading guns which were fitted on a forked piece of metal

Swivel guns mounted on a frigate of the 1770s. Author's photographs, courtesy of NMM.

and fired over the rail of a ship. They seemed to have been obsolete aboard English ships by the beginning of the seventeenth century, and there is no sign that anything replaced them during that century.

The swivel gun re-appeared around the beginning of the eighteenth century. Some breech-loaders have been found aboard the *Association*, wrecked in 1707, but these were of French origin, and probably intended for land use.[36] According to the 1716 establishment, small ships of the Fifth and Sixth Rates were to carry swivels on their quarterdecks. The number carried was approximately equal to the number of main deck guns carried. This type of gun was muzzle-loading, and carried a ball of half a pound. It was fitted with a long bar leading backwards from its breech. This was called the tiller, and was used to aim the gun. Its use was extended considerably in the 1770s, when it was allocated to ships of the line and frigates, for fitting to the tops and boats. Twelve were issued to all ships of 18 to 74 guns, though not to three-deckers.[37] Fore and main tops were fitted to carry three swivels on each side. The swivel gun was to a certain extent superseded by the carronade, especially on boats, but it remained in use until 1815.

Seven-barrelled Guns

These were rifled guns, able to fire seven balls at a time. They were invented by a Mr Nelson, and were established by an order of 1779.[38] A ship of 74 guns was to carry 20 for use in her tops; ships of 60 or 64 guns were to have 16 each; those of 50 and 54 guns, 12; those of 38 to 20 guns, 12; and sloops, 8. In a contemporary list of gunner's stores they are classed with the small arms, so presumably they had no fixed mounting.[39] They were probably short-lived, as the carronade soon came into use.

Chapter 19. Carronades

Invention

The Carron Iron Company was founded in 1759, near Falkirk in Stirlingshire. As the first modern ironworks in Scotland, it was an important harbinger of the Industrial Revolution. The company soon discovered that the casting of cannon could be a profitable line of business, and made its first guns in 1761. It first sold cannon to the Board of Ordnance in 1765. Though its prices were low, its proofs were not particularly successful so it strove to improve its product. It tried different types of ore, and imported skilled workers from southern English works. By 1769, the company had achieved some success and were casting up to 50 tons per week. Two years later the Board of Ordnance noticed that a large proportion of Carron guns were bursting on proof, and began enquiries. This eventually resulted in a detailed test of Carron guns early in 1773, including special proofs, and an assay of metal. As a result, large numbers were rejected, and it was ordered that the company was 'not to proceed in casting any more'. Carron guns already fitted to ships were to be removed.[1] This prohibition on the casting of long guns was not lifted until 1795, after carronades had been in use for many years.[2]

The company worked hard to recover from this disaster. More skilled labour was imported, and guns were bored from the solid. Though the Ordnance Board still refused to take any, Carron was experimenting with new lighter guns, and by 1776 claimed to be able to cast a 6-pounder of half the normal weight. Though the Board was unimpressed, the idea of a lighter gun began to take root at Carron.

Three men claimed to be the inventors of the carronade. General Robert Melville, though an infantry officer, provided the military expertise, and had the idea of a gun of light weight and heavy calibre as early as 1753. But he was mainly interested in very large fortress guns, firing mostly shells. The 68-pounder carronade was soon developed, but it was far less common than the smaller carronades, and the 100-pounder was a failure.[3] The carronade as eventually developed was used mostly by the Navy. Melville initially visualised the carronade as a version of the military howitzer, 'though heavier and more powerful'.[4] It was in fact to differ from the howitzer as it had a chamber, so that the thickness of metal would be greater where the charge was ignited, and it mostly fired solid shot, on a horizontal trajectory.

Charles Gascoigne was a partner in the Carron Company, and in overall charge of its gunfounding efforts. Though the original guns were known as 'gasconades', it is not clear what contribution he made to the design, except that he supervised the experiments with the first weapons, and presumably persuaded the company to finance them.[5]

Patrick Miller, an Edinburgh merchant and patron of art and science, also claimed the invention in later years. He said that he had been inspired by the leather guns used by the Swedes in the seventeenth century, and had first carried out experiments with a light 12-pounder, though there is no known record of this. Certainly he was instrumental in arranging the first actual use of a carronade, and in having them fitted to a privateer, the *Spitfire* of Liverpool, in 1779. Though he had no direct financial connection with Carron, he did much to publicise and promote the new gun, with eventual success.[6]

Characteristics

Several of the carronade's features were not fully realised by its inventors but were added later. The pivot under the gun, which took the place of the trunnions, is often thought of as one of the carronade's original and distinguishing features. In fact it was not fitted on the first generation of guns. Nevertheless, there were several important features, which together made the carronade unique from its conception.

Simply, it was shorter and lighter than ordinary guns. In general the fully-developed carronade was about a quarter of the weight of a long gun of similar calibre, or, put another way, a gun of a given weight could fire a shot four times as heavy as an equivalent long gun. Several factors made this lightness possible. First, it was designed as a short-range gun. Obviously this meant the barrel could be shorter. For example, an early 18-pounder carronade of 1780 was 2ft 4in long, whereas a normal gun of similar calibre would be at least 9ft long. This in itself allowed a considerable reduction in weight. Also, the shorter range necessitated a smaller charge of powder, between a quarter and a third of that of a long gun. This too contributed to lightness because the thickness of metal could be reduced.

Second, the carronade revived the old type of chamber, in which the bore was smaller where the charge was placed. Because of this, the thickness of metal in that area could be the same, but the outside diameter of the gun was greatly reduced so the weight of metal was correspondingly decreased. This type of chamber had always been used in mortars, in some cannon of the seventeenth century, and in the Russian 'unicorn' gun. It became unpopular because it tended to make loading more difficult. Though it was evidently considered for a new type of gun in the 1750s, it was not used. Its disadvantage was that it made it difficult to place the charge into such a gun, though this posed less of a problem with shorter guns, such as mortars or carronades.

The third characteristic was the reduced windage. Because of inaccuracies in the manufacture of both gun and shot, it had been common to allow one-twentieth of the bore for windage. This was now viewed as excessive, in particular because the boring of guns from the solid now allowed much greater accuracy. More-over, the amount of windage could now be made standard rather than proportional to the size of each gun. This gave a greater scope for reduction in higher calibre guns, like the carronade.

None of these ideas was entirely new. The need to reduce windage had been recognised most of the eighteenth century. The chamber, as we have seen, was an old feature, always used in mortars. Short guns, in the form of drakes and cutts, had been common in the seventeenth century, though they had declined in the early eighteenth, mainly because a change in fighting tactics had made close action much less common. By the 1780s the unimaginative tactics of the early part of the century were being increasingly questioned, and close action was to become more and more common over the next 25 years, culminating in Nelson's overwhelming victory at Trafalgar, and his famous signal 'engage the enemy more closely'. The carronade was successful because it came at precisely the right time, and because it was well produced and designed, not because of any great originality in its concept.

In shape it was rather different from the ordinary gun. Because it was short it had only one reinforce, and there was no swell of the muzzle – indeed the muzzle was considerably thinner than the main part of the barrel.

Trials and Acceptance

The carronade was first manufactured in autumn 1778, and was used to arm the Carronade Company's ships carrying goods to London. By the end of the year it had been advertised, and many orders had been received from private shipowners. The privateer *Spitfire* was fitted with a carronade at Liverpool, and it took part in several actions in the early part of 1779. By May that year the King's attention had been drawn to the gun, and he ordered trials to be carried out at Woolwich. These took place in the summer, and were attended by Charles Middleton, Controller of the Navy who was perhaps the most innovatory member the Navy Board had ever had. He was of the opinion that the trials 'were sufficiently decisive to prove that such guns may be used on the poops of all ships, and on the quarterdecks of others.'[7] He thought they would be particularly useful for frigates, as ships of 44 guns and less had large unoccupied spaces on their quarterdecks. On July 16 the Navy Board recommended the acceptance of Middleton's report, and proposed an establishment for fitting carronades on the poops, quarterdecks and forecastles of various types of ships.[8]

There was still much opposition to the carronade. By December 1779 the Navy Board was retreating from its previous proposals, and agreed that the number carried by frigates should be reduced. 'Captains of several of the frigates of 32 guns have complained that the foremost carronade on the quarterdeck came so much in the way of the rigging as to be in danger of carrying away the lanyards of the shrouds.'[9] In the following month it was agreed that that the establishment could be relaxed, 'it being impossible from the variety of their forms to fix any established number till more experience has been had in the using of them.'[10] In March 1780 it was reported from Plymouth that 'most of the captains at that port disapprove of carronades, and do not intend to take any.'[11] In October a letter signed by several distinguished officers stated that 'carronades are of little use in the Royal Navy'.[12]

The Navy Board gave some ground, and from March 1780

carronades were only to be fitted on the 'particular application' of the captains. On the other hand it believed that 'the advantages of carronades in strengthening the force of our frigates is so much out of the question that the choice should not be left to the opinion of any individual', and the established guns were to be carried except where they were in the way of the rigging.[13] The Board defended the gun, pointing out that some of the criticism was based on tests in long-range gunnery, which was not the carronade's forte. In the course of 1780 naval opinion began to turn in favour of the carronade. In March it was already being reported that captains were asking for more and bigger carronades, and wanted them to replace long guns on smaller vessels. More tests were carried out in July and October 1780, in which carronades of 12, 18, 24 and 68 pounds were tried against long guns of 3, 4 and 6 pounds.[14]

The carronade's success in action did much to turn the tide in its favour. It proved itself in several frigate actions in 1780–81, including that between the *Flora* and the French *Nymphe*. In 1781 the captain of the *Artois* praised the great effect of his carronades on the enemy, and in January, Captain Elliot of the 74-gun ship *Edgar* expressed pleasure at their performance in a fight with the Spanish. He denied there was any danger of the guns setting the rigging on fire.[15] The carronade's most dramatic success came in September 1782. The 44-gun ship *Rainbow* had been armed entirely with carronades, raising her gun power from 318 to 1238 pounds. She encountered the French frigate *Hebe*, and so shocked the captain by the power of the first broadside that he surrendered almost immediately. By the time the American War ended in 1783, the value of the carronade had been established.

Development

The early carronade was a very simple gun, descended from the howitzer and the coehorn mortar, with some influence from the naval swivel gun. Early weapons had a handle, or 'tiller' extending backwards and upwards from the button. Unlike the swivel gun, this was probably not held during firing, because early carronades were not normally fitted on the non-recoil principle. It may have enabled quicker traversing. The tiller became extinct soon after the American War, but it was replaced with another kind of handle, which originated from one side of the button, curved behind it, and met it again on the other side. This was still in use in the 1790s, and both the old and new types in store at that time were described as 'carronades with handles'.[16] It was no longer fitted in the 1800s.

The experience of the American War resulted in many revisions to the carronade's design. It seems to have been accepted that the first generation of carronades was too short, and this increased the possibility of setting fire to the rigging. Thus the length of the carronade was steadily increased over the next few years. The 18-pounder increased from 2ft 4in in 1780 to 2ft 6½in in 1781, and reached a maximum of 3ft 4in in 1793.[17] After about 1790, a further increase was achieved by adding a form of nozzle to the muzzle. This added little to the weight, but carried the blast a few inches further clear of the ship. After about 1805 the nozzle was hollowed out, perhaps to make loading easier. The nozzle also increased the strength of the foremost part of the muzzle which was always vulnerable, without itself suffering much from the effects of the blast. Because of this, the carronade

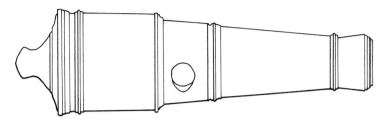

A 9-pounder of 1672, in the Tower of London. This gun may be a 'Punchinello', a short type of gun which, according to Pepys, Sir Anthony Deane experimented with around this time.

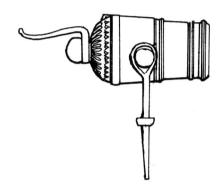

A very early version of the carronade, dated 1778. It is a 4-pounder, and is similar to the mortar from which it originated.

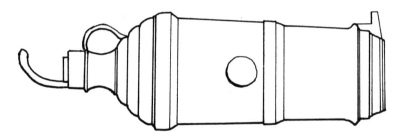

An early 18-pounder carronade, c1780. It is short, has no nozzle, and has trunnions and a tiller.

A model of a gunboat, showing an early type of carronade, with trunnions.

*The nozzle of a carronade, showing how it was hollowed out on the inside.
Author's photograph.*

did not need the swell of the muzzle like ordinary guns. The
nozzle was not counted as part of the length of the gun.

In general the carronade appears to have increased in weight
over this period. It was not the custom to list carronades according to their length, so it is not clear how much the increase in
weight was linked to their increased length. However, the gun of
1800 was usually about 10 per cent heavier than that of 1780.[18]
After that there was little change.

The trunnions of carronades seem to have been replaced during or soon after the American War, by a loop placed under the
gun. The screw thread through the button, which allowed the
gun to be elevated and depressed without the use of conventional
quoins and wedges, appeared around the same time. These
features were linked with the Carron Company's development of
a new type of gun carriage. Breech rings, to retain the breech
rope, were probably first used on carronades in the 1780s, at the
same time as they first appeared on long guns. It appears they
were not always fitted; a gun of 1808, for example, is shown without them.[19]

Sights were being fitted to carronades in the 1780s. A mounting for the breech sight was placed on the top of the breech ring.
On the older carronades the fore sight was fitted above the
muzzle. By about 1805 it had been moved back, to the reinforce
ring.

Types of Carronade

The 68-pounder was more similar to Melville's original invention than any other production gun, even the 100-pounder tested
in 1781. The 68-pounder was not one of the very first types tried
by Carron, but it appeared at the Ordnance Board trials in 1780,
and was adopted soon afterwards. It was not included in the first
Ordnance Board establishment in July 1779.[20]

The 68-pounder was the true 'smasher', though this name was
also applied to lesser carronades. It gained fame because the
Victory carried two at Trafalgar, and used them to considerable
effect. In fact its use was very limited. By an order of January
1782 it was to be fitted, at the captain's request, on the forecastle
of any ship able to carry it, but in July that year only one ship, the
Gibraltar of 80 guns, actually had any, and these were on her
quarterdeck.[21] At some point in or around 1782, the 74-gun
Egmont was ordered to carry 28 68-pounders on her lower deck,
but it seems that this order was never put into effect.[22] There
were none on the list of carronades carried in 1783, and it never
featured in any of the regular establishments. Despite the
68-pounder's success at Trafalgar, no ships on the 1807 Navy
List were fitted with any.[23]

The original 68-pounder, as tested in 1780, was 4ft long and
weighed 29cwt. By about 1790 there was a larger version of
30cwt. In 1796 the standard version was 5ft 2in long and weighed
36cwt.[24] Such guns were carried by the *Victory* in 1805.

The 42-pounder was not among the guns tested in 1780. It
does not appear to have been a standard weapon at any time,
though it was fitted to the *Rainbow* when she captured the *Hebe* in
1782. It was normally 4ft 3½in long and weighed 22cwt. It probably suffered from the same disadvantages as the 42-pounder
long gun, and presumably the 68-pounder carronade, in that its
ball was simply too heavy to handle in action.

The 32-pounder appeared relatively late in the lists, and there
is no sign of its existence before 1780, when it was stated that the
captain of the *Berwick* had acquired two unofficially. In that year
it was to be found mainly on the very largest ships, the *Victory*,
Duke and *Prince George*.[25] By 1794, when a new establishment
was introduced, its use was extended to many classes of ship,
including frigates. It also became very common on ships of the
line after 1797. By 1800, even 20-gun ships were able to carry it as
their main armament.[26]

The 24-pounder had appeared by 1780, though it was not mentioned in the establishment of 1779. In later years it was used on
some of the smaller classes of ship, especially on 20-gun ships and
brigs, and it became common on ship's launches. Normally it was

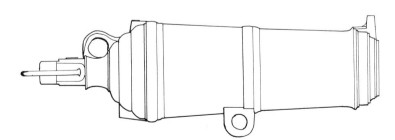

*A developed 68-pounder carronade, c1790. It is slightly longer than the early
version, and has a loop instead of trunnions, but it has still not acquired a nozzle.*

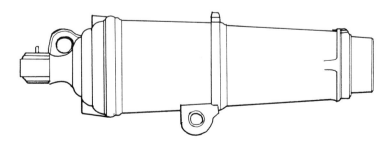

*A fully-developed 24-pounder, c1805. It has a nozzle at the muzzle, and a wedge
cast above and below the cascable. The lower wedge makes it easier to use a quoin to
elevate and depress the gun, the upper one was for fitting a sight.*

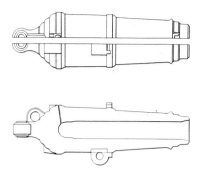

Details of a 24-pounder, c1815.

3ft 7½in long, and weighed 13cwt. The first gun, tested in 1780, had been 3ft long and weighed 11½cwt.[27]

The 18-pounder was one of the original carronades, and in 1779 it was to be carried on the forecastles and quarterdecks of all ships from 28 to 44 guns. Though never entirely supplanted, it was used less and less over the years, being replaced by the 32-pounder. The early guns were 2ft 4in long and weighed 8cwt. By 1793 3ft 4in guns were in service. After 1800 their length was slightly reduced. The standard gun weighed 10cwt, and was 3ft 3in long.

The 12-pounder was another of the original guns, and it was the most common on the establishment of 1779, being the only type allotted to ships of the line and to ships of 24 guns or less. Like the 18-pounder it tended to be used less in later years. The original gun was 2ft 2in long and weighed 5¾cwt. By about 1800 it weighed 6 to 6¼cwt, and was 2ft 8in long.

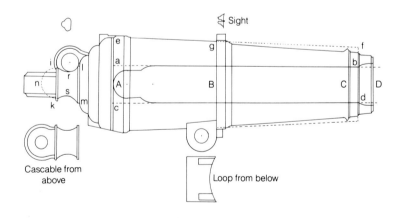

The proportions of a standard carronade, c1805. These were common to all carronades. (See Appendix page 267 for a table of dimensions.)

The Effect of the Carronade

The carronade was a great success, particularly in the wars with France between 1793 and 1815. Since the middle of the eighteenth century, tactics had been gradually modified, so that the line of battle became less rigid, and close action and mêlée

became far more common. The French Navy had declined in efficiency because of the disruption caused by the Revolution, and because the British never allowed it to recover from its initial disadvantages. These factors made it possible for British ships to get in close, and to fight to a finish, more than ever before. The carronade was usually mounted high on the upper works. At short range it could provide a devastating fire on the enemy's decks, often using case or grape shot. Many of the smaller vessels, on the other hand, carried carronades on their main decks, as their sole armament. The general decline in French seamanship and gunnery made it easier for such ships to get into action without first being overwhelmed by an opponent's long guns.

Much of the carronade's success, then, was fortuitous, but it did cause some deep consideration of the whole system of naval gunnery. A ship of the line, for example, carried 32-pounder long guns on her lower deck, and very often 32-pounder carronades on her quarterdeck, poop and forecastle. Her other armament consisted of 24-, 18-, or 12-pounders on her upper and middle decks. What purpose did they serve? They had neither the range of a 32-pounder long gun, nor the power of a carronade. A 32-pounder long gun weighed 55cwt, while a 32-pounder carronade weighed 18cwt. There was an enormous gap between the two, and the need for a gun of large calibre and medium length.

A gun which might have filled this gap was tested in 1796. It was a 32-pounder, about 4ft 10in long and 24cwt, and was designed by one Sadler. Of the 32 guns delivered for proof, 17 failed, and it was 'recommended that the service charge of the above guns may not exceed five pounds of powder and one shot'. It was tested in 1797 on the *Dart* sloop, but there is no sign of it after that.[28]

The next proposal, a 24-pounder designed by Captain Gover was in 1805. It was 6ft 6in long and weighed only 33cwt, compared with the 47cwt of a normal 24-pounder. It was first used on the frigate *Narcissus* in 1805, and large numbers were evidently manufactured. In December 1806 some old ships of the line were uniformly fitted with 24-pounders on all decks, standard guns on the lower decks, Gover-pattern guns on the upper decks, and carronades on the upper works. These ships gave quite useful service over the next few years, often being used as troop ships because their smaller crews meant there was some space for soldiers.[29]

These experiments did not prompt any immediate changes perhaps because the re-gunning of the whole Navy was too vast a task to contemplate in wartime. In 1812, however, the Admiralty was forced to reconsider the issue. War had broken out with

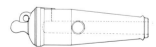

A Sadler 32-pounder of 1796. This was the only kind made. It was 4ft 10in long, and weighed 24cwt.

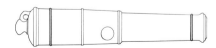

A Gover 24-pounder.

A Blomefield short 24-pounder.

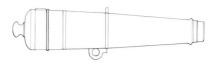

A Congreve short 24-pounder.

America, and the large, heavily-gunned American frigates inflicted a series of humiliating defeats on British ships. Something was needed urgently to reduce the differential between the British frigates and their larger American counterparts.

By this time the Gover-pattern gun was regarded as inadequate, as it could not be fired double-shotted. Two heavier types of 24-pounder had now been developed. One designed by William Congreve, the inventor of a type of rocket used in action in 1808, had a muzzle like a carronade. The other, designed by Blomefield, was of more traditional form. They were tested on two 38-gun frigates in 1813, and the Congreve pattern prevailed;

300 were ordered at the end of the year. In 1815 it was decided that First Rates should have Congreve 24-pounders on their upper decks.[30]

However, all these developments were too late to have any effect on the war, and the light 24-pounder was never used in action against its intended enemies, the Americans. These changes were only the beginning of a radical reform in gunnery, for in the 1820s and '30s most ships of the line were to be armed almost exclusively with 32-pounders of different lengths and weights. But in 1815 nearly all ships still carried traditional armaments, except where these had been replaced by carronades.

PART VI

The Distribution of Guns

Chapter 20. Early Armaments

Factors Affecting Distribution

In essence, there were two factors which influenced the number and quality of guns carried by a sailing warship: the design of the ship, and the availability of suitable weapons. Although the supply of guns was the responsibility of the Board of Ordnance, it could not instantly provide the weapons needed, with the limited and often irregular finance available to it. This was one of the reasons why early warships carried varied armaments, and also, as we shall see, why the plans made by late seventeenth and early eighteenth century administrators were often not implemented. Only in the second half of the eighteenth century, when the Ordnance Board was given the means to predict the demand for guns of particular calibres and types, were ships gunned with suitable armaments, rather than merely what was available.

There were several considerations in the design of a ship which affected her ability to bear an armament. Obviously the number of gunports limited the number of heavy guns which could be carried. Gunports were usually an integral part of the design of a ship, and they could only be altered during a major rebuild. Some gun positions, on the forecastle and poop, did not need ports, as the guns simply fired over the top of the gunwale, but comparatively few guns were mounted in this way, and they were invariably light in weight, if not necessarily in weight of shot.

The second factor governing what armament the ship could carry, was the strength of the decks which were to bear the guns. This was not always given due attention, especially around the middle of the seventeenth century, when many ships had their armaments increased without any serious consideration of the consequences. In the long term this factor had to be borne in mind, if the ship was not to be subjected to an undue strain.

The third factor was the overall stability of the ship. Heavier guns had to be placed on the lower deck, and progressively lighter weapons were on the middle deck, upper deck, quarterdeck and poop. British builders never seem to have made the elementary mistake of the Dutch designer of the Swedish *Vasa*, which had 24-pounders on her lower and upper decks, with the result that she capsized before leaving Stockholm harbour. A stable ship had to have her centre of gravity as low as possible, and heavy guns kept off the upper works.

The weight of the guns was an important factor in the overall weight of the ship. In the third quarter of the seventeenth century the weapons alone, excluding carriages, tackle, ammunition and other stores, could make up almost 10 per cent of a ship's total weight. Too heavy an armament would cause the ship to sink lower in the water, reducing her speed and bringing her gunports so close to the waterline, that when she heeled in a wind it would be impossible to open them, and the ship would not be able to use its most powerful armament. This problem was particularly apparent in the battles against the Dutch in 1666.

The most important consideration was the purpose for which the ship was designed, and the type of fighting she was intended for. A merchant ship would not carry enough men to fight her guns for long, and probably relied on a noisy first broadside to act as a deterrent. A frigate or sloop was designed for scouting or escort, and to a certain extent her armament was secondary to her sailing qualities. In a cutter or advice boat this principle was extended even further, and her armament would not be allowed to restrict her speed at all. In contrast the bomb vessel was designed round a very specialised form of armament, and was used against sedentary targets, such as towns and fortresses, so it did not need good sailing qualities. A ship of the line, on the contrary, was intended to fight battlefleets which might be reluctant to engage, so it needed reasonable sailing qualities, but these had to be balanced against its fighting power and efficiency.

Early Armaments

Battles have not always been fought broadside to broadside. The classic eighteenth century layout, with all the ship's guns mounted on the sides, was the antithesis of the Mediterranean galley, which had all its heavy guns firing forward. The arrangement of guns on the sailing ship of the sixteenth and early seventeenth centuries lay somewhere between these two extremes, with guns firing ahead, to each side, astern, and at various other angles. It was not generally assumed that the broadside was the main armament, and one experienced English captain wrote, 'It is requireable also that the bows and chases of these ships be so contrived that out of them as many guns as possible may shoot right forwards.'[1] Another said, 'a man of war pretends to fight most with his prow, that part is likeliest to receive shot'.[2] Methods of loading and firing were primitive and slow, so ships tended to reload away from the scene of the action. They made the best use of all available guns, on bow and stern and on both broadsides, during an attack. 'You are to fire your bow pieces upon her, and then your full broadside; and letting your ship fall off with the wind, let fly with your chase pieces, all of them, and so your weather broadside. The which being done, bring your ship about, that your stern pieces may be given also.'[3]

Another characteristic of armaments of this period was that many guns were intended to clear personnel from the decks of an enemy ship, rather than penetrate her sides. Boarding was still regarded as an integral part of a naval action, and light-weight and short-range upper deck pieces were carried. On the other hand, there was an exaggerated belief in the power of long-range gunnery, a factor which contributed towards the production of so many long-barrelled weapons of the culverin type. This view was somewhat discredited in 1588, when long-range gunfire failed to do any significant damage to the Spanish Armada. However, there was still some faith in long-distance firing, and chase guns were regarded as especially useful. 'In the first place, your chase guns are to be given; and coming somewhat nearer, your whole broadside in order, as your pieces will be brought to bear.'[4]

For all these reasons – the erratic availability of guns, and the division between the long-range chase guns, the medium-range guns on the broadsides, and the short-range lighter pieces on the upper works – armaments of individual Elizabethan ships were very varied. In the list of 1599 the *Elizabeth Jonas*, carried nine different types of gun. Most of the larger fighting ships, of 40 to 60 guns, carried about seven or eight different types.[5] The heavy battering pieces, the cannon and demi-cannon, were relatively rare. The *White Bear* was an exception in carrying three cannon and eleven demi-cannon, for larger ships usually carried about seven or eight of these heavy pieces. Culverins and demi-culverins were the most common guns, followed by their smaller cousins, sakers and minions. The largest ships also carried a few of the older breech-loading pieces, port-pieces and fowlers.

In the 1620s, as the English fleet revived from a period of neglect after the end of the Spanish War, not much changed in principle. The very largest ships, such as the *Prince Royal* and the *Bear*, had two cannon perriers and six demi-cannon, while the next group, the 'great ships', had two of each, and smaller ships had none. Culverins and demi-culverins were still the most common pieces, and the eighteen largest ships carried 12 to 18 of each. Sakers and minions were less common, but the smaller ships often carried 10 or 12 of the former. Port-pieces were only carried by the very largest ships, but most ships had four fowlers.[6]

What had changed since Elizabethan times was the distribution of this armament. Ships carried more than seven different types – a slight improvement on the earlier situation. Moreover, each type of ship carried a roughly standard armament, so that it is possible to divide the ships into classes, just by looking at the lists of guns. Six great ships, for example, had identical armament, and differences in the others were only slight. Twenty years of peace had allowed some order to be imposed on the fleet.

From the available evidence it appears that distribution of the armament remained the same throughout the 1620s, until the early '30s when some changes were made. In particular, there was a move away from the old breech-loading and anti-personnel weapons, such as port-pieces and fowlers. The *Victory*, for example, had the usual complement of four fowlers in the 1620s,

The Prince Royal, *first of the very large ships, arriving at Flushing in 1613.* Science Museum

Some of the Great Ships of the early seventeenth century, entering the Solent in 1623. NMM

but these were not carried in the '30s.[7] The very small pieces of the culverin type, such as falcons, also fell into disuse, and few cannon perrier were now carried. In their place the *Victory* carried two extra culverins, six sakers, and two more minions, so that her total number of guns remained at 42. Apart from two demi-cannon, all her armament was of the culverin type. In this she was typical of the fleet.

Civil War and Commonwealth

When the Civil War broke out in 1642 virtually all the Navy fell under the control of Parliament. The old Great Ships were of little immediate use because the King had no fleet with which to oppose them, but they served as a deterrent to intervention by foreign powers. Parliament built up a fleet of small fast frigates for use against Royalist privateers and gun-runners. These ships were originally captured or hired, but after 1646 Parliament began to build its own. These were gradually expanded in size over the years, and by 1650 some of them were almost as big as the old Great Ships, but they were much longer and lower, and carried more guns on the broadside, and fewer on the chase. They turned less easily than the old ships, and so tended to fight with one broadside rather than two, but because loading methods seem to have improved by this time, this was easier. It was during this period that ships first fought broadside to broadside, or 'yardarm to yardarm'. This tendency was reinforced during the First Anglo-Dutch War of 1652–54, when the English first began to fight in line of battle, thus using their broadside guns to full effect, and making chase guns less useful.[8]

The old ships gained many extra guns during these years. The *St George*, one of the few large ships to be fitted out in the 1640s, carried 52 guns in 1647, whereas in the 1620s she had carried a perfectly standard armament of 42 guns; the *Victory* carried 42 guns in 1636, and 64 in 1655; the *Happy Entrance*, a smaller ship, had 32 in 1636 and 40 in 1647; the *Rainbow* 40 in 1631 and 54 in 1652, and the *Leopard* 36 in 1636 and 46 in 1647.[9]

The new guns were positioned in spaces which had been vacant in earlier years, for the old ships had not been heavily gunned. Few heavy weapons had been carried on the quarterdecks and forecastles, because these areas had been reserved for musketeers, and the decks there were too narrow to give the gun room to recoil. Some of the great ships now had the area between the quarterdeck and forecastle filled in, creating a third deck which was armed with medium-calibre guns. Many of the new guns were of the culverin type, in particular demi-culverins. The *Victory*, for example, gained 12 more culverins and 14 demi-culverins, while her armament of demi-cannon rose only from two to six. The *Happy Entrance* gained four culverins and six demi-culverins, the *Convertine* two culverins and five demi-culverins and the *Leopard* nine demi-culverins. The *Unicorn*, on the other hand, gained heavier guns. She had six demi-cannon between 1636 and 1647, but 18 by 1652.[10]

Though the new frigates had originally been conceived as light and fast patrol vessels they also gained heavier armaments, especially the larger ships built after 1649, of which the *Speaker* was the prototype. In 1655 she carried an armament of 60 guns, though only four of these were demi-cannon. By the end of the decade this had been increased until she had 20 demi-cannon and 30 12-pounders, as well as smaller guns.[11] The smaller frigates retained more of their original characteristics, and were more lightly armed. The *Nightingale*, a Fifth Rate, had a main armament of 18 demi-culverins. The *Bristol*, a Fourth Rate, was originally fitted with 4 demi-cannon, but these were removed by 1654, so that her main armament was 24 culverins. The *Dover*, a similar ship, was always armed with culverins on the lower deck.[12]

This increase in guns, which continued for several decades yet, was to have serious long term effects. Ships became grossly overloaded for the tasks they had to perform. The problem was not immediately recognised, for wars were still fought mainly in the southern part of the North Sea, and in the English Channel, within a few days' sailing of the main base at Chatham. Large ships were fitted out for the summer only, and did not have to withstand the gales of winter.

Several frigates of the 1640's and '50s. By this time the word was usually used to describe two-decked ships. NMM

It is tempting to blame the naval administrators of the English Republic for the practice of over-gunning, which was often to hamper the Navy in its future development. In fact it had been initiated earlier, by their arch-enemy, King Charles I. When fitting out the *Sovereign of the Seas* in 1637, he had gone to great lengths to fit her with 100 guns, producing a heavy, and in some ways grotesque armament. She was the first ship to carry a large number of cannon-of-seven, and possibly the first to be fitted with a heavy armament on the quarterdeck and forecastle. Unlike many ships of the period she had broadside guns carried right up to the bow and stern. In these respects she pointed the way to the future, and represented a considerable advance in gun power. But even in the 1650s and '60s, when over-gunning was prevalent, her original armament was regarded as too heavy. She was allocated

only 95 guns in 1654, 90 in 1664, and 92 in 1666.[13] It was not until 1670 that she was again listed with her full armament of 100 guns.[14]

Early Attempts at Standardisation

The Commonwealth fleet of the 1650s was largely gunned *ad hoc*. When new ships were built, or old ones revived after years in reserve, the Admiralty Commissioners would ask the Navy Commissioners what guns were appropriate for the ship, and the Ordnance Board what was available, and thus arrive at an establishment for an individual ship. There appears to have been no single list of guns for the whole fleet. Estimates covering one

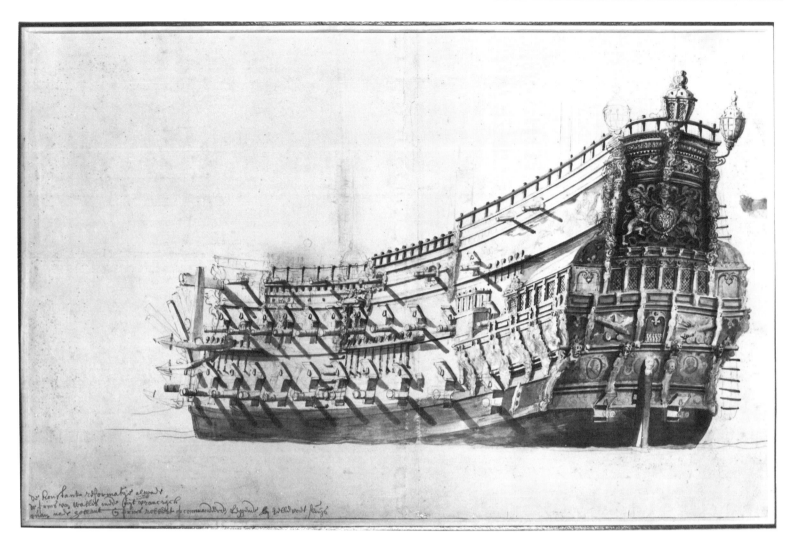

The Constant Reformation, *one of the great ships of the 1618 shipbuilding programme, drawn by Van de Velde in 1649. By this date extra guns had been added to the waist and quarterdeck, so that she was almost a three-decker.* NMM

ship of each Rate were sometimes prepared, as in January 1655,[15] but it would have been too time-consuming to prepare these for every ship. The Commonwealth and Protectorate were never entirely at peace, and had no time to take an unhurried look at the state of naval armament. There was a certain uniformity in that ships of similar design usually had roughly similar gun arrangements. Thus the *Dover* and *Dunkirk* both carried 24 culverins, 6 demi-culverins, and 8 sakers in 1655, the only difference being that the *Dover* also had two 3-pounders. On the other hand the *Leopard*, also of similar design, had 24 culverins, 12 demi-culverins, and 4 saker cutts. The *Jersey*, of similar size, had a much heavier armament of 22 culverins, 20 demi-culverins and 6 sakers.[16]

The restoration of the monarchy in 1660 brought some peace to the country, and some time to consider the matter of ships' armament more carefully. One new policy was that ships fitted out in peacetime were to have fewer guns than they would carry in wartime. This practice was initiated by an order of early 1664, and it continued into the next century. In general a peacetime ship carried about 20 per cent fewer guns than she would do in wartime.[17]

In the following spring the Admiralty and the Navy Board prepared, evidently for the first time since the Civil War, a list for gunning the whole fleet. The Ordnance Board was allowed to make some alterations to it, largely because there were not enough of certain types of guns in store.[18] It is not clear how far the establishment was applied in practice. It continued the trend towards more and heavier guns, especially for ships of the Fourth Rate and above, intended to take their place in the line of battle. All four First Rates were now to have cannon-of-seven on their lower decks, as were three Second Rates. All Third Rates, which in the past had mostly had culverins on the lower decks, now had demi-cannon. Most had 22, enough to fill all the broadside ports on the lower deck. Four Fourth Rates, including the *Leopard*, were given 10 or 12 demi-cannon. Fifth Rates, on the other hand, were now recognised as small scouting vessels unfit for the line of battle, and carried light armaments consisting mainly of demi-culverins.

Another war with the Dutch broke out in 1664. In the battles which followed the English did not have the easy victory they had expected, largely because the Dutch had learned from their defeats in the previous war. They had adopted the line of battle, and built new and bigger ships. The English produced another list of their fleet in 1666, reflecting some of the lessons learned in the last two years, and also the availability of guns.[19] It had some significant differences from the 1664 list and shared a further tendency to increase the weight of guns on most large ships. Though the First Rate *Royal James* was now given demi-cannon instead of cannon-of-seven, four Second Rates, including the new *Royal Oak* and *Royal Katherine*, now carried the larger gun. The *Leopard* now had 22 demi-cannon, a full complement, instead of 12. The *Yarmouth*, which had also been allotted demi-cannon in 1664, became the first native English ship to carry 24-pounders, a few of which had been produced in English foundries. Some Fifth Rates were given increased armaments. Three now carried culverins and two more had 12-pounders, heavier than any armament allotted to them in 1664.

The establishment of 1666, like that of 1664, was probably

intended as a reaction to a particular situation, rather than to provide a permanent guideline for gunning the Navy. There is very little information about what happened to the Navy's guns over the next few years, except that provided in Sir Anthony Deane's *Doctrine of Naval Architecture*. Here he provides lists of the Navy, with both numbers and weights of guns. Though these seem a little too cut and dried to reflect the reality of Charles II's Navy, Deane was one of the leading shipbuilders of his generation, and he certainly had access to the full facts. Most ships in Deane's list had either the same number of guns as in 1666 or slightly more, so it seems that the increase was continuing. This is confirmed by the list of guns carried by the *Fairfax* in 1672. She then carried 72 guns, as compared with 60 in 1666, though on her lower deck she now carried 24-pounders instead of demi-cannon.[20]

Chapter 21. The Establishments

The 1677 Establishment

According to his own testimony Samuel Pepys, in his capacity as Secretary of the Admiralty in 1674, 'first brought the establishment for men and guns for the whole fleet to be adjusted between the officers of the Navy and the ordnance, and chief officers of the fleet, and upon solemn hearing before the King and Lords of the Admiralty, and the measures thereof debated, signed by the King and the Lords, and so debated.'[1] The intention was to provide a permanent gun establishment for each ship, and to have the Ordnance Board work to keep the ships supplied with the appropriate guns. It was an important part of Pepys' general plan to impose uniformity on the fleet, which had been built up in a series of emergencies over the last thirty years, without any time to consider long-term implications.

The first instructions for the new establishment came in March 1674, when the Admiralty ordered the Navy Board to consider and propose a plan for gunning the whole Navy.[2] A draft plan was produced soon afterwards. Though it was not radically different from the one which was eventually adopted, no more was heard of it for some time.[3]

In 1677 Parliament voted £600,000 for building 30 new ships, and the Admiralty was galvanised into action. It was recognised that the gunning of the new ships was bound up with the plan for the whole fleet, and it was ordered 'that the adjusting that establishment and the measures thereof be referred to the Officers of the Navy and Ordnance, to be by them debated with some of the principal commanders of the fleet now in the way, so as to bring their joint report in next Saturday.'[4] A committee of officers duly met with the Navy Board; and a rough plan for the establishment for the new ships was drawn up. Evidently they had not yet succeeded in drawing up a plan for the existing ships of the fleet, for the great variety of types had defeated them. This task was to be 'put into the hands of the officers of the Navy [ie the Navy Board] to be made to answer in the great ships to the new ships of like dimensions, and in the lesser to be perfected by what measures

The Coronation, *one of the 90-gun three-decker Second Rates of the 1677 programme.* Kriegstein Collection

A three-decker 80-gun ship of the 1719 establishment. This picture emphasises the height of the topsides in relation to the ship's length, and the smallness of the guns on the upper deck. Science Museum

they can'.[5] Evidently the Ordnance Board had now been excluded from the discussions, perhaps to make it easier for the Navy Board to reach agreement. The flag officers and captains at first resented the Navy Board's presumption, believing themselves 'the only judges of it', but when the Navy Board's report was produced they conceded that 'themselves could not have done it so well as the officers have.'[6]

The new plan was presented to the Admiralty in June 1677, and approved. It was to be enforced by order in council, to make it binding on the various government departments involved, and to make it more difficult to amend. It was finally approved by the King at an Admiralty meeting in November, when he 'added thereto by his Royal hand at the top, enjoining the same to be strictly observed without any alteration to be made thereto upon any consideration whatsoever.' It was further approved by the Privy Council in December, and it was to be 'a solemn, universal and unalterable adjustment for the gunning and manning of the whole fleet (otherwise than by order of the King in Council)'.[7]

There are no records of how the decisions on gunning individual

ships were arrived at, but it is clear, from an analysis of their results, that the aim was for the weight of guns to be in proportion to the vessels' tonnage. In the original plan for the 30 new ships the weight of guns divided by the vessel's tonnage was .120 for a First Rate, .122 for a Second Rate, and .123 for a Third Rate. Of course it was not possible to be so precise for the various ships of the old fleet, but the Board did its best. On First Rates the weight of guns divided by tonnage ranged from .119 to .126, on Second Rates, with their greater variety it ranged from .110 to .145, but in most ships it was around .125. The heavy armament specified for Third Rates on Deane's list of 1670, was reduced and the weight of guns divided by tonnage was an average of .115. On the other hand, most Fourth Rates had the weights of their guns increased, sometimes by as much as a third, for they had originally been considered as patrol vessels rather than as ships of the line. A few Fourth Rates built before 1660 were given lighter armaments, perhaps because their decks could not bear anything heavier. The smaller ships of the Fifth and Sixth Rates were given slightly lighter guns, with a ratio of around .110. This reflected their increasing separation from the larger ships, which were intended for the line of battle.

Pepys was very proud of his new establishment, and said so in his letters and minutes, but in fact it was a dead letter from the beginning. No sooner had its final acceptance been announced at an Admiralty meeting than the Master General of the Ordnance rose to burst the bubble, 'observing that it was impossible that the said establishment as to guns be strictly put into execution, in that the Office of the Ordnance cannot gun His Majesty's ships otherwise than as the natures and weights of guns His Majesty is at present master of will admit.'[8] This was conceded by the Admiralty, who agreed that the establishment was merely a guide and a statement of the ideal, and could not be immediately implemented. Few ships were fitted for sea in the next eight years, and the Navy fell into decline, with Pepys and his friends driven from office for political reasons. It is possible that no ship was ever fitted according to this 'solemn, universal and unalterable' establishment.

The 1685 Establishment

In the past, most historians have assumed that the 1685 establishment was merely a proposal, and was never actually implemented. In fact it remained in force until 1703, though it was never strictly adhered to for all ships. It was in use throughout England's first European war, from 1689 to 1697, and in that respect it was far more important than the better known establishment of 1677, which was only applied, if at all, during eight years of naval inactivity.

The new establishment was first mentioned early in 1685, after Pepys had been recalled to office and the whole administration overhauled. Though there are no records of the discussion of it, it was evidently better thought out than the 1677 establishment. Availability of guns was considered this time, and lists were made of the total numbers of each type 'proposed' and 'on hand', with an account of 'excess' and 'shortage'. In fact there was a shortage in only three types: demi-cannon, 12-pounders and sakers, which amounted to a total of 222 guns, out of the 7581 needed. The establishment also paid rather more attention to the actual siting of gunports on individual ships. The 20 new Third Rates were no longer expected to have a completely uniform armament, as the

A 20-gun ship of the 1719 establishment of dimensions. It is equipped with swivel guns, and for rowing as well as sailing. NMM

builders had often deviated from the specification in the provision of gunports. Instead of 26 demi-cannon on the lower deck, most were to have only 22, with four culverins on the 'chase fore and aft', and more chase guns on the forecastle and quarterdeck. To some extent these arrangements were old-fashioned, in that chase guns had been rendered obsolete by rigid adherence to the line of battle. The new ships were also to carry a slightly heavier armament than in 1677: that carried by 70s increased from 124 tons to 127 tons, and in 1685 that carried by 90s from 159 tons to 160.[9]

The establishment only covered the types of ships already in service. Several new types were added to the Navy during the war, the best known being the 80-gun Third Rates. These were originally designed with two decks, but the last four ships were completed with three decks, because the two-deckers were found to be far too weak, and eventually all were rebuilt as three-deckers. The original gun establishment for the two-deckers[10] showed a strong return to chase armament, partly because of the need to cram so many guns into a small hull. Several new 60-gun ships were also built at the same time, and the 50-gun ship, out of favour since the 1660s, was revived. Thus new guns had to be produced, and new rules made. Because of the war situation, the establishment could not be adhered to exactly, and there was a certain amount of confusion in the gunning of ships. As early as 1695 the Ordnance Board had suggested a new establishment, but this had been turned down by the Admiralty.[11] In 1699 the Navy Board proposed a 'revisal of the general establishment of men and guns'.[12] The years of hard wartime service had shown that the ships were too heavily armed and that their decks were overcrowded with guns. The Lord High Admiral was informed that 'the guns which are established for the Royal Navy, especially those of the biggest rates, are too heavy for them, inasmuch as they do very much strain and weaken these ships'.[13] The latest war had been far longer and more extensive than any of the Dutch wars, and it was time for a new establishment.

The 1703 Establishment

Late in 1702 a committee of flag officers met with the Navy Board to consider how the Navy should be armed for the future. By December they had agreed on their proposals. Firstly, they wanted greater uniformity within the fleet. All ships of the same class (of 100, 90, 80, 70 guns etc) were to be armed with the same calibre of guns, though because all did not have exactly the same gunport distribution, they could not necessarily carry the same number of guns. There was now an increasing uniformity amongst the ships themselves. Though the establishments of dimensions, which were an attempt to ensure all ships were built to a common pattern, were not applied for a few years, there was a tendency to build all new ships of a certain class to a fixed specification. Moreover, there had been less technological change in the previous thirty years than there had been in the period before 1670, so the fleet was now much more uniform than it had been in 1677 or 1685. It was to become even more so in the next few years, though the administrators never adhered to one set of dimensions long enough to achieve their dream of a whole fleet built and fitted to a single pattern.

Secondly, the committee of 1702 proposed a great reduction in the weight of guns carried by all but the smallest ships. The Fifth and Sixth Rates, of 40 guns or less, were unaffected and retained their current armaments, but ships of the line underwent drastic reductions. The cannon-of-seven was abolished, and 100-gun ships were to carry the demi-cannon instead. The Third Rates were to have 24-pounders instead of demi-cannon, and the 50s, still officially regarded as part of the line of battle, were to carry no guns larger than 12-pounders.[14]

The Lord High Admiral was evidently satisfied with the proposals. He ordered the Navy Board to make out a list applying these principles to the individual ships, according to their gunport distribution. This was sent to the Privy Council and approved in July 1703. But the old mistake of 1677 had been repeated – the Ordnance Board had not been consulted, and the supply of guns had not been considered. Almost immediately it was discovered that ships could not be gunned according to the new establishment, and another Order in Council was issued, allowing variations to be made when necessary, until the supply of guns could be improved.[15] It is quite possible that the 1703 establishment was as much a dead letter as that of 1677. An analysis of ships gunned at Portsmouth shows that very few were fitted according to the establishment. Not one of the ships armed in the first five years carried the regulation armament, and the first ship to conform to it was the 50-gun *Colchester*, fitted in 1708. One more ship was given the established armament in 1713, two more in 1714, and one in 1716.[16] By that time the establishment was obsolete, and a new one was being considered. Ships deviated from the establishment in various ways. Many of the earlier ones retained their old armaments of 1685. By about 1707 most seem to have carried their main deck guns according to the 1703 establishment, and their forecastle and quarterdeck guns according to what was available. The 1703 establishment served as a guide for arming ships for 13 years, but it was never strictly applied.

The 1716 Establishment

The next establishment was considered by a committee of flag officers, who reported in the middle of 1715. In one respect they

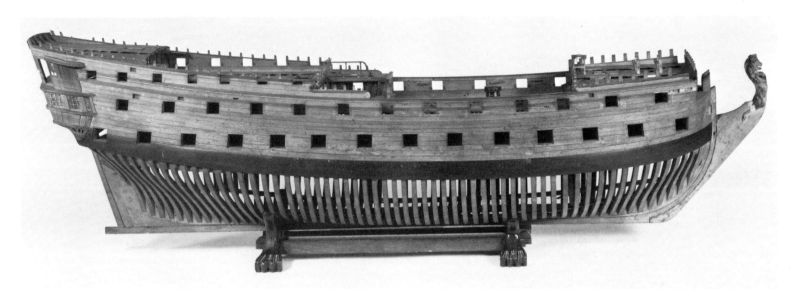

This model is of a very early 74-gun ship. There are signs that it has been altered, perhaps in an attempt to demonstrate how a three-decker 90-gun ship could be cut down. Smithsonian Institution

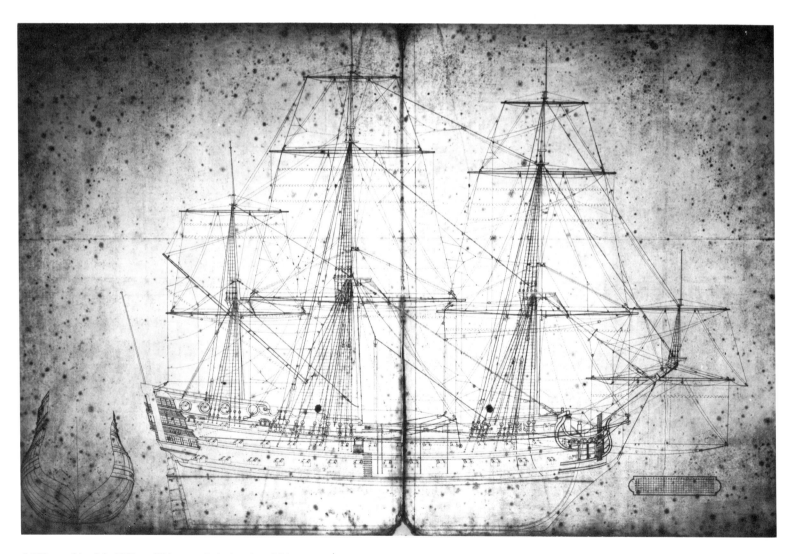

A 100-gun ship of the 1719 establishment. A rigging plan of this type was produced for each class in the establishment. Science Museum

continued the work of 1703, in that they imposed an even greater uniformity on the fleet. In the final version of the 1703 establishment different ships within each type were allowed to have different gunport arrangements. Now it was assumed that all ships with a given class, of 70 or 80 guns for example, would have an identical armament. This brought a mild protest from the Navy Board, who had not been fully consulted this time. They pointed out that many of the older ships did not suit the arrangements proposed by the flag officers. They conceded, however, that eventually the old ships would be rebuilt to the established dimensions, and would 'be made capable of carrying the guns proposed'.[17]

In another respect the trend of the 1703 establishment was reversed, and most ships were given heavier guns. The First Rates had their cannon-of-seven restored, and the 80-gun ships their demi-cannon, while the 60s now carried 24-pounders on their lower decks, and the 50s, 18-pounders. The 70-gun ships retained the 24-pounders allocated them in 1703.[18]

There was also an innovation. All guns were now described by their weight, rather than their ancient names. Thus the cannon-of-seven became the 42-pounder, the demi-cannon the 32-pounder, and so on. Even the saker, though not intended to be part of the new establishment, was henceforth described as the 5¼-pounder.

The Ordnance Board complained on the usual grounds that 'the guns in store could not comply with the same',[19] and was given permission by Order in Council to allow certain variations, especially on forecastles and quarterdecks. The establishment had planned there should be 6-pounders on the upper works of most ships, but these were in short supply. Old guns, including sakers (5¼-pounders) and 8-pounders were to be used instead. Nevertheless, it does seem that this establishment was put into practice more than the others, for most of its life was in peacetime, so there was less pressure on resources. Though by 1724 the Ordnance Board was still fitting old-style guns to many ships, the main gundecks were relatively unaffected by shortages, and the supply problem for the lighter guns seems to have eased by the 1730s.[20]

The 1733 Proposals, and the 1743 Establishment

The British Navy had not suffered a serious defeat since 1690, and in the first quarter of the eighteenth century it became unduly complacent, about the quality of its ships as much as anything else. This was dangerous, as other nations, especially the French and the Spanish, were building new navies, with new, larger and more powerful fighting ships. By the early 1730s some members of the Admiralty had become aware of this and in 1733 proposed a new establishment of dimensions. Though they failed to persuade the Navy Board that much larger ships were needed, and the new establishment was never ratified, ships were in fact built to it.[21] These new ships were only slightly larger than the old, and did not approach the dimensions of French and Spanish ships.

Since it could not have larger ships, the Admiralty tried to in-crease the power of the ones it already had. After consulting with the flag officers and the Navy Board, it proposed a new establishment of guns, which would put the ships 'in a much better condition not only of defending themselves from, but of annoying the ships of other maritime princes in time of war, who have not only (according to their several rates and classes) increased their weights of ordnance, but their number of men, to what were formerly allowed.'[22] The main intention of the new proposal was to increase the power of the guns carried. First Rates were to have 24-pounders on their middle decks again, instead of 18-pounders. The smaller Third Rates, formerly of 70 guns, were to have 32-pounders restored to their lower decks. It was recognised that this would add extra weight, so they were to carry only 64 guns instead of 70. Similarly, 60-gun ships were to carry only 58 guns, 50s were to carry 24-pounders instead of 18-pounders and 40s were to have 18-pounders instead of 12-pounders.[23]

As usual, the Ordnance Board objected. 'When it came to the Ordnance (where they are not all of a side) a remonstrance was drawn up and sent to the council against this establishment, particularly as to the guns, that it could not be complied with, without a considerable sum of money to enable them to cast the new guns where wanted'.[24] This time the Ordnance Board was more successful than usual. The Privy Council restored the 1716 establishment, and suggested that the new one be implemented when 'fewer ships are ordered to sea than are at present, and when some method be found for defraying the extraordinary expense occasioned thereby, that they may conform thereto gradually'.[25]

The situation remained the same for the next ten years. War with Spain began in 1739, and a further war with France already seemed likely. The size of some of the large Spanish ships, such as the *Princessa*, considerably shocked the naval administration, and in 1741 the dimensions of new ships were again increased slightly. It was recognised that the fleet needed more gun-power and the 1733 establishment came into effect in 1743, though only for ships built to the dimensions of 1741.

The 1745 Establishment

The increases in ships' dimensions of 1741 were clearly inadequate, and from 1744 a new Admiralty Board, on which Admiral Anson was the strongest member, forced greater changes. They formed a committee of flag officers to consider the dimensions of new ships, and ordered the master shipwrights to submit plans. Though the increases were greater than those resulting from previous establishments, they were still not far-reaching enough to match foreign ships, and they were a disappointment to the administration. Moreover, the shipwrights rejected suggestions that the three-decker 80s, the least successful ships in the fleet, should be replaced by two-decker 74s, on the model of the latest French ships. As regards guns, the principles of the 1743 establishment were retained for new ships, except that the 64s were once again to have 70 guns, and the 58s to have 60. This establishment was short-lived, and far more fundamental changes were on the way.[26]

Chapter 22. Types of Ship

The New System

The Anson administration carried out a very far-reaching reform of the whole Navy, in which gunnery was given as much consideration as anything else. It was 1755 before Anson was able to create a Navy Board to support him in his work, rather than obstruct him, but thereafter reforms began to take place very quickly. Before 1755 the gunning of ships was usually rather an afterthought. Before 1677 they were fitted with what was available, and after this date with what the flag officers or the Navy Board thought was most appropriate. After 1755 the best ships were designed round a specific armament. This was particularly true of the new 74s, which were the smallest ships to carry an effective battery of 32-pounders. The new type of frigate was designed to carry a lighter battery, of 12-pounders, high out of the water to allow good sailing qualities. Though guns were still removeable, and under the control of the Ordnance Board, the designers saw the guns as an integral part of the ship, far more than ever before.[1]

This heralded the end of the establishments, both of dimensions and of guns. That of 1745 was the last to be put into effect and the gun establishment was still applied to ships already built, and so in that sense lasted a remarkably long time. One ship built to the 1745 establishment, the *Britannia*, was to fight at Trafalgar in 1805. The Ordnance Board was now given advance warning of the need for guns, not by means of establishments, but by the Navy Board which informed it what ships were building, so that new guns could be ordered for them. Because each ship was usually designed round a particular armament, it became much less common to change a ship's guns during her career, which made it much easier to predict requirements in advance. The Ordnance Board was no longer faced with sudden demands, as it had been in 1677, 1703 and 1716, to re-gun whole classes of ships at once.

However, there were a few cases where an individual ship had her guns changed. The carronade began to replace many of the guns on the upper works, and even on the main decks of smaller ships, but this issue is complex and requires separate treatment. Some ships carried lighter guns in their old age, as their deck beams became weaker or their design became obsolete, and one type of gun, the 42-pounder, was gradually replaced over a period of about 30 years.

Paradoxically, after the initial burst of activity, the new system proved slow and piecemeal. For this reason it is better to consider ships by type and class, rather than as a whole.

The First Rates

Only five new 100-gun ships were built between 1755 and 1815, but because such ships had a long life, several generations were often in service at once. Thus this type, though small in number, showed as great a variety of armament as any other. The traditional gunport arrangement which was used up to the 1745 establishment, was for 28 guns on each of the main decks. This was modified for the *Victory* of 1765, the first post-establishment First Rate. In accordance with the policy of putting more guns on the main decks, and fewer on the quarterdeck and forecastle, she had 30 ports on the lower deck, 28 on the middle deck, and 30 on the upper deck. This arrangement became the most common, and it was used for two other ships, the *Royal George* of 1788 and the *Queen Charlotte* of 1790. The *Royal Sovereign* of 1788 had a rather old-fashioned arrangement, with 28 guns on the lower and middle decks, and 30 on the upper deck. Later, the 100-gun ship was expanded slightly to carry 104 guns, and the first such ship, the *Queen Charlotte* of 1810, had an arrangement of 30–30–30. Two more 104-gun ships were built, with an arrangement of 30–32–32, but these were not launched until the 1820s.[2]

On 100-gun ships the 42-pounders of the lower decks were replaced by 32-pounders.[3] This is the most striking example of the calibres of the main armament being altered during the lives of individual ships. During this period 100-gun ships always carried 24-pounders on their middle decks, most had 12-pounders on the upper deck (though the *Queen Charlotte* of 1790 had 18-pounders), and 6-pounders were standard on the quarterdeck and forecastle until about 1780, when they were replaced by 12-pounders.

Even larger types of ship were introduced towards the end of the eighteenth century. Two 110-gun ships were built. The first, the *Ville de Paris* of 1795, had 30 guns on the lower deck and on the middle deck and 32 on the upper deck; the *Hibernia* of 1804 had two more on each deck. Later, several 120-gun ships were built. The first, the *Caledonia*, was completed in 1808. She was to have several near-sisters, none of which were completed before 1820. Three ships of the *Nelson* class were also built, and completed in 1814–15. All the 120-gun ships had an arrangement of 32–34–34. All the large First Rates of 110 or 120 guns had 32-pounders on the lower deck, 24-pounders on the middle deck, and 18-pounders on the upper deck.

The Second Rates

The first post-establishment 90-gun ships were the *Sandwich* class of 1759–61. They were a departure from the old 90-gun type in that they had far fewer guns on the upper works: only two on the forecastle and none on the quarterdeck, compared with ten on

A model of a late 90-gun ship, c1760. This type had very few guns on the forecastle, but more on the main decks than the earlier ships. In 1773 guns were added to the forecastle, making them 98-gun ships. NMM

the quarterdeck on the older ships. In contrast they had more guns on the main decks: 28 on the lower deck, 30 on the middle deck, and 30 on the upper deck. This distribution remained standard for such ships until the type came to the end of its life, after 1815.[4]

The biggest change in this class was in 1778, when it was decided to fit eight guns on the quarterdecks of new ships, making them into 98-gun ships. They were still classed as Second Rates, despite having only two guns less than a 100-gun ship. To a certain extent this was justified by the fact that the calibres were rather lighter – the 18-pounders on the middle deck compared unfavourably with the First Rate's 24-pounders. The 98s invariably carried 32-pounders on the lower deck, and 12-pounders on the upper deck until the 1790s, after which most carried 18-pounders. The Second Rate was in decline by the end of the eighteenth century, and the construction of only one was started after 1801.

The 80-gun Two-decker

Few ships of this type were built before 1815. Only two were constructed in the 1790s and two were begun towards the end of the Napoleonic Wars, but not completed until 1815 and 1818.[5] The two ships of the 1790s, the *Caesar* and the *Foudroyant*, had particularly powerful armaments, with 32-pounders on the lower deck and 24-pounders on the upper deck. The *Caesar* had 9-pounders on the quarterdeck and the *Foudroyant* had 12-pounders. This armament made the two-decker 80 as powerful as the three-decker 98. The early nineteenth century ships were less powerful, with only 18-pounders on the upper deck. Though few of these ships were built in Britain, some were captured from France, Spain and Denmark, so that there were usually about ten in the fleet in the 1800s.

The 74-gun Ship

This type was the great success of the 1750s, and it remained the most common type of ship of the line until well after 1815. Most 74s were of the Common class – they had 28 32-pounders

A classic 74-gun ship, the Royal Oak *of 1769.* Science Museum

on the lower deck, 28 18-pounders on the upper deck, and 18 9-pounders on the quarterdeck and forecastle. As early as 1757, plans were made for the Large class, which was to have 30 24-pounders on the upper deck, and two less guns on the quarterdeck than a Common class ship. For a long time this armament was only fitted on French captures, except for two ships, the *Triumph* and *Valiant*, which were copied from the French *Invincible*. The Large class was augmented in the late 1790s, when 11 more ships were built to carry 24-pounders on the upper deck. This policy did not last long, and by 1800 the Common class had been revived. There was also an intermediate class of ship with 30 guns on the upper deck, but 18- instead of 24-pounders. Apart from six ships built in the 1790s, all such ships were prizes. The great majority of the 200 or so 74s which served with the British Navy were of the Common class, armed like the *Dublin* of 1757, except where carronades supplemented or replaced some of the guns on the upper works.

The 64-gun Ship

This was an expansion of the old 60-gun ship, and was built in Britain from about 1758. It had its heyday in the 1760s and '70s, after which it was found to be rather too small for the line of battle.[6] Numbers were supplemented by many captures from the French, Dutch and Spanish, and by six ships bought from the East India Company in the 1790s. In 1758 it was proposed that the 64 carry 32-pounders on her lower deck, but this plan was soon withdrawn, probably before any ships had been so fitted. Thereafter all 64s carried 24-pounders as their main armament, leaving them substantially weaker than 74s. They had 18-pounders on the upper deck, and 9-pounders on the forecastle and quarterdeck.

The 50-gun Ship

This type was no longer regarded as suitable for the line of battle after about 1755, so few were built for some years. It was revived in the 1770s, for use as a convoy escort and flagship for small squadrons. As it had 22 24-pounders on its lower deck, it was not much weaker than the 64, and it was much stronger than any frigate of the time, though it had poor sailing qualities. It had 12-pounders on the upper deck, and 6-pounders on the quarterdeck and forecastle.

The 44-gun Ship

This was an expanded version of the old two-decker 40 of the establishments period. It was largely out of favour in the 1750s and '60s, but like the 50-gun ship it was revived in the 1770s. It carried 22 18-pounders on the lower deck and usually had 9-pounders on the upper deck until about 1780, after which these were replaced by 12-pounders. The quarterdeck was unarmed and there were two six-pounders on the forecastle. Many ships of this type were later fitted with carronades on the main decks, as well as the upper works.

A model of a 32-gun frigate of the Richmond *class, thought from iconographical evidence to represent the* Juno *of 1757. The early 32-gun 'true frigates' were armed with a short 12-pounder which had been specially designed for their gundecks.* Science Museum

The 40-gun Frigate

In the early 1800s this was the largest type of single-decker 'true frigate' in service. Most ships of this class had been captured, though a small number were built from about 1797. Some carried 24-pounders, making them very powerful for frigates; the others had 18-pounders. Most had 9-pounders on the quarterdeck and forecastle, until many of them were replaced by carronades.

The 38-gun Ship

This was the largest type of frigate in common use in the late eighteenth century. Apart from captured ships, of which there were many, there were a few built in the 1780s, and many more in the 1790s, so that by 1797 there were 33 on the list. It carried 18-pounders on the gundeck, and 9-pounders on the upper works. Three ships, including the famous *Indefatigable*, were cut down from 64s and carried 24-pounders as their main armament.

The 36-gun Frigate

The 36-gun frigate was first introduced in the mid-1750s, soon after the 28 and the 32. It carried the same calibre of guns as the 32, and so it was only a little more powerful, which perhaps explains why this type did not catch on. The 12-pounder 36 was not produced in any great numbers. Only three were built in the 1750s, and a few were captured.

The 36 was revived in the 1780s and '90s, but with an 18-pounder armament, and was therefore very different from the old model. This type became very common, and by 1813 there were 70 of them in service, nearly all carrying 18-pounders. They also carried eight 9-pounders on the quarterdeck, and two 12-pounders on the forecastle.

The 32-gun Frigate

The 32-gun frigate, carrying 12-pounder guns as its main armament, was another of the great successes of the 1750s, though it was not as long-lived as the 74. It soon became the standard patrol and reconnaissance vessel, with 32 on the list by 1762, and 59 in 1783, of which 14 were building.[7] By the 1790s it had been outclassed by the larger French frigates, and was being replaced by 36- and 38-gun frigates. A new class of 32s, with 18-pounder guns, was built in large numbers after 1790. It was 120 tons larger than the 12-pounder ship, and must be considered as a separate type.

The 28-gun Frigate

This was the earliest type of 'true frigate' to be built in Britain, anticipating the 32 by two years. It was always overshadowed by the latter. At its peak, in 1783, there were 33 ships on the Navy list, after which this type slowly declined. It always carried 24 9-pounders on the gundeck. Early ships had four 3-pounders on the quarterdeck. Later these were replaced with 6-pounders.

The 24-gun Frigate

These were descended from the old Sixth Rates built in the time of the establishments. Few were added to the Navy after 1755, and most of these were captured. Some of the ships in service around 1760 had 20 9-pounders on the upper deck and a pair of similar guns on the lower deck, a very old-fashioned armament which pre-dated the unarmed lower deck of the true frigate. Later ships had 22 9-pounders on the main deck, and two 6-pounders on the quarterdeck. There were 11 24s on the list in 1783, including one building. By 1805 the number had declined to five.

122

The 22- and 20-gun Frigate

These types could also claim to be descended from the old Sixth Rates of the first half of the century. They invariably carried 20 9-pounders on the main deck, and two 3-pounders. Again few were built, though 14 were added to the fleet between 1793 and 1801, mostly by capture.[8]

The Sloop

This old term originally meant, as it often does today, a single-masted vessel. In the early eighteenth century sloops were often two-masted, rigged as brigantines, snows and ketches. By the 1750s ship-rigged sloops, with three masts, were being built. These carried 8 to 14 guns. Sloops of 8 guns had 3-pounders, those of 10 or 12 guns had 4-pounders, and those of 14 guns had 6-pounders. By the 1770s the smaller types had fallen out of favour, and 16- and 18-gun classes had been introduced. All sloops now carried 6-pounders. The 18-gun class was greatly augmented in the 1790s, and by 1805 there were 104 ship-sloops of all kinds on the Navy list. Until the introduction of the carronade most sloops carried swivel guns on their quarterdecks, approximately equal in number to their main armament.

Brig-sloops had two masts. They first appeared as a separate class in the 1780s, and there were 15 on the list in 1786, carrying 14 to 18 6-pounders. They were built in large numbers in the 1790s, and there were 64 on the list in 1805.

Smaller Craft

Various types were added in the last quarter of the eighteenth century, especially for escort and patrol duties. Cutters usually had 10 or 14 4-pounders. Schooners of the 1790s had four 3-pounders. Gunboats, introduced from 1794, were small vessels designed round large guns. Some carried three 32-pounder carronades, others had a single 32-pounder long gun. Another group, of rather different conception, had eighteen 18-pounder carronades, and two 24-pounders as chase guns.

Chapter 23. The Age of the Carronade

The American War

The Navy Board became very enthusiastic about the carronade after its initial trials and the first establishment was proposed in July 1779. Carronades were to be fitted in the empty areas on ships' upper works. Ships of the line, from 64 guns upwards, were to have none on the quarterdeck, as this area was already crammed with guns. They were to have two 12-pounders on the forecastle (four in the case of Second Rates, which had no long guns on the forecastle) and six 12-pounders on the poop, which had carried no long guns since the 1703 establishment had gone out of use. Ships of 100 guns had 8 carronades on the poop. Smaller ships, including frigates, sloops, and the intermediate group of ships carrying from 44 to 50 guns were now to carry carronades on their generally under-armed quarterdecks. Most were to have six 12- or 18-pounders, except for 44-gun ships which were to carry eight, and 50-gun ships which were to have two 24-pounders. All ships below the line of battle were to have either two or four carronades on their forecastles. Ships of these classes did not usually have poops.[1]

A few increases were ordered over the next few months. In August, cutters in the Downs under the command of Admiral Drake were to have two carronades for their stern chases.[2] In December there was a short-lived order to arm the quarterdecks of frigates entirely with carronades, except for the foremost port. This was the first attempt to use carronades to replace, rather than supplement, long guns. It is doubtful if it was ever actually done, because the order was cancelled the following January, and frigates were thereafter to be fitted at the discretion of the dockyard.[3]

It is not clear to what extent these early establishments were intended to be compulsory. By March 1780 the Navy Board was beginning to give way under the complaints of many captains, and carronades were now to be fitted only on the captain's application.[4] A few more orders were issued over the next few years. In January 1782, two 68-pounders were to be fitted to ships of the line if their captains requested them, but it seems that very few did.[5] In November the same year, it was authorised for large 36- and 38-gun frigates to have 24-pounders instead of 18-pounders on their quarterdecks.[6] By 1782, 167 ships and vessels, over a quarter of the fleet, carried some carronades, and many of these were armed according to the 1779 establishment.[7]

The Advance of the Carronade

No new orders relating to carronades were issued during the peace of 1783–93. A list dating from the beginning of 1793 shows that only a minority of ships were fitted with them.[8] Only 40 ships, out of 475 on the Navy list, were said to be fitted with carronades. Of these, all but two had already been fitted by 1782, so it seems that very few new ones were fitted during the peace and that many had been removed. Though there was much variation between the individual ships, the list roughly conformed to the establishment of 1779, taking into account the other orders issued since then. The 74-gun ships in particular had armaments similar to the establishment of 1779, as did 32- and 28-gun frigates. The three-deckers on the list, the *Victory*, *Duke* and *Prince George*, had rather different armaments, with a high proportion of 32-pounders among their carronades. Apart from the need to alter armaments to suit individual ships, and the fact that some new calibres of carronade had been added, the situation in 1793 was not far from the spirit of the orders of 1779.

The situation was rationalised in November 1794, when a new and compulsory establishment of carronades was drawn up.[9] There was some disagreement between the Ordnance Board and the Navy Board over it, but the view of the latter prevailed with the Admiralty, and the establishment was to be used for 'such

The gunwharf at Portsmouth in the late eighteenth century. NMM

ships as are now fitted out, and have not their carronades already prepared, and in the fitting of all ships which may hereafter be put in commission.'

The new establishment was not radically different from the old one in respect of the numbers of guns carried. All classes were to have eight carronades, except 50-gun ships which were to have 12, and small frigates, sloops and brigs had only six. Ships of the line still had none on the quarterdeck, and some classes, such as the 44s and 38s, actually carried fewer than they had done in 1779. The biggest difference was in the weight of guns. Now 32- and 24-pounders were common, even for 28-gun ships and 18- and 12-pounders were found only on poops of ships of the line, and on vessels of 24 guns or less.

Though this establishment was intended to be compulsory, some exceptions were made. Numerous captured and purchased vessels were added to the Navy, and special rules had to be made for each of these. In other cases individual captains were allowed variations in the armaments of their ships. In July 1796, for example, the 64-gun *Ardent* was 'allowed four 24-pounder carronades for the forecastle and four 18-pounders only for the poop, in lieu of the two 24-pounder carronades allowed for the forecastle and six 18-pounders on the poop.'[10] In October the *Maidstone* was 'allowed six 24-pounder carronades in lieu of 6-pounder guns'.[11]

The all-carronade armament, as tested on the *Rainbow* in 1782, had only a limited success. It was found that an enemy ship could keep out of range of the carronades and use her own long guns effectively; this was to happen several times during the War of 1812.[12] This was more of a problem with large ships than small ones, as the latter could use their manoeuvrability and sailing ability to get out of trouble. Thus in 1795 a new class of brig-sloops of 18 guns was ordered to carry 16 32-pounder carronades, and two long 6-pounders.[13] Such ships had been rare before the carronade allowed a small ship to carry an effective armament.

The arming of these brig-sloops introduced a new principle in that carronades began to replace long guns on many ships. This was greatly extended in March 1797, when it was ordered that all ships of the line being fitted out were to be prepared for carronades (usually 32-pounders) in place of the 9- and 12-pounder

long guns carried on the quarterdeck.[14] An exception was made in the case of the guns which would fire through the shrouds of the main and mizzen masts. Because of the danger of fire, these were still to be long guns of the usual calibre. For example, on a typical 74-gun ship, three of the seven ports on the quarterdeck would be reserved for long guns. In June 1799 this principle was also extended to frigates. The Admiralty examined 'the propriety of arming all frigates with carronades on the quarterdeck and forecastle on the outside principle, reserving two long guns on the forecastle and two on the quarterdeck as chase guns only.'[15] It was decided to do this with all ships fitting out. In 1800 more of the smaller ships, of 20 and 24 guns, were to have their 9-pounder long guns on the main deck replaced with 32-pounder carronades.[16]

Guns in the Wake of the Rigging

Because of the tumblehome (the narrowing of the hull above the waterline) the shrouds, which supported the masts, had to be mounted on projections from the ship's sides, known as channels. The shrouds passed between some of the forecastle and quarter-deck gunports, perhaps several feet outside the hull. A long gun would carry its blast beyond the shrouds, but a carronade would usually be too short to do this. The shrouds, vital to the ship's rigging, were covered with tar for preservation, and were highly inflammable. Hence many considered it undesirable to fit carronades where they would have to fire through the shrouds. Others preferred a uniform armament on each deck. Over the years the Admiralty and the Navy Board found it difficult to choose between these two principles.

The problem first arose in 1797, when carronades were first fitted to the quarterdecks of ships of the line. At this date, as we have seen, safety prevailed, and long guns were to be fitted 'in the wake of the rigging'. In 1799, when the time came to re-arm

Two of the French ships captured at the 'Glorious First of June', 1794. Such ships had considerable influence on British design. NMM

frigates, uniformity was evidently considered more important, and long guns were used only on the fore and after chase. There was perhaps slightly less danger of setting the shrouds on fire on a frigate than on a ship of the line, for the tumblehome was less, the channels narrower, and the shrouds closer to the ship's side.

In 1804 it was decided to fit carronades in all the ports on the quarterdecks and forecastles of ships of the line. This was evidently not a success, for in June 1805 the order was cancelled and all ships, down to 32 guns, were now to carry long guns in the wake of the rigging.[17] Those of 74 guns and more were to have 12-pounders, and those of 64 guns and less were to have 9-pounders. But some ships which had carronades fitted on the 'outside principle' sometimes retained them in the wake of the rigging.

Chase Guns

In the early eighteenth century, when the line of battle was still rigidly adhered to, all a ship's guns were fitted to fire on the broadside. When forming part of the line, the bow and stern were protected by the next ships in the line, and guns firing fore and aft, known as chase guns, were considered superfluous. A few ports were provided in the bow and stern, and guns could be moved into them from the broadside when necessary. But by the 1790s naval tactics were much less formal than in the early part of the century, and ships had much more need for bow and stern armament.

There were many difficulties in fitting an effective chase armament. At the stern the ship's structure was weak, and dominated

The Cornwallis, *one of the very last 74-gun ships. It has a 'round bow', and some attempt has been made to fit chase guns firing forward.* NMM

by the windows and balconies of the officers' cabins. In the bows the rigging of the bowsprit interfered with any guns fitted below forecastle level. Chase ports were usually provided at gundeck level in the sterns of ships of the line, below the level of the cabins, but on other ships chase guns were mostly mounted high up, on the forecastle, poop or quarterdeck. For obvious reasons, chase guns were particularly useful for long-range fire, and the carronade was inappropriate for such a task. On the other hand the heaviest guns, as fitted on the lower deck, would not be suitable, as the decks at the stern would not be strong enough to support them.

The first official mention of chase guns in this period was in 1797, when it was decided that two long chase guns could be fitted on the forecastles of all ships of the line.[18] Chase guns were normally to be of the same calibre as those of the upper deck. This created a slight anomaly, in that First Rates could have smaller chase guns than Third Rates. Frigates were more likely to be involved in chases than ships of the line, and by the orders of 1799 they were each to have four chase guns, two on the bows and two on the stern.[19] The calibres were not specified.

By an order of June 1804 the calibres of chase guns were regulated and rationalised. Ships carrying 74 to 100 guns were to have 12-pounders, those of 32 to 64 guns were to have 9-pounders.[20]

The Situation in 1815

As a general rule, the smaller the vessel the higher the proportion of carronades she carried in her armament. The very smallest vessels, schooners and cutters, often had all-carronade armaments. The most common type of brig-sloop had 16 carronades and two long guns. The smallest frigates, of 24 guns and less, had carronades on their main decks.

On ships of more than 24 guns the carronade had little effect on the main gundecks, and most carried the same types of gun as they had before its introduction. The carronade's domination of the upper works of such ships tended to increase over the years, and this had more effect at the smaller end of the range, for the quarterdeck and forecastle of a frigate carried a greater proportion of armament than that of a three-decker.

The carronade created many anomalies in the system of classifying ships according to their gun power. Until 1797 carronades were entirely additional to long guns, and only the latter were counted when the ship was classified, except in the case of very small vessels which had carronades on their main decks. After 1797, when carronades began to replace long guns on many ships, the number of guns against a ship's name in the Navy list (eg 74, 64, 32, etc) merely reflected a particular type of vessel, and did not reflect either the number of long guns, or the total number carried. This caused the Navy to be accused of deception, particularly during the War of 1812. The system of rating ships was not changed until 1816, after the end of the long wars with France, when it was totally re-structured.

PART VII

Gun Equipment

Chapter 24. Gun Carriages

Early Types

The oldest known gun mountings were of a very simple type. Each consisted of a long piece of wood with a groove cut in it to the size of the gun. The aftermost part of the carriage was solid, and it served to hold the chamber of the gun, which was breech-loading. The gun, apart from the removeable chamber, was held in place by straps of metal or rope. The chamber was wedged in place. Such mountings were common while the old type of breech-loader survived, but were in decline by the second half of the sixteenth century, and probably became obsolete by the first half of the seventeenth. There was no easy means of moving these mountings backwards and forwards, or about the decks of a ship, so they were suitable only for light guns, and those, especially breech-loaders, which did not need to recoil or be run in and out for loading. On such a mount the gun was only a little way above the deck, but this was no problem if the chamber was to be removed for reloading. Elevation and depression of the gun must have been seriously limited, but were only necessary at short range. Later guns, such as those found aboard the *Mary Rose* sometimes had a trapezoidal bottom on the carriage which, used with wedges, may have made elevation and depression a little easier. Her wrought iron guns seem to have been incapable of either recoil or traverse.[1]

The swivel type of mounting was probably the longest lived of all. It was certainly in use in the fifteenth century, and it was to survive as a standard naval mount until the swivel gun began to be replaced by the carronade after 1780. It too pre-supposed a very small gun which did not need to recoil. Essentially the mount consisted of a fork, usually placed on the upper rail of the ship, where it could rotate about its axis. The two prongs of the fork were fitted to the trunnions of the gun, so that it could be elevated and depressed. More sophisticated versions included a bracket which allowed the gun to be fixed at a certain angle during firing. The swivel could be used for both breech-loading and muzzle-loading guns. In the case of the latter, it was turned to point inwards during reloading. By the eighteenth century it was accepted that swivel guns should be of $\frac{1}{2}$ pound calibre. They were fitted to the smallest vessels, sloops and Sixth Rates, and

later to the tops of larger ships. They were not counted as part of the main armament.[2]

It is possible that some of the earliest ships' guns were mounted on field carriages, with a long trail and large wheels, as used for land artillery. Such carriages would have been most unsuitable. The long trail would have taken up too much space aboard ship, and restricted the room available for recoil. The large wheels would have served no useful purpose where there was no rough terrain to cover, and have made it impossible to run out the gun to its full extent.

Beds and Trucks

A ship's gun of any size, of about 3 pounds calibre or more, usually needed to recoil. This reduced the strain on the structure of the ship, and made reloading much easier. There is evidence that in the seventeenth century some ship's guns were loaded outboard, by a seaman climbing out on to the barrel of the gun.[3] Obviously this could only be done away from the scene of the action, and would certainly have been impossible in the broadside-to-broadside engagements which became standard by the middle of the century. It may have been suitable for merchantmen with reduced crews, as it saved the labour of hauling the guns out again after reloading, but a naval ship had enough men to haul on the gun tackles, and keep up a much higher rate of fire. Any naval gun which was too large to be either a breech-loader or a swivel needed a carriage which would enable it to be run in and out, and to recoil in a controlled manner.

Given this, the carriage had to be as small as possible, for space was always limited on a fighting ship. In particular, the carriage had to extend as little forward of the trunnions of the gun as possible, so that it could be run out far enough to clear the sides of the hull, and the rigging. Nor could it extend too far aft of the cascable, or the recoiling gun would need too much space in the middle of the ship. The gun had to be lifted 2 or 3ft above the deck. This was a suitable height for aiming and loading, and it would allow the gunports, particularly on the lower deck, to be placed higher above the waterline.

The carriage had to be run out by a limited number of men, often up an incline when the ship was heeling. In the early days it often had to be moved from one gunport to another. 'Bring me from the weather side to the lee so many pieces as we have ports to beare upon him' was one of the orders given by a captain engaged in a sea-fight in Captain John Smith's *Sea Grammar* of 1627.[4] The carriage also had to allow for elevation and depression, especially in the days when battles were fought at relatively long ranges.

The 'truck and bed' carriage, as evolved by the middle of the sixteenth century, fulfilled these requirements. It was based on four 'trucks', wheels which were small enough to take up little space, and which allowed the gun to be run in and out, and from port to port if necessary. Above the axles of these wheels was the bed, a flat piece of timber which provided the main strength of the structure, and also provided a base for the wedges at the rear, to control the elevation and depression of the gun. Two brackets, one on each side, were mounted vertically on the bed. Each had a semi-circular recess cut in its upper edge to receive the trunnions, and a series of steps behind that, for the levers which would help to elevate the gun. The two brackets were joined and the carriage given extra strength by a transom positioned between the brackets and below and just forward of the trunnion holes.

The earliest carriages of this basic type were recovered from the *Mary Rose*, lost in 1545. They differed from the later design in several respects. The bed was very large, extending beyond the brackets in all directions. The axles were mounted above the bed, whereas in later versions they were usually mounted below it. They were quite complex in construction, and seem to have been individually tailored.[5]

We have little detailed information about English gun carriages of the early seventeenth century. Unlike brass cannon they do not survive well underwater, so are found only on the best preserved wrecks. They do not last much better out of the water, and very few surviving guns have their original carriages. Plans of carriages are few, and not very detailed. The carriages found aboard the *Vasa*, lost in Stockholm harbour in 1628, are not strictly relevant to English ships, but they do give some indication of the extent to which they had developed since 1545. The bed had become rather smaller; it no longer projected forward or either side of the brackets. The aft part of the bed was now rounded and projected a few inches beyond the brackets to provide a base for the wedges used for elevation. The trucks were now placed under the bed, which tended to increase the strength of the carriage. The brackets were closer together forward than aft, and this conformed to the taper of the gun barrel. The forward truck was considerably larger than the after one. Each trunnion was held in its place at the top of the bracket by a cap-square, which was a piece of wrought iron that fitted over the trunnion. It was pivoted at its after end and locked into position by a key called the fore lock.[6]

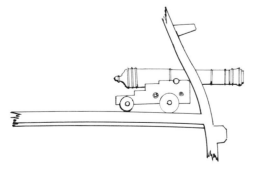

A gun carriage on a draught of a small ship, c1625.

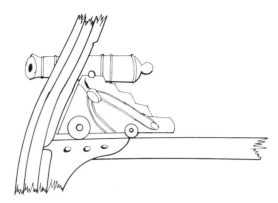

A gun and carriage forming part of the secondary armament of a bomb vessel of 1693. Though this drawing is taken from a rather crude draught, and the angles of the steps are unusual, it does give some impression of the rather narrow type of carriage used in the late seventeenth century.

All these features became standard in gun carriages. It seems likely that they had already been adopted in England by 1625. This is confirmed by plans which show similar carriages aboard small ships.[7]

This was to remain the standard type of gun carriage for another hundred years. There are a few glimpses of it in the later part of the century, in Sellar's *Sea Gunner* of 1691, in the Keltridge draughts of the 1680s and '90s, and a draught of a 70-gun ship of a similar date.[8] The only clear drawings and specifications date from the 1720s, when it was on the verge of obsolescence.[9] In principle it did not change much over these years, though its proportions may have altered somewhat. In the guns of the 1680s, for example, the tops of the brackets, under the cap-squares, appear rather narrow compared with those of the 1620s or 1720s.

The Truck and Axle Carriage

Some time around 1725 it was discovered that the bed of the carriage was not really necessary. The brackets were extended lower down, the axles were fixed by a more complex joint to give greater strength, and a separate surface, known as the stool bed, was provided for the sole purpose of supporting the wedge or quoin used for elevation. The bed was dispensed with, and the carriage made slightly lighter.

It is not clear exactly when this happened. In 1721 and in 1725 new regulations were issued by the Board of Ordnance for the dimensions of ships' carriages, which assumed that the old type of carriage was still in use.[10] Other drawings of the same period show the carriage without the bed. A drawing of 1732 clearly shows the new type of carriage, though in this case it is in use in a fortress rather than at sea.[11] Despite this, it is not unreasonable to assume that the new carriages were developed first at sea, where saving weight was more important than in a fortress. On the other hand, spending was restricted in these years, and it may have taken some time to replace all the old carriages.

The new carriage was to remain in service, unchanged in principle, until well after 1815. Each bracket was made in an upper and lower half. The lower edge of the bracket was hollowed out, presumably to save yet more weight. The ironwork was not very different from that of the old carriage. The cap-square, already described, held the trunnions in place. The bolts which held the

Details of the late seventeenth century carriage, from Sellar's Sea Gunner's Companion, *1691. It also shows some gunner's implements, such as the rope rammer coiled up in the right foreground. NMM.*

cap-square in position passed through both parts of the bracket, and also helped to hold the forward axle in position. Another bolt passed horizontally through the transom, binding the brackets together. Another horizontal bolt passed between the brackets just behind the centre of the carriage. This also supported the stool bed, which supported the quoin. Two vertical bolts passed through both halves of each bracket and through the rear axle, and another passed through both parts of the bracket near the centre of the carriage. The gun's breeching rope passed through a large eyebolt which was fitted on each side of the carriage, about halfway between the two trucks. In the latter part of the

eighteenth century two loops were also fitted behind the eyebolt, for some of the other tackle.

The Faults of the Truck Carriage

Despite its advantages, the truck carriage had many faults. By 1650 most ships had as many guns as gunports, and it must have been less common to move a gun from one port to another. Occasionally it may have been necessary to move guns into chase ports in the bow or stern, but the number of guns moved in this

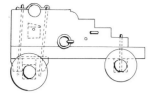

A late type of bed carriage, as specified by an establishment of 1725.

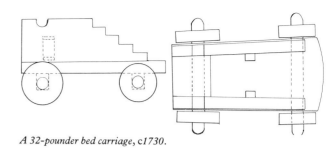

A 32-pounder bed carriage, c1730.

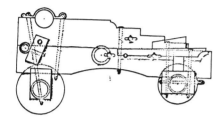

A mid-eighteenth century carriage, from the Danish Archives.

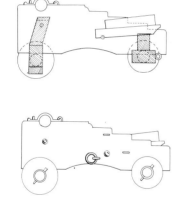

Another type of 32-pounder carriage, c1730. Unlike the one above it does not have a solid bed.

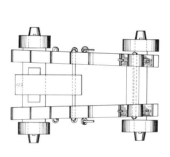

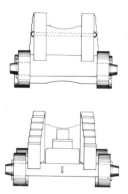

Details of a 32-pounder carriage, c1800, from a drawing in the NMM.

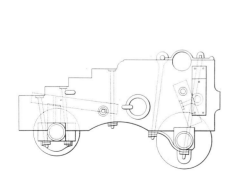

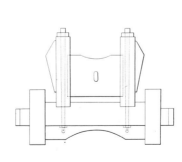

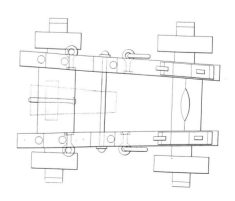

A slightly improved carriage, c1815. It has projections forward, to help keep the gun a sufficient distance from the side of the ship, and more projections from its sides.

The cap-square of a carriage, showing the fore lock which holds it in position.
Author's photograph, courtesy of NMM.

The truck of an early nineteenth-century carriage. It is held to the axle by a pin.
Author's photograph, courtesy of NMM.

manner was a very small proportion of the armament, so it cannot have been very useful to have had this capacity on all the carriages. On the other hand, a gun which broke loose from its mounting in a heavy sea would have been a great danger to all on the deck. At best the recoil of the truck carriage was unpredictable, and must have injured many men in the heat of battle, as 55cwt of 32-pounder rolled over feet and legs. It could be run out, elevated and depressed with no difficulty, but it was very difficult to traverse, for its wheels offered no help in moving it from side to side. This was no great problem when ships manoeuvred to allow their guns to bear, but more sophisticated tactics, especially in the war of 1812, caused some captains to think of other ways of mounting their guns.[12]

The system of restraining the recoil was not very efficient. The gun was allowed to run backwards for several feet, until the muzzle was far enough inboard to allow reloading. It was then brought up short by the breeching rope fixed round the cascable. This probably caused a severe jerk which strained the whole system. The wheels did nothing to slow the gun down. Nevertheless, the truck carriage remained the standard fitting throughout the age of sail. It was adaptable and robust, and more modern alternatives were only successful with lighter weapons.[13]

Carronade Carriages

From very early on the Carron Company believed that special carriages were necessary to get the best out of its guns. These were usually made by the company itself, and supplied as part of a package. There were many variations in the carronade carriage as it developed over the years, and as the guns were adopted for different kinds of ship, and different positions on board. Some carronade carriages were a reinterpretation of the standard ship's carriage, which had four trucks, brackets and quoins. These were used mainly on the smaller vessels, sloops and cutters. The standard type of carronade carriage, used on the poops, forecastles and quarterdecks of frigates and ships of the line, had two main parts.

The upper part, the bed, held the gun and enabled it to be elevated and depressed. It was fitted, by means of a bolt, to the second part, the slide, or training bed, which allowed it to recoil. The slide rotated about a pivot at its forward end, so the gun could be traversed.

There were two main types of bed, depending on whether or not the gun had conventional trunnions. The earliest guns had trunnions, and the bed was not unlike the carriage of a normal long gun, though slightly simplified, and without the transom and stool bed. In the later type of carronade, in which the trunnions were replaced with a ring under the gun, the bed was even simpler. It was a single piece of wood with an iron socket in its forward part, through which the ring of the gun rotated. Its rear part served mainly as a base for the elevating screw, and to hold ringbolts for the breeching tackle.

The slide, in either version, was essentially a long piece of timber with a hole cut along its centre. In early carriages the slide was rectangular. Later its fore edge was rounded off to allow better traversing. The foremost part was pivoted, either outside or inside the hull, according to whether the gun was to be fitted on the 'outside' or the 'inside principle'. On early guns the after edge of the slide was kept at a suitable height merely by placing a block of wood under it. This did not facilitate traversing, and on later carriages two small trucks were fitted under the rear part of the slide, to make it easier to move from side to side. Because the recoil was normally taken up by the bed, the slide did not have to recoil, so unlike conventional carriages it did not need to allow it to run back and forwards.

When the 'outside principle' was used, a timber was fitted outside the hull, just below the lower sill of the gunport. The foremost part of the slide was placed over that, and a pin was passed through both, providing the pivot about which the slide rotated. This type was certainly in use by 1781, and was probably the most common in the early days of the carronade, for it helped to carry the shorter gun outside the hull and the rigging. It was still being ordered as the standard fitting for frigates in 1799, and it was in use in 1808, for certain types of gun at least.[14]

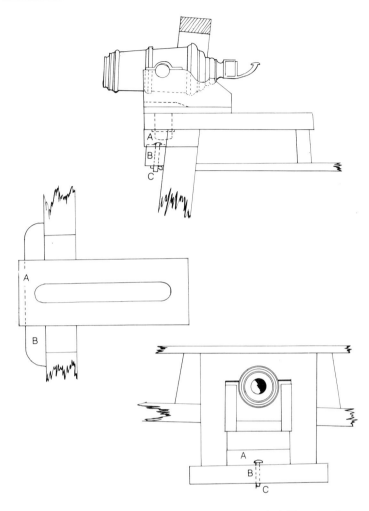

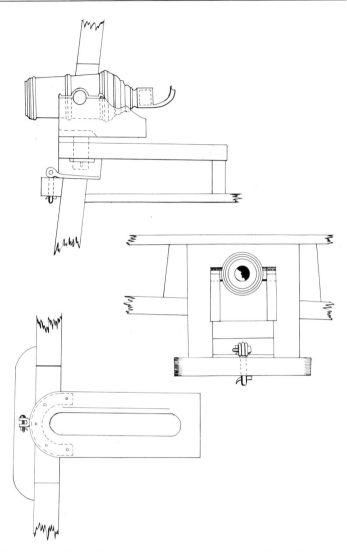

An early carronade mounting of 1781, fitted on the 'outside principle', so that the pivot was outside the ship.
A. A 5in thick piece of elm, with an iron plate let in the lower side of it, bolted to the ship's side.
B. Piece of oak 6in square, bolted to the ship's side.
C. Swivel bolt with fore lock.

A slightly more sophisticated arrangement than that shown on the left, also from 1781. The fore part of the slide has been rounded off, and the pivot pin is removeable.

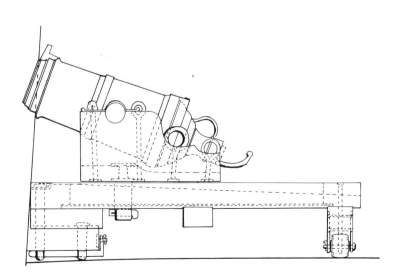

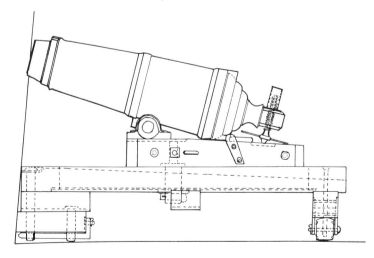

An 18-pounder trunnion carronade on its carriage, c1790.

An 18-pounder 'joint' carronade, also from 1790. The slide is virtually identical to that on the gun shown on the left, but the carriage is adapted for loops instead of trunnions, and is therefore much simpler in construction. The screw was used for elevating the gun and is protected by a leather cover.

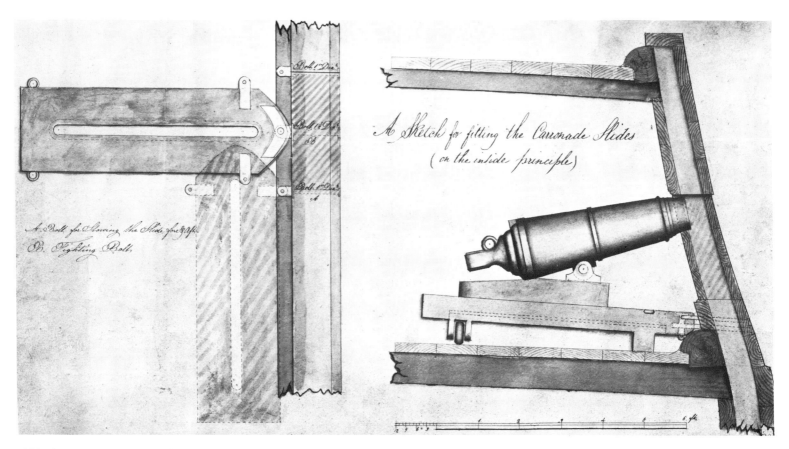

Slides fitted on the 'inside principle', c1795. The slide could be transferred to a different pin so that it could be stowed against the ship's side. Science Museum.

With the 'inside principle' the slide was pivoted inside the hull, round a bolt which was fixed securely to the ship's side. Up to the mid 1790s such carriages had only a very limited traverse, for the forward edge of the slide was usually cut square. Some extra traverse could be achieved by rotating the bed rather than the slide, but this produced great strain in the system, and often caused guns to overset. After 1796 the forward part was either rounded or pointed, to make movement easier. In some cases the slide could be transferred to a second or third pivot, fitted on either side, so that it could be stowed parallel to the side of the ship and the deck under the gun could be cleaned.[15] Nevertheless the position of the pivot inside the hull tended to reduce the amount of traverse available before the gun came up against the sides of the gunport. Conversely, the gun fitted by the 'inside principle' was better protected from enemy fire.

From about 1790 carronades were fitted with elevating screws. These passed through the cascable, and were turned to elevate or depress the gun. The top of each screw was covered, probably with leather, to prevent the ingress of water which would cause rust. The elevating screw probably had disadvantages in some circumstances. It would have been slower to operate than a conventional system of quoins, so carronades were provided with a moulding under their breeches, to aid the use of quoins should they become necessary.

Some carronades were fitted on the 'non-recoil' principle. This was invented by Bentham, the Inspector General of Naval Works, though a slightly different version, devised by a ship's carpenter named Bray, was used aboard improvised gunboats at

the siege of Acre in 1799.[16] Bentham's version was first used aboard the experimental sloop *Arrow* of 1796, which also had Sadler's guns. The captain's report was favourable, but little more was heard of non-recoil carronades until 1803, when another version was proposed by Peake, the Master Shipwright at Deptford.[17] Bentham pointed out that he was responsible for the original invention, which had 'not before attracted the attention of the Navy Board'.

Bentham claimed that he had first used the non-recoil gun in 1787, while he was serving with the Russian Navy. He had originally proposed that the gun be pivoted so that it could be turned to face inboard for loading, but he decided that this posed too much risk from an accidental discharge. Instead, the gun was to be carefully sited with its muzzle 4in outside the gunport, near enough to allow it to be loaded without recoiling it, but far enough out to avoid damage to the rigging. Its greatest advantage was that it needed very little space, but not everyone agreed with Bentham's claim that reloading was safe and easy. Specially designed carriages could be used for this system, but most of those fitted were conversions of the standard carriage.[18]

Bentham made great claims for his invention, and believed that it could be applied to the largest guns, on the lower decks of ships of the line. In practice it was used only for carronades. By an order of July 1804 it was to be used 'on all ships which may be armed in this manner'.[19] Not all ships were suitable, and on the 80-gun *Gibraltar* for example, the sides were too thick to allow non-recoil carriages and conventional ones were fitted.[20]

Another improvement was produced in 1805, by Mr Ward of

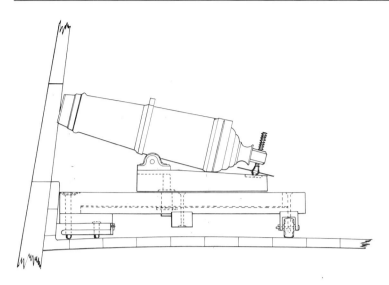

A 32-pounder carronade as fitted to the sloop Helena *in 1804. This appears to have been a standard mounting.*

A model of a carronade mounting. Science Museum.

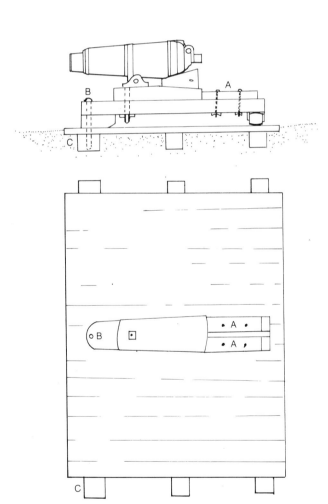

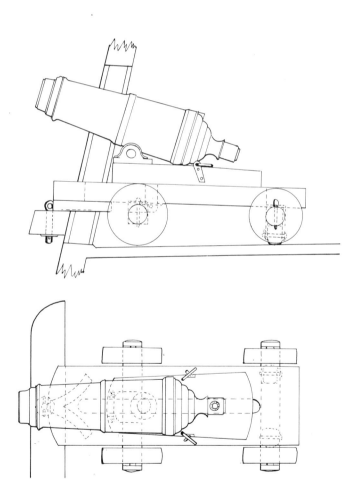

A 32-pounder carronade on its carriage. This type was used at the siege of Acre in 1799, and was claimed to be the prototype of the non-recoil system.
AA. Pieces of 3in plank bolted to the lower carriage to prevent the upper carriage recoiling.
B. Front pin of the lower carriage.
C. Pieces of wood in the ground, for pivoting the carriage.

An 18-pounder carronade. An order of July 1808 stipulated that the two aftermost carronades on the poop of a ship of the line were to be fitted in the manner shown, so that they could be moved to the stern and used as chase guns. The trucks were not used when the gun was in its normal position, and they were reversed when it was used in the chase, so that the larger ones were at the rear, to help reduce recoil.

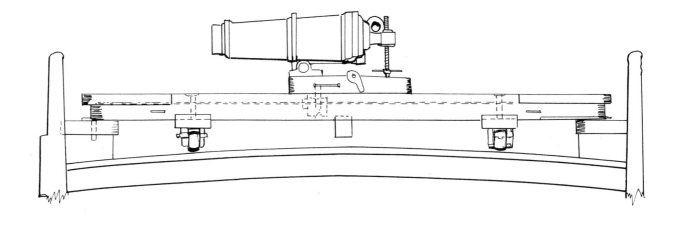

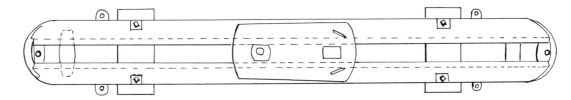

A double-ended carronade slide on a gunboat of 1797. It could be used to fire the gun from either side of the ship.

Sheerness Yard. It is not clear exactly what was involved in his invention. An Admiralty letter of September refers to a model 'showing an improvement in the fitting of carronades by means of an elevating screw', but these had already been in use for at least ten years.[21] The captain of the *Dauntless* tried out some guns on carriages designed by Ward, and preferred them to 'those fitted with the chocks outside', as they were 'better protected from the enemy's fire'.[22] This is possibly a reference to a new type of chock which began to appear around this time. These were shaped to fit under the small chocks under the rearmost part of the slide, to provide enough elevation when the ship was heeling, and to make it easier to run the guns out.

The conventional type of carriage was still used for some carronades. By an order of 1808, the two aftermost carronades on the poop were to have dual-purpose carriages, which had the pivot forward and small trucks at the rear, as on other carronade carriages, but also had the large wooden trucks of ordinary

carriages, so that they could be removed to a stern port when needed in a chase.[23] The large trucks were raised off the ground in the normal firing position. When the gun was moved to the stern they had to be swapped round so that the largest ones were now at the rear, to help arrest the recoil.

Another type of truck carriage was used on small vessels on which the carronade was the main armament. It was not unlike the ordinary carriage, though it was fitted for lugs rather than trunnions, and the stool bed was formed by placing a piece of timber over the rear part of the brackets.

Many other experiments were already taking place in the design of gun carriages as the wars ended in 1815, the most important being those by Congreve, who was trying to find better ways of arresting the recoil of guns. None of these had any real effect for some time and the main weapons of warships were still carried on carriages based on a design first used in the sixteenth century.

Chapter 25. Powder, Shot, and Stores

The Supply of Powder

Gunpowder, like printing and the compass, was one of the great inventions which shaped the post-medieval world. Its use aboard ship was well established by the sixteenth century. English governments had long recognized its importance, and its

manufacture was subject to strict controls. It was a mixture of three ingredients: saltpetre, sulphur and charcoal. Of these, only charcoal was readily available in Britain. During the seventeenth century attempts were made to produce native saltpetre, but it was expensive and of rather poor quality. Far superior supplies came from India, and were shipped by the East India Company. Sulphur was invariably imported, mostly from southern Italy.[1]

Early powder sometimes had less than 50 per cent saltpetre, but by the middle of the seventeenth century it had risen to $66\frac{1}{2}$ per cent, and by 1670 to 75 per cent, which was to remain standard. Some formulae stipulated equal quantities of charcoal and sulphur; others 15 per cent charcoal and 10 per cent sulphur. The ingredients were ground down and mixed together. In the early days this was done by hand. Later, as demand increased enormously, mills were built, most of which were operated by water power. They had to be in south east England, close to the offices and arsenals of the Board of Ordnance, but a good distance from the main centres of population, for explosions were not unknown. There were two main mills in England: one at Faversham in Kent, already in existence by the late sixteenth century and owned by Daniel Judd in the seventeenth; and one at Waltham Abbey, probably founded in 1560. The government bought the Faversham mill in 1760, and the Waltham Abbey mill in 1787. Both were expanded under government control. In 1774 Faversham had eleven water mills and five horse mills, and was capable of producing 364 tons of gunpowder per annum. There were also mills at Dartford, founded in 1732, and owned by Pike and Edsell.[2]

Types of Powder

Early powder, called 'serpentine' powder, was simply made from charcoal, saltpetre, and sulphur, which were ground down and mixed together. This type of powder had several disadvantages. The ingredients had a tendency to separate themselves if the powder was subjected to vibration. It absorbed moisture very easily, but there was no space for circulation of the air, which would have aided combustion, and its performance could be made even more unpredictable by pushing it together too tightly or too loosely inside the gun.

These problems were largely solved by the invention of 'corned' powder. After mixing, the powder was wetted and then passed through a sieve to form grains of a desired size, according to the type of gun it was to be used for. The use of corned powder was first noted as early as 1425 but its use spread only slowly. It was too powerful for most heavy guns, and at first it was reserved for muskets and similar. It was used in France by the middle of the sixteenth century, and in England soon afterwards. It was common by 1625, and around that time Captain Mainwaring wrote of serpentine powder, which 'we never use at sea in ordnance, nor small shot, both because it is of small force, and also for that it will (with the air of the sea) quickly die and lose its force.'[3]

In 1783 it was suggested that charcoal could be charred in 'cylinders' or ovens, rather than the traditional kilns. These would burn it much more uniformly, and contribute significantly to the powder's efficiency. Powder made in this way was introduced to the Navy around 1800. When issued to ships, the new cylinder powder was marked with red lettering to distinguish it from ordinary powder, which was marked in blue, or re-cycled powder, which was marked in white.[4] The weaker powders were to be used for close action, or for salutes and tests, and cylinder powder was reserved for distant engagements.

Charges of Powder

Improvements in the quality of powder meant that the amount used for a charge could be reduced. The weight of the charge also depended on the type of gun, for a short gun like a carronade used a lighter charge, in proportion to its weight, than a longer gun,

while a culverin had a heavier charge, in proportion to the weight of shot, than a cannon. In addition the size of the charge varied according to what was being fired by the gun, for example a double-shotted gun, fired at short range, used less powder than a single-shotted one.

In 1587, when serpentine powder was still in use, a culverin had a charge equal to the weight of the shot, and a cannon had a charge two-thirds of the weight of shot.[5] By 1672, with corned powder in general use, a cannon used powder half the weight of shot and a culverin two-thirds.[6] In the early years of the eighteenth century the smaller guns, which of course had a greater length in proportion to their bores, carried a proportionally greater charge. For example, the powder of a 42-pounder was 43 per cent of the weight of the ball, while that of an 18-pounder was 55 per cent, and a 9-pounder, 83 per cent. These charges were considerably reduced in 1725, but the principle remained the same. A 42-pounder was to have powder 40 per cent of the weight of the ball, an 18-pounder 50 per cent, and a 9 pounder 66 per cent.[7] This scale remained standard until the end of the century, when the new cylinder powder was introduced, and charges were further reduced. A charge of 33 per cent of the weight of the ball was now standard in normal circumstances, and 25 per cent when the gun was double-shotted. Carronades, which had previously used powder 12 per cent of the weight of the ball now used 8 per cent.[8]

Cartridges

By the beginning of the seventeenth century it had been found more convenient to load the powder in a prepared cartridge, rather than to shovel in loose powder with a ladle. Cartridges were made up aboard ship by the gunner and his crew. The powder was issued and stored in barrels, except for a few ready-use cartridges. The gunner was issued sheets of cloth or paper with which to make up the cartridges, until the end of the seventeenth century when he was provided with made-up bags instead.

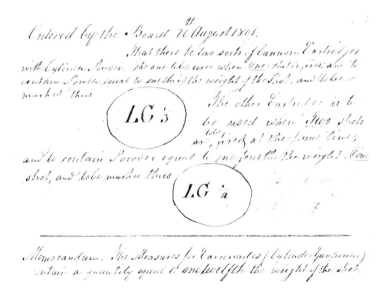

Instructions on how cartridges were to be marked-up, 1801. Great care was required when using cylinder powder as there was a danger of overloading the gun.

In the seventeenth century the main materials for cartridges were paper and canvas. Thus in 1655 the *Sovereign* was to be issued with five reams (2500 sheets) of 'paper royal', and with 500 ells (1875ft) of canvas.[9] Canvas had the disadvantage that it did not burn completely, and left burning traces in the chamber, and paper, that it became soggy and difficult to handle in wet conditions. Because of this, canvas tended to fall into disuse in the eighteenth century. In the 1720s parchment cartridges were common. They were issued alongside paper ones, in the proportion of three parchment to four paper.[10] But parchment must have been rather expensive, and there is no trace of its use in later years. Flannel cartridges were introduced in 1755 because they, like paper ones, were totally consumed in the explosion. In 1793 it was ordered that some cartridges, to be used for grape- and case shot, should have bottoms of flannel and tops of paper.[11] After this, flannel seems to have gained in popularity, and it was said 'Flannel cartridges are preferred to paper, because they do not retain the fire, and are, therefore, less liable to accidents in loading.'[12] Its disadvantages were that it weighed one-fifth more than paper, and was more expensive.

Round Shot

The simple cannon-ball was the main projectile of all navies, and especially of the British. Other types of shot served to damage the rigging, or kill and maim the men on the decks of an enemy ship. Round shot was the most dense, and therefore the heaviest shot that could be fired from a standard gun, thus it had the greatest range and penetrating power. It was by far the best means of penetrating the enemy's hull, and British tactics gave it great prominence. Between 1600 and 1815 it was issued in far greater numbers than any other projectile. In 1655 a Third Rate carried 1040 round shot for its demi-culverins, along with 320 double-headed hammered shot, and 150 tin cases for grape-shot.[13] By an order of 1717, ships were to carry 20 extra rounds of ball shot for the upper and middle deck, and 30 for the upper deck.[14] In the 1780s a 74-gun ship had 2800 rounds of ball shot, compared with 166 of grape shot, 84 of double-headed shot, 115 of Langrel (or langridge), shot and 173 of canister shot.[15]

Early round shot was often made of stone. This was lighter than iron, but it tended to cause more damage because it shattered on impact, and possibly it had a greater effect in destroying the timbers of an enemy ship. But stone shot was difficult and expensive to manufacture. As the rate of fire of guns increased enormously, and the iron industry grew in scale and efficiency, it became completely obsolete. It was rare by the 1580s, and only a few rounds survived into the seventeenth century, for use with perriers and similar guns. Stone had fallen completely into disuse by the middle of the century.[16] Thereafter, round shot was invariably cast in iron. Musket balls could be made by dropping a piece of lead from a shot tower, but cannon-balls were too large for this, and lead was too expensive, so clay moulds were used to make iron shot. Standards of accuracy improved throughout the eighteenth century, especially after the introduction of the carronade made a tight fit more necessary. It is believed that cannon-balls were painted black after this time, to protect them from rust which would have affected their fit.

Shot Used Against the Rigging

Though firing into the rigging was not a normal tactic of the British Navy, a ship had to be ready for any eventuality, and it might find itself outnumbered and obliged to disable its pursuers. Round shot did not have enough spread to cut many rigging lines, or make large holes in the sails. Something different was required.

Making round shot at Woolwich arsenal in the eighteenth century. NMM.

Types of shot used in the late seventeenth century. British Library.

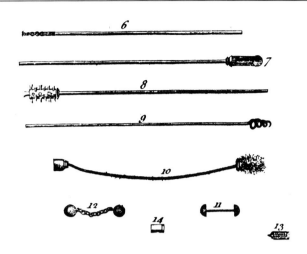

Gunner's implements and types of shot, 1769, from Falconer's Marine Dictionary.
  6. A worm, for removing a charge.
  7. A ladle.
  8. A sponge.
  9. Another type of worm.
  10. A flexible rammer and sponge.
  11. Bar shot.
  12. Chain shot.
  13. Grape shot.
  14. Canister shot.

The oldest and simplest form of shot used against the rigging was bar shot, or 'double-headed hammered shot'. Essentially this was dumb-bell-shaped, with a heavy part at each end and a narrower bar in the middle. There were many variations of this type: 'double-headed' sometimes meant a shot with a sphere at each end; 'hammered shot' had cylinders at each end, and 'bar shot' was simply a bar of iron with strips of wood bound to it at each end, to make it as thick as the gun's bore, and more inflammable. In the 1620s 'cross bar shot' was described as 'round shot with a bar of iron through it'.[17] In 1677 a distinction was made between 'hammered double-headed shot', which was presumably forged, and 'double-headed cast shot', which was evidently moulded. The latter type was only used by guns which had their calibre measured in pounds, so it is possible that it had been captured from the Dutch.[18] In 1815 'double-headed or bar shot' was described as 'a ball cut into two equal parts and joined together by a bar of iron'.[19] The length of shot also varied, from twice the calibre, to about six times the calibre, in extreme cases.[20]

Chain shot had a heavy ball or hemisphere at each end, which were joined by a length of chain. It had a greater spread than bar shot, and could do more damage to rigging. Though it is described in all the main nautical dictionaries, it does not appear on the lists of gunners' stores actually carried, so its use must have been rare in the British Navy, unless it was simply included in the category of 'double-headed shot'.

Langrel shot was also intended to damage the enemy's rigging. It consisted of 'bolts, nails, bars and other pieces of iron tied together, and forming a sort of cylinder, which corresponds to the bore of the cannon'.[21] According to Falconer, writing in 1769, it was 'never used in Royal ships, but very often by privateers and merchantmen'.[22] In apparent contradiction, the *Bedford* was listed in 1779 as carrying four rounds of langrel for each of her upper deck, quarterdeck and forecastle guns.[23] In 1625 the term evidently had a different meaning, as it was 'made like a shackle, and may be shortened when it is put in a piece, and flies out at length when it is shot out.'[24]

Star shot was a more sophisticated version of chain shot. It had four heads, linked together by chain, so that it would spread itself wider. There is no evidence that it was used by the British Navy.

Anti-personnel Shot

In principle, anti-personnel shot consisted of a large number of small balls, which would separate either on leaving the gun or on reaching the enemy deck, thus hitting a large number of men. There were two main types, grape shot, and case or canister shot.

Grape shot was 'a combination of balls . . . put into a thick canvas bag, and corded strongly together, so as to form a sort of cylinder, whose diameter is equal to that of the ball'.[25] It was in use in 1725, though it was allocated only to ships of the Third Rate and below. In the 1770s, three to seven rounds were issued per gun, with more for the quarterdeck and forecastle guns. It remained in common use in 1815.[26]

Case shot, also known as bace and burr, burrel, and canister shot, was probably older. In 1625 it was 'good to ply amongst men which stand naked, plying of their small shot'.[27] It differed from grape shot in that the balls were put inside a can, which shattered on impact. In 1655 the *Sovereign* was to be issued with 180 tin cases for its demi-culverins, and 30 for its sakers. In 1779 the *Bedford* had grape shot for all its guns, but about six rounds per gun of canister shot for just its upper deck, quarterdeck and forecastle guns.

Wads

In 1627 'waddings' were 'okum, old clouts or straw, put in after the powder and the bullet'.[28] According to Falconer in 1769, a wad was 'a quantity of old rope-yarns, hay and co, used to confine the shot or shell, together with its charge of powder, in the breech of a piece of artillery.' They were 'peculiarly necessary in naval engagements, because without thus being retained in its chamber, the shot would instantly roll out of the chace by the agitation of the vessel'.[29]

Wads were usually made up on board ship, and the gunner was issued with pieces of old rope and cable, known as junk, for this purpose. The *Sovereign* had 50cwt of junk in 1655, and a 74-gun ship of the 1770s was issued with 5 tons.[30] This was enough to provide one wad for every round, including grape and double-headed shot. In 1779 the policy was changed, and one-third was issued in wads, with the remaining two-thirds in the form of junk.[31]

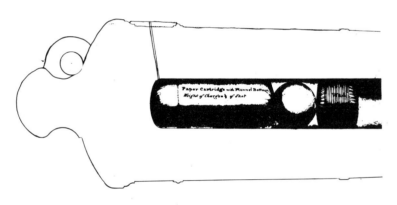

Part of a gun of 1796, showing the wad, ball, and cartridge in place.

Tompions

In 1627 a 'tomkin' was defined as 'a round piece of wood put into the piece's mouth and covered with tallow'.[32] According to Mainwaring's dictionary of 1625, it was 'put in there to keep out the rain and sea water from washing when the pieces lie without board'.[33] It did not change much over the years. Large numbers were issued: the *Sovereign* was to have 800 in 1655, for 95 guns; and a ship of the 1770s was allowed four per gun.[34] We can discount any idea that they were used as a substitute for wads, for there were not nearly enough to provide one for every shot, but they were clearly regarded as expendable. Presumably they decayed very quickly due to the effects of the water and it is therefore unlikely that they were decorated, like modern ones, with ships' crests and badges. The evidence of models suggests that their outer surfaces were either flat, or were turned to a rounded shape. In 1677 they were issued in only two sizes, great and small, which suggests that they were not intended to fit with any great accuracy.[35] By the 1770s they were made in different sizes for each calibre of gun.[36]

Other Stores

The gunner of a ship of war was responsible for a very important department, and he had a great variety of stores under his care. There were spares for almost everything, including axles, beds and trucks for the carriages, nails, baskets, and sheepskins to cover sponges. The gunner was in charge of the small arms of the ship, including muskets, pistols, bayonets, swords, axes, and all their sheaths, bandoliers, powder and shot. Under his supervision was the armourer, who might be called on to repair any metalwork on board the ship, whether associated with the guns or not. He needed a complete set of tools, including vices, hammers, braces and files, and in later years a camp forge was carried so that he could carry out repairs when a convenient shore could be found. On a 74-gun ship of the 1770s the total value of the gunner's stores was £7478, of which the guns accounted for about £3185.[37] This comprised about a sixth of the total cost of a fully equipped ship.

Chapter 26. Gun Tackle and Equipment

Gunports

The gunport, with its opening port lid, was one of the inventions which made the heavily-gunned sailing warship possible. The port itself was simply a rectangular hole in the hull, with one of the ship's frames forming each side, and horizontal timbers known as sills forming the top and bottom edges. It meant the heaviest guns could be carried on the lower deck, just above the waterline, thus lowering the centre of gravity, and allowing much more room for guns than if only the weather decks were used. The port lids could be opened for battle or for ventilation, and closed during heavy weather. The year 1500 has been given for the invention of the gunport, but this seems too clear cut, and has been much disputed.[1] It must have developed quite naturally from the loading ports which were often fitted to ships intended to carry awkward cargoes, such as timber. In any case, gunports were quite common on English ships by the second decade of the sixteenth century.

The gunport lid served three main purposes. On the lower deck it kept out the sea when the ship was heeling, or the waves threatened to enter the ports. On most ports, they helped to make

An early eighteenth century model, with a side-opening port in the wake of the shrouds. Author's photograph, courtesy of Science Museum.

the deck space habitable by keeping out water, wind and cold air. On all ports, they helped protect the gunners from return fire by the enemy. In the seventeenth century, port lids were fitted on all ports. After about 1700 they were no longer fitted to ports in the waist[2] and on the quarterdeck of two- and three-decked ships, where the deck was uncovered and not used as a living space. This in effect negated the third purpose of the lid, which was to protect the gunners.

The standard type of gunport lid was hinged at its top edge. This protected the gun from rain in action, and meant that in the event of damage it would close itself, which was its safest position. Other types of port lid were used in some cases. Those of a fireship were intended for ventilation rather than for guns, and were hinged at the bottom edge, so that when the fire burned through the rope, the port would fall open rather than closed. On many seventeenth and early eighteenth century ships the ports above the channels were made in two halves, and hinged at the sides. The shrouds tended to narrow above those ports, and could make it difficult to open a conventional lid. They were also used on the forward ports of some ships, where a normal lid might interfere with the bowsprit's rigging. Such ports became extinct as the channels were raised in the course of the eighteenth century.

The Construction of Port Lids

A typical port lid was made up of six or eight timbers. Three or four of these were placed side by side, and lay vertically on the completed port. On top of these were placed three or four rather thicker planks, which ran horizontally at right angles to the first layer of planks. Often the run of the outer planks was arranged to match the run of the ship's side timbers at that point. Sometimes thicker planks were used in line with the wales of the ship. On earlier ships the outside plank was larger than the inner, to give a better seal when the port was closed.

The lid invariably had two hinges. Each hinge was made in three parts. A long arm extended almost all the way down the outside surface of the lid, and was bolted to it. It was often made in a decorative shape, particularly on the big seventeenth century ships. The top part of the arm projected above the port, and had a spigot on its fore and after side. When the lid was fitted to the hull each spigot was placed inside a gudgeon, and the pin of the latter was put through a hole in the ship's side, just above the port, and clenched in position.

Several eyebolts were fitted to the port. Either one or two, according to the type of port, were fitted on the outside and attached to the tackle to raise the port. One or two more were fitted on the inside, to help hold it shut. By an order of 1778, a small scuttle with a sliding lid was to be cut into every alternate port, to give some degree of light and ventilation when it was not possible to open the whole port.[3] By a further order of 1782, it was made clear that a scuttle was not to be cut on the equivalent port on the opposite side of the ship, but on the next one along, so that the scuttles were staggered.[4] After 1789 all ports were to have a scuttle[5] and after 1809 small pieces of glass, known as 'illuminators', were also to be fitted to all ports.[6]

Port Tackle

The port lid was opened by means of port tackle. In the seventeenth century this consisted of a single rope fixed to a ringbolt in the centre of the port, just above its lower edge. This rope passed through a hole in the side of the ship, just above the gunport. It was led under the beams of the deck above, and fitted to a block. Through the block ran another rope called the tackle fall. This was rove through another block, which helped to give mechanical advantage when raising the port. In the eighteenth century a double tackle was used on many gunports. Two ropes now passed through the hull, and were attached to eyebolts fitted to the bottom part of the port hinges. The two ropes joined together inside the hull, and the port tackle was operated as before. The double tackle first began to appear on the lower ports of the largest ships around 1705. By the 1750s it was often fitted to the upper decks of ships of the line, and on the main decks of frigates, but it never completely replaced the single tackle on smaller ships.

Obviously the port tackle would have very little leverage on a closed port, and it only became efficient when it was about half open, so a bar was used to push the port open some way, and to raise it until the tackle became effective. In 1716 all tackle falls were of 2in rope. Port ropes for guns of 24 pounds and above were of $2\frac{1}{2}$in rope, and those of lesser guns were of 2in rope.[7] In the 1780s, port ropes were usually of 3in rope, and tackle falls of 2in.[8]

Breechings

It was said that a 32-pounder gun with a normal charge on a level platform would recoil 11ft.[9] There was not room for this on the crowded decks of a ship, especially since it could not be guaranteed there would be a level platform, thus the recoil had to be restrained. This was the purpose of the breeching. Each end of this thick piece of rope was fitted by means of an eye-splice to a ringbolt on the side of the ship, either side of the gun. The rope

Gunports on the Victory. *The separate pieces of timber from which they were constructed and the shape of the hinges can be clearly seen. The port tackle is not fitted here, but above the port in the background are the leather coverings over the holes where the tackle entered the hull.* Author's photograph, courtesy of HMS *Victory.*

Open gunports on the Victory, *showing the port tackle in use, and the ringbolts.* Author's photograph, courtesy of HMS *Victory.*

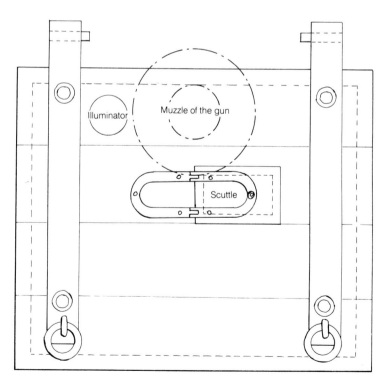

Part of the Victory's *stern. The outline of a hidden port, directly under the window, can just be discerned.* Author's photograph, courtesy of HMS *Victory*

A view of the gunport (from outboard), 1814, showing the illuminator and the scuttle. From a drawing in the PRO.

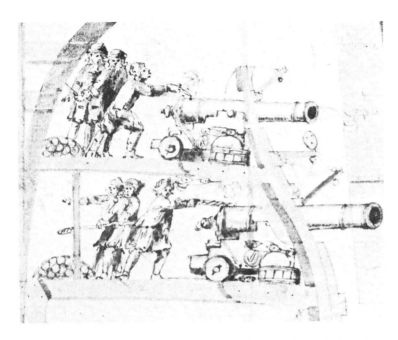

Guns in use, c1690. The shot appears to be stored under tarpaulins on the deck. A linstock is being used. The Earl of Pembroke.

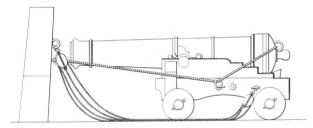

A gun run in, c1815, with the breech tackle at its full extent.

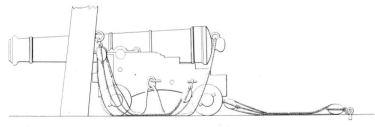

The same gun run out, with the train tackle attached to the rear of the carriage.

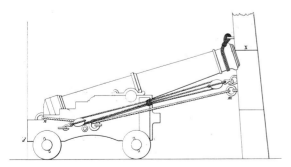

The gun stowed, showing how the muzzle lashing was used.

passed through eyebolts on each side of the gun, and was spliced to the button of the cascable. Blomefield pattern guns had rings on their cascables, and on these the rope was merely passed through the ring, so there was no need for splicing. Normally a breech rope was three times the length of the gun. Sometimes they stretched in use, and this created problems with carronade slides, for it allowed the bed to hit against the end of the slide, causing damage.[10]

In 1716 breech ropes were 6in in circumference for guns of 24 pounds or more, 5in for guns from 12 to 18 pounds, and 4in for 9- and 6-pounders.[11] They tended to become thicker over the years. In 1749 it was recommended that the breech ropes of 42- and 32-pounders should be increased by 1in in circumference, and that they should be long enough to let the guns run back to the hatch coamings, without touching them.[12] By the 1780s 7in ropes were used for 32- and 42-pounders, and $5\frac{1}{2}$in ropes for 12- and 18-pounders.[13]

Gun Tackle

A lower deck gun with its carriage and ammunition might weigh as much as 3 tons, and it often had to be moved out through its port up the deck of a heeling or rolling ship. Though 15 men were provided for this task in the eighteenth century, it could not be achieved by muscle power alone, and some tackle was needed. A gun tackle consisted of a rope fixed to a single block, passed through a double block, back through the single block, and through the double block again. A hook was fixed to each block. One of these was placed through an eyebolt in the side of the hull, just above the eyebolt of the breech rope, and the other was put through an eyebolt or ringbolt in the side of the gun carriage. Every gun had one tackle on each side, and together they were used to run the gun out. In 1716 tackles were of $2\frac{1}{2}$in rope for guns of 24 pounds or more, and 2in for smaller guns. The tackle had blocks of 8 or $6\frac{1}{2}$in.[14] In the 1780s the ropes were of 3in diameter for guns above 24 pounds, and 2in diameter for 9- or 6-pounders.[15]

Other Tackle

A train tackle was similar to a gun tackle, except that it was fixed between the gun and a ringbolt near the centre line of the ship. It was used to prevent the gun from running itself out when the ship was heeling. It is not clear when it was introduced. Seventeenth century ships do not appear to have been fitted with the requisite ringbolts along the deck, though the gun carriages had fittings at the rear.[16] Some such fitting was necessary to keep the gun in place when reloading, but how it was done during this period remains something of a mystery. Even in the mid-eighteenth century, when the central ringbolts were certainly in use, the train tackle was not issued separately. 'If you exercise the lee guns, and it blows fresh, you must keep one tackle hooked to the ringbolt on the deck, near the coamings, and the other tackle hooked in the ring in the train of the carriage. But if you exercise the windward guns, keep both tackles hooked to the ship's side, and the train of the carriage.'[17] By the 1780s three tackles were issued per gun. Presumably one was to be used as a train tackle if necessary.[18]

When a gun was out of use for some time, it was elevated to its

A carronade and its tackle, c1790. Science Museum.

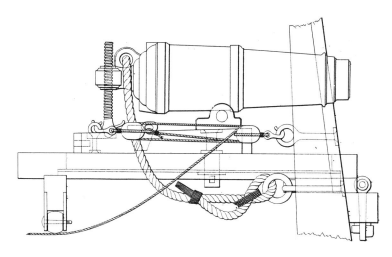

A carronade, c1815. The tackle had changed little by this time.

The guns of a three-decker, c1750. The gun on the gundeck is stowed out of use and its tackle is frapped. Those on the middle and upper decks are run out ready for firing, and the one on the quarterdeck is run in, for loading. NMM.

greatest extent by removing the quoin from under its breech. It was then run forward so that its muzzle rested just above the upper sill of the port, and it was lashed there by means of a muzzle lashing of 2in rope. The tackle was also 'frapped', that is, several turns of rope were taken round the breech ropes and the tackles on each side, and round the gun itself, to hold it in position.

Loading Implements

In the days before cartridges became common, a ladle with a long handle was used to put the powder into the gun. By 1625 it was recognised that this was 'not very convenient to be used in a hot fight at sea', and 'brass ladles upon stiff ropes', or cartridges, were recommended instead.[19] The ladle was now used mainly by the gunner and his crew, to make up cartridges in the filling rooms. Not many were needed for this, and in 1655 the *Sovereign* had only 30 for 95 guns; in 1780 four per deck were issued for the larger ships, and three for ships of 50 guns or less.[20] The ladle was different from the 'copper powder measure', of which two were issued for each type of gun. Presumably the latter were used when more accurate measurement was required. Ladles were fitted to long poles, which often had a sponge fitted at the other end. These were probably designed for use in routine cleaning of the gun – they must have been difficult to use in action.

Sponges were needed to clean the gun out after firing. There was always the danger that a fragment of burning cartridge would be left in the barrel, and this would cause the next charge to explode prematurely, which was very dangerous for the crew. Sponges attached to staves were no use, because there was not room to wield them between the muzzle of the gun and the closed gunport. Rammers were necessary to force the charge home, but again one attached to a wooden stave would be little help. The 'flexible rammer' was used to carry out both these functions, and it was the most useful of the gun crew's implements. It was a thick piece of rope, with a rammer head at one end, and a sponge at the other. In the 1660s enough of these were carried to allow the issue of one per gun, though it is not clear if they were made in different sizes to match the guns' calibres.[21] By the 1780s one was still issued per gun, in sizes to match each bore.[22]

The worm, or wadhook, was used to remove a charge without firing the gun. A few were issued for each deck. It was a long stave, with a spiral of iron at one end. Buckets of water were used to wet the sponge, and the budge barrel was used to collect any powder left on the decks after firing. From early times wooden cylinders known as cartouches were used to carry the cartridge to the gun, and protect it from accidental ignition. At least two were issued for each gun.

Training Implements

A gun had only a limited traverse from side to side, partly because of the narrowness of the port. It was not easy to take advantage of the available traverse with a conventional carriage, for the wheels operated in the wrong direction. The side tackles might have been of some use, but their effect was limited because of the positions of the ringbolts on the ship's sides. The crew was therefore expected to manoeuvre the gun by means of crows and handspikes. A crow was defined in 1815 as 'an iron lever ... furnished by a sharp point at one end, and two claws at the other ... to direct and manage the great guns by moving them into their ports, and levelling and pointing them to any particular object.' A handspike, or a 'gunner's hand crow lever' was 'shorter and flatter' than the handspikes used in stowing the hold and in a windlass. It was 'armed with iron claws, for the purpose of managing the artillery.'[23] In the 1780s 'crows of iron' were issued at the rate of one per gun, while 'hand crow levers' were 6ft long for guns of 18 pounds and above, and were issued at the rate of three to every two guns.[24] By an order of 1779 additional eyebolts were to be fitted between the ports to give extra leverage to the side tackles, when the gun was being trained. It is not clear to what extent this order was applied, or how long it lasted.[25]

Elevating and depressing the gun was somewhat easier because it could rotate on its trunnions. All guns were designed with their centre of gravity aft of the trunnions, so they tended to point upwards unless the breech was supported. A wedge known as a quoin was placed under the breech. Before 1725 it rested on the bed of the carriage and after this date on the stool bed. Quoins were also tapered on their sides, so that they could be turned round to lift the breech higher if necessary. Each had a handle at its wider end, to facilitate pulling it out. Two quoins were normally issued for each gun, and they could be used in conjunction to give maximum depression.

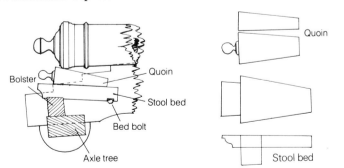

Details of the quoin and stool bed of a late eighteenth century gun, from a drawing in the National Maritime Museum.

Early Firing Systems

All guns had a touch hole drilled in the breech, where the powder was ignited. The captain of the gun was issued with a powder horn, from which he poured powder into the touch hole, to prime the gun. He also had a priming iron, or priming wire, which he used to prick the cartridge and release a little powder, so that the fire would spread easily to it. The charge was ignited simply by placing a lighted match to the touch hole. The match was held by a linstock, 'a short staff of wood about three feet long, upon one end of which is a piece of iron which divided into two, turning from one to another, having each a place to receive a match and a screw to keep it fast. The other end is shod with iron to stick it in the ground.'[26] In the mid-seventeenth century one was placed between every two guns, but by the 1760s they were only used on small ships. Sheets of lead, known as aprons, were tied across the touch holes of guns when they were loaded but not in use, to prevent accidental firing.

Locks

The practice of keeping lighted matches on deck had its obvious dangers, and in the 1750s the first attempt was made to replace them. Hollow tin tubes were placed in the touch holes for priming, and flint locks were issued for the exposed guns on the quarterdeck and forecastle, so that the match was unnecessary. The naval administration recognised that these changes could not be made overnight, and they were to be 'introduced by degrees'.[27] It seems that the innovations did not initially catch on and it was complained that the tin tubes, though they helped to stop the spread of powder about the deck, often flew out in action. Tubes and flintlocks had to be re-introduced in the late 1770s, and became standard.[28] The gun captain fired the gun by pulling on a lanyard attached to the lock, thus keeping himself out of the way of the gun's recoil. Locks were issued in two sizes; one for 9-pounders and above, and one for smaller guns.[29]

A gun lock. Although this example dates from 1819, it is probably similar to those in use from the 1770s. Author's photograph, courtesy of NMM.

Chapter 27. Magazines

Powder Storage

Powder was by far the most difficult of a ship's provisions to store. It was subject to two dangers, that of water which would render it useless, and that of fire which would detonate it and perhaps destroy the whole ship. Neither was easy to avoid on a ship in battle, but fire was obviously the most dangerous, so powder was always stored in the hold, away from enemy fire, rather than on the decks where it was less endangered by bilge water. For long- and medium-term storage, powder was kept in barrels which had hoops of copper or wood rather than iron, to prevent sparks.

There is not much information about the seventeenth century magazine. Certainly it was in the hold, probably forward. Deane's longitudinal section of a Third Rate of 1670 shows the forward part of the hold divided off into one or two parts, and also a compartment right aft.[1] The after part seems unlikely to have been a magazine, if only because it opened onto the steward's room, where provisions were issued, so it seems likely that the fore part was used. Beyond that we know little, for the draughtsmen of the age, Dummer, Coronelli and Phillips, show us very little below the main gundeck in their longitudinal drawings of ships. This suggests that there was nothing special about the magazine and that it was simply a part of the hold or the orlop deck set apart from the rest, and kept locked to prevent careless handling of powder.

By the early part of the eighteenth century it is clear that most ships had their magazine in the forward part of the hold, where powder was stored in large quantities in barrels. This had an advantage over the midships position, in that bilge water was expected to run down to the centre of the ship, and would not collect at either end. The after part of the hold was generally favoured by French designers, but the hull was rather narrow there, and provided less room for storage. The forward position for the magazine was to remain standard for British ships of the line and for most frigates, though a few had it amidships, perhaps to allow more space. Smaller vessels, such as sloops and gunboats, often had it aft, perhaps because the chase guns took up so much space on these vessels, or so the powder would be under the officers' cabins, where it could be more easily guarded in a ship which had no marines for such a task.

In the seventeenth, unlike the eighteenth century, the amount of powder carried increased substantially. The late eighteenth century powder barrel was designed to carry 90 pounds of powder. The number of shot carried tended to increase over the years, but the amount of power needed for a given number of guns stayed roughly the same throughout the century because the amount needed for each shot was reduced. Thus the amount of powder carried by a 100-gun ship increased from 330 barrels in 1655 to 390 in 1677, but remained steady in the eighteenth century at 480 in 1722, and 479 in 1801.[2]

Filling Rooms

Filling rooms were used to make up the cartridges ready for action, and to store some of them ready for use. Naturally they had to be close to the powder rooms, and so were usually to be found in the fore, lower part of the hull. Again details of seventeenth century practices are rather vague, and it is not known whether a permanent space was provided in the early part of that century. Possibly the gunner's store room, which was situated forward on the orlop deck above the powder room, served a dual purpose. The filling room had a clear identity by the early years of the eighteenth century, for it was mentioned in contracts for ships, and can be seen on some draughts.[3] It was placed well forward on the orlop deck, with a small hatch to connect it to the powder room below. It was often furnished with a few powder chests, which were placed between the deck beams so that they could hang down below the level of the deck. Presumably these could be used to secure ready-use cartridges. Sutherland wrote in 1711, 'It will be very requisite to have the filling room as low as the ship can possibly bear it, and have half it in the lower powder

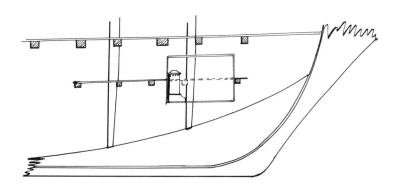

The magazine on a 40-gun ship of 1722. There is no palleting in the hold, and the lantern is still inside the filling room, which is 'hanging' below the orlop deck.

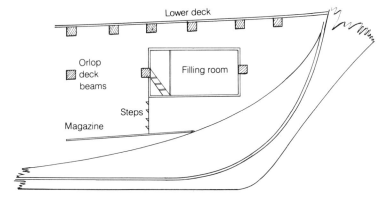

The Humber, an 80-gun ship of 1728. The magazine is clearly in the hold, and the powder room 'hanging' under the orlop deck.

room and half in the store room.'[4] In accordance with this, many draughts of the early eighteenth century show the filling room forward of the magazine on a separate deck of its own, above the floor but lower than the orlop.

In 1716 the Admiralty ordered that future powder rooms should be fitted like those tried experimentally on the *Royal Oak* and *Royal George*.[5] It is not clear how these differed from the previous pattern, but in the following years the filling room seems to have been fitted in the hold, just forward of the magazine. This was a safer position than just below the orlop. It was made possible by the fact that ships were increasing in size, and their bows tended to be fuller. Though this position was to be the most common for ships of the line until the end of the sailing ship era, some ships, up to the 1740s, still had the powder room on the deck below the orlop.[6] Frigates and smaller ships, however, often had it hanging between two decks.

By the early 1700s the filling room was being fitted with permanent furniture. That of the *Russell*, begun in 1707, was to have 'shelves and lockers and all other particulars as shall be necessary and convenient.'[7] By 1757 a filling room was to have 'proper shelves for stowing [filled cartridges] with shifting battens, drawers and co.'[8] In general a late eighteenth-century filling room had shelves round three of its sides, leaving one side clear for communication with the magazine. The filling room in the hold was still on a slightly higher level than the magazine, because the made-up cartridges needed rather more protection from bilge water than powder barrels, and because the deadwood of the hull tended to rise at that point. In most ships the filling room was not partitioned off from the magazine, so the barrels could be passed upwards, and the two rooms could share a common source of light.

Middle and After Magazines

On the largest ships, it soon became clear that a single source of powder was not enough to keep all the guns supplied in action. This was recognised in an order of 1716, by which 'ships of the first, second and third rates of 80 guns have a middle and after powder room, the third rates of 70 guns and fourth rates have an after powder room, and the fifth and sixth rates have a powder

chest in the most convenient place'[9], in addition to the main magazine, of course. The middle and after powder rooms were approximately square in plan, and rather smaller than the forward ones. Early ones, for example in 1708, were situated to one side, but by the 1730s they were usually placed on the centre line of the ship, away from the water running down the sides. Some early ones were on the orlop deck, but by the middle of the century they were usually in the hold, built up a little above the keelson to keep them clear of the bilge water.

Another type was the 'hanging' magazine. This had a deck which hung below the orlop, but its top was above that level, so that cartridges could be passed out. It had the advantage of keeping the powder well clear of the bilge water, but still below the gundeck where there was a danger of fire. It was fitted on some First Rates, for example the *Royal George* of 1756 and the *Victory* after her repair of 1803. It was most common on small two-deckers, such as 64s and those 74s which had a fine run aft. On such ships there was less space for a powder room below, because of the fineness of their lines. After powder rooms in frigates were usually placed in the hold, but they often had a structure built above the level of the orlop, for passing up cartridges.

After powder rooms were usually built round the lowest part of the mizzen mast, though that of the *Royal George* of 1756 was considerably forward of that position. The *Victory* had an after powder room as well as two hanging magazines, but most three-deckers merely had a middle powder room between the mainmast and the fore capstan, in addition to the fore and after rooms. Middle and after powder rooms were fitted with shelves on three sides, like filling rooms. They too had removeable battens to hold the cartridges in position.

Safety Devices

There is no clear evidence that those of the seventeenth century had any particular safety devices, beyond the fact that they were partitioned off from other parts of the hold, and entry was strictly controlled. By the 1690s the interior of the magazine was carefully prepared, and contracts demanded that the builder 'plaster with lime and hair, and line with slit deals all bulkheads and places where the powder comes'.[10]

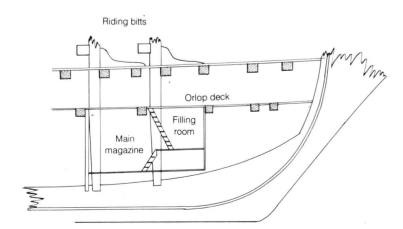

The Devonshire, *an 80-gun ship of 1742. Both the magazine and the filling room are in the hold, below the orlop deck. This remained the standard layout for large ships after this date.*

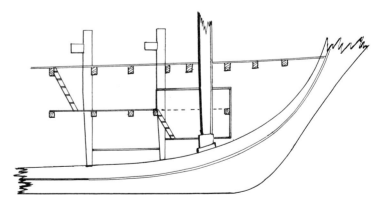

An early 32-gun frigate of 1762. Because the bows are sharper than those of a ship of the line, the filling room had to be higher, so that it could still hang below the orlop deck. This system continued to be used on frigates.

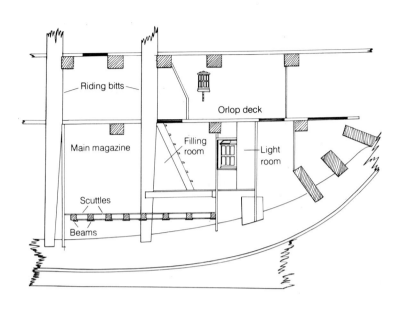

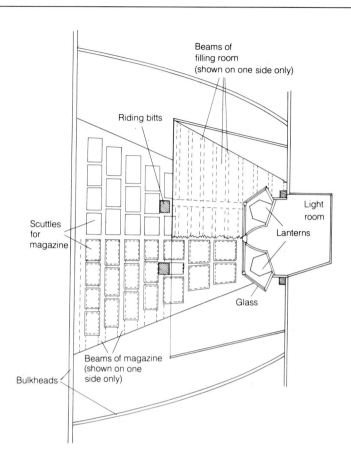

Details of the magazine of the 70-gun Dorsetshire, *of 1757. The system of palleting shown is fully developed. Any later changes were minor. Cross-section (above) and plan view (right).*

By the beginning of the next century there was much concern about powder rooms. One ship, the *Carlisle*, blew up in the Downs, and the accident was attributed to the fact that the yeoman of the powder room, who was responsible for the magazine under the direction of the gunner, was not employed in peacetime. The rating was immediately restored to all ships in sea pay.[11]

In 1702 Captain Peddar produced on invention 'having contrived a greater security for the preventing any miscarriages by candles in the powder rooms of His Majesty's ships'. It was tried out on the *Boyne* and *Chichester*, and the officers of Chatham and Sheerness dockyards reported very favourably on it. It was agreed that the 'charge of each ship will be very small, considering the great security.'[12] Unfortunately the reports do not tell us what the invention was, but it seems reasonable to assume that it was the 'light room' as this begins to appear on the draughts of ships soon afterwards. In effect the lantern which lit the powder rooms and the filling room was put into a separate compartment. There was a glass partition between the light room and the magazine, but this was carefully sealed, and there was no direct communication between the two rooms, for both had to be entered by separate hatches on the orlop deck. When the filling room and the magazine were put on nearly the same level, as began to happen before long, the light room illuminated both. A typical light room on a large ship was an irregular shaped compartment, built around the foremast. From it, on the after side, opened two compartments which contained lanterns. These were angled slightly outwards, to give a greater spread of light. The after and middle powder rooms also had their own light rooms, usually with a single lantern, and also entered by a completely separate hatch.

In 1715 there was concern that some powder, especially that kept in cartridges, was being damaged by damp. To remedy this it was decided to floor the powder room and the bread room with palleting, which was to be 'made in the nature of hatches, to lay loose, so as to be taken up without tearing them to pieces, whenever there is occasion to clean and water passages under them, to give air and search these parts.'[13]

In 1716 more reforms were carried out in the design of powder rooms, and all ships were to be fitted out in a similar manner to the *Royal George* and *Royal Oak*. The full extent of these changes is not clear, but it was decided that the after powder room should be placed closer to midships, and not close to the ship's side, as it had been earlier, and that 'no more of the fore powder room be lined with lime and hair than is absolutely necessary for the preservation and security of the powder only'. The officers of Chatham yard agreed that the powder rooms on the *Royal Oak* and *Royal George* were 'very useful and secure from fire and other accidents, either from the enemy, contiguousness of the store rooms or from any service that may occasionally be performed to the fore and after parts of the ship and mast, and likewise for the better airing, preserving, opening or repairing those parts of the ship.'[14]

In 1734, pallating was further improved. The officers of the dockyards were to consider 'whether by raising the present pallatings, or by laying a platform a small distance above that, and leave the space between vacant, or by only laying deep ledges upon the present pallating, and the whole charcoal filled in between them to inhale the damp, and a platform of dry deals laid over them.'[15] In fact both seem to have been done. Charcoal was used, and the filling room was put on a separate floor above the

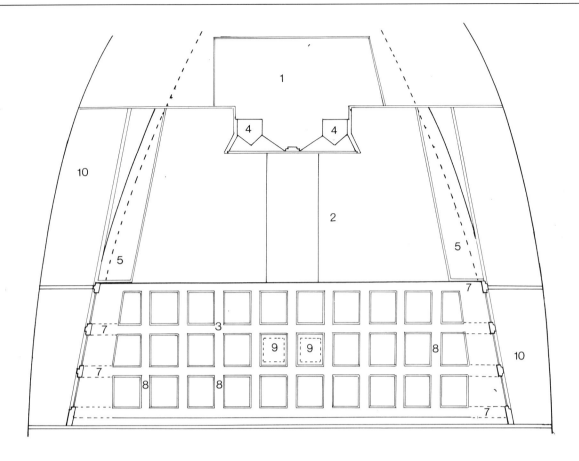

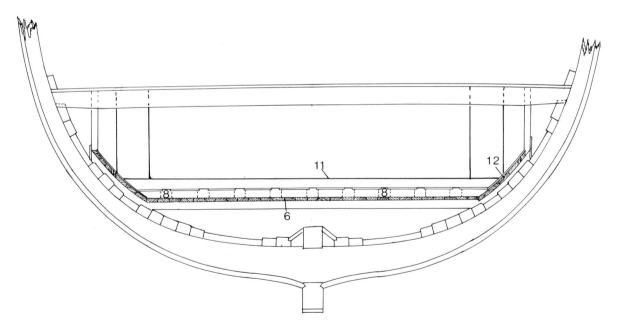

The magazine proposed for the Courageux *of 1797. Plan view (top), cross-section at after part of magazine, looking forward (bottom).*

1. *Light room.*
2. *Filling room.*
3. *Magazine.*
4. *Lights.*
5. *Filling room shelves.*
6. *Three-inch plank below the magazine pallating.*

7. *Cross beams of the pallating in the magazine.*
8. *Fore and aft beams.*
9. *Hatches below, for access to the hull for repairs.*
10. *The wings.*
11. *Deck of filling room.*
12. *Plank of magazine continued up sides to help keep water out.*

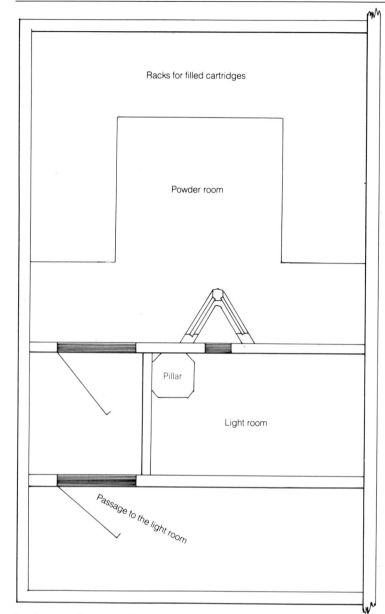

Powder room of a 74-gun ship, 1808.

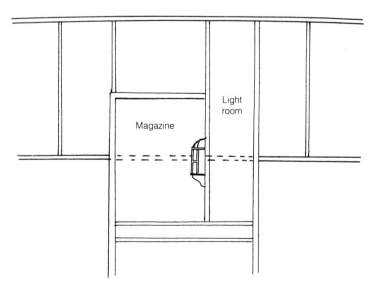

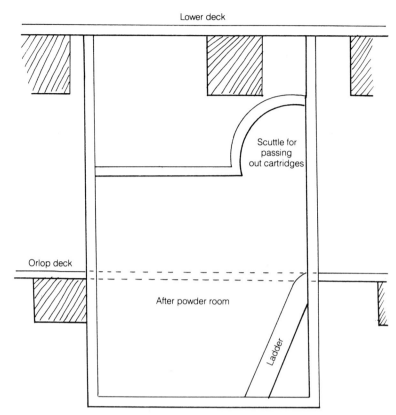

After powder room of a 64-gun ship, c1770. This type of hanging after powder room was common on the smaller two-deckers, and on ships with a fine run. On other ships the after powder room was in the hold.

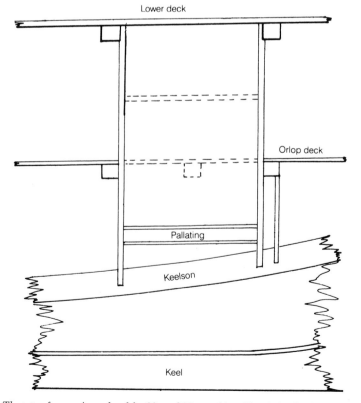

The type of magazine ordered for 32- and 28-gun ships, May 1781. Sections through the aft part of the powder room, left and above.

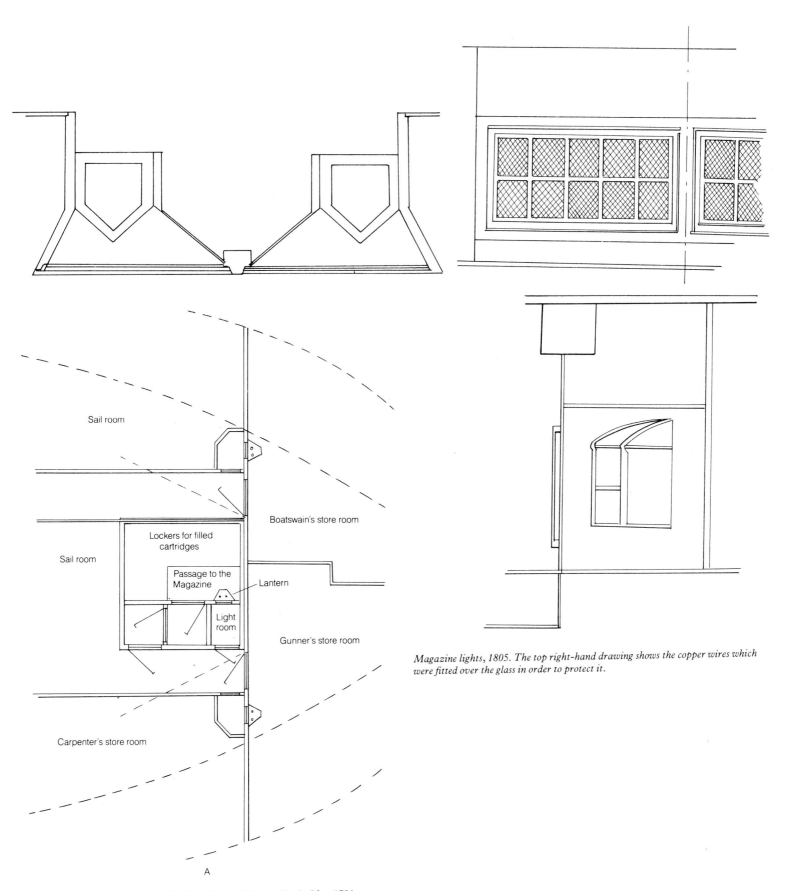

Sail room

Boatswain's store room

Lockers for filled
cartridges

Sail room

Passage to the
Magazine

Lantern

Light
room

Gunner's store room

Carpenter's store room

A

Plan of the type of magazine ordered for 32- and 28-gun ships in May 1781.

Magazine lights, 1805. The top right-hand drawing shows the copper wires which were fitted over the glass in order to protect it.

pallating. In 1738 it was ordered that the pallating flat in magazines be raised higher, in order to improve the preservation of the powder.[16]

The pallating flat can be seen on draughts from the mid-1740s, though this does not prove that it was not used earlier. In essence the pallating formed a floor for the magazine, intended to prevent the powder from seeping out, and to stop bilge water from entering. It was also arranged so that the pallating could be lifted to allow the inspection and repair of the hull underneath, for there was not always room for a man to crawl underneath. It was made up of a framework of thick pieces of timber, running fore and aft and athwartships. Each of the rectangles thus formed was closed by a scuttle fitted on top of it, in a recess cut round the edges. A solid deck was put underneath, to complete the seal. Because of the overlap between the scuttle and the timbers, there was presumably less risk of leakage than with normal planking. The space below the scuttle held the charcoal, which was intended to absorb damp. Normally the pallating flat ran some way forward of the powder room itself, and under the floor of the filling room. The filling room was raised a few inches above the pallating and its floor was constructed from conventional planking.

The method of lining the powder room was specified in more detail in the late eighteenth century. According to a contract of 1779, the builder was to 'part off filling rooms, plaster and single line the same on the outside, and plaster and double line the same within, the first with slit deal lining upon mortar as usual, and on that lining to bring a dry lining fastened with brads punched up and their heads puttied all round'.[17]

More improvements took place over the years. In 1780 it was decided to have 'a piece of plank let down square from the platform, to break in some degree the quantity of water that runs up the ship's side when she rolls above the said platform, with limbers that the violence of the water by being so suddenly obstructed may not blow the scuttles off the platform; and also to vent air in its return to the water course.'[18] In 1799, after the loss of the *Boyne* by an explosion, copper bolts were introduced to replace iron ones in many places in order to prevent sparks, and planking was continued some way up the sides of the magazine, to help keep the water out.[19] In the following year sheet copper was to be placed in other parts of the magazine, to help keep rats out.[20] In 1804 it was discovered that the hanging magazine of the 98-gun ship *Atlas* had been placed forward of the mizzen mast by

mistake, and it was ordered that it be moved aft, to its usual position on a 74-gun ship. All three-deckers were to be fitted this way in future.[21] In 1805 guards made from copper wire were to be placed round magazine lights, to protect the glass from accidental breakage. Despite these precautions ships continued to be lost, and in 1807, for example, the 74-gun *Ajax* was destroyed by fire and explosion.

Storage of Shot

Shot was much easier to stow than powder, the only problems being its comparatively great weight, and its tendency to rust. The latter was largely disregarded in the days before the carronade, for the windage of the gun was sufficient to allow for any inaccuracies in the size of the shot. Certainly from 1670, and probably much earlier, shot was kept amidships, forward and aft of the pump well, in the hold. This helped keep the centre of gravity low, and it also had the advantage that any rapid use of shot would not alter the trim of the ship. On the other hand it was exposed to water, and therefore to the danger of rust. The shot was stored in a locker which was a simple rectangular box, with an angled and hinged lid on top. There were two shot lockers and it appears that often each was divided vertically into several sections, to store different types and calibres of shot. By the middle of the eighteenth century a third locker was provided, in the hold just aft of the magazine.

In the seventeenth century there does not appear to have been any specific provision for the storage of ready-use shot about the decks. A drawing of about 1690 shows it kept in piles, and held together by a cloth or tarpaulin covering.[22] In the early years of the next century racks for round shot were placed around the sides of the ship, between the gunports. By an order of 1780 these were to be replaced by holes cut round the hatchway coamings.[23] Possibly the reason for this was to move weight away from the sides of the ship, in the belief that this would improve its stability and reduce the strain on the frame timbers.

It is not clear how other types of shot were stored. Certainly the round shot racks can have been of little use, but the use of other shot was rare enough for it to be treated separately, so for long-term storage it is probable that a part of one of the shot lockers was partitioned off.

PART VIII

Accommodation

Chapter 28. General Layout

Basic Requirements

A sailing warship, particularly one operated by such an active and aggressive force as the British Navy, had to fill many demanding roles. It had to carry a large number of guns, and consequently a large crew, within a very confined space. All its own stocks of spare parts had to be stored, as well as ammunition, and supplies for several hundred men, so that it could be independent of the shore for months at a time. Because wood could only be grown to limited sizes, it was difficult to build bigger ships without a great increase in expense, yet the demands put on ships by politicians and strategists increased radically over the years. Aboard a warship on active service, space was in extremely short supply, and every inch was put to full use, often doubling up for several purposes. Thus the gundeck served as the eating and sleeping area for several hundred men, as well as a platform for many tons of weaponry. The after cockpit was a berth for the midshipmen, as well as a primitive operating theatre in time of action. The captain's cabin was sacrosanct on French ships, but on British ones it housed several guns, and therefore had to be cleared of furniture in time of battle.

Principles of Design

Several factors influenced the allocation of space aboard ship. Of these, the most obvious was the large number of men carried. Comparsions with modern warships are perhaps a little too complex to be valid, but the *Victory*, for example, was comparable in length to a Second World War escort sloop, but carried about five times the crew. Likewise a sailing warship needed to carry about ten times the crew of a contemporary merchant ship of similar size.

The warship, of course, needed a large crew to operate the guns. Merchant ships were often armed, but they usually relied on deterrence, or the shattering effect of a first broadside, rather than the high rate of fire which British warships achieved in the late eighteenth century. Because of the continual need to improve this rate of fire, the number of men allocated to a gun of a given size tended to increase over the years. Thus a pair of 32-pounders had a crew of ten men in 1677, and 14 in 1800.[1] Ships of a given rate tended to increase in size, so that a First Rate of 100 guns was 1700 tons in 1682, and 2142 tons in 1765. But much of this increase was due to the need to accommodate a larger crew. The *Britannia* of 1682 had a crew of 784 men, at approximately 2.17 tons per man. The *Victory* when first launched in 1765, had a nominal crew of 850, at 2.52 tons per man. This small gain in space was largely swallowed up by the extra hold space needed by eighteenth century ships which were expected to spend far longer periods at sea, further from their bases.

Because the seamen's accommodation doubled up for other purposes, ship designers did not specifically take it into account, except in one very important respect. The space between the decks, though cramped, had to be large enough to allow men to move and work without extreme discomfort. Designers were never generous in this provision, and one eminent surgeon attributed the prevalence of lunacy among seamen to the fact that they continually knocked their heads on deck beams.[2] However, the actual space, between the top of the plank below and the bottom of the beam above, was never much less than 5ft 6in, for under this the seamen would have been unduly hampered in their work at the guns. This measurement did not vary greatly over the years, or from ship to ship.

This factor had a profound effect on the design of ships. It meant that a ship with a given number of decks would be a particular height above the water, irrespective of her length. It contributed greatly to the success of such ships as the 74-gun ship and the frigate, which were the optimum length for their number of gundecks. On the other hand 44-gun and 80-gun two-deckers were too high for their lengths and had very poor sailing qualities.

Despite the need to cram the maximum number of men aboard, considerable space had to be saved for the officers, according to rank. A petty officer was allowed 28in for his hammock, twice the allocation of space for a seaman. An admiral had several rooms to himself, and took up the space of about two hundred seamen. Though the contemporary class system meant that the difference in status between a senior officer and the common seaman was enormous, it is worth remembering that unlike the Army, which drew its officers from the highest social classes, and its soldiers from the lowest, the Navy had a strong middle class element. In general naval officers were less aristocratic than army officers, and

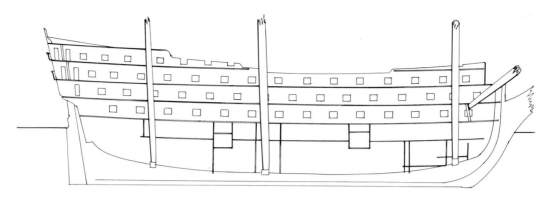

The Royal George *of 1756, which has a standard three-decker layout. It has two stern galleries, and three rows of windows. There were hanging magazines aft and midships, and a main magazine forward in the hold, three full decks of guns, a forecastle and quarterdeck, and an unarmed poop.*

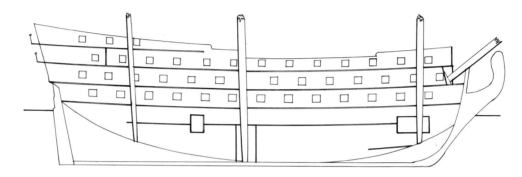

A small three-decker, the Humber *of 1708. It has three full decks, but no forecastle or poop, and only a lightly armed quarterdeck. This layout represents a transitional stage in the development of the 80-gun ship from a two-decker to a full three-decker.*

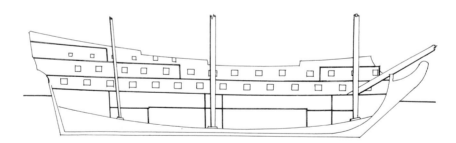

An early two-decker – a 70-gun ship from Deane's Doctrine *of 1670. It has two full decks of guns, a quarterdeck, forecastle, and poop, and a full orlop deck below the waterline. The height between the decks was not great, but it increased near the stern to make room for the officers' cabins.*

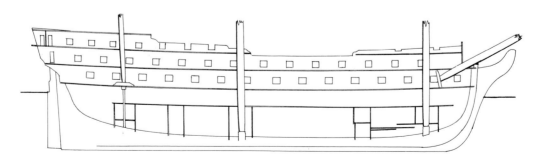

A 74-gun ship of the 1790s. In principle little had changed since 1670, though the ship was much larger. It has two rows of stern windows, and one gallery.

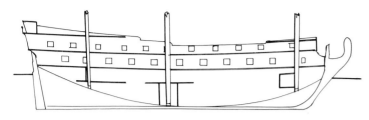

A small two-decker, the 40-gun Diamond *of 1722. As with the 80-gun ship, some re-arrangement was necessary to enable such a small ship to have two decks, so there were platforms in the hold instead of a continuous orlop. The poop was very small, and the quarterdeck and forecastle unarmed.*

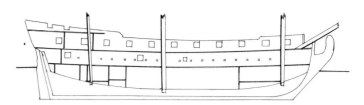

A 24-gun ship of 1740. In a sense this was a forerunner of the frigate, but because the lower deck had some gunports it had to be kept some distance above the waterline, thus raising the centre of gravity and increasing windage. Nevertheless the lower deck was still very low, and the guns could not have been used in a heavy sea, or when the ship was heeling to any extent. It has no forecastle and a small quarterdeck.

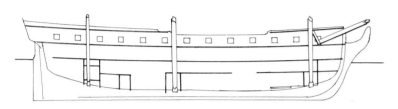

The 'true frigate' as developed in the 1750s, represented here by a ship of the 1790s. The ports on the lower deck have been abandoned, allowing the waterline to be a little lower. Like most Fifth Rates, this ship has three platforms in the hold, the midships one being used to stow the cables.

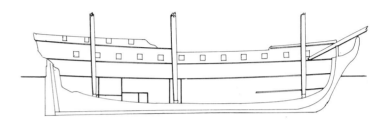

A Sixth Rate of 1775. Apart from being smaller, the main difference from the Fifth Rate's layout is that there is no platform amidships in the hold, and the cables are stowed on top of the barrels. This was typical of Sixth Rates.

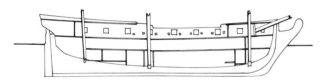

A late eighteenth-century ship-rigged sloop. It differs from the Sixth Rate in that it has no guns on the quarterdeck and forecastle, and the platforms in the hold are lower down, so that there is little room for stores under them. The lower deck is still not full length, and has taken on some of the characteristics of the orlop of a larger ship.

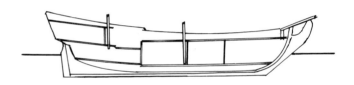

A royal yacht of about 1680. It has two decks running the full length of the ship, and a small cabin under the quarterdeck, but the decks are not continuous. The subdivision is quite complex for such a small vessel.

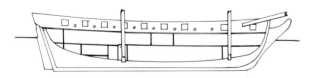

A brig of 1797. This has two decks, which are almost continuous, except for a slight step aft of the mainmast, to allow more headroom in the officers' cabins. The lower deck is well below the waterline, and there are no gunports on this level, perhaps to allow room for the galley.

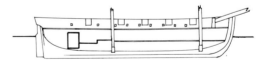

A brig-rigged gunboat of 1804. This also has two decks; the lower one does not run the full length of the vessel. The hold is very small, and such vessels could only make short voyages.

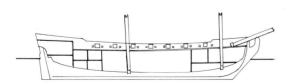

A 14-gun brig-rigged sloop of 1740. There is no lower deck in midships, and there is a type of 'hanging cabin' in the stern, for the captain. It is not clear whether the crew lived in the hold, or were crammed into the space forward; the former seems more likely.

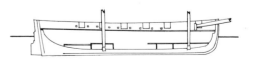

A small gunboat of 1797. There is no continuous lower deck and what there is is on several different levels. The upper deck is continuous.

seamen, while no more socially acceptable than soldiers, had great skill, and demanded some respect from their officers. They were never automatons like soldiers, and when relations between officers and men broke down around the end of the eighteenth century, the Navy was severely disrupted by a series of mutinies.

Lying in status between the seamen and the commissioned officers was a large block of warrant officers, of varying skills and social backgrounds. This group included surgeons, chaplains, and schoolmasters, men of some education; and boatswains, carpenters and gunners, who had risen through the ranks by years of hard experience. It also included masters' mates and midshipmen, who expected to become commissioned officers some day. The road to a commission was never completely closed to the common seaman, and some of the most famous commanders, including Admiral Benbow and Captain Cook, began as seamen. There was not a great gulf between officers and men, as in the Army, but a gradual increase in privileges which was linked with pay, rank and responsibility. The allocation of accommodation reflected this. Single cabins, of varying quality, were offered to nearly all the senior warrant officers, while the junior officers, and the petty officers, had slightly superior accommodation to that offered to the men.

Room not only had to be provided for every member of the ship's company to sleep and eat, but for their food and drink to be stowed. In the seventeenth century, when few ships operated far from home bases it was possible to get by with three or four months' provisions. By the late eighteenth century, war had spread to the West Indies, the Mediterranean and India. It was normal to have six months' supplies in these areas, though up to twelve months' worth of certain commodities were sometimes carried.

Another design problem of warships was that it was very difficult to keep the centre of gravity low. If the guns were to operate efficiently they had to be placed a certain minimum distance above the waterline, but their great weight tended to raise the centre of gravity. This, combined with the weight of the masts, sails, and rigging, many feet above the hull, meant there was a danger of capsize in a poorly designed ship. The only way to counteract this was to place weight as low as possible inside the hull. Iron and shingle ballast were placed on the floor of the ship, and above this there were several tiers of barrels, filled with food, drink, and other stores. The stowage of the hold required special skills. The ship had to be properly trimmed, but the different types of stores had to be accessible, incompatible goods apart, and items like rum and gunpowder, for different reasons, secure.

Deck Arrangements

The allocation of much of the space aboard ship was dictated by very compelling reasons. Stores, as we have seen, had to be kept in the hold. Gunpowder was also kept below decks to protect it from danger, though special measures had to be taken to keep it away from bilge water, and to ventilate it.

The lowest deck, the orlop, served a variety of purposes. On larger ships the cables were stowed there, so that they could drain into the bilges after they had been brought up. The cables alone took up a good deal of space, but room also had to be found for several storage areas. These housed items which were neither heavy, valuable, nor dangerous, such as spare rigging, timber for hull maintenance, and thousands of other articles which were

needed for emergencies, or for the everyday running of the ship. On the orlop they did not obstruct the guns, were safe from enemy fire, but were reasonably accessible. The sails were also stored on the orlop, usually down the centre line of the ship, between the cables, where they were safe from bilge water and water running down the side of the ship. They were close to the hatches through which they were brought on deck.

On ships of the line the orlop was also used for accommodation. Although it was dark and ill-ventilated, some regarded it as a privilege to sleep there, because it did not have any of the inconveniences of the gundeck. The space among the cable tiers was allocated to senior seamen, and others who, for various reasons, were to be separated from the rest of the crew. A berthing plan of 1796 shows this area was to be used by quartermasters, quarter gunners (all petty officers), midshipmen and ships' boys.[3]

Like all decks, the orlop accommodated some officers near the stern. It had the great advantage that cabins there did not have to be taken down in action. Two non-combatant officers, the surgeon and the purser, were berthed there, as were some midshipmen, the master's mates, and surgeon's mates. Several store rooms, for marines' and seamen's clothing, and for the officers' personal belongings, were also near the stern of the orlop. Right aft on this deck was the steward's room, where provisions were issued by the purser's assistant.

The orlop, however, only existed in its full form on two- and three-deckers. Frigates had a number of platforms in the hold, rather than a continuous deck, which were not used for accommodation except in the earliest ones. On smaller vessels, as always, some eccentric arrangements had to be made to fit everything in.

The bulk of the crew slept and ate on the lower deck on virtually all ships, and also on other decks on some types of vessel. For example, on a three-decker, there was also some room on the middle deck, so conditions were perhaps a little less cramped than on other ships. A 100-gun ship of the late eighteenth century, for instance, had a crew of about 850 men. A large two-decker 74 was almost as long, and had a crew of 650 men, but the 100-gun ship had two decks on which to house the men. Even if a substantial portion of the middle deck was taken up with cabins for the admiral and his staff, there must still have been room for many members of the crew, though no detailed figures are available to prove this.

The crews of two-deckers were probably the most cramped of all, except on the very smallest vessels which undertook only very short voyages. Most of a two-decker's crew was crammed into the lower gundeck. The remainder, the number of men required to operate two full decks of guns, as well as those on the quarterdeck and forecastle, had to share their accommodation with the guns. On frigates the crew and most of the officers lived on the lower deck, or berthing deck, just on the waterline. They received as much light and air from above as the crew of a ship of the line, through the gratings of the upper deck, but of course they got none through the sides of the hull, as a frigate had no gunports at this level. A frigate's crew benefited from the fact that they did not have to share their accommodation space with the guns. This would have been an advantage, especially at meal times, as there must have been room for the mess tables. On the other hand, they had to share the deck with all the officers except the captain.

Smaller vessels, such as brigs and schooners, had a single gundeck, with an accommodation deck below that. On this, space had to be found for all the store rooms, cabins, mess tables and hammocks, which would be distributed over several decks on a larger ship. The very smallest vessels, such as the gunboats of around 1800, sometimes only had a single weather deck, which was not even continuous throughout the vessel's length. Below that there was no real deck – men lived in the hold, with stores and ammunition. The short voyage range of these vessels made such conditions more bearable.

Apart from the 'standing' warrant officers (the boatswain, carpenter, gunner and cook) all the officers lived in the stern. A few had cabins on the orlop of the larger ships. Others had cabins in the gunroom, aft on the lower deck, while the gunroom itself was often used by the midshipmen. In a frigate the gunroom contained no guns, for it was aft on the lower deck, just above the waterline. It housed nearly all the officers, except the captain. There were no great advantages in the officers being accommodated in the after cockpit and the gunroom, except that they were segregated from the common seamen. Only tradition, and their proximity to their duties on the quarterdeck, kept the officers aft on the lower decks.

The other officers' cabins, fitted aft on the upper deck, the middle deck, the quarterdeck and even the poop, had more substantial advantages. They could be fitted with stern windows and sometimes galleries, so that they would be well ventilated and lit.

On frigates and sloops the captain lived aft on the upper deck, and had sole use of the only row of stern windows. On two-deckers the wardroom officers had one row of stern windows; the captain was accommodated directly above or below, and usually had a stern gallery as well as a row of windows. On three-deckers there was an extra row, for the admiral, and a few three-deckers even had a fourth row, built above the poop, for the master and first lieutenant. Though the actual distribution of the officers' cabins altered over the years, the captain was nearly always given the most comfortable part of the ship, unless he was overshadowed by an admiral. He was also given good access to the conning position on the quarterdeck. The watch-keeping officers, too, were placed near the steering position.

Apart from the absence of women, a sailing warship was a microcosm of contemporary society. The accommodation reflected this, the captain or admiral being allocated much more room than a seaman, just as on shore he would live in a mansion, rather than a cottage or a hovel. All ranks had to bear hardship while at sea. The perils of disease, drowning, and accident were equally distributed. Rewards in the form of pay, glory, and prize money were far less egalitarian, as was the distribution of space on board ship.

Chapter 29. The Layout of Cabins

The Early Period

In the early seventeenth century, seamen as well as officers were often allowed cabins. In the 1620s it was suggested that there should be 'built between every two ports hanging cabins to fold up to the decks for the lodging of men.'[1] Captain John Smith recommended that 'care should be had that there be not two comrades upon one watch, because they have more room in their cabins to rest.'[2] Referring to high-built ships, Boteler commented, 'the common seamen like it well enough, as coveting a store of cabins.'[3] In 1642 the *Victory* had at least 56 cabins, many of which were probably double, for a crew of 260 men.[4] Such cabins were probably not very comfortable. In 1659 a newly joined boy described it thus: 'That night I was put into a cabin to sleep, a thing much like some gentleman's dog kennel, for I was forced to creep in upon all fours, and when I was in and set upon my breech, I could not hold my head upright; but being very weary, I slept indifferently well.'[5]

Several factors combined to bring about the end of this system. Many captains regarded it as unhealthy, and prejudicial to discipline. 'These cabins are no better than nasty holes, which breed sickness, and in a fight they are very dangerous, as causing much spoil in their splinters; so that in all long voyages, especially to the southwards, the lodging of the common men in hammocks is far more wholesome and preferable.'[6] The use of cabins tended to restrict the circulation of air about the decks, and made it more difficult to inspect the hull for damage and rot. Furthermore, there was a gradual change in gunnery tactics. More guns were crammed into a given space, more men were allotted to handle them, and a much greater rate of fire was expected. All the changes tended to point against having cabins which cluttered up the deck. Finally, the hammock which was being used more and more provided a satisfactory and flexible alternative. There was a gradual reduction in cabins during the first three-quarters of the seventeenth century. A Third Rate of the 1660s was allowed eight cabins aft on the orlop, two aft on the gundeck, six on the roundhouse and two on the poop, though there was no rule preventing the captain having more constructed if he wished.[7] In 1673 the issue was tackled firmly and decisively.

The 1673 Establishment

In 1673 a new Admiralty commission, with King Charles II at its head, and Samuel Pepys as its secretary, became concerned about 'the very great charge and many other inconveniences rising by the unlimited number of cabins on ships'. These caused 'the pestering of the ship' and 'contracting of sickness', causing officers to 'neglect their duties and mis-spend their time in drinking and debauchery', and 'the danger of fire'. Furthermore, it was 'a charge not in any degree allowed in French or Dutch ships.'[8] For these reasons, the first regular establishment of cabins was drawn up, which stipulated that the captain could no longer allocate them to his favourites at his sole discretion. It defined the cabins on each rate of ship, and stipulated which officer was to occupy each. On three-deckers, which would usually carry an admiral and his staff, the commander still had some discretion, for there were 18 hanging cabins on the middle deck, to be used 'as the captain pleaseth to dispose of them', and six cabins which were unallocated. On smaller ships the captain had no such rights. A First or Second Rate had a total of 55 cabins. A Third

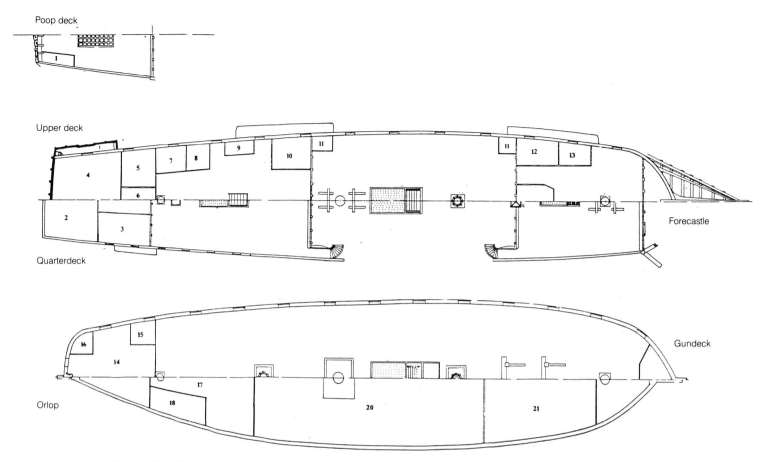

Poop deck

Upper deck

Quarterdeck

Forecastle

Gundeck

Orlop

A reconstruction of the cabins of a Third Rate, c1670, based on Deane's Doctrine, *and the 1673 establishment of cabins.*

1. Trumpeters.
2. Master starboard, lieutenant port.
3. Chief mate or 2nd lieutenant starboard, minister (chaplain) port.
4. Great cabin, for captain.
5. Captain's bedplace.
6. Captain's pantry.
7. Second mate and 'land' (marine?) officer.
8. Second mate and pilot.
9. Half cabins for servants.
10. Carpenter starboard, boatswain port.
11. Coxwain and midshipmen, under the gangways.

12. Cook starboard, boatswain's mate port.
13. Midshipman and carpenter's mate.
14. Gunroom.
15. Gunner and surgeon.
16. Standing cabins (probably for supernumerary officers).
17. Cockpit.
18. Purser's cabin and steward's store room and bedplace.
19. Surgeon's and captain's store rooms.
20. Cable tiers.
21. Boatswain's, carpenter's and gunner's store rooms.

Rate, without the large number of dependents carried on a flag-ship, had only 32. A Fourth Rate had 21, a Fifth Rate 12, and a Sixth Rate, 7. The size of the cabins was also stipulated. 'No standing cabins on the middle deck of the first and second rate ships to be more than six foot long fore and aft, and five foot upon the deck. No cabin in the steerage and forecastle of a third and fourth rate ship to be more than 5ft 9ins long, and four inches [sic] wide upon the upper deck. In the steerage of a fifth rate ship, no cabin to be more than 5ft 6ins long, and 4ft wide upon the upper deck.' No cabins were allocated to the lower ranks, except for the two or four 'upon the poop for trumpeters'. Judging by their appearance on models, they were more like dog kennels than cabins.

The principles of the 1673 establishment were largely re-inforced by the 1686 establishment,[9] so remained standard for nearly three-quarters of a century. A few piecemeal changes were made over the years, and some significant alterations were made

in 1745, but these concerned the structure of cabins rather than their layout. There was a completely new establishment in 1757, which took into account such factors as the development of the wardroom, the introduction of new types of ship, such as the 'true frigate', and the relocation of the captain's cabin on the upper deck rather than the quarterdeck. This establishment was recon-sidered in 1783, but no substantial changes were made, so (though there were some changes to individual cabins) it re-mained in force as the basis of cabin layout until well after 1815.

The Use of the Stern

Since classical times ships' officers had been housed in the stern. Captains, masters, and officers of the watch used the quarterdeck when on duty, so that they could supervise the steer-ing and cast an eye over the sails. It became recognised that the

Quarterdeck

The cabins of a First Rate, c1680, from a document in the Pepysian Library, Cambridge. Unfortunately there is no key to tell us what all the cabins are for, but the elaborate subdivision, and the use of the small cabins between the ports, especially on the middle deck can be seen.

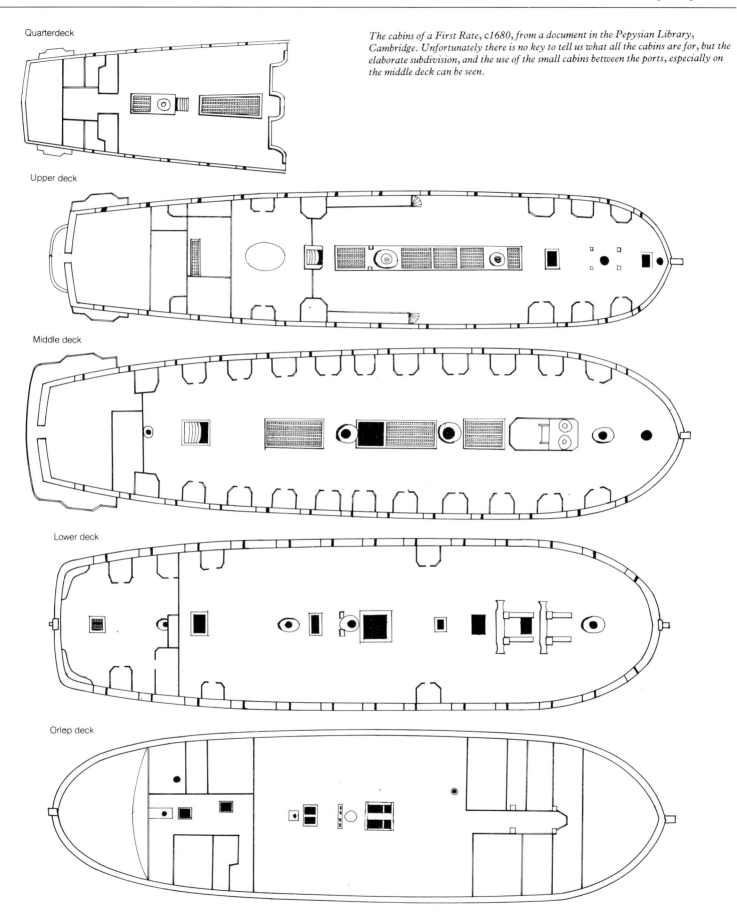

Upper deck

Middle deck

Lower deck

Orlop deck

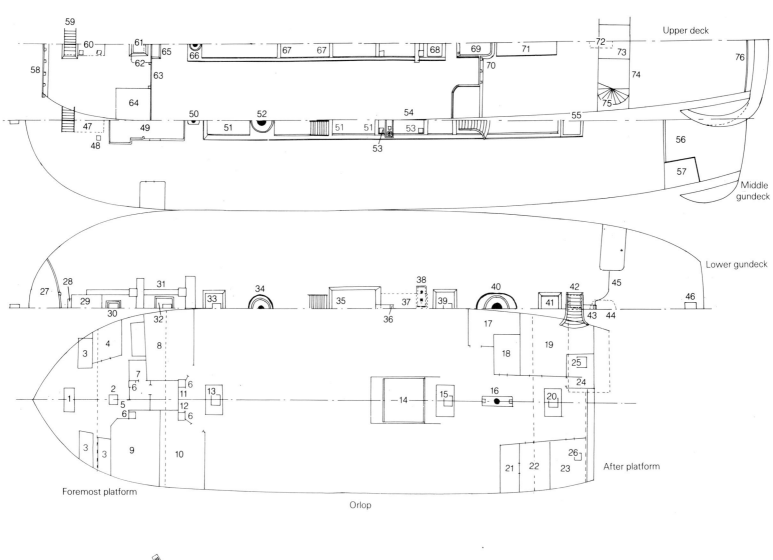

Upper deck

Middle
gundeck

Lower gundeck

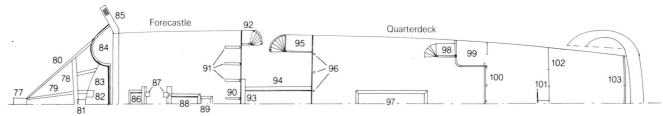

Foremost platform

Orlop

After platform

Forecastle

Quarterdeck

The deck arrangements of the Ossory, *a 90-gun ship of 1711. This is probably the earliest plan to show a steering wheel.*

Foremost platform
1. A scuttle to a convenience in the gunroom.
2. A scuttle to the powder room.
3. Powder chests.
4. The filling room.
5. Doorways to the powder room.
6. The fore and main bitts.
7. The light room.
8. The surgeon's store room.
9. The sail room.
10. The boatswain's store room.
11. A small convenience for the carpenter.
12. A small convenience for the boatswain.

Orlop
13. A hatch and scuttle to the hold.
14. The well and shot lockers.
15. A hatch and scuttle into the hold.
16. The step of the main capstan.

After platform
17. The captain's store room.
18. The surgeon's cabin.
19. The captain's or flag officer's store room.
20. A hatch and scuttle to the fish room.
21. The slop room.
22. The purser's cabin.
23. The steward's room.
24. Doorway to the after powder room.
25. Scuttle into the after powder room.
26. A scuttle into the fish room.
Note. The dotted lines at the platform are bulkheads in the hold for the powder rooms and fish room.

Lower gundeck
27. The manger.
28. Pillars in the step of the bowsprit.
29. The partners for the foremast.
30. A cap-scuttle to the powder room.
31. The main and fore bitts.
32. A hatch and scuttle to the foremost platform.
33. Fore hatch with a scuttle.
34. Step of the main jeer capstan.
35. The main hatch.
36. The viol block.
37. The partners for the mainmast.
38. The pumps.
39. A hatch to the shot lockers with a scuttle.
40. The partners for the main capstan.
41. A grating for light to the after platform.
42. The steward's room hatch.
43. The messenger block.
44. Partners for the mainmast.
45. Bulkhead of the gunroom.
46. Bread room hatch.

Middle gundeck
47. The partners for the foremast.
48. Fore jeer bitts.
49. The cook room.

50. Step of the small jeer capstan.
51. The long coaming carlines and head ledges.
52. Partners of the main jeer capstan.
53. The main topsail sheet and fore bitts.
54. The pumps.
55. A hatchway for the bulkhead to the gundeck.
56. Bulkhead to the wardroom.
57. Lieutenant's cabin.

Upper deck
58. The collar or beakhead beam.
59. A hatchway for a staircase to the middle deck.
60. The fore partners and the fore topsail sheet and jeer bitts.
61. Hole for the chimney.
62. A pantry for the boatswain.
63. The bulkhead to the forecastle.
64. The boatswain's cabin.
65. A companion for light to the cook room.
66. Partners for the small jeer capstan.
67. The long coaming carlines and head ledges.
68. Fore and main topsail chesstree blocks.
69. A hatchway to the upper deck.
70. Bulkheads of the lower coach.
71. A grating for air and light to the middle deck.
72. Partners for the mizzen mast.
73. A pantry.
74. Bulkhead of the great cabin.
75. Stairs to the quarterdeck, and cabin under them.
76. Screen bulkhead.

Forecastle and head on the flat
77. The lion.
78. The cross pieces.
79. The carlines.
80. The upper rail.
81. The stem.
82. Knighthead.
83. The bulkhead.
84. The house of easement.
85. The cathead.
86. A hatchway for a staircase to the upper deck.
87. Fore topmast sheet and jeer bitt with their cross pieces.
88. Grating.
89. Chimney stack.
90. Plank for the sides of the belfry.
91. Blocks for the running rigging.
92. Gangway and ladder to the upper deck.

Quarterdeck
93. Cross piece to the main topsail sheet or gallows bitts.
94. Carline from the quarterdeck to the gallows.
95. Gangway or ladder to the upper deck.
96. Breastwork stanchions.
97. A grating.
98. Gangway and ladder to the roundhouse.
99. Cabin.
100. Bulkhead of the upper coach.
101. The steering rowle.
102. Bulkhead of the captain's cabin.
103. Screen bulkhead.

stern was the area for the officers' accommodation, for like others on board ship, they needed to be close to their stations. Officers like the surgeon and the purser had no particular need to be on the quarterdeck, but their business took them to the after cockpit, where the purser issued his provisions and the surgeon had his dispensary and operating theatre. The more junior officers, the masters' mates and midshipmen, also spent time on the quarterdeck learning navigation, and the marine officers kept nearby the officers they were expected to protect in the event of mutiny. This grouping was reinforced by the tendency of men of like status to associate.

Either as a cause or a consequence of this, the stern became more comfortable and grandiose than other parts of the ship. It lent itself to the windows and galleries which dominated it for much of the period, and it was often given great quantities of carved decoration. The captain and admiral often had a stern walk, but the captain of a frigate had to make do with a row of windows, as did the wardroom officers on a late eighteenth-century ship of the line. Commissioned officers mostly had well aired and well lit cabins on the upper decks, but the more junior officers were placed below on the orlop. Nevertheless, all officers down to midshipman rank were berthed at the stern, except the standing warrant officers, the boatswain, carpenter and gunner, who had invariably risen from lower deck rank and accommodation.

Supernumeraries and Reformadoes

According to many accounts, the Restoration Navy was plagued with 'gentleman captains' – ex-Cavaliers and their offspring, who attained positions of command because they were owed favours by the King, but had no knowledge or experience of the sea. One of the many complaints against them was that they filled the ship with their own favourites. According to Pepys, they surrounded themselves with 'footmen and barbers and serving men'.[10] They also attracted other impecunious gentlemen, who were regarded as socially superior to seamen, but had no specific role or command. According to Pepys, 'These gentlemen reformadoes are good for nothing but to impoverish their captains and enslave them, for fear of their friends forcing them at the end of the voyage to give certificates of their deserving better than they deserve, and all the voyage long doing dishonour to the service.'[11]

These men took up many of the extra cabins on late seventeenth century ships, especially on three-deckers. They were largely abolished from smaller ships by the 1673 establishment, which ordered that 'each officer to whom any of the said cabins are therein so designed, may enjoy the same as of right belonging to his place, without being subject to be dispossessed thereof by his commander or other superior officer.'[12] Captains were restrained from building extra cabins, so on most ships there was no space for the reformadoes. First and Second Rates were an exception, for on these ships they were allowed to occupy the 'lower great cabin', aft on the middle deck, and the canvas cabins on the middle deck were for 'mates, pilots, pursers, midshipmen, and other officers as the captain pleaseth to dispose of them'. The lower great cabin was eventually to develop into the wardroom, as the supernumeraries gained in status and responsibility, and became watch-keeping lieutenants.

The Midshipmen's Berth

One of the great achievements of the Pepysian Admiralty was to abolish the useless men aboard ship, and to institute a standard system for training naval officers. The result was that the reformado was gradually replaced by the midshipman, who had a specific role in the ship, was fully subject to discipline, and was regarded as being under training to become a lieutenant and eventually a captain. His situation was ambiguous in many respects. He was not completely inexperienced when he became a midshipman, for according to Pepys' regulations he had to have served at least two years at sea; this was raised to four years at the beginning of the eighteenth century. He was not always from an educated background, for an older type of midshipman, raised from the lower deck, continued to exist alongside the newer type of naval cadet. Though the midshipman was often very young, he was also expected to bear a certain amount of responsibility, taking charge of a party of seamen or one of the ship's boats, for example. Nor could he be certain of reaching commissioned rank. Far more midshipmen were appointed than would ever be needed to fill all the vacancies for lieutenants, so it was not unknown for there to be middle-aged midshipmen.[13]

The midshipman was given the lowest form of officers' accommodation, on the airless, lightless orlop deck. For most of the eighteenth century the midshipmen were berthed in the after cockpit, in the space left between the cabins and store rooms. They slung their hammocks there, or in the cable tier, along with some of the petty officers. Near the end of the century midshipmen's berths were built on ships of the line, one on each side of the ship, just forward of the store rooms on the orlop. On frigates they were positioned forward of the rows of officers' cabins on the lower deck. The midshipmen's berth was shared with the master's mates, who had often been promoted from midshipman rank and were working towards a commission, and the surgeon's mates, who were qualified in their profession, and therefore considered to have officer status.

The Gunroom

The space aft on the lowest gundeck, or the berthing deck on frigates, was known as the gunroom. As a living space, it had both advantages and disadvantages. On two- and three-deckers it was above the waterline, and could be ventilated in good weather by opening gunports, both at the sides and at the stern. On the other hand, it was too close to the waterline to be fitted with windows and galleries. It could be partitioned off, and usually was in the early part of the eighteenth century. The orders of 1757 specifically forbade this and demanded that the gundeck be kept clear.[14] Space in the gunroom was restricted by the fact that the tiller moved under the deck above. Only areas outside the sector of the tiller could be used for setting up cabins or for slinging hammocks.

Like the after cockpit, the gunroom was used for officers of rather ambivalent status. Originally, as its name implies, it was used by the gunner. 'No officer, but his captain, is accommodated like him; he challengeth the gunroom as his hereditary estate, where he struts about like any crow in the gutter.'[15] In practice this meant that he had a small cabin for himself in one of the after corners, and the rest of the area was used by his mates and his crew. This custom orginated in the days when gunners were rare and highly skilled, and had to be attracted by good pay and conditions.

The gunner's hold over the gunroom tended to decline over the years. By the late seventeenth century it had four cabins, one at each corner. In 1673 one of these was allocated to the gunner, and the others to the surgeon and two of his mates. Later the surgeon and his mates moved below, to be near the dispensary and operating theatre, and the gunroom cabins were taken over by other officers of middling status; and junior lieutenants, the lieutenants of marines, the chaplain, and the pilot (if one was carried permanently).

At some point in the early eighteenth century, the gunner's crew was displaced from the gunroom, and had to make do with finding space among their fellow seamen, or at best in the cable tier. Their place was taken by the growing class of boys training to become midshipmen. They went under various titles: captain's servants, volunteers per order, king's letter boys, and volunteers first class. They were of sufficient social status to be apart from the other ship's boys and because they were all young, had to be kept away from the desires of the older men. On most ships they probably only used the gunroom as a mess, for it would have been difficult to sling hammocks there. They appear to have slept in the cable tiers. In later years the gunroom also served as a schoolroom, and an office. On a 74-gun ship of 1812 it is described thus, by a chaplain who had his cabin there: 'opposite to me, the junior lieutenant possessed the larboard transom cabin. Right and left were the sail-cloth cabins of the captain's clerk, the pilot, and the two lieutenants of marines. Between us, from the stern to the mizzen mast, a table was fixed, at which the clerk's assistants, ship's boys learning to read and write, etc., etc., were employed during the day.'[16] These tables, known as school tables, had been established by an order of 1702.[17]

On frigates, the gunroom was rather different. As the ship had no poop, and no full orlop, there were only two decks, and the upper deck was taken up by the quarterdeck and forecastle. Because the space under the quarterdeck was used for the captain's cabin, only the lower deck was available for the accommodation of the crew, and nearly all the officers. The first generation of frigates, built during the Seven Years War, had purser's and surgeon's cabins on the after platform, as on a ship of the line, but this practice soon ceased, and by 1775 these had been moved up to the lower deck. The gunroom retained its historic name, though there were no guns on that deck, and the only connection it had with the gunner, was that he was one of several officers berthed in that area. This type of gunroom had more in common with the wardroom of a ship of the line, except that it was almost on the waterline. This meant that it had no natural light, but had the advantage that cabins did not have to be cleared away in action. The gunroom itself does not seem to have been partitioned off from the rest of the deck, though a canvas screen or curtains may have been used for this purpose.

Specialist Warrant Officers

The specialist warrant officers fell into two main categories: those who were regarded as having a social status which entitled them to walk the quarterdeck along with the lieutenants, and those without this status. The master was one of the former group, but he was a special case, for in some respects he had more privileges and responsibility than the lieutenants, who were his nominal superiors. In addition, the first group included those officers who had qualifications in professions which were equally useful on land and on sea: the surgeon, purser, chaplain and sometimes the schoolmaster. The second group consisted of men who had risen from the rank of common seamen. It included the boatswain, gunner, carpenter and cook.

In 1673 the surgeon was berthed in one of the cabins in the gunroom. By the early years of the eighteenth century he had moved to a cabin on the orlop, where his accommodation was to remain. The purser was always placed on the orlop, where he could be close to the store rooms, and the steward's room. The chaplain was not highly regarded on some ships. The 1673 establishment allocated him a cabin on Third Rates and above, 'afore the roundhouse ... on the larboard side', but there was no provision for him on smaller ships, a situation which sometimes led to conflict.[18] Likewise there was no specific space allotted for him on the deck plans of frigates drawn up in 1775, perhaps because it was not expected that a chaplain would serve on such a small ship. In the early nineteenth century, the rise of the Evangelical movement made the government pay more attention to the chaplain's role, thus his status tended to rise. An order of 1805 stipulated that he was to take over the old gunner's cabin in the gunroom of a ship of the line, but his status on smaller ships was still indeterminate.[19]

The boatswain and carpenter were regarded as having equal status, and were usually berthed in similar accommodation. In the seventeenth century they were placed by the bulkhead of the forecastle. This was confirmed by the orders of 1757, but in the early nineteenth century this area was largely occupied by the sick berth, so they were moved down to the orlop, where they were given cabins forward, near their store rooms. In small ships they lived, like all the other officers and men, on the lower deck. In 1728 it was decided that they needed cabins to prepare their accounts, and the dockyards were ordered to 'build two small cabins next the side, between the decks, joining them to the lieutenants and masters cabins, for the surgeon and gunner, two in the midships, next the side, for the boatswain and carpenter.'[20] This remained the practice with the new frigates of the 1750s, except that the boatswain's and carpenter's cabins were eventually moved aft to join the others.

The cook remained under the forecastle, where he was near his galley. The gunner of a ship of the line remained, as we have seen, in the gunroom until the early nineteenth century when he was displaced by the chaplain, and thereafter was housed forward on the orlop deck, near one of the sail rooms, and close to the carpenter and boatswain.

The Development of the Wardroom

From the 1670s onwards there arose a group of officers of approximately equal status, ranked just under the captain. In the early seventeenth century there had been only one lieutenant on a ship, as an understudy for the captain. By the early eighteenth century there were three on large ships, and more were to be added, so that Third Rates had four or five by the middle of the century, and First Rates had up to nine by the end of the century.[21] The marines became more established as part of the ship's complement, and after 1755 they were administered by the Admiralty rather than the Army. By the middle of the eighteenth century a Third Rate had three marine officers and these, like

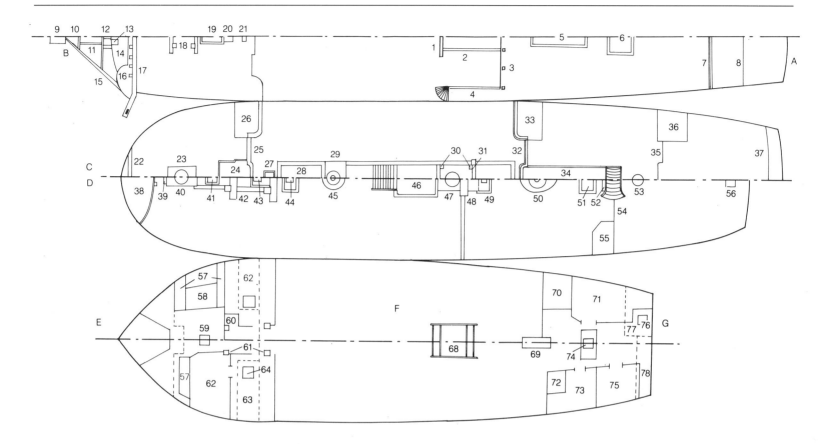

The decks of the Resolution *of 1708.*

A. The quarterdeck
1. Cross piece to the main topmast sheet or gallows bitts.
2. The carling from the quarterdeck to the gallows.
3. The breast works stanchions.
4. The gangway and ladder to the upper deck.
5. A grating.
6. A hatchway for the bell ladder to the upper deck.
7. The bulkhead to the roundhouse.
8. A lieutenant's cabin.

B. The forecastle and head on the flat
9. The lion.
10. The cross pieces.
11. The carlings.
12. The stem.
13. The knighthead.
14. The bulkhead.
15. The upper rail.
16. The house of easement.
17. The cathead.
18. The fore topsail sheet and jeer bitts. with their cross pieces.
19. A grating.
20. The chimney hole.
21. A hole for the steam of the furnace.

C. Upper deck
22. The bulkhead or collar beam.
23. The partners for the foremast.
24. The cook room.
25. The bulkhead of the forecastle.
26. The carpenter's cabin.
27. A scuttle.
28. The long coaming, carlings and head ledges.
29. The partners for the jeet capstan.
30. The main topsail sheet and jeer bitts.
31. The cross piece to the main jeer bitts.
32. The bulkhead of the steerage.
33. A lieutenant's cabin.
34. A grating.
35. The bulkhead of the great cabin.
36. the captain's dressing room.
37. The screen bulkhead.

D. Gundeck
38. The manger.
39. The pillars or step of the bowsprit.
40. The partners of the foremast.
41. A scuttle to the powder room.
42. The main jeet bitts and their spars and cross pieces.
43. A hatch with a scuttle to the foremost platform.

44. The fore hatch with a scuttle.
45. The step for the jeer capstan.
46. The main hatch.
47. The partners for the main mast.
48. The pumps.
49. A hatch with a scuttle to the shot locker.
50. The partners for the main capstan.
51. A grating for light and air to the cockpit.
52. Steward room hatch.
53. The partners for the mizzen mast.
54. The bulkhead of the gunroom.
55. A lieutenant's cabin.
56. The bread room scuttle.

E. Foremost platform
57. Powder chests.
58. The filling room.
59. A scuttle to the powder room.
60. The light room.
61. The fore and main bitts.
62. The sailroom.
63. The boatswain's store room.
64. A scuttle into the boatswain's lower store room.
65. The carpenter's store room.
66. A scuttle into the carpenter's lower store room.
67. Doorways to the powder room.

F. Orlop
68. The well and shot lockers.
69. The step of the main capstan.

G. After platform
70. The surgeon's cabin.
71. The captain's store room.
72. The slop room.
73. The purser's cabin.
74. A hatch and scuttle into the fish room.
75. The steward's room.
76. A scuttle into the after powder room.
77. A doorway to the after powder room.
78. Platform abaft the bulkhead.

Note. The dashed lines are bulkheads in the hold for the powder room, fish room, and carpenter's and boatswain's lower store rooms.

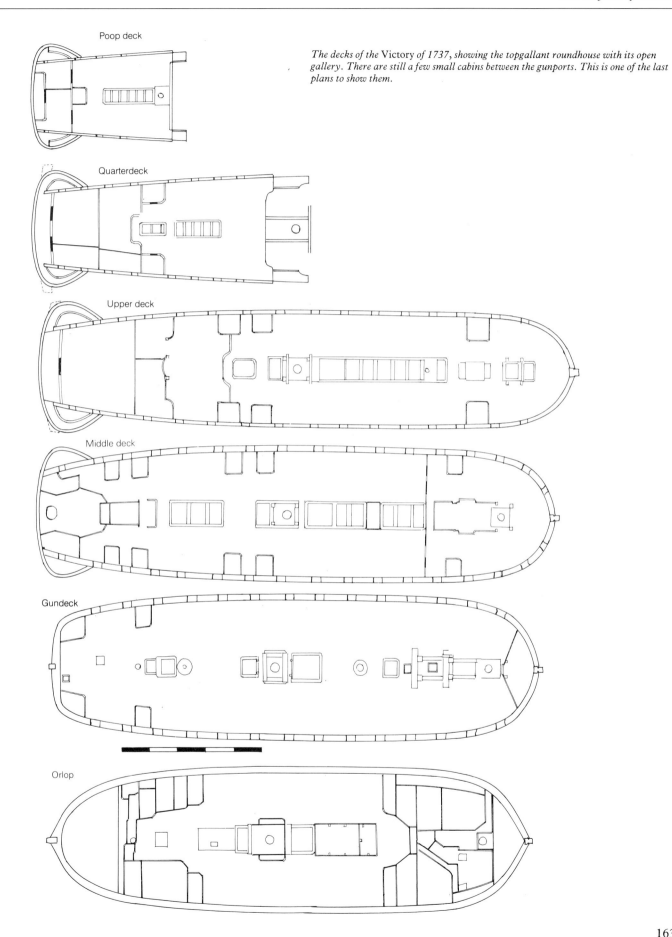

Poop deck

Quarterdeck

Upper deck

Middle deck

Gundeck

Orlop

The decks of the Victory of 1737, showing the topgallant roundhouse with its open gallery. There are still a few small cabins between the gunports. This is one of the last plans to show them.

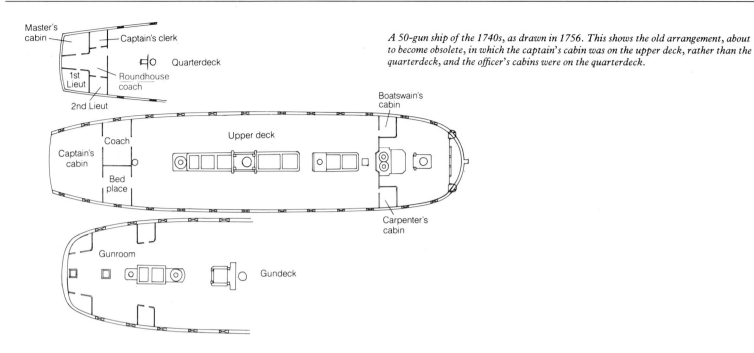

A 50-gun ship of the 1740s, as drawn in 1756. This shows the old arrangement, about to become obsolete, in which the captain's cabin was on the upper deck, rather than the quarterdeck, and the officer's cabins were on the quarterdeck.

Master's cabin

Captain's clerk

Quarterdeck

1st Lieut

Roundhouse coach

2nd Lieut

Captain's cabin

Coach

Upper deck

Boatswain's cabin

Bed place

Carpenter's cabin

Gunroom

Gundeck

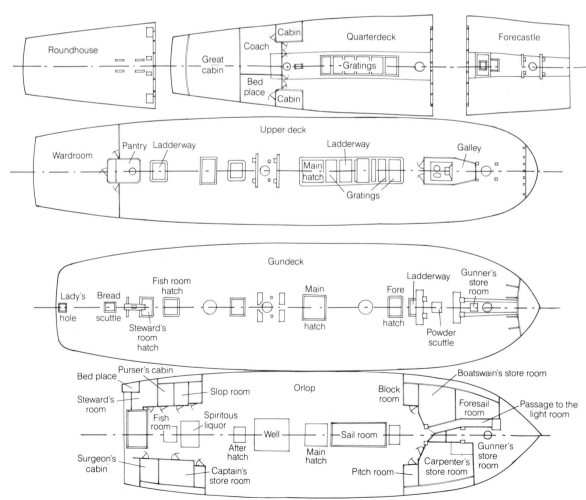

Roundhouse

Great cabin

Coach

Cabin

Quarterdeck

Forecastle

Bed place

Cabin

Gratings

Wardroom

Pantry

Ladderway

Upper deck

Ladderway

Galley

Main hatch

Gratings

Gundeck

Lady's hole

Bread scuttle

Fish room hatch

Steward's room hatch

Main hatch

Fore hatch

Ladderway

Powder scuttle

Gunner's store room

Bed place

Purser's cabin

Slop room

Orlop

Block room

Boatswain's store room

Steward's room

Fish room

Spiritous liquor

After hatch

Well

Sail room

Main hatch

Foresail room

Passage to the light room

Surgeon's cabin

Captain's store room

Pitch room

Carpenter's store room

Gunner's store room

The standard arrangement of a 74-gun ship, from the 1750s onwards.

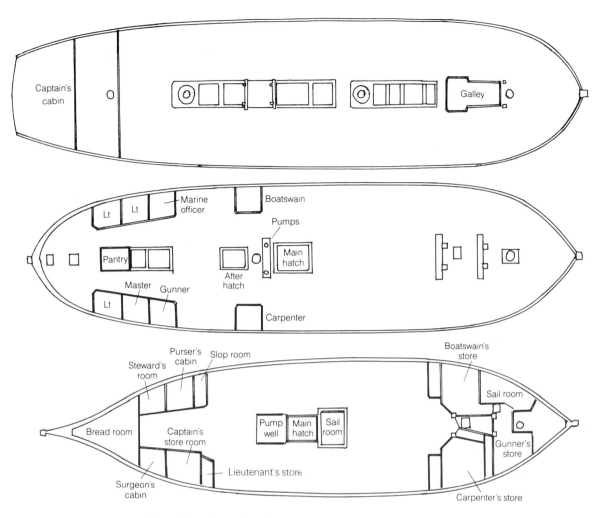

An early frigate of 1762. The purser and surgeon still have their cabins on the orlop.

naval lieutenants, held the King's commission. The highest rank-ing warrant officers included the master, surgeon, pursuer and chaplain. The master had always had high status, as the most competent seaman and navigator on board the ship. The other officers usually had a good general education, and middle class manners, which entitled them to some respect. The surgeon, however, was the only member of his department who had full parity with the commissioned officers. His mates, who might be equally well qualified in medicine, remained below in the cockpit with the more junior officers.

This group of junior commissioned officers and senior warrant officers began to mess together around the beginning of the eight-eenth century. On a ship of the line, the area they used for meals and recreation was aft on the upper deck, or on the quarterdeck. It was at least one deck above the gunroom, and thus well above the waterline. This meant that it could be well lit and ventilated. It usually had a row of stern windows, though rarely a stern gallery, and two quarter galleries.

There are two contradictory theories about the origin of the wardroom. One suggests that it was originally a room in which valuables taken from prizes could be stored, the other, that it was a room for the watch officers. A store room for valuables would have to be in the bowels of the ship, and a room for watch officers would have to be on deck, or at least close to the steering position,

so the evidence tends to suggest the latter theory is correct. The first known appearance of the wardroom is on the Phillips print of the 1690s, where it is described as being for the use of 'volunteers and land officers' (ie the marine officers).[22] It was aft on the middle deck, was well furnished, and had its own stern gallery, making it vastly superior to the gunroom below. Though it was well below deck level, it was close to the whipstaff. This was to re-main the standard position for the wardroom on three-decked ships.

It was in the same position according to an order of 1703, which decreed that the marine officers were to be allowed half the wardroom on a three-decked ship, half the steerage on a two-decker Third Rate, and on Fourth Rates 'a convenient part of the steerage to be divided by canvas'.[23] This seems to imply that the wardroom was only used on three-deckers at that time. It appears again on a set of deck plans of ships of around 1710.[24] On a three-decker 90-gun ship it is aft on the middle deck, close to the lieutenant's cabins. On a three-decker 80-gun ship it is in a simi-lar position, with the lieutenants and the captain of marines accommodated nearby and on a two-decker 70-gun ship it is not specifically mentioned, though there was a space on the quarter-deck which could have served as a wardroom. This area, known as the roundhouse, continued to be used for marine officers' cabins for many years, and is also shown on a drawing of an old

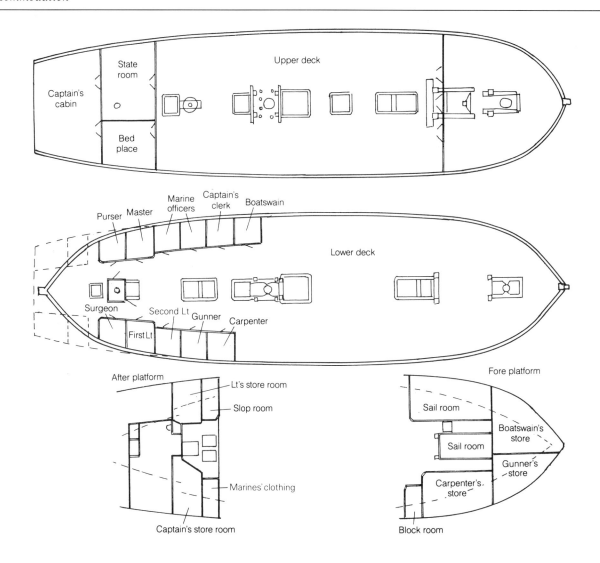

A 28-gun frigate of 1775. All the officers' cabins are now on the lower deck, except for the captain's.

50-gun ship in 1756. There was room between the cabins for a communal space for their inhabitants.[25]

However, by 1756 the wardroom had a clearly recognisable position on other two-deckers. Following the orders of 1745, it had taken over the old site of the captain's cabin, on the upper deck under the quarterdeck, for reasons which will be examined later. It was to remain there until the first quarter of the nineteenth century.

The wardroom also provided cabins for some of the officers entitled to use it for eating and recreation. Up to eight cabins could be constructed along its sides, though most of these were of a rather temporary nature, and had to be taken down for action, or even in the daytime. The most desirable cabins were furthest aft, for they had stern windows of their own. One of these was for the first lieutenant, and it also enclosed the door to one of the quarter galleries, which was therefore reserved for the sole use of that officer. The corresponding cabin on the other side was smaller, and there was a passage beside it to allow the other officers access to the remaining quarter gallery, which was allocated to the master. Both these cabins had the substantial advantage

that they contained no guns, which as well as providing more space, meant that they sometimes became permanent, and did not need to be taken down for action. Not all the wardroom officers could sleep in the wardroom itself; chaplains and junior lieutenants slept in the gunroom, and surgeons and pursers in the after cockpit.

Smaller Ships and Vessels

By the late eighteenth century there were many smaller vessels such as cutters, schooners, and brigs, which had only a single enclosed deck, which often did not even run the entire length of the vessel. On these ships the officers were still grouped near the stern. The complement of officers varied considerably according to the size of the ship, which might be commanded by lieutenants, or even warrant officers. The commander invariably had a larger cabin than the others, and smaller cabins were usually grouped around it.

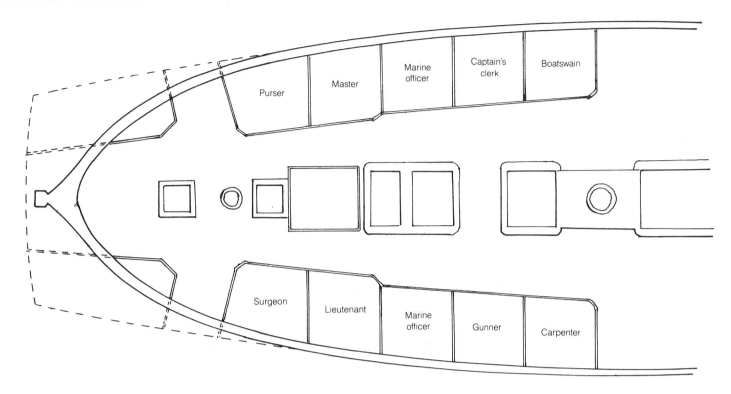

The cabins of a 20-gun ship arranged according to the orders of 1776. The layout on other frigates was similar, but the bigger ones had more lieutenants. The areas aft shown by the dashed lines are probably bread rooms. No cabin was to be more than 6ft in any direction.

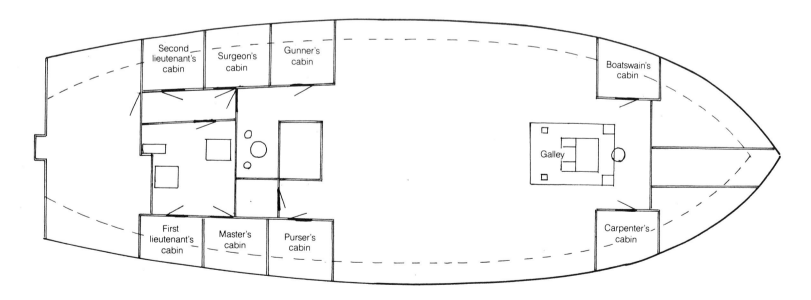

The cabins of an early nineteenth century Sixth Rate. A second lieutenant had just been added to the complement of such ships, and this plan was intended to show how his cabin was to be fitted in.

The Royal William *of 1719, showing four rows of stern windows, indicating the presence of a topgallant roundhouse. It has not yet acquired a gallery, as had the* Victory *of 1737. Author's photograph, courtesy of NMM.*

The Topgallant Roundhouse

During the first half of the eighteenth century the small cabins of the trumpeters on the poops of large three-deckers tended to increase in size, so that by the 1720s they had become full cabins. The first stage of this process can be seen on a three-decker of the 1690s, on which the separate cabins have merged and acquired some decoration.[26] Another model, perhaps of the First Rate *Britannia* as repaired in 1700, shows a slightly larger structure, while on the *Royal William* of 1719 the cabin is fully developed, with stern windows cut through the taffrail.[27] The topgallant roundhouse was included in the 1719 establishment of dimensions, for First Rates only. By this stage it had clearly become too grand for the trumpeters. It was divided into two and used by the master and the first lieutenant.

The topgallant roundhouse, or poop-royal, reached its peak on the *Victory* of 1737, where it was fitted with open stern galleries. Even at the time, Ackworth, the Surveyor of the Navy, disapproved of this, and wrote in 1740 'This post will bring an order to fit the *Victory* [of 1737] for Sir John Norris; he has promised to take the ship as she is, but complains much of her height abaft, treble balconies and co, which I was much surprised to hear of; our ships were too heavy, too loose and too high without these additional encumbrances, which I am sure cannot add beauty, but must be in every respect disagreeable.'[28] The *Victory* went down with all hands in 1744, and much of the blame was attributed to her high topsides. The topgallant roundhouse was omitted from the 1745 establishment of dimensions and it was not to be heard of again.

Chapter 30. Captains and Admirals

Traditional Accommodation

The disparity between the captain's accommodation and that of his officers was as great as that between officers and seamen. On a seventeenth-century king's ship, the captain was often the sole representative of the upper classes, except for his lieutenant, the military officers, and perhaps some of his servants, who were totally dependent on him for their positions. Gentlemen captains were given prominence in the latter part of the seventeenth century, but they had existed for a long time previously. Socially they regarded themselves as infinitely superior to the technicians who ran the ship, and they expected accommodation to match. This attitude was coming under fire by the end of the seventeenth century, by which time a captain was expected to have a reasonable knowledge of seamanship, but he still maintained the right to the biggest and best cabin in the ship. In the late eighteenth century his claim tended to be reinforced by the more utilitarian argument that the commanding officer was often expected to maintain his authority for months or years on end without reference to higher authority, and to do this he needed to be segregated from other men, and to have, in the relative spaciousness of the great cabin, a retreat from the stresses of command.

The captain, of course, lived in the stern. Until the second quarter of the eighteenth century his cabin was on the upper deck. This was well above the water level, so that he was able to have stern windows, galleries and quarter galleries. Until the late seventeenth century he was often the only officer to enjoy these amenities, for the stern at the level of the quarterdeck was usually planked up solid, with only very small windows. Moreover, the deck was very narrow on the quarterdeck because of the great tumblehome of the sides. The position on the upper deck was far more desirable. The cabin above, known as the roundhouse, was given to the master, who later shared it with one or more lieutenants.

The early accommodation of a seventeenth century captain is described by Boteler. The cabin itself was known as the great cabin, which was 'the retiring place for the captain, and where he sleeps and eats.'[1] Forward of that, before the bulkhead of the great cabin, was the steerage, where the helmsman operated the whipstaff. A change was taking place by the 1630s. 'Of late, in His Majesty's ships of the first and second rank, they have (for state sake) lately framed a fair and pleasant room over the steerage, wherein the captain usually eats, and this they call the coach; for no other reason, as I think, but because it resembles a land coach without wheels.'[2] It is unclear from this statement whether reference was being made to a separate cabin, built on the quarterdeck, or merely a raising of the 'roof' above the steerage, to give the captain more headroom. This form of coach was rather short-lived, and disappeared in the 1650s, so there are few pictures and models which show it clearly. Those that do tend to suggest that it was not a separate compartment. It seems to have begun at the break of the quarterdeck, and extended a few feet above it, with windows and carvings. It did not extend the whole width of the ship, for a gangway was left on each side to allow men to pass back and forth rather than having to climb over it. It did not reach as far back as the mizzen mast, so it cannot have protected the

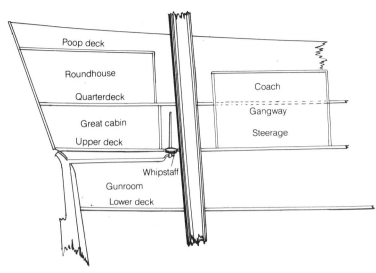

Possible arrangement of the stern cabins, c1630.

A vestige of the old arrangement of the coach can be seen in this model of a 100-gun ship, c1670. A small gangway running along each side of the cabin meant the coach could be built higher without interrupting the work on deck.

helmsman, though it must have restricted his view even further. It meant the quarterdeck itself could be a little lower, but it made it very difficult to fit guns in that area, which is probably why it became obsolete after about twenty years. A relic of it can be seen on a model of about 1670, on which the fore part of the quarterdeck is raised, with a passage leading past it on each side, much lower than the deck in the middle.[3]

However, the terms steerage and coach remained in use for many years. They became synonymous, and described the area in front of the great cabin, still used as a dining room by the most senior officer on board. On a two-decker it was still close to the whipstaff until the invention of the wheel, so the term steerage had more relevance than it did on a three-decker.

Three-deckers

The first three-decker was the *Prince* of 1610, but she did not have a fully armed upper deck, unlike her successor, the *Sovereign of the Seas* of 1637. Other ships followed in the 1650s,

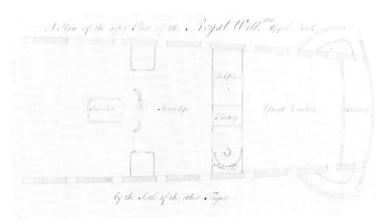

The admiral's apartments on the Royal William *of 1719. British Library.*

'60s and '70s, until by the mid-1680s there were about 20 three-deckers in the fleet. Such ships usually carried an admiral. Though there were more three-deckers than admirals by 1680, not all ships were available at once, and those that were, usually served as flagships.

On a three-decker the best cabin was on the upper deck, above the middle and lower decks. This was higher than a two-decker's upper deck but tumblehome had not narrowed the hull too much at this point. It was fitted with quarter galleries, and was much more suitable for stern galleries than the upper deck of a two-decker, as it was higher above the waterline. This cabin was therefore appropriated for the senior officer on board, in this case the admiral. As on a two-decker, it was known as the great cabin, and the space forward of it, used as a dining room, the steerage.

This left two more stern cabins, one above on the quarterdeck and one below on the middle deck. The middle deck cabin had some desirable features, having stern windows and quarter galleries, but it was far from the weather deck, though close to the whipstaff. Therefore it was initially given to reformadoes and supernumeraries, and was later to develop into the wardroom. This left the quarterdeck cabin for the captain. It was rather a small cabin and had no stern windows or quarter galleries. Its size was further restricted because the area forward of it was used for other officers – second captains, masters, lieutenants and mates. By the end of the century, however, it had gained windows and galleries. The pattern of a three-decker's after cabin arrangement was established very early, by 1673 at the latest. It was to remain the same for more than a century and a half, with the gunroom on the lower deck, the wardroom on the middle deck, the admiral on the upper deck, and the captain on the quarterdeck. Two-deckers, on the other hand, were to undergo a radical change in the course of the eighteenth century.

The Change in Position of the Captain's Cabin

By the early eighteenth century the position of the captain's cabin on a two-decker, aft on the upper deck, had begun to lose

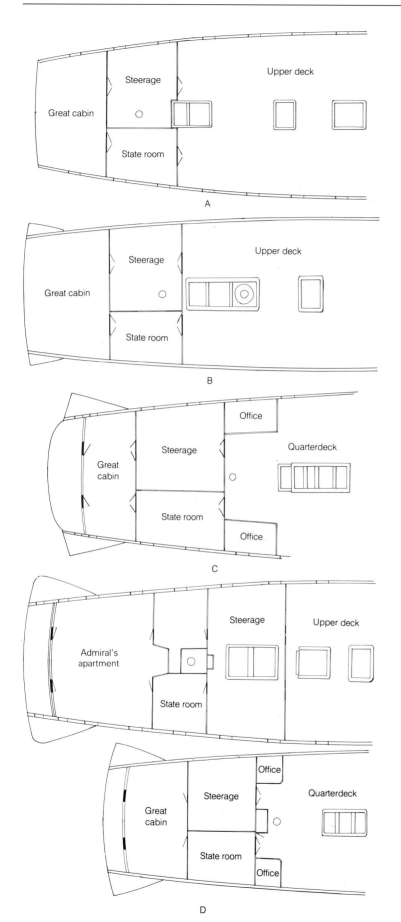

The interior of a captain's cabin in the mid-eighteenth century. It shows a gun and the hanging compass. Though, in this case the window is hinged and opened outwards, the sash window, which slid up and down, seems to have been much more common. NMM.

The arrangement of captains' and admirals' cabins, as established by orders of 1784.
A. Andromache, *32 guns.*
B. Gladiator, *44 guns.*
C. Edgar, *74 guns.*
D. Britannia, *100 guns (showing both the captain's and admiral's accommodation).*

some of its attractions. It was no longer close to the steering position, which had moved from the upper deck to the quarterdeck upon the introduction of the wheel. By the 1730s the practicality of the open stern galleries on the upper deck was being seriously questioned, for it was found that they were too near the waterline to be safe in a following sea. There was a general move to abolish them, and replace them with galleries on the quarterdeck. By the 1690s quarter galleries were permitted on the quarterdeck. There was a general reduction in tumblehome at this level, so that the quarterdeck cabin was not much narrower than the one on the upper deck. A cabin on the quarterdeck could be well-ventilated and lit, because a companion on the poop deck above could be fitted with glass panels, and opened in good weather. It also allowed the captain a view of the sails, without leaving his cabin. It would not be surprising if, from about 1710 onwards, captains coveted this cabin.

However, this upward movement does not appear to have been officially recognised until 1745. Early in that year a group of flag officers and captains recommended that the great cabins on 60- and 70-gun ships change places with the accommodation for other officers which was on the quarterdeck.[4] This was confirmed a few months later by the committee which drew up the 1745 establishment of dimensions. This proposed 'that captains' cabins on ships of 60- and 70-guns be upon the quarterdeck', while 'the captains' cabins of 50-gun ships and downwards be under the quarterdeck'.[5] In 1757 the latter proposal was amended, with an order that 'ships of 50 guns built by the establishment of 1745, or of dimensions equal thereto, to be fitted with a great cabin, bedplace and coach for the captain upon the quarterdeck.'[6] The arrangements on older ships were to remain the same, and 'such of the ships of 50 guns as are of inferior dimensions, or may be fitted already with a great cabin, bedplace and coach for the captain under the quarterdeck, they are to be continued so', even though the new policy of fitting a double main capstan would have restricted the room for such a cabin, and 'the foremost bulkhead of the coach is to be disposed of at such a distance abaft it as to give sufficient room for the sweep of the bars thereof.'[7]

On the smallest two-deckers, of 40 and 44 guns, the great cabins remained on the upper deck. There was little choice, for they did not normally have a poop deck, though they sometimes had very small cabins built on the quarterdeck for the master and lieutenant. By the orders of 1745, these were no longer to be fitted, and the captain's cabins were to be built clear of the capstan bars, as on the older 50-gun ships. In this respect the 40-gun ships were similar to the new frigates, which were already being built.

Frigates and Smaller Ships

On a frigate, the captain was the only officer to live any distance above the waterline. He had quarter galleries and stern windows, but he was too close to the waterline to have an open stern gallery. The length of his cabin was restricted, like that of a 40-gun ship of the 1750s, by the need to fit the capstan just forward of it. However, after the first generation of frigates the capstan was fitted on the upper deck and the quarterdeck. Thus the part of the capstan on the upper deck was mainly used for coiling the messenger round, while the part on the quarterdeck was where the bars were normally fitted, so space had to be left between the

capstan and the foremost bulkhead of the cabin. This meant that the cabin terminated just forward of the mizzen mast. On smaller vessels, the captain was accommodated below the waterline like all the other members of the ship's company, though he was usually given the aftermost cabin in the vessel.

Flagships and Private Ships

In some cases a three-decker did not carry an admiral. This of course meant there was extra space for the other officers, who could move to the next best cabin. Thus the admiral's cabin on the upper deck would be taken over by the captain, and the captain's former cabin on the quarterdeck would be shared by the master and the first lieutenant, leaving extra room in the wardroom.

Conversely, many two-deckers carried admirals, especially in peacetime, or on minor stations. In this case, the admiral took over the captain's cabin and the captain moved below to the wardroom, where he was given a cabin twice the size of a normal one, with access to stern windows and with a quarter gallery of its own. Two or more officers, depending on the number of admiral's staff, were thus displaced from the wardroom. The most junior officers would eventually find themselves slinging a hammock in the wardroom itself, or finding extra space in the gun room.

Subdivisions of Cabins

The arrangement of the captain's cabin became established in the course of the eighteenth century, initially according to custom. One thwartships bulkhead separated the great cabin proper from the rest of the accommodation. The remaining part was divided in two by a fore and aft bulkhead. The larger part, known as the steerage, served as a lobby and office accommodation and the smaller part was set aside for the captain's sleeping quarters, or 'bedplace'.

The admiral's cabin was of course larger. It usually had two internal athwartships bulkheads. Again the great cabin was aftermost and largest. It had access to the stern galleries and windows. Either the middle or the foremost part was used for the dining cabin, while the remaining section was further divided. In some cases a pantry was set in the middle of the whole structure. The sleeping cabin was partitioned off by a fore and aft bulkhead, and the remaining space served as a lobby. In the first half of the eighteenth century, when a spiral staircase was fitted on three-deckers, its lower end rested in the lobby of the admiral's cabin.

Dependants and Assistants

Captains and admirals had assistants, who were usually appointed at the former's nomination. The captain had a clerk, who was largely responsible for keeping the ship's account books, and writing the captain's letters. The admiral's secretary prepared orders for the squadron or fleet, and helped the admiral with his administrative tasks. These officials had cabins, which also served as offices, near their superiors. In 1673 the admiral's secretary on a three-decker was accommodated on the quarterdeck, forward of the roundhouse. The captain's clerk's cabin was established in 1708, 'the better to enable them to perform their business and secure their books and papers'.[8] On larger ships it was initially situated at the forward bulkhead of the captain's cabin. Eventually its use was extended down the scale, and in 1772 it was ordered that all frigates should have one, if there was room.[9] Opposite the captain's clerk's cabin was the master's cabin, which was used as much as a chart room as for living in, for the master had another cabin in the wardroom.

Captains and admirals also had large numbers of servants. Some of these actually carried out domestic duties, while others were gaining experience to become midshipmen and eventually officers. The latter group was lodged with the other cadets, in the gunroom or midshipmen's berth. The others usually lived among the crew, though sometimes they were allowed some special accommodation of their own. According to the 1673 establishment, two 'half cabins for servants' were to be allowed in the coach of Third Rates, and there can be little doubt that many of the small cabins on three-deckers were used for the admiral's servants. Later there was no regular establishment for such cabins, but room could be found for them near the officers' quarters.

Chapter 31. The Structure and Fitting of Cabins

The Factors Involved

Most naval administrators regarded cabins in a rather negative way, seeing them as a feature to be given as little attention as possible. There was no such thing as a watertight bulkhead, and no attempt to use cabins to add to the structure's strength. Some of the bulkheads, at the break of the poop and the forecastle for example, helped to keep the weather out, but most merely served to segregate the different ranks, and give privacy to some. Above the waterline, the structure of cabins was as temporary as possible, so that they could be dismantled during action.

The position of the guns was a decisive factor in cabin arrangements. Cabins were usually built round them. The typical officer's cabin in a wardroom contained a gun, and the captain's cabin had several. Unlike the French, the British never designed the quarterdeck armament so that the captain's cabin would be free of guns. Nevertheless, the areas free of guns, particularly in the after part of the ship, had some desirable cabins. In the seventeenth century there was some attempt to build cabins between the guns, so that the occupants need not be disturbed during routine maintenance, though they would almost certainly have to be taken down in time of action. Such cabins, rare on ships of less than three decks, were very small and inconvenient, and became obsolete in about the middle of the eighteenth century.

Permanent Cabins

There is little detailed information about the bulkheads of early seventeenth century ships. They were often festooned with carvings, and on models they have a permanent look about them. It is probable that the bulkheads of the poop, quarterdeck and forecastle were solidly constructed, and were not taken down in action. For most of the century, bulkheads still retained some residual role as defensive structures, and needed some strength. Those at the breaks of the quarterdeck and forecastle had three large projections, which might reflect their origins as defensive structures, able to cover one another with their gunfire. In the 1690s the builder of an 80-gun ship was to 'set all the bulkheads up on oaken plank fayed on the deck at the foot of the stanchions,

of ten inch broad and four inches thick, laid with hair and tar, and the seam leaded.'[1] The screen bulkheads, which separated the stern cabins from the galleries, were also permanent.

Usually bulkheads were reasonably clear of the guns, but in the eighteenth century they became lighter in structure, and more mobile. Even so the captain's cabins on late eighteenth-century frigates were permitted some semi-permanent bulkheads. By an order of 1779, they were to have 'one firm bulkhead at the fore part of the captain's apartments, and fixed between two guns so as to admit of their being worked in case of a surprise in the night. The after bulkhead to be of canvas, and fixed as the captain shall desire.'[2]

Cabins were also often permanent in the early seventeenth century. According to Boteler, 'In a fight [they] are very dangerous, as causing much spoil with their splinters'.[3] On the *Victory* in 1642, at least 12 of the cabins were described as 'standing'.[4] They are described in a contract of 1666 with no suggestion that they should be removeable.[5] According to the 1673 establishment, a few standing cabins were still to be fitted in the gunroom, presumably aft of the last gun.

Bulkheads and cabins on the orlop deck remained permanent, largely because they were linked to the store rooms, and these had to be kept secure. Moreover, there was no need to take such cabins down in action. There is little detailed information on their construction. In the late seventeenth century it seems that the bulkheads in the hold were made of weatherboard. Later they were probably built of deal placed between timber frames, like the cabins and store rooms.

The structure of cabins on frigates and smaller vessels could obviously be more permanent than those of ships of the line, as most were on decks which did not mount guns. However, there was some provision for removing them, if only to inspect the timbers underneath, and to repair shot damage between wind and water. They too seem to have been built of deal between timber frames. In the 1800s, the doors of such cabins were sometimes made with vertical wooden bars across a window, or with horizontal slats. This would have let some air into these ill-ventilated spaces.

The stern of a First Rate of c1690, from the Phillips print. W. is the gunroom. T is the wardroom, 'allotted for volunteers and land officers'. V. is a typical small cabin between the gunports. Above is 89, 'the coach or council chamber', with the oval table which was a regular feature of this compartment. S. is the state room, or admiral's cabin. Q is the captain's cabin, and forward of that is the cuddy, 'which is commonly divided for the master and secretaries officers'. The areas numbered 96 are the trumpeters' cabin. The tiller is 105 and the whipstaff 103.

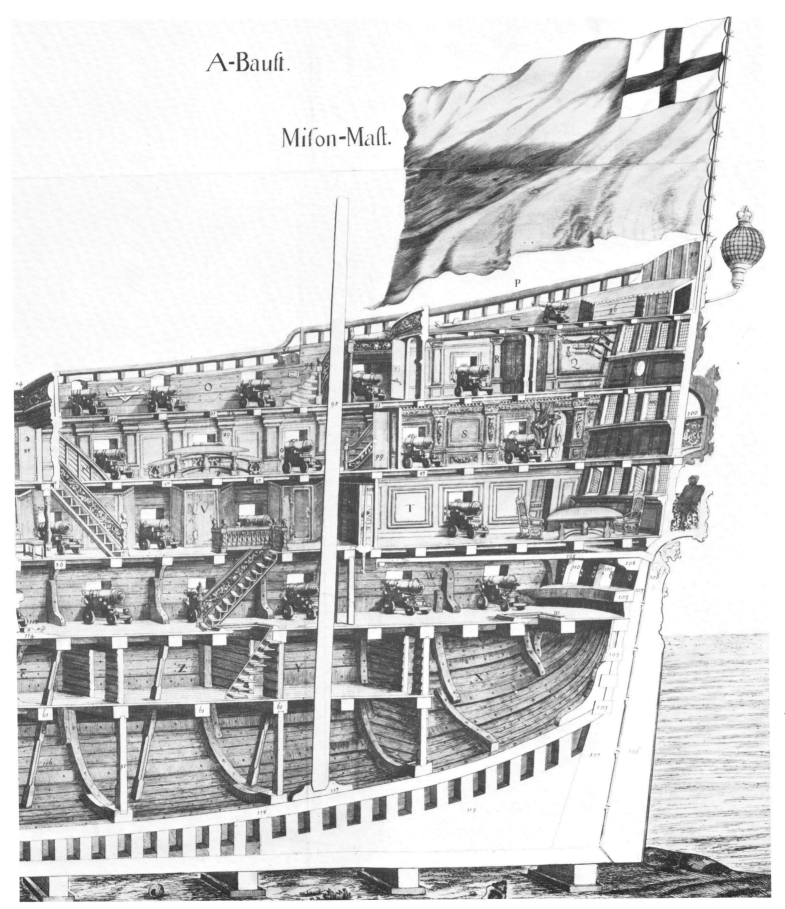

A-Bauſt.

Miſon-Maſt.

The cabins of an early nineteenth century First Rate. Those of the captain and admiral are well furnished with deal panelling, but the wardroom and gunroom are much more spartan.

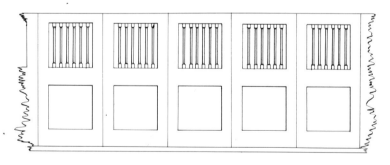

The cabins of a frigate of 1814, showing the vertical bars which were common by this time.

Moveable Frames with Deal

In the early eighteenth century there was a distinct move away from permanent cabins and bulkheads, and various orders specified how different partitions were to be constructed. By an order of 1718, care was to be taken that all bulkheads were fitted under

beams. The dockyards were 'To fix pillars, stanchions, or stiles of oak in the wake of them'. The partitions of the captain's bedplace were to run athwartships, 'without their being encumbered with breaks or projections, and to fix them in grooves so as they may be easily taken down and put up again.' The partitions of the other cabins were also to be put in grooves, 'with thick pieces fayed up to the deck from beam to beam, and not with shelves under the beams, as practised in some of the yards.'[6]

In the following year it was decided that 'all cabins and linings of the sides of ships of the Royal Navy may be framed and panelled with deal, in regard it has been found by long experience that cabins framed and covered with canvas are as dear and not half as durable'.[7] This indicates that some cabins were perhaps a little too removeable – in 1745 those of the *Dreadnought* and *Falkland* were thrown overboard in action. For their replacement, it was decreed that the bulkhead of the captain's cabin 'be panelled with deal placed in grooves, those athwartships with hinges on the top to go with pins, and those at the bottom with bolts, the cants to be in three pieces placed in the middle between the guns, so as to be out of the way of traversing them fore and aft, the cants next the side to be screwed or fastened with spikes.'[8] In the same year this system was made standard for ships of 50

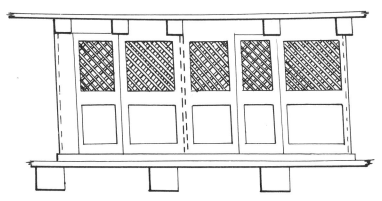

Side view of the wardroom pantry, on a 64-gun ship of 1779. It is possible that latticed partitions such as these were used in other places, such as the cabins and store rooms on the orlop.

The internal partitions of a captain's cabin on a model of about 1780.
Author's photograph, courtesy of NMM.

Part of the admiral's cabin on the Victory, *showing how the bulkheads could be hinged upwards in action.* Author's photograph, courtesy of HMS *Victory.*

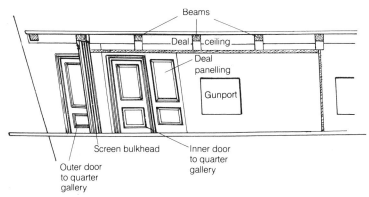

The fittings of the great cabin of the Dorsetshire *of 1757.*

guns and less. Larger ships were to have bulkheads 'panelled with deal, placed in grooves so as to be easily taken down out of the way of the guns.'[9]

Around this time there was a tendency to build some permanent cabins in the wardroom, where they could be kept clear of the guns. Larger ships were to have 'two in the stern of the wardroom, contrived so as to have only one window in each cabin, and that one of the quarter galleries be left in common', implying that the other was to be accessible only through the cabin, and was reserved for the sole use of its occupant. There were also to be two cabins on the gundeck, 'on the transom, where there is room to put them up, clear of the after gun.'[10]

Such cabins were largely abolished by the orders of 1757, which introduced a new puritanism in the structure of officers' cabins. In general, canvas curtains replaced wooden partitions in areas above the waterline. Wooden bulkheads were retained to seal off the wardroom, the captain's cabin, and the space under the forecastle. These were to be fitted 'in such a manner that they may be taken down or disposed of out of the way of fighting the guns or doing mischief by the enemy's shot in the shortest time

possible.' They were to be 'framed of deal, with slit deal panels wrought strong, light and plain'. None of the panels were to exceed three feet in width, and they were to be 'fitted with hinges and shifting pins through the joints thereof on the upper part, and below to fall in a rabbet prepared to receive them in the cant, with a batten before them, or small bolts for their confinement in their places, from which place the bulkhead may be taken quite away, or turned up under the beams, as shall be found most suitable to the service.'[11]

The screen bulkheads, separating the cabins from the stern galleries, were also to be made more mobile. In the past they had been 'fitted with double sashes and double shutters, by which the whole bulkhead requires to be $7\frac{1}{2}$ or 8 inches in thickness, is troublesome to take out, heavy and cumbersome to stow away when preparing for action, and with difficulty restored to their places again after it is over.' In future they were to be lighter. They were to be 'fitted with a single sash and a single shutter, and the height be so divided that the depth of the sash may be equal to the panel below, that both sash and shutter may be buried therein when taken down, by which the quantity of glass will be reduced,

175

the cabin made warmer in winter; the panels, by being reduced more than one third, will become more portable.'[12]

Care was also to be taken that the cants, which were thin timbers nailed to the decks, were neither close to the gunports, nor more than 3in thick. They were to be fitted in three parts, thus leaving space for the two doors which adorned each bulkhead, and they were to be removeable, in case it was necessary to traverse the guns yet further, or to caulk the decks under them.

By this time the fixed bulkhead above the waterline was the beakhead bulkhead, right in the bows. The orders of 1757 stayed in force for many years, and they were to some extent reaffirmed in 1802 when the dockyards were instructed 'to cause no other than the foremost bulkhead to be fitted in any of His Majesty's ships.'[13] The structure of cabins did not change much, except that after 1795 stern galleries, and therefore screen bulkheads, were no longer fitted. When the galleries were restored around 1810, they were constructed differently, and there was no need for the screen bulkhead.

Hanging Canvas Cabins

Hanging cabins were in use during most of the seventeenth century, though there are no details of their construction. On the *Victory* in 1642, three were fitted on the 'chief deck', and 18 on the lower deck. The orders of 1673 allowed six on First or Second Rates, but none on any other ship. Canvas was out of favour as a material for cabins in the early eighteenth century, but in 1744 Captain Dandridge of the *Mary* suggested that 'if the ships bulkheads and co were taken down, and canvas ones put up in their room ... it would be a great saving to the government, because they would easily furl up in time of engagement.' Moreover, officers' cabins were 'quite needless, because good berths for hammacoes might be made in the gunroom, and canvas curtains, properly contrived to fall before them, would look more ship-shape.'[14]

The Navy Board heartily agreed, as did a committee of sea officers which met to draw up a new establishment in the following year. They suggested that wardroom officers should be allowed 'double hammocks, and canvas curtains to hang before them in the said wardroom.'[15] Though this idea does not seem to have been adopted in the final version of the orders, in 1757 it was strongly revived. Canvas curtains were to be used for all cabins in the wardroom, including the two aftermost, which had been permanent in the past. Canvas was also to be used in the gunroom. The wardroom was to be parted by a bulkhead, and 'from thence to the stern a space enclosed on each side (for three or four berths) by canvas hanging loosely before it like a curtain, or laced below and above, with a parting in the middle of each berth, to go in and out, and to roll up in the daytime when not wanted.' Cabins in the gunroom were to be 'fitted in the same manner ... except there is to be no deal bulkhead.'[16] In 1757 a marine officer's cabin was described as 'a place between two guns, about seven feet long and four feet wide, and divided only from some hundred hammocks by a little canvas or an old sail, where there is no light but a candle, nor any air but what is unavoidably very foul.'[17]

The orders on cabins do not seem to have been fully obeyed, and in April 1778 the Navy Board ordered 'that the framed cabins in the wardroom may be taken down, and canvas for curtains issued in lieu thereof'. The orders of 1757 were still to be complied with.[18]

Framed Canvas

Most of the tiny cabins between gunports, which so clogged up some seventeenth century ships, were made of canvas stretched across wooden frames because this was light and cheap; it is thought that some may have been made of deal. They were either square or trapezoid in shape, being angled inwards towards the centre of the deck, perhaps to allow more room for maintenance of the guns. The number of such cabins tended to be reduced in the next century. Though a deck plan of a three-decker of the 1740s shows a few small cabins of this type between the guns, they are rectangular, and the fact that they are shown on a deck plan makes it unlikely that they were made of canvas.[19]

Canvas on frame was out of favour by 1719. It had evidently had some use for great cabins and wardrooms, but was found 'as dear, and not half as durable' as deal, and was to be replaced. It came into favour again in 1778, for the bulkheads of great cabins and wardrooms.[20] Its use was extended by an order of 1808, which stipulated that the partitions separating the cabins from the wardroom were to be of stretched canvas, 'to be hinged and hooked up to the deck'. The divisions between the different cabins were still to be canvas curtains, which could be rolled up.[21] In 1812 a chaplain described his cabin in the gunroom as being made of 'canvas strained on a wooden framework, with a door of the same materials, and a small window in each, opening on hinges, and intended to admit as much light as could enter from the stern port hole, and the after port on the ship's starboard side.'[22]

Mica and Glass

For most of the seventeenth century glass was an expensive and rare commodity in England, and it was rarely used aboard ship. Mica, or Muscovy glass, was used instead. This came only in small sizes, and was more opaque than glass. It was used, for example, in 1678 in the *Dartmouth*'s refit, 'for glazing the cabin windows, bulkhead lights and officers lights with Muscovia glass.' Pieces of this mica have since been recovered from the wreck of the ship off Mull.[23] Because the mica came in small pieces, the windows had to be subdivided into many parts, which were then leaded together. These divisions were sometimes diagonal and crossed over one another.

In 1688 the French developed a new method of making plate glass, by casting it and then grinding the surfaces of the sheet smooth. This technique seems to have reached England about five years later, and in 1702 the use of stone-ground glass was established on many parts of ships.[24] Panes of glass tended to be rather larger than those of mica, and this changed the appearance of sterns and windows quite considerably. They had fewer subdivisions, which now invariably ran horizontally and vertically. Around this time, the shape of lanterns began to change, for the same reason.

In some cases, sash windows were fitted in the gunports in the area of the wardroom and the great cabin. They can be seen on a model of around 1703, a model of the *Royal George* of 1756, and on the *Victory* at Portsmouth. All these ships were First Rates, and it is not clear if windows were fitted only to such ships, or if modelmakers omitted them on less important models. Ships of the Third Rate and above often had windows cut in the side, near the quarterdeck and poop, which gave the officers more light.

Model of the Royal George *showing the windows fitted in the aftermost gunports.* Author's photograph, courtesy of NMM.

Their surrounds were heavily carved, like the windows of the stern galleries. These windows seem to have gone out of favour by about 1745.

Throughout the period there were also windows in the bulkheads, and in some of the internal cabins. It is clear that most standing cabins had some glass by the beginning of the eighteenth century, and in 1812 a chaplain's cabin had glass in two internal windows, each consisting of four panels. Companions were built on the poops of ships of the line, or on the quarterdecks of frigates, to allow light into the captain's cabins below. Glass was sometimes even used in the interiors of cabins. For instance, in 1702 an admiral's secretary was allowed glass in 'nests and presses for papers'.[25]

Beds

Roughly speaking there were three types of officers' beds. 'Standing beds', or bedsteads, seem to have been similar to those used on shore, and as a standard issue were reserved for captains and admirals. In the 1680s one bedstead was issued to each ship of the Fourth Rate and above.[26] It is possible that junior officers provided their own, though few would have had room for them, and it would be difficult to stow them away in action. Admirals, on the other hand, suffered from no such restrictions. In the 1780s Rodney provided himself with a large and a small mahogany bedstead, as well as a field bedstead, and two cots.[27] Captains, however, sometimes had difficulty in finding room for theirs. In 1718 it was complained that on smaller ships their bed-

places were 'too small for their standing beds'. It was ordered that bedplaces should be at least 6ft 4in fore and aft.[28]

Standing beds seem to have gone out of favour by the end of the eighteenth century, and they were not provided for in the stores of 1794.[29] By 1745 junior officers were issued with double hammocks, with two clews instead of one at each end. By the 1790s, cots were in use as an alternative to double hammocks. According to the list of 1794, a First Rate carried 20 cots or double hammocks, enough for all the wardroom officers, the captain, and perhaps the standing officers. In addition, 14 spare wooden bed bottoms were carried, without canvas. A 74 carried 18 cots, and a frigate 10, while smaller vessels had only two. The cot was described as 'a machine of about six feet in length, and usually about 2ft 3in wide; made of coarse canvas, and strained on an oaken frame; provided with such bedding as the owner may choose; and when slung, suspended by cords from each extremity to hooks in the beams above. It is commonly slung athwartship; but I found it more convenient to hang mine fore and aft.'[30]

Tables

Few cabins were large enough to hold their own table. According to a cabin list of 1686, similar in most respects to that of 1673, only the most senior officers, such as captains, admirals and senior lieutenants, plus standing officers such as pursers and surgeons, had cabins with 'deal tables in them'.[31] The standing officers probably had their own tables because they tended to mess alone rather than communally, or because they were judged to need them to prepare their accounts. Such tables were described in a contract of 1690. They were to be 2½ to 3½ft long, 'with legs of oak, deal tops, deal rails, a third part of the top to hang with hinges with a swing leg to reduce it, and a drawer to each.'[32]

Communal tables, for the gunroom and wardroom, were used in the eighteenth century. By an order of 1797, wardroom and mess room tables were to be made of wainscott rather than deal. By the 1800s, wardroom tables were made in suitable lengths to fit the space available, and had iron legs.[33] The captain's cabin had three tables on a ship of the line, and two on a frigate; they were made of wainscott. The tables in the midshipmen's berth, established in 1802, were made of deal, as was the school table, for use in the gunroom for teaching the midshipmen and boys. A writing table was issued to each ship, presumably for the captain's clerk.[34] If any of the other officers wanted tables in their cabins they must have had to provide their own, which must have been very small, and probably folding.

Other Furniture

Of all the areas aboard ship, the wardroom was probably the best furnished from the public purse. As well as the table, and a chair for each of the occupants, it included a sideboard at its foremost end, and a place to sling a quarter cask of wine.[35] Captains and admirals could provide themselves with much more, and Rodney in the *Gibraltar* had three tables, numerous chairs and sofas, and other items.[36] On a more modest scale, the chaplain of 1812 furnished his cabin with 'a writing desk, camp stool, looking glass etc.', in addition to his bedding.[37]

By the late eighteenth century the wardroom was apparently provided with a heating stove, at the officers' expense. The facetious *Duty of a Purser*, published around 1770, advised, 'When you go to sea for a three month cruise at the end of autumn, do not carry with you a stove for the wardroom, but pretend that you have forgot to buy one, or that you have left it ashore to be mended, and you will save at least half a cauldron of coals.' The same source implies that officers were allowed candles for their cabins, though some captain's orders insisted that they be extinguished at a fixed hour of the evening, as a precaution against fire.[38]

Pantries

By the early eighteenth century admirals were allowed pantries close to their cabins. On a plan of the *Britannia* of 1719, a pantry was constructed along the centre line, passing between the steerage and the great cabin. It was used by the admiral's steward to store some food, and prepare light meals. Full meals for the officers were usually prepared in the galley. In the later part of the century, a similar pantry was to be found attached to the wardroom of a ship of the line. It was also near the centre line, passing through the wardroom bulkhead. It was rather more permanent than the officers' cabins, being made of framed deal, with latticed windows. It was divided into two parts: the aftermost and smallest part served the wardroom, and was situated entirely within that compartment; the forward part was for the captain.

Finishing and Decoration

The decoration of officers' cabins varied enormously according to their rank. At one extreme, the gunroom and cockpit were extremely bare, unless their occupants took it upon themselves to hang curtains, or other adornments. At the other extreme, an admiral's cabin could be decorated with carvings and paintings, at great expense to the state.

Between these two extremes was the wardroom, which had a minimum of decoration. The rudder head was covered with deal, and served as a small table. The transom under the stern windows was also covered, and disguised as a bench seat. The canvas of the officers' cabins was painted, probably as skilfully as the crew could manage.

Captains were better provided for. Their cabins often contained carved works, until 1703 when these were banned. They were lined with wainscott, until 1704 when this was replaced with stamped leather. According to an order of 1719, they had sometimes been lined with canvas, but this was to be replaced with deal, 'without any sort of moulding or corniche'.[39] The space between the deck beams above was usually filled in this way, to provide a continuous surface. By orders of 1792, the spaces between the beams of the great cabins were to be filled with putty, to give a smoother finish, and floor cloths were supplied, usually in a black and white chequer pattern.[40] Many admirals would have improved on this by supplying themselves with carpets.

Chapter 32. Hammocks

The Allocation of Space

If there is a single aspect of seventeenth and eighteenth century naval life that seems intolerable to the modern mind, it is the crowded conditions in which the crew lived. It is difficult to believe that men could tolerate such conditions for months and years at a time, yet they were largely accepted by contemporaries. The mutineers of the late eighteenth century made no mention of crowded conditions in their complaints, perhaps because they were inured to them, and recognised that there was no way to operate a warship efficiently with a smaller crew. The only solution to the lack of space would have been to take away some from the captains and admirals and give it to the seamen, but this would not have been sufficient to alter the position radically. Some contemporaries were sensitive to the hardship. Captain Middleton ordered that the officers and petty officers should not encroach on the seamen's space, 'that the seamen may not be deprived of the space allowed them, which at best is found full insufficient'.[1] A seaman of the early nineteenth century wrote, 'the great disparity in numbers between the crew of a merchant ship and that of a man of war occasions a difference in the internal arrangements and mode of life, scarcely conceivable by those who have not seen both.'[2]

Most took lack of space for granted. It was not easy to fit all the hammocks into the given space, but few officers found it necessary to describe how this should be done, even in the manuals for aspiring officers which were produced in the early nineteenth century. Much was dictated by custom and practice and one thing is clear: the place where a man slung his hammock was largely determined by his role in the ship, so he was usually close to the part of the ship where he performed most of his duties. Thus the allocation of berths was closely related to the organisation of the crew.

The Organisation of the Crew

The crew of a large sailing warship included several hundred seamen. Each man was allotted a specific role in each operation which had to be performed, for instance trimming sails, raising anchor, fighting fire, engaging an enemy, or cleaning the decks. This produced a very complex list of individual duties, but it was simplified to a certain extent by dividing the crew into groups, associated with either functions or parts of the ship. Marines formed a natural group of their own, as did specialists, such as carpenters and gunner's crew. The remaining seamen fell easily into two categories: those who were skilled and agile enough to work aloft in the rigging, and those who were not. The former group was divided into three, one party for each mast. The less active or able men were put in three categories, associated with the three main divisions of the ship's decks. The forecastle men carried out some skilled tasks with the anchors, and helped work the sails of the foremast. The afterguard was based on the quarterdeck. It usually provided the helmsman, and was constantly under the eyes of the officers. The least skilled group were called the waisters. They heaved on ropes and pushed capstan bars, and carried out the most menial tasks.

Each of these groups was commanded by a petty officer known

as the 'captain' of the fore top, of the afterguard, and so on. A group could be allocated a specific task during a particular evolution. For example, aboard the *San Domingo* in 1810, when 'tacking ship with the watch' (that is, using one watch only, without calling the off-duty watch on deck) the marines hauled on the main brace, the poop afterguard operated the crossjack braces, and the main-top men the fore topsail brace, the waisters and forecastle men the fore tack, the fore-top men the fore sheet, and so on.[3]

The 'idlers' formed another part of the crew. These men performed tasks which were only needed in the daytime, and they could sleep all night, except in action or dire emergency. A 74 of 1809 had 49 idlers, including armourers, sailmakers, coopers, officers' servants, butchers, hairdressers, barbers, tailors and cooks. The groups within the crew eventually became known as 'divisions', and each was put under the care of a particular officer for purposes of discipline and welfare. Though this system was only formally introduced in the 1750s, it appears that the subdivision of the crew had been common for many years.[4]

The crew was also grouped into watches. Most of the men, that is all the topmen, waisters, afterguard, forecastle men and many of the specialists and marines, were divided into watches, so that a sufficient number would always be on duty at any given moment. Some operations, for instance raising anchor and setting sail, or tacking in difficult conditions, required the full crew to be on deck or aloft. Others, such as minor sail-trimming or small changes of course needed less men. Until the nineteenth century, most captains seem to have preferred a two-watch system. This meant that half the men, with the exception of idlers, were on

deck at the same time, though at night not all of these would be actively employed, and on some ships they were allowed to sleep, or at least to rest, on deck. One important effect of this system was to alleviate the overcrowding below, for nearly half the hammocks would be empty while the ship was at sea.

By the early nineteenth century, the three-watch system was becoming fashionable. This allowed a seaman a full night's sleep for two nights out of three, whereas he would never have had an uninterrupted night's while at sea in the old system, only getting four hours in his hammock for one night in two. The new method met with some resistance, and 'captains, prejudiced in favour of old customs, cannot divest themselves of the idea that their ships would not be safe with less than half the ship's company upon deck.'[5] The use of the three-watch system also depended on whether the ship had a full complement, and a sufficient number of skilled men. It was recommended that the three-watch system should be used as a reward for crews that had worked well and become reasonably efficient. However, it can be assumed that the two-watch system was more common for most of the period. Its hardships could be mitigated by dividing each watch into two sections, so that on occasion only a quarter of the crew needed to be on deck.

The Hammock

Hammocks, or hammacoes as they were more commonly known in the seventeenth and eighteenth centuries, were evidently first used by the aboriginal Indians of the Caribbean, and

A hammock on the Victory, *showing the spreader and the bedding inside. Behind this is a hammock which has been lashed up. This was often done when the occupant was on watch, or when it was not possible to use the hammock racks because of bad weather.* Author's photograph, courtesy of HMS Victory.

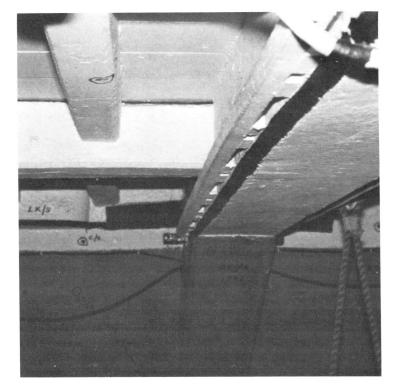

Racks along the edge of one of the middle deck beams of the Victory. *These may be the racks which began to be fitted in the 1750s to replace the nails on which hammocks had previously been hung.* Author's photograph, courtesy of HMS Victory.

were later adopted by European seamen. They were in use in the English Navy by 1597, when canvas was ordered 'to make hanging cabins or beds . . . for the better preservation of their health.'[6] By 1629 they were issued to one man in two for overseas service, but not in home waters where cabins were still used.[7] They seem to have been in general use by the middle of the seventeenth century.

A hammock was defined as 'a piece of hempen cloth, six feet long and three feet wide, gathered together at the two ends by means of a clew, and slung horizontally under the deck, forming a receptacle for a bed for the sailors to sleep in.' A clew was 'the combination of small lines by which it is suspended, being formed of knittles, grommets and lanyards.' Knittles were 'small lines, composed of two or three rope yarns, either plaited or twisted'.[8] These were passed through holes along each end of the hammock, and met at a grommet, or ring of rope. To the latter was attached a lanyard, which was used to hang the end of the hammock from a hook or rack on the deck beam above.

Hammocks came in two sizes, single or double. The latter was of course larger, with two clews at each end. It was issued only to officers and certain petty officers; the common seaman used the single hammock. In the early years of the nineteenth century each seaman was issued with two hammocks. A captain of 1804 wrote, 'The establishment of two hammocks to each man, so conducive to the preservation of health, is always to be complied with if it be possible'.[9] But this had not always been the case. A First Rate of the 1680s was issued with 1000 hammocks for a crew of 780 men, enough for one each, and some replacements for those worn out or damaged.[10] Similarly, a First Rate of the 1790s was issued with 900 hammocks for a crew of 850 men, with 260 extra for a long voyage.[11] According to the captain's orders issued on the *Pegasus* in 1786, a few hammocks were to be scrubbed every other morning, and spare ones issued in their place. This would not have been necessary if two had been issued to each man. However, another set of captain's instructions of the same year mentions that there were two hammocks per man.[12] Moreover, the hammock nettings had been extended to the waist of the ship by about 1780, which implies that more hammocks were in use. Clearly the custom of two hammocks per man became established in the late eighteenth century.

Hammocks were regarded as the property of the government, and were issued by the boatswain, on loan to each man. Midshipmen and junior officers also used them, for few had the privilege of a double hammock, and even fewer a cot or a standing bed. A First Rate of the 1790s had only 20 cots or double hammocks, and a ship of 24 guns or less had only two.[13]

Other Bedding

The hammock was only 'a receptacle for a bed for the sailors'. Each seaman also had a bed, or mattress, which in 1760 was '5ft 10in long and 2ft 3in broad, measured by the seams when made', and a bolster or pillow which was 'as long as the bed is broad, and 1ft 5in in breadth'. Both were to be 'made of good Bremen cloth, or other cloth of equal goodness, and good clean sweet wool and white flocks'.[14] In 1757 contractors had been given permission to use wool instead of 'good dry rag flocks', because of a shortage of the latter.[15] The seamen also had a blanket and a 'coverlet', four quarters (4½ft?) broad, and 6ft long. Sometimes the coverlet was replaced with an extra blanket.

Unlike the hammock, the bedding was not issued to the seaman but bought from the purser out of his wages, unless he came on board with his own. 'He then demanded of the boatswain a hammock for me, . . . and as I had no bed clothes, procured credit for me with the purser for a mattress and two blankets'.[16]

The Space for Hammocks

By the late eighteenth century most captains issued standing orders to their officers and crews, and some of these still survive. None say very much about how the hammocks were to be arranged below decks, implying that such matters were better left to tradition, and the organisational skills of the boatswain and first lieutenant.

The space available for slinging hammocks was of course very restricted. On a two-decker, only the beams under the upper deck, and those in the cable tier, were normally used. According to one set of instructions, the space under the cable tier was reserved for the quartermaster, sailmakers, gunner's crew, and those who worked in the hold. According to another, it was allocated to quartermasters and quarter gunners, idlers, midshipmen and boys, to a total of about 100 berths.[17] Whatever the case, it was used for those who were separated from the rest of the crew for reasons of rank or morality, and accommodated only a small number of the 650 crew on a 74-gun ship.

The other spaces underneath decks had various uses. There was some room below the quarterdeck, in the area not taken up with officers' cabins, but it was open to the elements, and was only used for hammocks when a large number of supernumeraries were borne. The space under the forecastle was reserved for certain warrant officers, and later for the sick. That under the poop was reserved entirely for the captain. The gunroom, aft on the lower deck, was largely used for cabins and other purposes, and in any case much of it was useless for slinging hammocks because of the sweep of the rudder. Thus on a 74-gun ship, the lower deck, which had an area of less than 6000 square feet, had to accommodate about 500 men.

In practice even less space was available. Because of the tumblehome of the hull, the upper deck, under which the hammocks were slung, was somewhat narrower than the gundeck. Some of the space near the sides of the hull was unusable because of the knees which supported the upper deck, and a hammock slung above one of the guns must have been very restricted indeed. Yet more room was taken up by the petty officers, who slept nearer the ship's sides and were allowed more room than the common seamen. Moreover, large areas near the centre line were useless, because they were occupied by masts, capstans, gratings, and the manger. The latter could occasionally be used for sleeping, but it was damp and uncomfortable. Some captains tried to contrive ways to make it easier for men to sleep near the gratings. 'Any man or men who sleep near the hatchways or scuttles, who feel any draught of wind, or are subject to be wet in their hammacoes from seas or rain, are to acquaint the first lieutenant, that painted canvas screens may be neatly nailed up to make their berths as comfortable as possible'.[18] However, the space directly under the gratings could not normally be used, so that, all told, only about two-thirds of the 6000 square feet was really available for berthing.

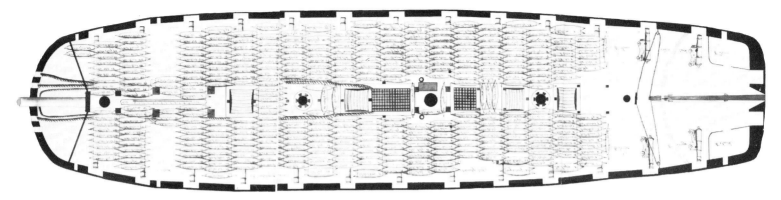

The hammock arrangement of a mid-eighteenth-century Third Rate. It still had the pre-1771 form of steering arrangement. The empty area near the bows is for the sick berth. NMM.

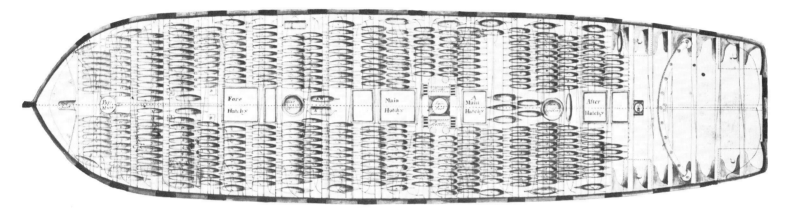

The hammocks of the Bedford, *c1780. The last three rows are for marines. Traditionally they were berthed between the officers and the seamen, in order, it is said, to help prevent mutiny.* NMM.

Hammock Arrangements

The common rule appears to have been that each man was allowed a space 14in broad for his hammock. Though this sounds impossible, it is something on which all sources agree. 'The berths marked out for the ship's hammocks are on the exact allowance of 14in broad to each man.' The problem was mitigated by the fact that 'a man on one watch hangs by another in the other watch, so that whoever sleeps below is not so crowded as if all that belonged to one watch slept next one another. But in harbour, when all the seamen sleep in all night, they find it very inconvenient.'[19] It is possible that hammocks could have been slung on slightly different levels, if the lanyard was long enough. The 14in refers to the distance between the hammock nails on the beams above. After 1754 specially designed racks were used, being 'more commodious to the beams than the nails normally employed.'[20] Presumably these maintained the 14in spacing, and indeed tended to make it even more exact. However, it is possible that each seaman slung his hammock a little higher or lower than his neighbour, to give himself more room. There is no direct proof of this, but it must be remembered that the bed was 2ft 3in wide, and it would have been difficult to cram into a 14in space, though it was a little narrower than the 28in space left when one watch was on deck.

The allocation of berths was under the control of the first lieutenant, but his scope was limited. It is not clear whether the dockyard, or the ship's carpenter, first fitted the hammock nails or racks, but it can be assumed that if the ship was not new, the nails were already there, and were not likely to be moved. Most hammocks were slung fore and aft, in neat rows running across the ship, beginning at the bows just aft of the manger, and working aft. A few were slung athwartships, especially near the centre line, where there was not much space between gratings and other encumbrances. At the end of each athwartships row was a berth for a petty officer. They were allowed a space of 28in each, which was 'not to be pinched'.[21] The rows were interlocked, so that the clews of one row crossed with those of the next.

Every man's hammock had a number, which indicated where his berth was. 'Every hammock has its appropriate place. Below, all the beams are marked; each hammock is marked with the corresponding number, and in the darkest night, a sailor will go unhesitatingly to his own hammock.'[22] Most ships seem to have had a separate series of numbers for each watch, so that in a two-watch system every number was duplicated, and in general a man would sleep beside the man with the corresponding number when the ship was in port, and do the same job as him on watch.

The numbers reflected the divisions in the crew. The marines were berthed aft. Traditionally it was believed that they should protect the officers against mutiny, but they do not seem to have done much to prevent the mutinies of the late eighteenth century. However, they were close to the officers' cabins on the quarter-deck and upper deck, where they mounted guard. The seamen were berthed by divisions, from just aft of the manger. On a frigate of 1805, the forecastle men occupied the first 28 spaces (or 56 if two watches were off duty at once). They were followed by fore-top men, main-top men, mizzen-top men, waisters, the afterguard, and then the marines and idlers.[23] This seems to have been a typical arrangement. On three-deckers there was probably more space. Though the extra deck was largely occupied by officers' cabins, it seems likely that the additional deck space provided by it was greater than the room required by the larger complement needed for such a ship. On frigates the berthing deck was probably a little less crowded than the lower deck of a ship of the line, on which it had to be used for officers' cabins as well as for the crew.

In tropical weather, crews often preferred to sleep in the open air. Captains resisted this, for reasons of discipline and health. One ordered that hammocks were not to be slung under the boat booms. Another allowed them to be slung under the forecastle, half deck, booms and gangways, though the men were not to be allowed to sleep on the deck itself.[24]

The Stowage of Hammocks

When a man was on watch his hammock had to be lashed up to the beams to make room for his neighbours. Early in the morning, the hammocks were unslung, rolled up, and, from the middle of the eighteenth century, put into the hammock racks round the decks of the ship. The actual speed with which this was done varied from ship to ship, but captains insisted that it be done quickly and promptly, and midshipmen were not excused. According to one set of orders, 'The boatswain is to pay particular attention that when the hammocks are piped up, they are taut and neatly lashed, so that no bedding appears. No clothes are to be stowed in them. He is to see that every hammock is up, excepting those of the sick.'[25]

Hammocks had to be washed, and like clothing they could be hung from parts of the ship to dry. Again, captains regulated when this could be done and forbade hanging them from certain places, such as the shrouds, or under the gangways.[26] In the evening, the hammocks and bedding were taken out of the racks and set up below. One captain ordered that this be done a quarter of an hour before sunset, one division at a time, to prevent confusion[27] When a man was on watch, the man in the adjacent berth was responsible for taking his hammock below when the time came to set them up.

Chapter 33. The Messes

The Organisation of the Messes

In the loosest sense, a mess was a 'company of the officers or crew of a ship who eat, drink and associate together'.[1] Among the seamen, it had a slightly more specific meaning: 'The crew of a man of war is divided into little communities, called messes. These eat and drink together, and are, as it were, so many families.'[2] Though it had strong social implications, the mess was essentially an administrative unit, round which the issue of seamen's food was based. Each mess had its own table, and this formed the centre of its activity.

The seaman had few liberties, but choosing his own mess was one. He often had no choice as to whether he wished to be in the Navy, nor which ship he was to serve on. He did not choose who he worked with, or where he slept, but he was allowed to choose the companions with whom he ate. The first lieutenant did not attempt to allocate men to messes, but, within certain limits, allowed them to choose their own. Firstly, men could not change messes on impulse, as this would cause enormous confusion in the distribution of food. Traditionally, any man who wished to change could do so on the first Sunday of each month, after seeking the formal permission of the first lieutenant. Secondly, there were limits on the size of each mess. The upper limit, of about eight men, was imposed by physical conditions – it would have been impossible to seat more men at a table. The lower limit was usually imposed by those in authority. If there were too few men in some messes, it would increase the strain on the others. In the *Pegasus* in 1786, every mess was ordered to have at least four men.

Other captains specified six, which seems to have been a more common number.[3]

There was a further restriction, based on rank and function. The marines never messed with the seamen, partly because the officers tended not to encourage the two groups to mingle, and partly because of custom and mutual dislike. Petty officers were also kept apart from the seamen on some ships, for obvious reasons of discipline. 'The men are to mess in messes of six each, the boatswain's mates and petty officers by themselves, or with some other petty officers.'[4] However, the great mass of the men, the common seamen who made up about 70 per cent of the ship's company, had the right to choose their companions from within their own group.

The Situation of the Messes

As in many other respects, the crew of a two-decker seem to have had the worst deal when messing space was allocated. On three-deckers there would have been some space on the middle deck. In the seventeenth century most of the space between the guns on this deck was occupied by tiny cabins for the junior officers, but these were abolished in the eighteenth century, which presumably left the space free. On a frigate, the lower deck had no guns. This did not leave much extra room for slinging hammocks, but it did make space for more mess tables.

On a two-decker, it appears that all the men messed on the lower gundeck, where much space was taken up by guns, as well as hatchways, capstans and other obstacles. However, this does not at first sight seem possible. A 74-gun ship had 28 guns on the lower deck, four of which were in the gunroom, where the crew did not mess. This left 24 guns, with 24 spaces between them,

A mess table, c1800. This illustration also shows how the plates and bags were stored, and how the guns were lashed. The large projections on the breeches of the guns are probably imaginary, but the rest of the picture is accurate. NMM.

including one space forward of the foremost gun. If a maximum of eight men had been allocated to each space, only 192 men could have been seated at one time, and on a 74-gun ship with a crew of about 650, there were nearly 600 seamen and petty officers.

One possibility is that the men dined by watches, but this seems unlikely. Captain's orders usually give a specific time at which the hands were to be piped to dinner, and often allowed them an hour and a half for their meal, if there were no pressing tasks to be performed. The implication is that all the crew dined at once, except for a few lookouts and helmsmen on duty. Clearly more space must have been needed.

A print of 1796 provides a few clues.[5] It implies that there were two rows of messes down each side of the ship, one close to the side and the other inboard, presumably between the breech of the gun and the row of hatchways along the centre line. This is possible, though it would have been rather cramped. The same document clearly shows that more tables, seven in this case, could be fitted along the centre line, in the spaces between the hatches, gratings, capstans, pumps and so on. However, this print raises as many questions as it answers. Though it claims to represent the 74-gun ship the *Vengeance* it ignores the existence of guns, and allocates 20 tables along each side, with 20 more inboard of these. With a total of 87 mess tables, there would clearly have been room for 600 men, but it is difficult to believe that this much space would really have been available.

However, there is another arrangement which is just conceivable. There is no doubt that there was room for 24 tables between the guns, and another seven at the centre of the deck. As the print suggests, more could be fitted in the unobstructed area between the guns and the centre of the ship, as follows: more than 12 tables could have been fitted on each side (not as many as 24), one opposite each gun and one between the guns, to a maximum of perhaps 20 on each side. With eight men to each table, 568 men could have eaten at once. This is not an unreasonable figure, and would have left a total of 71 men without a table, who would have to have stayed on deck during the meal.

There is no support for this theory in any other documentation. All the available pictures of messes show them situated between guns, and Falconer refers to a 'birth' as 'the room or apartment where any particular number of the officers or the

A container recovered from the wreck of the Invincible, *possibly used for bringing the crew's provisions from the galley to the mess.* Author's photograph.

ship's company mess can reside. In a ship of war there is normally one of these between every two guns.'[6] This takes no account of frigates, which were already in use in Falconer's time, and it does not specifically deny that messes could also be elsewhere on the lower deck. It is difficult to see how else the ship's company could have been accommodated.

The Equipment of Messes

The focus of each mess was its table. There is little specific information about its construction, but presumably it was designed at a suitable length and breadth to fit between two guns. It seems that the outboard end rested against the ship's side, and was held up by a batten. The other end was supported from the beams above by two ropes, one leading to each corner. When not in use it could be raised up and hung from the beams. In the early nineteenth century the ropes were replaced with a Y-shaped iron supporter.

A bench was placed on each side of the table. A rack was hung from the side of the ship at one end of the table, to hold the seamen's cutlery. Other utensils, including bowls and tubs, were used to fetch the food from the cook or steward. In general the seamen preferred to supply their own plates and cutlery, but often press-ganged men had little option but to buy them from the ship's purser if they could not find another supplier. One seaman, the 'cook of the mess' was responsible for fetching the others' food. Uncooked items, such as cheese and biscuits, were collected directly from the steward on the orlop deck. Others came from the cook, who used a pin to mark off each mess as it was provided for.

Seamen's Belongings

Seamen had very little money, and did not expect to keep it long. 'Their money is lavished with the most thoughtless profusion; fine clothes for his girl, a silver watch and silver buckles for himself, are often the sole return for years of labour and hardship. When his officer happens to refuse him leave to go on shore, his purse is sometimes with the coldest indifference consigned to the deep, that it may no longer remind him of pleasures he cannot command.'[7] His main property consisted of his clothes and his bedding. For these he was provided with a bag, known as a ditty bag, which was hung up beside his mess. Any further property, including valuables, could be kept in a chest. On a large ship, only one chest was provided for every eight men, and it was kept below when the ship was at sea. On frigates, where there was more room below decks, one chest was provided for every two men, and it largely replaced the ditty bag.[8]

Heating and Ventilation

In most cases heating the lower deck was unnecessary. Most ships spent far more time in the Mediterranean or the Caribbean than in the North Sea and the Baltic, and summer in the English Channel was warm enough for most. Moreover, in the evening when the gunports were closed the massed human bodies on the lower deck created their own warmth. 'On the same deck with me, when the crew was complete, slept between five and six hundred men; and the ports being necessarily closed from evening to morning, the heat in this cavern of only six feet high, and so entirely filled with human bodies, was overpowering.'[9]

Moveable iron stoves were first issued in 1783, one for each deck. Though they might also have helped heat the ship, their main purpose was to help air it, whether at sea, or laid up with no crew on board. Lack of a proper circulation of the air caused two problems. It accelerated the decay of the hull's timbers and it increased the level of disease and discomfort amongst the crew. It was often impossible to open the gunports for days or weeks when there was bad weather, and of course in a frigate this was never possible. The stoves could help to create a satisfactory airflow. Each consisted of an iron pan placed on top of a four-legged frame.[10] Though it had been intended that one should be issued for each deck, they seem to have partly fallen out of use by 1794, when the boatswain's stores of a 74-gun ship listed only one 'small iron stove, Brodie's, with printed instructions'.[11]

There had been earlier efforts to solve the problems of ventilation. One of the first was proposed by Sutton in 1741. Pipes were led from the galley stove to the various decks. Another development came in 1757, with Dr Hales' ventilators, which were operated by bellows and pumped air to each deck. The captain's orders regulated the use of these, usually stipulating that they be operated for at least one hour in each watch when the ports were

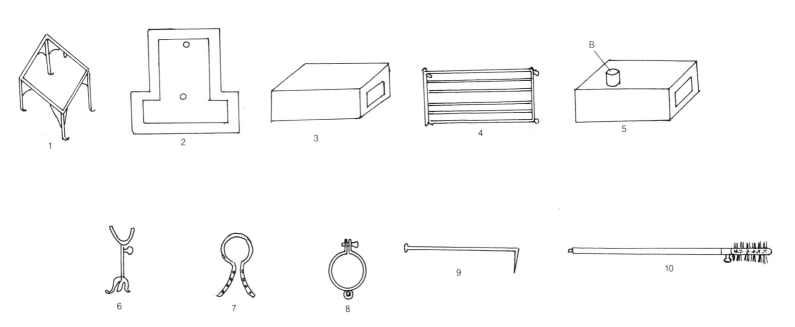

1 to 5. *A 'stove for airing ships', c1783.*

1. *An iron frame, with four legs and four braces, for the stove to stand on.*

2. *A cast iron and wrought iron pan with shelving or sloping sides, which was fixed to the iron frame, fig 1. It had holes which the stubs of the frame fitted into.*

3. *An oblong box, open on top and bottom, with a door at one end, which stands in the pan, fig 2.*

4. *A cast iron grated bottom, with four short feet, which stands in the box, fig 3.*

5. *Another cast iron box, which stands on fig 3 and grated bottom fig 4, completing the stove except for the funnel or copper tube with elbows, which is fixed on the part B, fig 5, to convey the heat and smoke away from the stove.*

6, 7, 8 and 9. *Several fittings which supported and held together funnel pipes.*

6. *A standard with three feet, a sliding rod with a fork, and a set screw to fix the fork at any height.*

7. *A collar with two flaps and several nail holes so it could be fixed at any position to hold up the funnel pipe.*

8. *A jointed couple with a screw, to fasten over the joints of copper funnel to hold them together.*

9. *A spiked rod. The spike was driven in one end of the funnel and bent to any length in order to hold up the funnel pipe.*

10. *A round brush with a long handle and a set screw to clean the funnel pipes.*

closed. In 1773, the windsail was introduced. This was a canvas tent-like structure, placed over a hatch and turned towards the wind so that some air was directed below decks. At first they were issued to three-deckers, but they did not entirely replace the Hales ventilator. In 1785 a different system was tried aboard the *Royal Sovereign*. A fan was placed under the galley stove, to pipe hot air to the decks below. In 1794 a new instrument, known as White's ventilator, was introduced.[12]

Lighting

In the age of sail, artificial light always involved a naked flame, and this of course was potentially very dangerous. Between 1793 and 1815, ten ships were lost because of fire, eight of which were of the line of battle.[13] Other notable casualties included the *Sovereign of the Seas*, burnt in 1697, allegedly as the result of an accident with a candle. Obviously the mess decks had to be lit in the evening, and the purser issued candles, and the boatswain lanterns. Great care had to be taken that they were extinguished when the crew bedded down. One of the main duties of the master at arms was to patrol the decks at lights-out, to ensure this. In Captain Middleton's orders, a midshipman was to go down at least once an hour to make sure that no lights were lit below decks.[14] Men were allotted special stations for fire-fighting so that they would be ready if fire, the most fearful emergency known to seamen, broke out.

PART IX

Internal Fittings

Chapter 34. Hold Stowage

Iron Ballast

One of the major considerations when stowing a ship's hold was to keep the weight, and therefore the centre of gravity, sufficiently low. Obviously the most efficient way of doing this was to place heavy weights as low as possible in the ship. Metal, in the form of lead and iron, provided the most obvious means of doing this. Lead, despite its cost, was the most efficient of these. Boteler and Mainwaring mention lead, but not iron, as a possible form of ballast.[1] In 1627 it was suggested that only ships with 'sharp and narrow floors, which carry much ordnance, and have three decks whereby the ordnance is carried high' needed iron ballast. Other ships could carry coal instead.[2] Iron ballast does not seem to have been used much for at least the next century, and there is little contemporary mention of it. The *Royal Katherine* of 1664, for example carried 145 tons of ballast, but this was evidently stone or shingle.[3] In 1676 the Admiralty decided that the new galley frigates should have 'iron ballast out of the Tower if it can be had'.[4] This seems to indicate the rarity of its use; it was discussed by the Admiralty itself rather than treated as a routine matter, and it had to be obtained from the Tower, rather than from stocks in the dockyards. The galley frigates were designed for fast sailing. As late as 1752, a list was produced showing ships with only one type of ballast, which it can be assumed was to be shingle. But by 1756 another list shows nearly all the ships mentioned carrying large quantities of iron as well as shingle.[5] Lead ballast was also in use at this time, but only for the royal yachts, which were regarded as very fast sailers.[6]

Iron ballast, sometimes known as 'kentledge', came in the form of strips known as pigs. These varied in size, from 3ft × 6in × 6in, to 1ft × 4in × 4in, and in weight, from 320 to 56lbs, but the largest of these sizes was by far the most common in the late eighteenth and early nineteenth centuries.[7] A pig had a hole at each end, to make it easier to lift. To be efficient, the iron had to be laid as low as possible in the ship, but it could not be put right in the centre of the hold, because the keelson and limber boards would lift it too high. Burney suggests that it should be at least 5in away from

the limber boards, and kept from sliding inwards by strakes of fir nailed to the internal planking.[8] But some plans show it brought right up to the limber boards, stowed diagonally on top of them, and even on top of the keelson. Others show it outside the line of hatchways and the well of the pump, perhaps to allow room for the movement of stores. In general, frigates seem to have had it closer to the centre than ships of the line, probably because their floors were less flat.[9]

The bottom level of the hold was already divided into sections, known as 'rooms', by the athwartships riders which were part of the structure, and were known, for this purpose, as 'sleepers'. Within each room, several rows of pigs ran out from the centre of the hull. Close to the keelson, the pigs were piled two high; the top ones were known as 'riders'. Where they were three high, they were called 'double riders'. Most pigs ran fore and aft, but some ran athwartships where the shape of the ship dictated it. The greatest quantity was usually placed forward of midships, where the floor of the ship was widest, and the ballast could therefore be kept lower. The rows tended to reduce in length and depth towards the bow and the stern, and the ballast did not extend very far towards the extremities of the ship. On frigates and smaller vessels where the run aft was very fine, little ballast was placed aft of the pump well. A few tons were kept spare for shifting about, to alter the ship's trim.

The quantity of iron ballast was usually decided by the ship's designer. In the 1750s the amount seems to have varied considerably, even among ships of a similar type. For example, in 1756 four 90-gun ships, the *Prince*, *Ramillies*, *St George* and *Prince George*, carried 102, 50, 98 and 50 tons respectively, while the *Cambridge* and *Newark*, both 80s on the 1745 establishment, carried 71 and 150 tons respectively.[10] In the same year, Captain Rodney of the *Dublin* had a dispute with the Navy Board about the amount to be carried, and later removed some iron and shingle, against its instructions, but to the improvement, he claimed, of the sailing qualities of his ship.[11] By 1796, the amount of iron ballast was standardised for each type of ship.[12]

Shingle Ballast

Even when iron ballast was carried, a ship usually carried on average about four times as much shingle, though the proportions

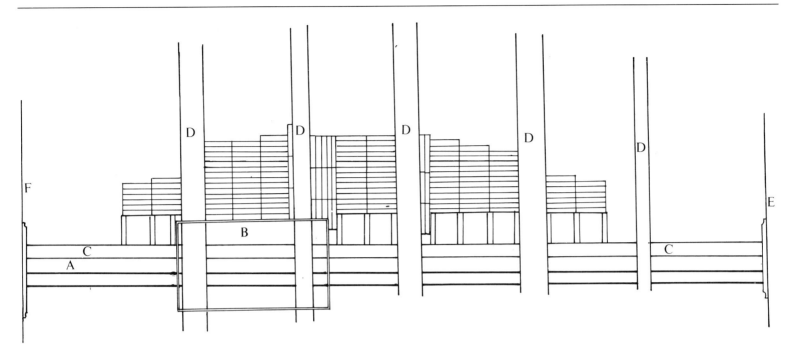

Iron ballast in the hold of a 74-gun ship, c1780.
A. The keelson.
B. The well.
C. A rising to the ceiling.
D. The riders.
E. Bulkhead of the fore hold.
F. After bulkhead.

could vary considerably. This ballast served two purposes. Like iron, it helped keep the ship's centre of gravity low, and it also provided a suitable surface for stowing the casks in which provisions were kept. One of the problems with shingle was that it tended to be infected with bilge water and become noxious. One of the duties of the master of a ship was to 'see that the ballast is sweet and clean'.[13] The shingle was placed on top of any iron ballast, and was extended outboard of it, and closer towards the bows and stern. It was easier to fit into awkward spaces, and easier to shift than iron, therefore it was often moved during minor adjustments to the ship's trim.

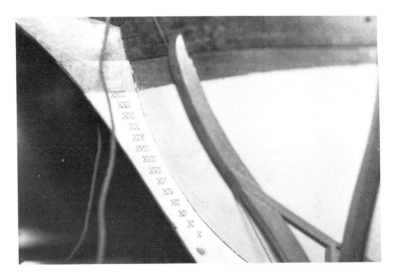

Draught marks on the cutwater of a mid-eighteenth century ship.

The Trim of the Ship

There were three main factors to be taken into consideration when finding the correct trim of a ship. First, it had to be sunk to a suitable depth in the water so that, on one hand, the gunports were a reasonable distance above the water, even when the ship was heeling and on the other hand so that it was deep enough to create resistance to leeway. Second, the centre of gravity had to be kept correctly positioned, possibly by the use of a carefully judged quantity of iron ballast. Too much iron would cause stiffness, and the ship would roll too violently and too often, making it an unsteady gun platform and causing damage because of the shaking. Too little would make it crank, so that it would not be able to carry much sail, or keep its lower gunports out of the water when heeling. Third, the ship's waterline had to be at an optimum angle to the keel, for good sailing. On most ships this meant that the stern was sunk lower in the water than the bows, and the ship was 'trimmed by the stern'.

The first and last of these factors depended at least as much on the weight and distribution of stores and provisions as on ballast. The ship's depth in the water depended on the total weight carried, and the difference in the waterline at the bow and the stern depended on how these weights were distributed. In general the weight above the waterline, the masts and yards, the guns, and the structure of the ship itself, was fixed and beyond the control of the ship's officers. The stowage of the hold, including distribution of provisions as well as ballast, was used to control the trim.

The master of the ship, responsible under the captain for her sailing, was in charge of the stowage of the hold, rather than the purser, who was responsible for most of the goods kept there. When the master took up his office he was to discover all he could about the sailing qualities and trim of the ship, either from previous masters or the designer. During his service he was 'attentively to examine her qualities at sea, that he may suggest any alteration in her stowage as he may think likely to improve

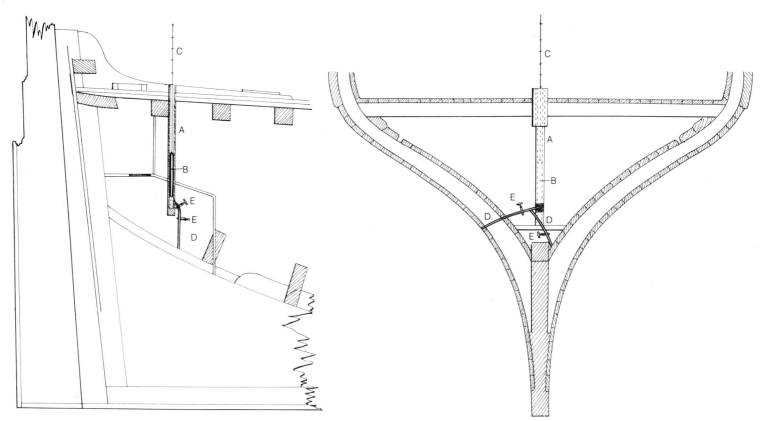

Floats, as fitted to a 74-gun ship, c1780. Profile (above) and cross-section looking aft (right).
A. Hollow tube, 4¼in square.
B. Copper float, 4in square, 9in long.
C. Wooden rod, marked to show draught of water.
D. Lead pipes, one leading to the hold, the other to outside the ship.
E. Sea cocks.

them.'[14] He had to maintain the best trim during the ship's voyage, even though some of her stores would be consumed. Sometimes it was necessary to fill empty casks with seawater to keep them a suitable weight. In other instances, casks were broken down into their individual staves to save space in the hold. By the 1680s, lead numerals were fixed at intervals on the stern-post and stempost, as an indication for the master of the ship's draught of water both fore and aft.[15] In the 1780s a more complex system of floats was adopted. These were intended to aid in 'trimming the ship when at sea', by giving instant information on the draught of water both fore and aft. Holes were cut in the hull at each end for inlet pipes, which led to chambers with floats, which raised and lowered battens marked off in feet. The float itself was made of copper. In 1780, they were to be fitted on all ships of more than 20 guns, on the captain's application. In 1782 they were to be fitted regardless of the captain's wish, but in 1788 it was forbidden that they be fitted without special order. In 1796 the officers of Portsmouth Dockyard wrote, 'Frequent applications are made to us to take away the floats, being in general thought of very little use, often out of repair, and the pipes frequently leaking, the water often gets among the bread.' It seems likely that they fell out of use soon afterwards.[16]

Supplies Carried

In the seventeenth century, English ships were usually expected to carry enough provisions for four months. In the 1660s, it was found that French ships were being built to carry up to six months' supplies, and, according to Pepys, the most recent group of English ships was designed likewise. There is some reason to believe that his claim was exaggerated; in any case it would have been many years before the whole fleet could be rebuilt in such a way.[17] In the eighteenth century, ships operated much further from their home bases, but it was not generally possible to improve on carrying six months' worth of stores. Ships were stored according to need. Those intended for service in the Channel were never far from the main dockyards, and carried food for three or four months; those going further afield were equipped for six months.

Water was easier to replenish than food, for it could be obtained at any convenient creek or river. Therefore it was customary to carry water to last only half the period of the food. Nevertheless it had to be used frugally and it was another of the master's duties to ensure this. Water was the heaviest, bulkiest, and in many respects the most important of the supplies caried. A 74-gun ship of the 1790s, for example, carried 219 tons of water, compared with 183 tons of other stores, including food, alcohol and fuel.[18]

Seamen in the age of sail would not have remained obedient for long if they had only water to drink. Originally they were issued with one gallon of beer per day on home service, to supplement the water. When on foreign service, wine or brandy could be substituted for beer, at a rate of a quart of wine or half a pint of brandy per day. In the 1740s Admiral Vernon discovered rum in the West Indies, and he insisted that it be diluted with two parts of water, believing that this helped prevent drunkenness. Thus water was still needed for drinking. Rum soon became the traditional drink of the Navy, though beer was still issued in home waters, and at the beginning of a voyage.

The seaman's diet was very simple. The staple was 'bread' or biscuit. In 1677 each man was 'to have for his allowance by the day one pound avoirdupois of good, clean, sweet, sound, well bolted with a horse cloth, well baked and well conditioned wheaten biscuit'.[19] About 30 tons' worth were needed on a 74-gun ship for four months.[20] Bread was wrapped up so it was protected and unlike other provisions did not have to be stored in casks, though it had to be kept clear of the bilge water.

Meat, in the form of salt pork or beef was issued four days a week. In the seventeenth century, fish was issued on the other days, for the government wished to encourage the fishing industry as a 'nursery for seamen'. On meatless days each man was to have 'the eighth part of a full-sized North sea cod 24 inches long, or a sixth part of a haberdine 22 inches long, or a quarter part of the same sort, if but 16 inches long.'[21] Fish was less common in the eighteenth century, though ships were issued with nets and lines to catch their own on long voyages. Other perishable supplies, also kept in casks, included butter, cheese, peas, and raisins. Coal and wood were carried, mainly for the galley stove.

Divisions of the Hold

The largest hold was the main hold. It occupied about half the length of the ship, extending from where the riding bitts were level with the break of the forecastle, to a little forward of the mizzen, under the break of the poop. It was divided into two parts, the fore and the after hold. The pump well, situated about two-thirds from the forward end, was the main division. However, there was no actual partition, and the well extended only part of the way across the hold. The after hold seems to have been used for ready-use stores, and was regarded as slightly more secure than the main hold. Each hold was reached through a series of hatches, one above another, cut through several decks to form a continuous passage through which casks could be raised or lowered. Ships of the line usually had three such series. The main hatchway, the largest in the ship, was just forward of the mast and the pumps. The after hatchway was just aft of the mainmast and

the fore hatchway was well forward to give access to the forward part of the main hold.

The main hold was used for provisions such as water, meat, beer, cheese and butter which required neither special care nor security. Fish, with its strong smell, was kept apart from other goods, in the fish room which was fitted aft of the main hold and separated off by a partition. It was entered by way of a small scuttle cut in the orlop deck. Beer was too bulky to pilfer in significant quantities, but the increasing use of spirits in the second half of the eighteenth century made it necessary to create a space where they could be kept safe. By an order of 1776, the dockyards were to 'cause a bulkhead to be put up in the after part of the hold in all ships whose captains shall apply to you for it', for 'the security of their wines and spirits'.[22] The 'spirituous liquor room' was aft of the fish room, under the after cockpit, where it could be easily guarded. The master kept the keys to this room and the after hold, and 'when they are wanted, he is to deliver them to one of the master's mates only, strictly charging him not to suffer a light to be carried into the spirit room; to attend himself, without quitting on any account, either the spirit room or the after hold when it is open'.[23]

Aft of the spirit room and the fish room was the after powder room, which was under the control of the gunner. Aft of that was the bread room. At this point the deadwood lifted the frame timbers high above the keel, so that there was relatively little danger from bilge water. On the other hand, the hull was narrow and the sides were steep, so space here was rather restricted. Because of this, the bread room extended above the orlop deck, at which level gratings were sometimes placed for the bread to lie on. The bread room was, according to an order of 1686, to be double lined with dry seasoned slit deals.[24]

On early ships the bread room continued all the way to the transoms of the stern. By the end of the eighteenth century a tiny compartment known as the 'lady's hole' was separated off aft of it, roughly on a level with the orlop. It may have derived its name from the 'lady of the gunroom', an aged seaman responsible for that compartment, and who kept his stores there.

Forward of the main hold was the main magazine. Forward of that was another small, irregular shaped compartment known as the fore-peak. This was used mainly to store wood and coal for the galley stove.

The partitions in the hold were simply constructed, from vertical cants and horizontal planks, or around 1690, weatherboard.

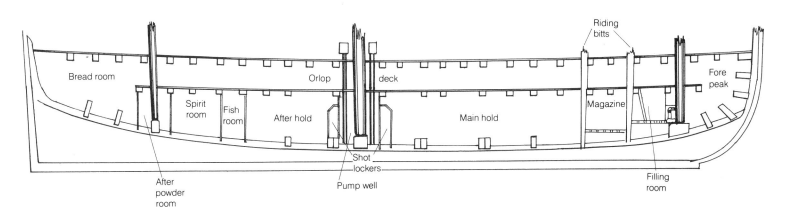

The subdivision of the hold of a 74-gun ship in the 1750s.

They were sometimes covered in deal, and plastered to make the goods more secure. They were not caulked, and there was no suggestion that they were intended to act as watertight bulkheads should the ship spring a leak.

Methods of Stowage

Most provisions, with the notable exception of bread, were kept in casks of various sizes. The biggest, known as leaguers, were 4ft 6in long, and had a maximum diameter of 3ft. Their capacity was 150 gallons each, and they were used exclusively to hold water, in the lowest tier of the larger ships. Butts, containing 108 gallons, also seem to have been common on large ships, at all levels in the hold. Smaller casks, including puncheons, hogsheads, barrels and half hogsheads, formed the main stowage on smaller vessels, or filled up the spaces near the sides of the ship on larger ones.

The hold was stowed in several layers, known as tiers. The ground tier was at the bottom. It contained the largest barrels, which held much of the water and beer, which were heavier than meat and other provisions. The shingle ballast was arranged so it provided a relatively level surface, and the casks of the ground tier were sunk into it, to a depth of about a quarter of their diameter. Like all casks, they were stowed 'bung up and bilge free', to minimise leakage. They were arranged in rows running fore and aft, with the bilge, or widest part, of one cask opposite the ends of those in the next row. The space near the sides was occupied by smaller casks, and care was taken that the whole tier was kept level, to make it easier to stow the one above. The next tier was arranged in similar fashion, but generally with smaller casks. Each cask was placed in the 'canting' of the one below. In other

words it fitted into the space where two rows met. When necessary, wedges were driven between the casks to prevent them moving about.

Large ships usually had three tiers, smaller vessels had only two. In 1814 the 60-gun ship *Newcastle*, designed by the emigré French naval architect Barralier, was criticised because it could not stow a full tier of butts as its third tier, and had to use puncheons instead.[25] Smaller ships carried as many tiers as convenient, and used suitable sizes of cask.

Diagonal Bracing and Iron Tanks

Towards the end of the Napoleonic Wars several changes occurred which were to alter the traditional system of hold stowage. Firstly, in 1811 Sir Robert Seppings introduced his new system of diagonal bracing, which replaced the athwartships riders which had been used in the past. It gave ships much greater strength. It also meant that the iron ballast, which had mostly been laid fore and aft between the riders, had to be laid in a different pattern. It was now often laid diagonally like the riders, or placed within the triangular and diamond shapes formed by them.

Not long afterwards, another far reaching change took place. By an order of 1814, rectangular iron tanks began to replace the casks of water in the holds of ships. These could hold a greater quantity of water in a given space than casks, because much less space was wasted between them. They were shaped specially for each ship, and laid directly above the floor riders. There was no need for shingle ballast (with all the problems it caused when unclean), for the tanks did not need to be sunk into anything to hold them in place. Iron tanks therefore entirely superseded

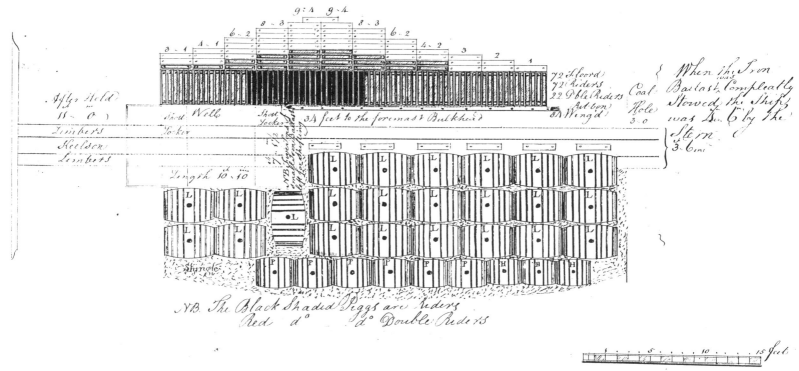

The ballast and ground tier of the frigate Artois *in 1794, showing how the casks were placed in the shingle.* PRO.

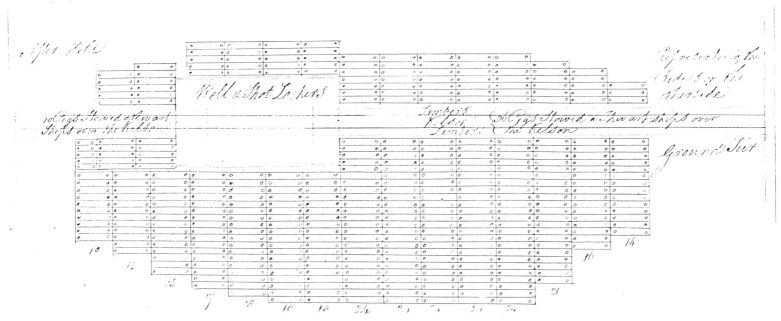

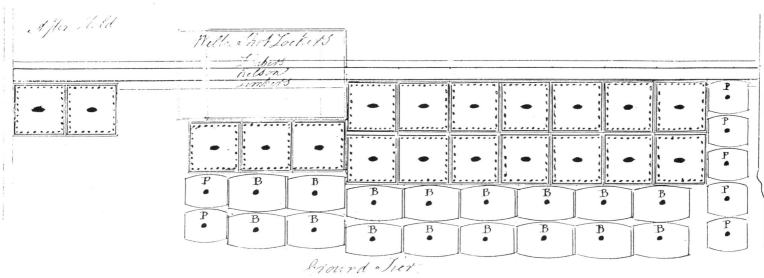

The iron ballast (above) and water tanks (below) of the Barrosa, *a frigate of 1812.*

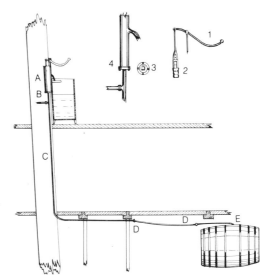

Truscott's pump as fitted on the Havock *of 1805.*
A. Pump on the upper deck.
B. Pipe to carry water to ship's hold, ¾ in interior diameter.
C. Pipe to carry water to tank on the upper deck.
D. 'Union screws to shift in lengths as wanted'.
E. Leather hose.
1. Handle to pump.
2. Upper box.
3. Cap or ring with valve.
4. Joint with four screws.

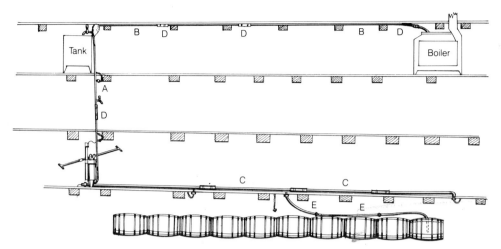

Trustcott's pump.
A. Pipe to convey water to the upper deck.
B. Pipe to convey water to the boilers.
C. Pipe in the orlop deck with cap screws to which suction hoses from the hold could be fitted.

D. Leather hoses with spring wires placed between ends of pipe, to prevent damage from the ship's motion.
E. Leather suction hoses, with tinned and coppered swivel screws and copper ferrules. These were 11in long and could be shifted along the hoses' length as required.

shingle ballast. However, this change took many years to implement. By 1815 only a minority of ships had been so fitted and 3343 iron tanks issued. A 100-gun ship carried 100 tanks, a 36-gun ship 30, and a small sloop had 12.[26]

The iron tank was made possible by the fact that it was no longer necessary to raise the container out of the hold to extract its contents. In 1812, Truscott's pump had been introduced. This had a flexible tube, which could be inserted into any of the casks in the hold, and used to pump its contents out. It could convey water to a tank on the quarterdeck where it was issued to the crew, or directly to the boilers of the galley.

It was first tested aboard the *Malta* and *Bulwark*. The captain of the latter ship reported 'Truscott's apparatus for conveying water from the casks in the hold to the decks and forward to the ship's boilers . . . fully answers every purpose propounded by the inventor, and will materially tend to lessen the labour on board His Majesty's ships, by obviating the necessity of casks being hoisted on deck.'[27] The device was generally adopted, and Truscott was promoted from lieutenant to commander.

Chapter 35. Store Rooms

The Orlop Deck

A man of war had to be ready to operate away from bases and dockyards for many months, and prepared for almost any eventuality. Thousands of separate items were necessary to keep the ship afloat and operational. Spare parts for the rigging, the hull, the guns, and all the fittings were needed, and medical supplies, clothing, and bedding had to be stored. Tools for metal workers and woodworkers were carried, sometimes including a camp forge so that the armourer could carry out his work on a convenient shore. The hold was designed to stow items in bulk, where the inaccessibility of an individual cask did not matter. Other stores had to be kept in store rooms, on racks, on shelves, and in drawers, where they could be reached very quickly in an emergency.

The orlop deck was ideal for these purposes. It was below the waterline, so it was relatively safe from gunfire, and articles kept there would not impede the ship's guns. Unlike the hold, it was flat, and so it could be used to lay out cordage and cables. It was free from bilge water, except that which ran down the sides, so it could be used to store spare sails and any other items which would perish when wet. Largely because of the absence of guns, it was easy to divide into compartments, sealed off with strong bulkheads, and locked with the keys which were under the control of a particular officer. This was important because many stores, such as rope and copper, were quite expensive and easily disposed of on the black market.

The orlop deck never extended the full length of a ship. Even on two- and three-deckers, it stopped some way short of the stern, to allow room for the bread room. On some ships, particularly in the seventeenth century, it also ended some way from the ship's stem; this was rarer in the eighteenth century. On frigates it was divided into three parts, one forward, one midships and one aft, which were used for different purposes (they were called platforms in the hold). The foremost division was used for stores, the midships one for cables, and the after one for other stores. Smaller Sixth Rates did not have a middle division, though this did not in itself affect the distribution of their store rooms. On other ships, the orlop deck was fitted at several levels to allow for the rising and narrowing of the hull. In many cases the magazine interrupted the deck, for it was on a higher level than on a two-decker. Other small vessels had no orlop at all. The berthing deck served for stores as well as accommodation. The very smallest gunboats kept almost all their stores on small decks built just above the floor of the ship.

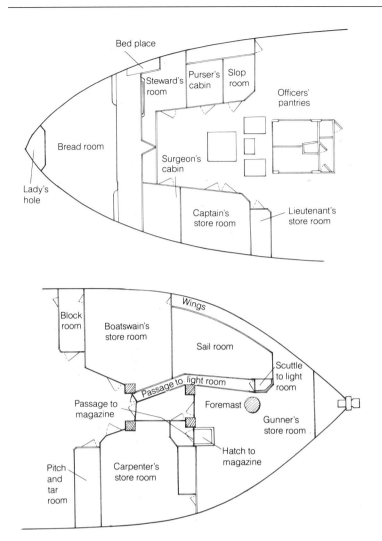

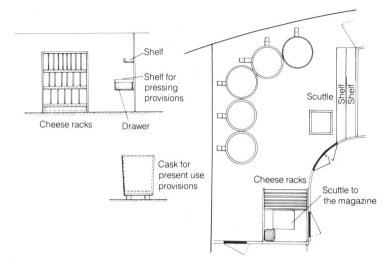

Drawers in the carpenter's store room of the Wellesley *and* Melville *of 1814.*

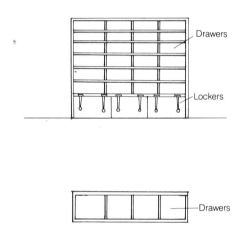

Details of the steward's room.

The store rooms etc, of the Dorsetshire *of 1757. This arrangement was fairly standard after about 1715. Plan aft (top), plan forward (bottom).*

Warrant Officers' Stores

Virtually all the items kept in store were under the direct control of one or other of the ship's warrant officers: the surgeon, purser, carpenter, boatswain and gunner. The latter three kept their stores forward on the orlop, or on the fore platform. The boatswain, carpenter and gunner were the 'standing officers' of the ship, so called because they would stay with her even when she was out of commission. They were largely responsible for maintenance: the boatswain for rigging, the carpenter for the hull and for all wooden fittings including masts, yards and boats, and the gunner for the guns and all their tackle. Between them they needed large stocks of material, either for spares or for ready-use. To facilitate accounting, the three stores were invariably kept separate. This resulted in a rather complicated subdivision of the fore platform, for it also had to have one corridor giving access to the magazine, and one to the light room, when it came into use.

The gunner's store was forward, right in the bows of the ship. It was fitted with racks and drawers for a wide variety of items such as spare ropes and blocks for the guns, parts for the trucks and carriages, locks for the guns, materials for making cartridges, and substances for painting and preserving the various pieces of equipment. Because the armourer, the principal metal worker of the ship, was under the command of the gunner, the store also included his tools, and a certain amount of spare ironwork.

The boatswain had perhaps a wider variety of stores than any of the warrant officers. His largest single item was spare rope to repair the rigging. This was coiled on the deck, or hung on specially designed stands with projecting arms. He also kept blocks of various sizes, and all the materials which were needed to treat and maintain the rigging. Racks and drawers were fitted to hold the numerous smaller items. The boatswain's store was fitted on the port side, often aft of a separate sail room. The carpenter's store was on the opposite side of the ship. It was of course mainly equipped to hold wood, in all shapes and sizes. In 1808 it was ordered that it be fitted with lead cisterns to hold paint and oil, instead of keeping them in buckets.[1]

The Wings

The orlop deck was below the waterline so the hull around it was particularly vulnerable. Shot which penetrated the hull in this area was 'between wind and water', that is, just above the

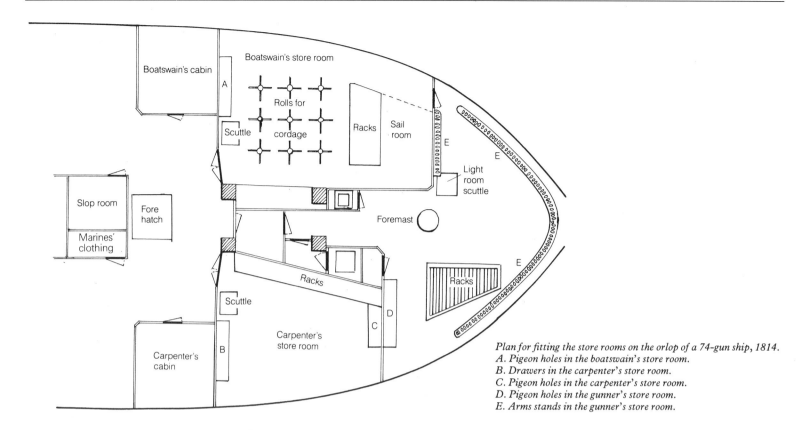

Plan for fitting the store rooms on the orlop of a 74-gun ship, 1814.
A. Pigeon holes in the boatswain's store room.
B. Drawers in the carpenter's store room.
C. Pigeon holes in the carpenter's store room.
D. Pigeon holes in the gunner's store room.
E. Arms stands in the gunner's store room.

waterline, but where water might still be able to enter because of the action of the waves, or because the heel of the ship altered. Any holes in this area had to be sealed instantly, and in action the carpenter and his crew were stationed with wooden plugs ready to hammer them into place. To allow them easy access, the store rooms and cabins on the orlop were partitioned off from the sides of the ship. The passages thus created were known as the 'wings', or the 'carpenter's walk'. They were of course very narrow, particularly because they included the knees of the gundeck. Though one would have expected them to be kept clear ready for use, in 1805 it was ordered that they be widened to make room to stow powder barrels.[2] In 1808 it was ordered that they be floored with gratings, instead of ledges which had been customary in the past.[3] Wings were only needed on two- and three-deckers. On frigates and smaller ships, the orlop deck was well below the waterline in any case, and the cabins and other fittings on the lower deck were already removeable. They were not always needed in midships on two- and three-deckers. Generally a row of stanchions was fitted to keep the cables away from the sides of the ship; in the early nineteenth century this seems to have developed into a more solid structure.

Sail Rooms

Ships carried an enormous amount of sailcloth. A 74-gun ship of 1773 had nearly 9000yds of canvas, 2ft wide, made up into 27 sails, and spares. Much of this was kept aloft when the ship was at sea, but taken down when she was in harbour for a long period. Some sails, such as the studding sails, were only taken out when needed. There were also many spare sails, so that stronger canvas could be used in higher winds. One of the great dangers to sails

was mildew, which was caused by damp. Sails had to be dried before they were stowed away, and then carefully folded to save space. The rooms where they were stowed were on the orlop, carefully chosen to avoid damp and also to allow them some airing. One traditional site was in the bows, near the boatswain's store room and just aft of the gunner's store room. On larger ships, there were also sail rooms behind the warrant officers' stores. This area was not always entirely satisfactory. The wings did not always keep the sails far enough from the sides to prevent damp, and the rooms were not close to any of the large hatchways, so it must have been difficult to get a large sail out onto the deck.

In the early years of the eighteenth century further sail rooms were added to two- and three-deckers, down the centre line of the orlop, between the pump well and the store rooms forward. These were well clear of the bilges and the sides of the ship. The wet cables were stowed on each side of them, and though the water from these was expected to drain into the bilges, it must have tended to raise the moisture level in the area of the orlop. Usually two sail rooms were fitted in the cable tier of a ship of the line, between the fore and main hatches. Later, frigates had one. The sail room in the bows was retained, but it probably served more as a store for spare rolls of canvas, and a workshop for the sailmaker.

The Cockpit

On ships which had a continuous orlop, either side of the space amidships, aft of the store rooms, was filled with cable tiers, and a line of sail rooms, hatches, and the well of the pump ran down the middle. Aft of this was an area known as the cockpit. The space in the middle of this served as a berth for the junior officers and

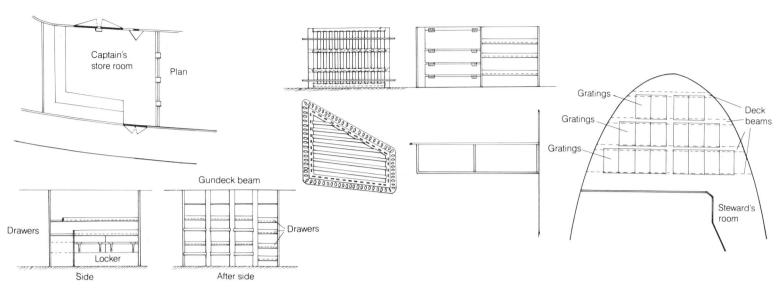

Details of the captain's store room.

Left. Racks for the gunner's stores, with racks for small arms round them. Right. Colour chest and shelves in the boatswain's store room.

The gratings of the bread room on a 74-gun ship, c1810.

midshipmen, as an operating theatre for the surgeon in action, and to give access to the fish room and the spirit room, by way of hatches cut in the deck. On each side of the cockpit were cabins and store rooms, kept away from the sides of the ship, like the store rooms forward, by the wings. On a ship of the line, two officers had cabins there, the surgeon, so that he was close to his operating theatre and store room, and the purser, so that he was near where he issued provisions. The other rooms were for stores.

The slop room housed the clothing which was issued and sold to seamen as they needed it. Next to that was another room for marines' clothing. Though there were far fewer marines than seamen, the store was not much smaller, for the marines' dress was much more elaborate. On the other side were store rooms for the captain and the lieutenants. These officers lived high up in the ship, so their cabins had to be cleared and dismantled for action. Their more valuable and bulky goods were kept below. Often they supplied their own food, to supplement that issued by the government, and it is possible that some of this was kept in the store rooms, as well as in the pantry on the upper deck.

Another compartment in the cockpit was the surgeon's dispensary. Originally this was rather small, but it became bigger and more elaborate in the early nineteenth century, as naval medicine made some advances. Around the same time, enclosed midshipmen's berths were added on each side of the cockpit. These were used mainly for recreation and eating; the midshipmen still slung their hammocks in the cockpit itself.

A frigate's orlop differed from that of a ship of the line in that, after the first generation of these vessels, no-one was accommodated there. The cabins and the midshipmen's berths were placed on the lower deck, though the store rooms remained on the orlop.

The Steward's Room

The aftermost compartment on the orlop deck was the steward's room. Here the purser's chief assistant, the ship's steward (not to be confused with the captain's steward or the wardroom stewards) issued provisions to the cooks of each mess for the day's meals. Bread could be issued easily because the steward's room was close to the bread room. On ships where the orlop deck was continuous other provisions were brought aft from the after hatch, and weighed out. Large bins, probably made by cutting large casks in half, were provided for short-term storage. In 1808 vats or casks were to be used instead of bins, presumably because they preserved provisions better.[4] Apart from the room itself, there was a larger area on the edge of the orlop deck, where stores could be weighed and issued. Inside the steward's room was a small area for the steward's bedplace; he was probably the most junior member of the complement to be given the privilege of a fixed and private space for his bed.

Chapter 36. Cooking

The Situation of the Galley

In the early seventeenth century, there was considerable controversy about where to put the cooking stove. The main possibilities were under the forecastle or in the hold amidships. The forecastle position had its disadvantages, because there it would 'hinder the use of the ordnance', and 'lie over the powder'. Moreover, 'a man of war pretends to fight most with his prow, that part is likeliest to receive shot, which if any chance may come amongst the bricks of the cook room, they will spoil more men than the shot.' The prow was 'the most important and pleasantest part of the ship', and it was 'where the chief offensive force of the ship should lie', and it should not be spoiled by placing the cook room there.[1]

Part of Dummer's draught of a First Rate of c1680, showing a globular kettle enclosed in a brick firehearth. Tables for preparing the officers' food are aft of the stove. Science Museum.

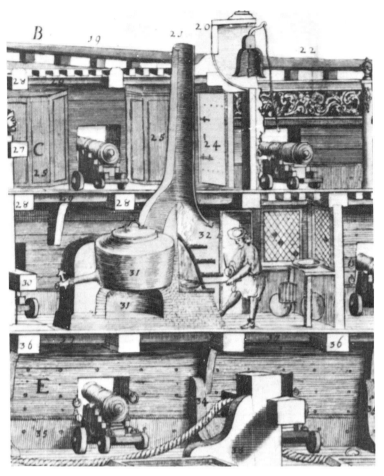

The Phillips print of the 1690s shows a different shape of kettle. No 32 is the grill for the officers' food. NMM.

On the other hand, 'when the cook rooms are in the midship, especially in great ships, they must needs occasion a great hazard of the spoil of the drink and victual stowed in the hold, in the vicinity of the fire and the heat thereof; and are also very offensive by the smoke; and moreover, whensoever the cook-rooms are thus placed, the burthen and lading of the ship, and so the weight and charge thereof, must of necessity be stowed at both her ends; whereby she cannot choose but be much weakened, and become subject to that kind of warping which in sea language is called camber-keeled.'[2] The Commission of Enquiry of 1618 decided in favour of the position under the forecastle, 'because in the midship and in the hold the smoke and heat so search every corner and seam, that they make the oakum spew out, and the ship leaky, and soon decay. Besides, the best room for stowage of victuals is thereby so taken up that transporters must be hired for every voyage.'[3] After that, two-deckers and smaller ships carried the cook room under the forecastle, forward on the upper deck. On three-deckers it was forward on the middle deck, so its chimney had to pass through two decks before discharging its smoke. On a few frigates of around 1780, it was carried forward in the hold, perhaps because its normal position under the forecastle tended to interfere with the cables and riding bitts. The very smallest vessels sometimes had it amidships, because there was so little space in the bows.

Early Stoves

Not much is known about the early seventeenth century galley stove. It is possible that it was as simple as the one found on the Swedish *Vasa* of 1628. This ship had a compartment in the centre of the hold lined with bricks. Above this a large cooking pot was suspended. Possibly the transfer of the stove from the hold to the forecastle resulted in it becoming a little more sophisticated, for the decks were quite low under the forecastle, and there was less room to swing a pot, so it had to be incorporated as part of the structure. The stove consisted of two main parts: a fireplace built of brick, which held the heat of the fire, and a metal container for the food, which was usually boiled.

The Copper Kettle

Copper was regarded as the most suitable material for a cooking pot, largely because early iron did not stand up so well to heat. In the 1750s there was a theory that copper contributed to scurvy, and several ships were fitted experimentally with iron kettles, but this did not last long, and copper remained predominant until the 1780s.[4] The copper kettle was made up of several plates riveted together. The late seventeenth century kettle appears to have been round in shape, rather like a cauldron. By the 1700s it was cylindrical, with a height of about two-thirds its diameter. A horizontal pipe with a tap was fitted near the bottom of the side, to run off the water. The bottom of the kettle was flat, or slightly curved. The top had a removeable lid, about half the diameter of the whole kettle. By the 1680s, all ships of the Sixth Rate and above had two kettles, placed side by side in the furnace. They were known as the fish kettle and the small kettle.[5]

The Firehearth

The basis of the system was the ash pit, above which the kettles were placed. Until the 1750s, bricks were normally used to contain the heat of the furnace, and to build up the structure. Bricks were placed all round the pit, enclosing the kettles (except for their tops), leaving an opening at one side. This was closed by an iron door, which was hinged and could be bolted shut. Horizontal pipes ran through the brickwork, forward of the kettle. The ash pit also had an opening in the top, to allow the smoke to escape through a funnel. Several layers of brick were placed under the ash pit, to keep the fire away from the wood of the deck.

This was the most basic type of firehearth, and was suitable only for boiling. Parts were added to the structure to give scope for more sophisticated cooking. In the seventeenth and early eighteenth centuries, the brickwork on the after side of the main stove formed a separate furnace, with iron racks for grilling. This was used for the officers' food. By the 1740s a separate internal compartment, similar in shape, was being fitted on the opposite side to the ash pit. This was used as an oven.

Even the most basic firehearth used a considerable quantity of bricks. In the 1680s a First Rate needed 2500, a Third Rate 1500, and a Sixth Rate 600.[6] In 1718 it was complained that the working of the decks often caused the bricks of the firehearth to work loose, and the forecastle beams were to be carefully kneed to prevent this.[7]

The Iron Stove

Iron firehearths were first proposed in 1728, because the 'great weight of brickwork' was overloading and straining some of the small sloops.[8] They had become fairly general in 1757. One was fitted to the *Dorsetshire*, launched in that year, and in May the Navy Board issued a detailed list of dimensions for stoves for each class of ship.[9] The kettle was rectangular in shape and still made of copper, but in a single piece, divided into two unequal parts. These were known as double kettles. The smaller compartment was a little more than half the volume of the larger. The larger one had a round lid, the smaller one an oval one. Round kettles were still being made in 1777, but they may have been intended for old ships which still had brick hearths.[10]

The firehearth was made of iron, and built round the double kettle. It was approximately square in plan, the double kettle being fitted on its after part, and raised above the deck by 2ft 3in to 2ft 6in, according to the size of the ship. Under it was the after fireplace, reached by a door in the side. In the foremost part was another fireplace, fitted with racks for grilling, and an arm to hold a spit. Between the two fireplaces, just above deck level, was the oven, also reached by doors in the side. Both fireplaces led to the funnel, which was placed over the forward part. A fan was placed

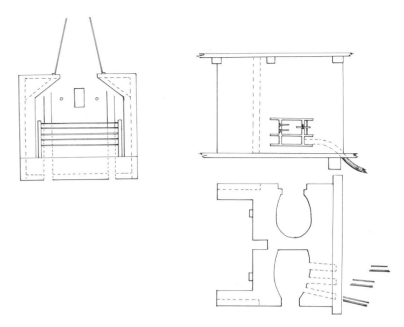

Cross-section and plan of a brick hearth of 1741 showing the Hales ventilators, hence the pipes which can be seen leading out of the stove. NMM.

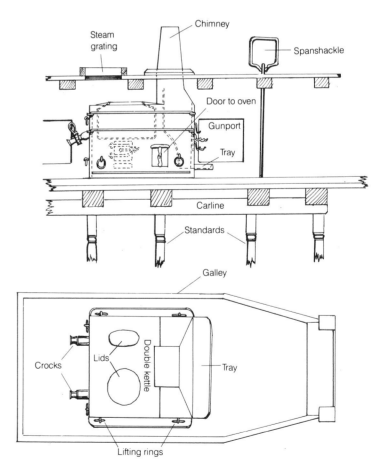

The iron firehearth of the Dorsetshire *of 1757. This is one of the first recorded examples of this type of stove.*

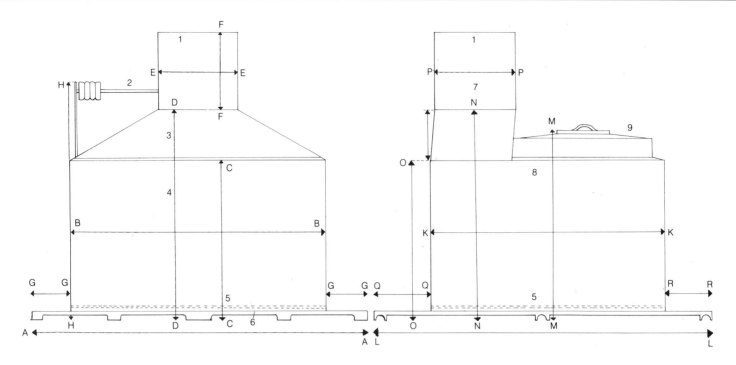

Dimensions of firehearths, c1775.
1. *Lower part of the chimney funnel.*
2. *Chain wheel and spindle of smoke jack.*
3. *The sloping cap.*
4. *Front of body of hearth.*

5. *Additional bottom.*
6. *The bearers.*
7. *Side of sloping cap.*
8. *Side of body of hearth.*
9. *Boiler cover.*

Dimensions

Rate or no of guns	Front (in ft. and in.)								Side (in ft. and in.)							
	A–A	B–B	C–C	D–D	E–E	F–F	G–G & G–G	H–H	K–K	L–L	M–M	N–N	O–O	P–P	Q–Q	R–R
100	9.8	7.4	4.6	5.11	2.3	2.2	1.2	6.8	6.11	9.11	5.3	5.11	4.6	2.3	1.8	1.4
90	9.6	6.11	4.6	5.10½	2.2	2.1	1.1	6.7	6.7	9.8	5.0	5.10½	4.6	2.2	1.7	1.2
80	8.8	6.8	4.4	5.8	2.2	2.1	1.0	6.6	6.4	9.0	4.11	5.8	4.4	2.2	1.7	1.1
74	8.4	6.4	4.4	5.8	2.2	—	1.0	6.6	6.2	8.10	4.10	5.8	4.4	2.2	1.7	1.1
64	7.9	5.9½	4.3	5.7	2.1	—	1.0	6.5	5.9	8.3	4.9	5.7	4.3	2.1	1.6	1.0
50	7.2	5.4	4.2	5.7	2.0	—	0.11	6.5	5.1	7.5	4.8	5.7	4.2	2.0	1.6	0.10
44	5.6	5.0	4.0½	5.6½	1.11	—	0.3	5.3	5.0	7.2	4.6	5.6½	4.0½	1.11	1.6	0.8
38	5.2	4.8	4.0½	5.3½	1.11	—	0.3	5.3	4.9	6.11	4.5½	5.5½	4.0¼	1.11	1.6	0.8
36	5.2	4.8	3.10	5.3½	1.11	—	0.3	5.3	4.9	6.11	4.3	5.3½	3.10	1.11	1.6	0.8
32	4.10	4.3½	3.10	5.3	1.10	—	0.3	5.3	4.7	6.7	4.3	5.3	3.10	1.10	1.4	0.8
28	4.9	4.3	3.10	5.3	1.10	—	0.3	5.3	4.6	6.6	4.3	5.3	3.10	1.10	1.4	0.8
24	4.8	4.2	3.10	5.3	1.9	—	0.3	5.3	4.0½	5.11½	4.2½	5.3	3.10	1.9	1.4	0.7
20	4.7	4.1	3.10	5.3	1.9	—	0.3	5.3	4.0	5.11	4.2	5.3	3.10	1.9	1.4	0.7
18	4.2	3.8	3.8	5.0	1.8	—	0.3	5.3	3.9½	5.7½	4.0	5.0	3.8	1.8	1.3	0.7
16	3.10	3.4	3.7	4.11	1.7	—	0.3	5.3	3.7	5.4	3.11	4.11	3.7	1.7	1.2	0.7
14	3.7	3.1	3.4½	4.8½	1.6	—	0.3	5.3	3.2	4.10	3.9	4.8½	3.4½	1.6	1.1	0.7

A–A *The extreme width of the bottom plate.*
B–B *The width of the body of the firehearth.*
C–C *The height of the hearth from the sloping cap to the deck.*
D–D *The height of the hearth to the head of the cap to which the square joint of the chimney funnel is fitted.*
E–E *The diameter of the lower joint of the chimney funnel.*
F–F *The height of the low joint of the chimney funnel from the upper part of the sloping cap.*
G–G *The distance which the additional bottom plate projects out from the body or side of the hearth.*
H–H *The height of the chain wheel of the smoke jack to the deck.*
K–K *The depth of the body of the firehearth from front to back.*
L–L *The extreme depth of the additional bottom plate from front to back.*
M–M *The height from the deck to the top of the boiler cover.*
N–N *The height from the deck to the head of the cap to which the square joint of the chimney funnel is fitted.*
O–O *The height from the deck to the sloping head or cap.*
P–P *The diameter of the lower joint of the chimney funnel.*
Q–Q *The distance which the additional bottom plate projects before the fore part of the hearth.*
R–R *The distance which the additional bottom plate projects abaft the aft part of the hearth.*

The funnel recoils back 1½in from the front of the hearth.

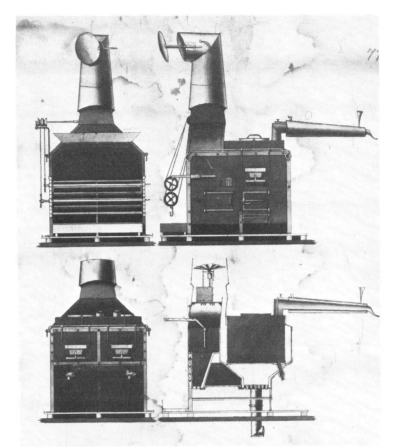

Above. A firehearth fitted to the 100-gun Royal Sovereign *in 1785. The main innovation is that it has a pipe and fan leading to the deck below, for heating and ventilation.*

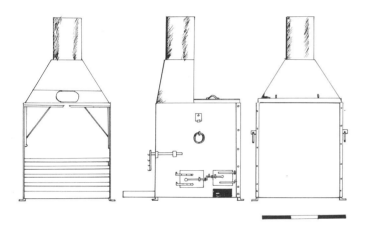

Left. A firehearth for a gunboat at Leith, 1797.

inside the funnel, to help turn the spit. Rings were fitted to the sides of the furnace, apparently for lifting it into place when it was first fitted. Bars were placed along the sides, either as hand-holds or for equipment. The whole structure rested on a flat metal base, and the deck underneath was specially strengthened to hold it, with deck carlines that were thicker than usual.

The new hearth had several advantages. It took up less space than the old one, and probably weighed less. It was much simpler to fit, as it could be hoisted in one piece. The oven, between the two furnaces, must have been more efficient. The extra features, such as the turnspit, were also an advantage.

The Brodie Stove

The Brodie stove began to replace the old type of iron fire-hearth in the 1780s. In 1781 the dockyard officers were ordered to buy no more 'firehearths of the old construction', as the Navy Board was 'intending to enter into a contract with Mr Brodie for fire hearths of a new construction'.[11] In fact it does not seem to have been radically different from the old type. It was much less

of a break with tradition than the issue of the first iron stoves in the 1750s. It appears that the boilers were now iron, and were an integral part of the construction; otherwise the changes were small. The Brodie stove was described as 'a firehearth of a new construction, with kitchen range, folding top bar, two sliding racks for spits, a trivet bar and two swing cranes with a stay to each, two ovens which are heated without any extra fuel, two square iron boilers with two covers to each, two brass cocks with set screws to plugs, a circular plate with two sliding rods and sockets for the mouth of the funnel.' Other equipment included spits, wheels for driving them, and various spare parts.[12] It was said to be capable of distilling water, and indeed a still led from the top of the hearth. Any quantities produced by this means must have been very small, and were probably used for medical purposes. It is not clear how many of the above features were new.

Smaller stoves, described as 'stewing stoves with trivets and grates', were issued in 1787. Seven were issued to a First Rate, five to a 74-gun ship, three to a frigate and two to a sloop. Each stove had two grates and one trivet. It is not clear how they were used.

Lamb and Nicholson Stoves

A new type of stove, made by the company Lamb and Nicholson, was first tested in 1809, aboard three ships of the line, the *Aboukir*, *Royal Oak* and the *Blake*. It had a still, which was not an entirely new feature, capable of producing four gallons of fresh water per day and was said to use less fuel. It had three boilers instead of two, so that 'potatoes can always be boiled separate from meat and soup'. Following favourable reports from all three captains, it was adopted generally in 1810.[13]

Chimneys

The galley chimney was in two parts. The lower one, an integral part of the stove, conveyed the smoke up to the level of the forecastle deck. The upper one raised it above the level of that deck. In most cases the chimney could be moved around to suit the wind. The lower part was roughly conical on a brick stove, and shaped like a truncated pyramid on an iron stove. It gathered the smoke together near the centre line of the ship, and passed it through the deck.

From the outside the upper part of the chimney was the most prominent feature. It was placed on the forecastle deck, between the belfry and the mainmast. The simplest type was shaped like a truncated cone or pyramid, and merely carried the smoke some way above the deck, without regard to wind conditions. In cross section it was round or rectangular, or a more complex shape which was a combination of a cone and a pyramid. The smoke was simply discharged through the opening in the top.

Another type of upper chimney was made in the form of a cowl, which could be turned round to face away from the wind, to prevent the smoke being blown back down. This appears between

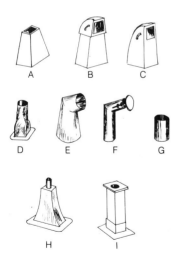

Types of galley chimney.
A. Simple wood chimney, used for various ships up to about 1760.
B. A similar base to A, with a wooden cowl which can be moved according to the wind direction. Note the handle to help turn it.
C. The 'sentry box' type, which can also be moved according to the wind direction.
D. A copper tube on a 20-gun ship of 1745.
E. A metal cowl on the Victory.
F. A cowl with plate, to prevent the smoke blowing back.
G. A simple metal cylinder, as used on the Boyne *of 1790.*
H. An unusually shaped chimney on the Warrior *of 1781.*
I. A wooden pipe on a 60-gun ship of 1719. Possibly it was lined with metal inside.

1690 and 1740 in a type of 'sentry box' form. It was made of wood and was square in section with sides which narrowed slightly as they extended upwards. The top was rounded off, with a hole on one side for the discharge. Because its base was square, it could be turned in any of four directions. A variation of this was a shorter cowl which could be placed on top of the square chimney (described above). Only the top part needed to be moved, or when the wind or the ship's heading changed.

Though copper is mentioned as a material for chimneys as early as 1686, most of the early eighteenth century ones seem to have been made of wood. Copper chimneys, usually the simple cylindrical form, are seen again late in the century, for example, on the *Boyne* of 1790. The copper cowl appeared in the 1720s, though it did not become standard until the nineteenth century. It was shaped like a bent pipe, usually narrowing towards its top end. Sometimes the bend was curved, sometimes angular. As it was round in cross-section, it could be turned to any angle. In some cases a round copper plate was fixed vertically a short distance away from the discharge, to prevent a sudden gust from blowing the smoke back.

The Cook Room

The galley on a two-decker was behind the forecastle. In the seventeenth century it helped to give the forecastle bulkhead its distinctive shape, with its three square projections, one in the centre for the cook room, and one on each side for the standing officers' cabins. In the eighteenth century the bulkhead became straighter, though the cook room still projected slightly. Even though the galley on a three-decker was on the deck below, the bulkhead of the forecastle was of similar shape. After the introduction of the iron stove in the middle of the eighteenth century, the part of the bulkhead immediately aft of the galley had two large doors which opened outwards, to allow for its fitting and removal.

From the later part of the seventeenth century the galley was sealed off from the rest of the forecastle within a six-sided compartment, which had sides narrowing towards its foremost end. This helped to prevent the pilfering of food, and perhaps also to protect the stove from damage in action. At the after end of this compartment, on the side of the stove which was traditionally used for preparing the officers' meals, were shelves and working surfaces for food preparation. In the late seventeenth century, on Third Rates and above, this area was often fitted with mica or glass windows. Often in the eighteenth century a bench was fitted in the waist, against the cook room bulkhead. Perhaps this was for the comfort of the watch on deck, who might find some warmth there, or perhaps it was reserved for the warrant officers who had their cabins nearby. In any case, it tended to disappear in the second half of the century, as double doors were introduced to facilitate the fitting of the iron stove.

Livestock

It had long been the custom to carry some live animals to provide fresh food. Cows and sheep were sometimes carried in the manger without any special provision. In 1808 sheep pens were to be made in two parts, and fitted between the main hatchway and the capstan. The bottom of the pen was to draw out on each side of the deck so it could be cleaned. The upper part was on skids, the lower on trucks.[14]

Hens were particularly useful aboard ship, as they could be fed from scraps of biscuit and even from the cockroaches which inhabited the hold, and in return they provided fresh eggs. In 1690 hen-coops were to be 6ft 2in long, 2ft 7in high, 1ft 9in broad at the bottom and 1ft 8in broad at the top. They were made of deal, with a trough at the back. In 1755 it was complained that 'breeding hencoops' were being fitted to ships. These took up more space, and got 'in the way of exercising the small arms', so ordinary ones were to be substituted.[15] In 1779 it was ordered that an additional hen-coop be fitted to ships on Channel service.[16] In 1808 they were to be placed around the foremost capstan, and to have sliding bottoms to facilitate cleaning.[17] In 1814 a new design was proposed, evidently more rectangular than the old one.[18]

By the end of the eighteenth century it was customary to keep pig sties under the forecastle, but they were displaced by the sick bay in 1801, after which they were put in the waist.[19]

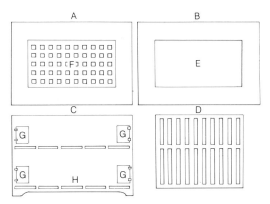

A chicken coop of 1814.
A. Plan of the top of the coop.
B. Ground plan.
C. The fore and aft side outside front, profile.
D. The fore and aft side inside front, profile.

E. Walk for the fowls.
F. Grating on the top.
G. The doors to thwartships coops.
H. Drawers.

Chapter 37. Sanitary and Medical Arrangements

The Problem of Health

Even by seventeenth or eighteenth century standards, life on a man of war was not healthy. Diseases abounded, with scurvy, rheumatism, and fevers being among the most common. Seamen were also susceptible to numerous injuries from everyday work as well as from battle. Infectious diseases were a great hazard, for they could decimate a ship's company and isolation or escape was impossible. These problems became greater as ships spent longer periods at sea, and as the press gangs lowered their standards in the quest for seamen. It is estimated that in the wars between 1793 and 1815 about 80 per cent of fatalities were caused by disease and accident, and only about 7 per cent by enemy action. Around 80,000 men perished from disease and accident during these years.[1]

In one respect, at least, it was easy to maintain sanitary conditions aboard ship: there was no great problem in finding a place to dispose of human waste, though actually getting it overboard might require some effort. Sanitary accommodation aboard ship, although crude and extremely uncomfortable by modern standards, was simple and effective, and considerably healthier than conditions in the growing industrial towns of the late eighteenth century.

The Lee Chains

The simplest way for a seaman to relieve himself was to go to the channels, which were platforms extending from the sides of the ship, intended to spread the rigging. On the lee side, the wind and the heel of the ship would tend to carry the waste well outboard, and make the seaman's task easier. Here there was no difficulty in passing water, and even defecation was possible, with the

aid of suitable slings or holding points. The provision of more sophisticated facilities was already rather inadequate, and this primitive method may often have been resorted to.

Sometimes the lee chains could be dangerous. 'I narrowly escaped drowning, for going into the main chains to exonerate nature, the ship yared to port and heeled so deep to starboard, the side whereon I was, that I were dipped head and ears, the affright of which, together with the surface motion of the sea, almost forced me from my hold. If it had, I could not have escaped.'[2]

In the third quarter of the seventeenth century, round enclosures were built on the main channels of some three-deckers. In some paintings, trunking can be seen leading out from below them, and it seems reasonable to assume that these erections were used as heads for the junior officers, being replaced by roundhouses late in the century. Certainly they were conveniently close to the many small cabins on the middle deck, though it is not clear how they could be reached, except through a gunport or down the ship's side.

A small roundhouse built over the channels of the Royal Katherine *of 1664, with trunking leading down from it. It seems likely that this was used as a toilet by the officers.* Author's photograph.

The Head

By the 1620s the beakhead was recognised as 'a place for men to ease themselves in'.[3] Yet for many years after that no models show any specific provision for this. It was not a prudish age, and the embarrassment of the modeller would not have been a cause of omission, though his lack of skill or concern for mundane detail might have been. It is possible that the seaman simply leaned over the side, as he did at the chains.

'Seats of easement' are first known to have appeared in British ships in the 1680s. Each seat was simply a box with a round hole in the top. The man sat on the box, and discharged through the hole. The earliest ones were placed in the outboard, aftermost extremities of the head, where they overhung the water. There were no gilded carvings at that point, and the waste could go straight into the water, unless the heel of the ship, in combination with the wind, caused it to hit the side. In the early seventeenth century the task of cleaning up any such mess was reserved as a punishment for liars.[4]

Free-standing seats of ease began to appear in the 1690s. They were closer to the centre line, and further forward. Because the waste had to find its way through the decorations and rails of the head, these seats were fitted with vertical wooden conduits underneath, to make sure that it was carried out safely. These seats were usually cubical boxes. By the late eighteenth century, three or four seats were often placed together in a row on the larger ships. Even so, there were not very many for the crew of a large ship. There seems to have been no standard arrangement of seats, and there were many variations. Seats could be built like thrones, or tiered like steps, for example. Some had a keyhole shaped aperture, rather than a round one.[5]

Few ships had as many as one seat for a hundred men. The *Victory*, for example, had six seats for about 800 men below the rank of petty officer. This suggests that other areas, such as the lee chains, were still used.

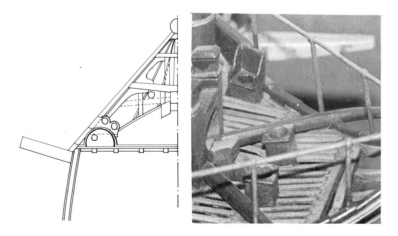

Left. Plan of the head of the Suffolk *of 1765, showing the roundhouse and the seats of ease. Right. Seats on a model of a 74-gun ship of the 1790s, including two of the 'throne' type.* Author's photograph.

The Piss-dale

In shape the piss-dale was not unlike a modern urinal. It was probably made of lead, and can often be seen in pictures and

A piss-dale on a model of the 1700s. Author's photograph.

models, fitted to the side of the ship in the waist. It had piping which conducted the water out through the ship's side by a simple scupper arrangement. It first appears on models in the 1680s. Though it is rarely seen on models after that date, in 1801 it was defined as 'a place set apart on either side of a ship of war, for the people to piss in to prevent the decks being wetted in other places.'[6] By 1865 it was described as 'now almost abolished',[7] so it can be assumed that it survived into the nineteenth century, though by that time it makes no appearance on draughts and models.

The Quarter Galleries

Quarter galleries began to develop in the early seventeenth century, as a synthesis of the military-looking turrets which had been fitted to some Elizabethan ships, and the open galleries which were fitted round the sides of the stern and later covered over. By 1637 when the *Sovereign of the Seas* was completed, the galleries were fully developed. Though their shape changed over the years to suit the current fashion, they remained in use until the end of the age of sail. It is not clear how soon they were used as toilet

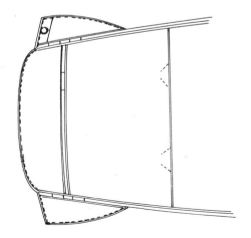

The captain's cabin of a 74-gun ship of the 1750s, showing the seat and hole in one of the quarter galleries.

accommodation for the officers, but because they overhung the water this aspect must have been fairly obvious. For most of the seventeenth century they were fitted only at upper deck level on two-deckers, and upper and middle deck level on three-deckers. Single-deckers had none, and only a window and a decorated badge on each quarter. Thus only admirals and senior captains had the use of these facilities. Galleries on the quarterdeck began to develop in the 1690s, and these would have been used by the master and the lieutenants. Later ships with a topgallant round-house had galleries at four levels. They were also fitted on frigates and on some smaller vessels, for the use of the captain only.

Captains and admirals had two quarter galleries each, but per-haps only one needed to be fitted out as a head, with the other being used as a store, or for observing the sails without leaving the cabin. In the wardroom of a ship of the line the cabins were arranged so that one gallery was accessible only through the first lieutenant's cabin. A passage was left between the cabins on the other side so that the remaining officers had access to the other one.

The quarter gallery could not have provided much privacy, for it was surrounded with glass on three sides. Until the late eight-eenth century its amenities were very basic. A bench seat with a round hole cut in it was fitted on the aftermost edge. Presumably there was some form of piping to carry the waste out of the ship, especially from the upper galleries. Discharge pipes can occasion-ally be seen on models, under the galleries. As with the head, the contrast between gilded and decorated carvings and the menial use to which the accommodation was put, must have been strik-ing.

The Roundhouse

Clearly the arrangements described so far did not make much provision for the junior officers and the commissioned officers on a frigate who did not have the use of a wardroom. It is quite likely that many made their own arrangements, by bringing a commode on board. Admiral Rodney, despite his access to two quarter gal-leries, brought his own 'night stool with pan' on board his flag-ship.[8] Possibly such items were also used by the occupants of the after cockpit, for example. For even when better facilities did begin to develop for the middling ranks in the 1670s, they were at the head of the ship, a long way from the berths of those who would use them. Moreover, they were confined to the larger ships; the officers of a frigate or a sloop would have no special facilities of their own.

The roundhouse first appears on a model of 1675. It was placed at the outboard end of the beakhead bulkhead, where it overhung the sea. Usually one was fitted on each side of the ship, though an

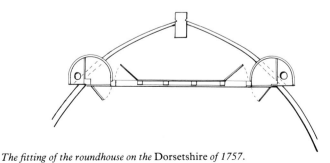

The fitting of the roundhouse on the Dorsetshire *of 1757.*

early model shows only one.[9] Since it appeared before the quarterdeck quarter galleries, it may have been intended for the lieutenant and master in the first instance, but later it was used mainly by the warrant officers of the after cockpit. By 1815, after the development of the sick bay under the forecastle, the two roundhouses had different uses. 'The one on the larboard side being appropriated to the private use of the mates, midshipmen and warrant officers, the other on the starboard side, to the use of the sick bay.'[10] The use of the different facilities must have been dictated as much by custom as anything else. Captains' orders, for example, make no mention of who was to use what.

Inboard Seats

Smaller vessels had no beakhead bulkheads, and therefore no place for roundhouses. Often they had little space on the head itself. In some cases, the seats were fitted inside the rail of the forecastle, with discharge pipes leading overboard. One model, of a sloop of about 1750, shows a seat inside the bulwark of a round bow. Another, of a frigate of 1780, has the seat placed on top of the rail itself, just forward of the cathead, with the hole overhang-ing the outside of the ship. These seats would certainly have been more sheltered than the head itself, but they would have afforded even less privacy. However, the eighteenth century seaman had no such expectation, and even his officers accepted sanitary prac-tices which in the later nineteenth century would have been abhorred.

The Water Closet

In May 1779 the Navy Board ordered the fitting of a cistern and water closet on all ships with quarter galleries. Presumably this meant a flushing toilet system, but there is no further refer-ence to it, and no detailed descriptions of how it was to be con-structed. This seems to suggest that the order was soon forgotten, and few ships were so fitted.[11] The order came soon after a number of developments in the design of the water closet. Andrew Cummings took out a patent for one in 1775, the first in the history of patents; Prosser designed another in 1776, but the most successful model was produced by Joseph Bramah in 1778. It is possible that this was the one adopted for ships.[12]

The Bramah water closet.

The Surgeon and his Stores

On the face of it, a ship of war was well provided with medical staff. Each ship had a surgeon, and some mates who were also fully qualified surgeons. The number of mates carried bore a rela-tion to the ship's size. There may have been three or four on a

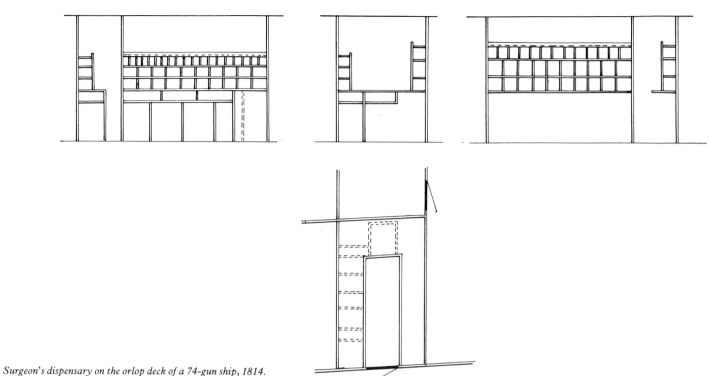

Surgeon's dispensary on the orlop deck of a 74-gun ship, 1814.

ship of the line, giving a higher proportion of medical practitioners to patients than one would expect today. But it must be remembered that in the days before anaesthetic the capabilities of a surgeon were rather limited. His profession had not long been separated from that of the barber. The surgeon could bleed a patient, and amputate limbs when necessary, but he could do little more. The upper classes held much higher regard for the physician, but good ones could rarely be enticed to enter naval medicine. Surgeons there were in plenty, because they were poor and unfashionable, and necessary in the carnage of a naval battle. They had little training in the treatment of disease, which was a much more serious enemy to the seaman than the musket or cannon.

The surgeon was a wardroom officer, and his cabin was on the orlop deck. His mates ranked with the master's mates, and lived on the orlop. The surgeon was given a small dispensary on this deck, which in the early eighteenth century was 'near the dimensions of an overgrown sea chest'.[13] In the early nineteenth century it was considerably expanded, and fitted with racks for his instruments and medicines. The space in the after cockpit was reserved for use in action as his operating theatre. In 1809 he was issued with an operating table, to be fitted 'opposite the dispensary, in the centre of the cockpit, between the stanchions'.[14] Before that, it is said that some of the midshipmen's sea chests were put together to make a suitable surface.

The Sick Berth

Until the early nineteenth century there was no established position for the sick berth aboard a man of war. According to a mid-eighteenth century account, 'the place commonly allotted for the sick, is either the part of the gundeck called the bay, which is the most unwholesome part of a ship; or, what is nearly as bad,

and very incommodious, the fore part of the hold.'[15] Nor was it a well organised area. 'I was much less surprised that people should die on board, than that any should recover. Here I saw about fifty miserable distempered wretches, suspended in rows, so huddled upon one another that not more than fourteen inches was allotted for each with his bed and bedding; and being deprived of the light of day as well as of fresh air; breathing nothing but a noisome atmosphere of the morbid streams exhaling from their own excrements and diseased bodies . . . I could not comprehend how it was possible for the attendants to come near those who hung on the inside towards the sides of the ship, in order to assist them, as they seemed barricadoed by those who lay on the outside.'[16]

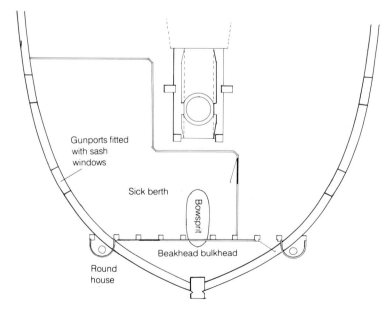

The official plan for fitting the sick bay on two- and three-deckers, 1801.

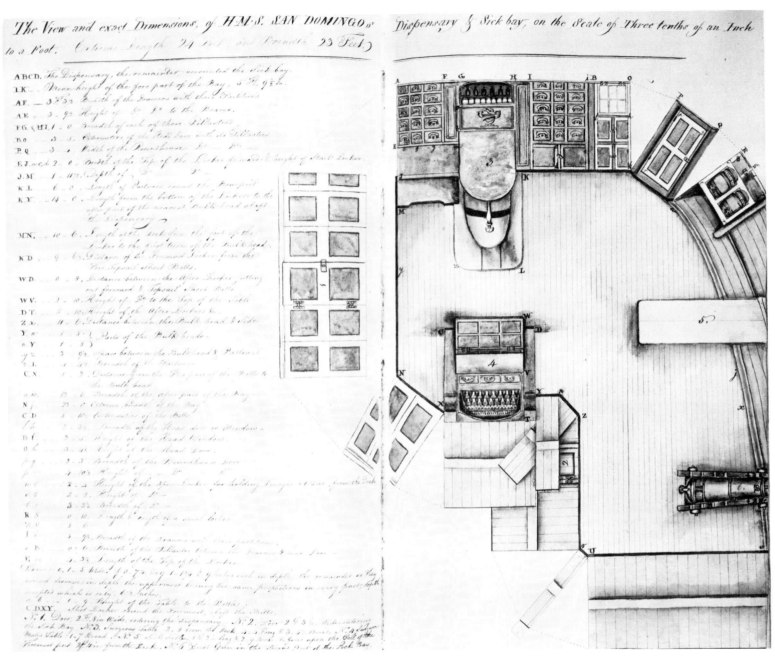

A very detailed drawing of the San Domingo's *sick bay in 1811*. NMM.

As a result, many surgeons preferred to use the sick bay as little as possible. 'There is seldom occasion to remove the sick in any ship, from their proper beds, into one place; and it is done only, when their number is so increased, so as to make it inconvenient for other men to attend them when separate.'[17] 'There is nothing so apt to increase, and even generate, contagion, as a number of sick together, unless uncommon attention is paid to cleanliness and ventilation. This is so true that, unless where the complaint is very catching, it is best not to separate the sick; for if they are a good set of men on board, those who are confined by sickness will be better nursed and tended by their mess mates than in a sick berth.'[18]

If a sick berth was absolutely necessary, the best medical men of the late eighteenth century recommended that it should be either in the gunroom or under the forecastle, where isolation and ventilation were easier. However, the evidence is that the mass of ships merely used one or two of the rows of hammocks on the lower deck, and this can be seen, for example, on a hammock plan of the mid-eighteenth century.[19]

The Improved Sick Berth

There was some improvement in conditions in the late eighteenth century, largely because of the efforts of doctors such as Lind, Blane and Trotter. Lessons were learned from disasters, such as the great loss of life from scurvy during Anson's famous circumnavigation of 1740–44. Lime juice, and other substances, provided some protection against scurvy. The requirements of blockade service, and the great shortage of skilled seamen, also inspired some improvements. One result of this was a new type of sick bay. The gunroom was not chosen for several possible reasons: it was already used by too many groups of men, was a difficult place to sling hammocks, and had no toilet facilities of its own.

Instead, the new sick berth was placed under the forecastle, 'furnished with all the requisites of a hospital, and with access to the head for necessary purposes.'[20] Evidently this area had been used for pig sties, until Admiral St Vincent ordered that they be moved to the waist. Captain Markham of the *Centaur* was given credit for developing the new sick berth in the late years of the eighteenth century. The starboard side of the forecastle, to one side of the cook room, was sealed off for the 'sleeping place'. For-

ward of the cook room was the dispensary. The sick had direct access to the roundhouse, and provisions were made for much better ventilation than there had been in the past: 'over the midships is a large sky light, which gives a cheerful appearance to the whole, and in warm weather is thrown open, to cause a fresh current of air to pass through the ports and head window.'[21] There were other versions of the new sick bay. That fitted to the *San Domingo* in 1812–14 was a different shape and did not have a separate dispensary, but it was similar in general principle. Of the new type it was said, 'A sick berth of these dimensions, in the larger class of 74s, gives room sufficient for 22 people to hang up their beds, with full advantage to attendance and purification.'[22] The new type of sick bay was established on two- and three-deckers by an order of 1801. A further order of 1808 specified that the sides were to be made of deal because canvas had been found insufficient.[23]

PART X

The Ship's Boats

Chapter 38. The Uses of Boats

The Boats' Functions

The pure sailing ship, unaided by auxiliary engine or steam tug, and usually without capacity for rowing, needed boats for reasons almost undreamed of by the captains of powered vessels. Sailing warships rarely came alongside a pier or wharf, partly because they were difficult to manoeuvre and control without an engine or oars, and partly because of the fear that pressed men might desert given the slightest chance. Everything – men, supplies and equipment – had to be brought to the ship in boats, and it often had to rely on its own, especially where dockyards were few and far between. Smaller ships, frigates and less, usually had some capacity for rowing, but evidently they rarely did so, and the ship's boats were used to move when there was no wind, or in a confined space when it was unfavourable. In the days when signal codes were primitive and limited in scope, boats had to be used, at sea as well as in harbour, to carry messages which were too complex to transmit in any other way. Even after the signalling system had become more sophisticated, captains and other officers had to be taken to conferences and briefings. Boats also had purely military purposes, for cutting-out expeditions against moored ships, for landing troops and guns, and even for independent patrols. Some boats were armed with cannons or carronades for these roles. The idea of ship's lifeboats only originated in the early nineteenth century, but the use of a boat for rescue, for example of a man overboard, began to develop in the late eighteenth century, and gave ships' boats yet another task.

The ship's boats had two main advantages over the ship herself. Though nearly all could be sailed, they were much easier to row than any kind of sailing warship, and were thus far more manoeuvrable and had much greater freedom of movement. Also, they had a much shallower draught, and could land at any beach or jetty. The tasks carried out by boats were so varied, and the requirements so demanding, that no single boat could fulfil every function, so a ship had to carry several boats, designed for different purposes.

Moving the Ship

A sailing warship needed a broad hull, to enable her to carry sail when the wind was on the beam, and a large underwater body to support the weight of her guns, and provide room for the stores and provisions for her large crew. Both these features tended to make the ship difficult to row, for they created a resistance that human muscle power could not successfully overcome. Certainly some ships, such as galley-frigates, were designed to row almost as efficiently as they could sail, but evidence suggests that they were not entirely successful and did not row well. One of the early galley-frigates is reported to have made a speed of only three knots with her crew working very hard, and it is doubtful if she could have kept this up for long.[1] Oar ports were retained on sloops and many frigates into the nineteenth century, but there were few cases where they were used to advantage. The smaller vessels, such as cutters, seem to have used their sweeps more often, and in the 1790s a large class of gunboats was designed especially for rowing. But the largest ships, the ships of the line, had no provision at all for rowing. To work efficiently, an oar or sweep had to be kept close to the waterline, and the deck layouts of the largest vessels made this impossible.

A ship's boat, on the other hand, provided three different methods of moving the ship in unfavourable conditions. Towing was the most obvious. Several boats could be used at once to tow the ship, with the crews taking it in turns to row to allow them some rest. It was not a very efficient method, and it gave the ship very little headway. It was mostly used in an emergency, for example during a pursuit, or when the current was likely to carry the ship into danger. It was only necessary on the open sea and in deep water, where there was no possibility of using anchors, or buoys, or attaching a line to the shore.

Kedging was used in shallow water. The smallest anchors, the kedge and the stream, could be suspended under the ship's boats, taken ahead to the limit of the cable, and then dropped in the water. The cable was then hauled in, and the process repeated. To work efficiently, especially when there was an unfavourable wind or current, two anchors had to be employed, otherwise the ship lost ground while its anchor was being laid out.

Kedging could assist during a pursuit in shallow water. In 1812, for example, the USS *Constitution* used this method to

The cutting-out of the Hermione, *1799.* NMM.

Landing troops. The boat in the right foreground is a specially designed landing craft; some of the others are ships' launches. NMM.

escape from a British squadron off New York.[2] It was used much more often in the confined space of a river or harbour, when the ship had no room to tack against an unfavourable wind. However, it was exhausting work for the men. Some were needed to row the boats carrying the anchors, and others to haul at the capstans and work the cables.

Warping involved attaching the end of the cable to a fixed object, a mooring buoy, a tree or post on shore, or a specially provided mooring post in the water. Obviously it was less labour intensive than kedging, in that only the cable, and not the anchor, had to be rowed out, and the labour involved in actually lifting the anchor out of the water was avoided. Moreover, a fixed object provided a much more secure grip. When conditions allowed, warping was used in preference to towing or kedging. Suitable buoys and posts were often provided in rivers and dockyards.

Anchoring and Mooring

Boats could also help in ordinary anchor work. They could be lowered to help cat or fish the anchor, or to clear obstructions from it. A boat was also essential if the ship was to pick up a permanent mooring buoy, for it would be very difficult to sail the ship right up to the buoy and just as difficult to pick it up with a boathook from the ship's decks. Most ships seem to have kept their boats lowered ready for use when they were entering or leaving a harbour or anchorage. Boats were used to lift the buoy rope of an anchor which was stuck fast in the ground, and thus launches and longboats were often fitted with a davit and winch specifically for this purpose. Ships' boats were also used to help clear the hawse. If a ship which was moored with two anchors was allowed to swing with the tide, her cables would become tangled unless great care was taken; boats could be used to unravel them.

Military Uses

The best known and most dramatic use of a ship's boats was for a cutting-out expedition. The boats were filled with men and rowed into a harbour or anchorage to attack and capture an enemy ship, often within range of the shore batteries. This form of attack was particularly common in the French Revolutionary and Napoleonic Wars, and many ships were captured in the small harbours of the Mediterranean and the Caribbean. The most celebrated example probably took place in 1799 when the *Surprise* launched boats carrying over 100 men to recapture the former British frigate *Hermione*, under enemy batteries said to mount over 200 guns. They succeeded in overcoming a Spanish crew of 365, with only 12 wounded, and retook the ship.[3] Not all such attempts were successful. In 1804 the frigate *Galatea* attempted to recapture the sloop *Lilly*. Four boats with 90 men were sent in, but the enemy was fully warned of their intentions. Only 20 men returned unwounded and the *Lilly* remained in French hands.[4]

Boats could also be used to land troops, marines, or seamen on an enemy held coast. The scale of such operations varied enormously. For a full invasion, such as the many attacks on Caribbean islands in the eighteenth century, much planning was needed. The Army provided most of the troops. They were carried on hired transports, and specially designed landing craft were used to put them ashore. The role of the ship's boats was purely sub-

sidiary. At the other end of the scale, an individual captain might order an attack on a shore installation, such as a battery or a signal station, on his own initiative, using his own seamen, marines, and boats. Ships' boats had a role in many other types of operation, best illustrated by the part the Navy played in the Peninsular War, which began in 1808. In that year the 74-gun ship *Alfred* landed 300 marines at Figuera in Portugal, to support a local revolt against the French. A few weeks later this foothold was used by Sir Arthur Wellesley to land 13,000 men, beginning the British intervention in the war.[5] Four years later Sir Home Popham operated on the north coast of Spain, with a force which included two ships of the line and several frigates. He cooperated with the Spanish guerrillas to harass the French forces. Using the superior mobility that such a coastline gave to ships, he mounted raids on various points, eventually capturing the city of Santander. He held down enough of the French forces to contribute decisively to the success of Wellington's campaign on land.[6]

As well as landing troops, guns were sometimes landed in their support. In 1812 Popham landed three cannon to attack enemy positions near the town of Lequeitio. Such a force was puny at sea, but on land, where heavy guns could only be transported with great labour and difficulty, it could prove decisive. Heavy guns could be slung under a boat, or laid in its bottom, so that its stability was not affected. Other guns were used to arm the boats themselves, either for cutting-out expeditions, or for defence during other tasks, for example when filling water casks on a hostile shore.

Ships' boats, especially the more seaworthy ones such as cutters, could even carry out independent patrols over a period of several weeks. Thus in 1742, during Anson's famous voyage of circumnavigation, a 22ft cutter cruised off Acapulco for 43 days, with a crew of seven, watching for a Spanish treasure galleon.[7]

Transport

When warships were in port they usually remained moored to buoys off the main dockyards, or at anchor in one of the main

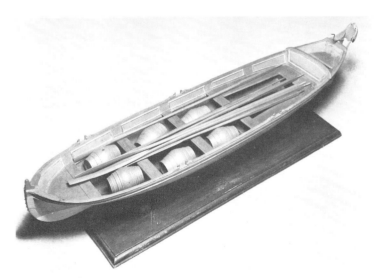

A model showing a pinnace carrying casks. These are too small to be the ones in which water for the ground tier was carried, and the largest casks were normally transported in the launch or longboat. NMM.

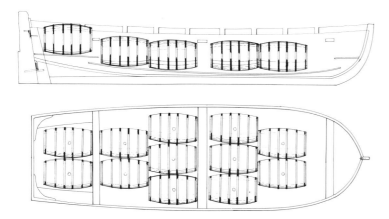

A Third Rate's launch, 1804, specially designed to carry 12 butts of water. A First Rate's launch carried 14 butts.

Men being carried ashore in a pinnace, c1750.

anchorages such as the Downs, the Nore, Spithead, St Helens Roads, Torbay or Cawsand Bay. In the immediate vicinity of a dockyard they could be manned and supplied by yard craft and hired hoys, though the ship's boats would also contribute to the job of fitting-out. Where such facilities were not available, for instance on foreign service, in a small port, a little used anchorage, or an isolated place, the ship had to rely solely on her own boats for support. Because food, water, and provisions were usually kept and transported in casks, boats were often designed to carry casks of a particular size. This was especially true of the largest boat, the longboat or launch, which had full bows and a substantial breadth, with a suitable distance between the fixed thwarts to enable the largest casks to be carried. There is evidence that barges and pinnaces, though designed primarily for other tasks, were also able to carry a significant number of smaller casks.

Of all the provisions which had to be brought in by the ship's boats, water was the most important. Normally a ship carried

water for only half the period of time it carried food and other stores. Thus an eighteenth century ship fitted and stored for foreign service would have provisions for six months, but water for only three. She was expected to replenish her water supply at any suitable creek or river, when the opportunity arose. The longboat or launch was designed to carry the maximum number of water and other casks possible without upsetting seakeeping abilities.

Men also had to be brought on board ship, on their first joining, on transferring to another ship, leaving the service, or even, for trusted members of the crew, for shore leave. Again, dockyard craft did much of the work involved in this, and special press-tenders were often used to bring the recent victims of conscription on board. However, the captain was expected to be independent to a certain extent, and in the 1740s ships of the first three rates were issued with an extra boat specifically to assist in the pressing of men.[8]

Flogging round the fleet. The victim is tied to the triangle made up of capstan bars, as in the right-hand boat. A drummer sits in the bows. NMM.

One of the most unpleasant uses of boats was for the custom of flogging round the fleet. A man sentenced to several hundred lashes by a court martial would be lashed to a triangle made of capstan bars erected in a boat, and rowed round all the ships in the anchorage, receiving about 25 lashes at each unless the surgeon decided he could stand no more, in which case he was revived and the flogging resumed another day. Each of the ships sent one of its boats to witness the punishment, and the rogues march was played as it took place.

Communication

Officers had far more opportunities for leaving the ship than men, and it was assumed that they would not desert. Their duties often called them ashore to the dockyard, or to other ships, and they were also allowed a certain amount of shore leave. Specialist officers such as carpenters and gunners would often need to converse with dockyard officials, and lieutenants would lead press gangs. The captain would spend much of his time in harbour conferring with his superiors, or supervising the storing of his ship. The boats which carried the officers on such business did not need to be very seaworthy, as they operated in sheltered waters, but they often had to cope with adverse currents, and captains liked to be rowed ashore efficiently and quickly. These boats, though they could occasionally be sailed if necessary, were designed mainly to row well, and to a certain extent for the comfort and prestige of those they carried.

At sea, the problems of communication were rather different. Until the later years of the eighteenth century, the system of flag signals was very limited, and a commander had only about 30 or 40 messages, all tactical, at his disposal. Ships could come within hailing distance of one another, but this could disrupt the order of the fleet, and it was generally better to send messages by boat, if the weather permitted. A full system of flag signals, which used special flags to make numerals and words, had been developed by 1801, but it did not end the need for communication by boat. Officers like Nelson relied very heavily on briefing their captains before an action, and seaworthy boats were necessary to bring them aboard the flagship.

Safety

In general, ships' boats were not intended to save lives. Until the early nineteenth century there was no attempt to make them seaworthy in very bad weather so that they could survive even when the parent ship had sunk. Seamen were expected to take their chances with wind, weather, and the hazards of the sea, and no serious provision was made for their safety. There were cases where the boats did help save some men from a shipwreck, but this was not one of their primary functions.

In saving the seaman who was unlucky or careless enough to fall overboard, boats had a slightly more significant role. The biggest difficulty was in getting the boat into the water fast enough. In the seventeenth century longboats were generally towed, but it would have taken some time to get a full crew into one, and as most seamen could not swim, the chances of survival were slight. The practice of towing boats died out in the early years of the eighteenth century, and the davit, which would have enabled the quick launching of a boat, was not to be introduced for many years. After that, it is possible that a cutter or gig could be used for rescue purposes, though examples of this are rare.

Function and Design

Ships' boats had to be designed for a great variety of tasks and conditions. Some were carried on board ship, some hung from davits, and some towed astern. The weight of the boat, and therefore its construction, was very much influenced by how it was to be carried. Ships had to have boats capable of landing at quays

Rescue. The crew of the Ramillies *take to the boats as the ship sinks after damage by a hurricane in 1782.* NMM.

and jetties, in heavy surf, or that could be dragged up a beach. Some boats were designed to operate in rough seas, others to be rowed in harbour, some had to carry a large crew with a small load, others had a small crew for a heavy load. Some were armed with guns or carronades, or carried anchors. Obviously no single boat could meet all these requirements, so a ship had to carry several. Mid-seventeenth century ships carried two or three, but the number had risen to six by the 1800s. The demands on boats tended to increase over the years, as the scale of warfare widened. Ships were expected to operate ever further from their home bases, the number of cutting-out expeditions and landings tended to rise, and the skill and resourcefulness of the seamen grew. It was a considerable task for the boatbuilder to fulfil all these needs.

Chapter 39. Boat Construction

Types of Construction

Clinker and carvel were the two main systems used to construct the boats of British warships. The most important difference between the two was that in the first the planks overlapped and were joined together along their edges, while in carvel build they did not. As a consequence, carvel boats were built with a fairly strong structure of ribs, which was constructed first, and in principle their construction was similar to that of ships. Clinker-built craft had their planks fitted first, over a purely temporary structure of wooden moulds. The frames, which were relatively light, were added later.

There were other methods of constructing wooden boats. For example, there were ways of joining the edges of planks together without overlapping them, and there were many systems which combined the advantages of clinker and carvel. In the Netherlands, for example, it was normal to build a large ship by laying the planks of the bottom first and then fitting the frames, and so proceeding as with carvel build. A radically new system, diagonal planking, was introduced in the 30 years after 1815.

Nevertheless, carvel and clinker were the only two systems used for ships' boats in the British Navy before 1815. If local craft with different structures were sometimes acquired by individual captains on foreign stations, there is no clear record of this and no evidence that other methods were used for boats built in Britain. Culturally and historically, the two methods represented very different traditions. Clinker build had been the standard system of the Vikings, and had spread in Britain during their period of dominance. It was particularly common on the east coast, though it was used to some extent in all parts of Britain. It was well adapted to small vessels, particularly those hauled up on a beach, and it was within the capabilities of local boatbuilders. The smaller ports were filled with traditional craftsmen with a knowledge of clinker building, but the more sophisticated shipwrights, particularly those of the royal dockyards, had little experience of it.

Carvel build was the more 'intellectual' form of construction, in that the builder worked from a prepared plan, and less by 'hand and eye'. It was carried out in the dockyards, for it was merely a scaled down version of the method used for large ships. Each major dockyard had its master boatbuilder, but other boatbuilders were not distinguished from the rest of the shipwrights in the yards. Shipwrights were merely sent to work for the boatbuilder as needed, and it was not considered necessary for them to have any more specialised skills. The boatbuilder himself was in line for promotion to master shipwright, and some, such as Pollard of Portsmouth, did reach that rank. Because the yards nearly always worked in carvel, the shipwright could move easily between ships and boats.

Because of this, and the fact that carvel boats were considered easier to maintain, most of the Navy's boats, and nearly all those built in the dockyards, were of carvel build. Carvel-built boats could also be constructed in private yards, for like ships they were often contracted when a dockyard's resources were overburdened. Clinker-built boats were nearly always built in private yards. Since the two main types of clinker-built boats, yawl and cutter, both originated at Deal, yards in that town supplied many of these craft in the eighteenth century.

Design

Though traditional boatbuilders usually worked by 'hand and eye', without a prepared set of plans, there is evidence that the Navy, preferred its boats to be built by more sophisticated methods, particularly from the beginning of the eighteenth century. No seventeenth century plans of boats have survived, and there is no direct evidence that they were used then, though they were certainly in use by about 1700. In the later part of the eighteenth century there was some attempt to impose standardisation on the yards, and draughts of standard types were sent out to them in the 1790s. Even cutters, though clinker-built, had standard plans by this time.

Even in the seventeenth century, the actual dimensions and scantlings of boats had been subject to a high degree of central control. The establishment of boatswains' stores of 1686 imposed specific dimensions on boats of each type,[1] and these would have been detailed enough to dictate much of the shape. Similar, more detailed sets of dimensions were issued over the years.

The designer of a boat began by drawing out the shape of the keel, stempost, and sternpost, and marking out the shape of the gunwale along the length of the boat. The actual shape of the hull was drawn out by a process known as 'whole moulding'. Until the late sixteenth century this system had been used for major ships. Then it was replaced by more sophisticated methods and by the beginning of the seventeenth century was retained only for boats. The essence of whole moulding was that a single 'mould' or template was used to make the shape of each frame along the length of the boat. The mould was formed by a single segment of a circle, whereas on a large ship it was formed from several segments of different circles. The actual position of the mould at each frame station was determined by two theoretical lines known as the rising line and the narrowing line. The rising line was a curve drawn on the sheer draught, or side view, of the boat. In midships

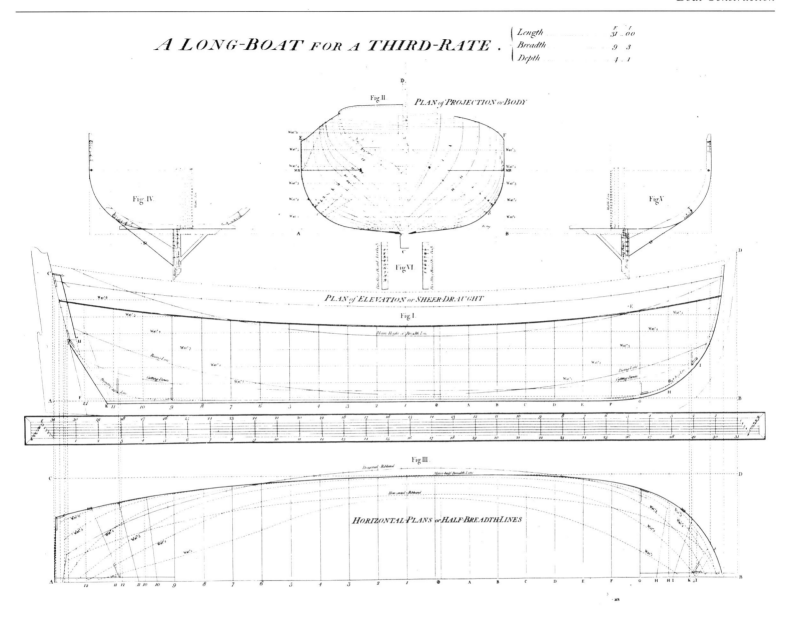

A plate from Stalkaart's Naval Architecture *showing the system of whole moulding as applied to a long boat in 1782. The top left- and right-hand drawings show how the mould is combined with other pieces to form the shapes of the individual timbers. The rising line and the main half-breadth line, which determine the basic shape of the hull, can be seen in the other drawings.* Science Museum.

it was just above the top of the keel, and it curved upwards towards the bow and the stern. It indicated the position of the lowest part of the mould at different stations along the hull.

The narrowing line was drawn on the plan view of the boat. In midships it was well out from the keel, and it indicated the maximum breadth of the ship. It curved inwards towards the bow, which it met at the sternpost. It also tapered towards the stern, but never met it, for a transom was fitted. In the bows the mould rose some way above the keel. The narrowing line was joined to the mould at each frame by a diagonal straight line, which formed a tangent to the curve of the mould, and joined the top of the keel. Near the stern, a concave curve was used instead of a straight line. This helped to create finer lines and direct the water to the rudder. Above the widest point in midships, the shape of the frame was carried upwards by a vertical, or almost vertical straight line, also tangential to the mould. Near the bow and stern

this was not necessary, for the rising line had carried the mould upwards, so that its centre was higher than the side of the boat, and therefore it was cut off before it reached full breadth. This meant that the narrowing line was purely theoretical; only in midships did it represent the actual breadth of the boat. Builders disagreed about the methods of drawing the narrowing and rising lines. Some favoured segments of circles, others ellipses, or more complex shapes.[2]

Carvel Building

The builder began with the keel, stempost and sternpost assembly. The keel was straight, and usually made in one piece. The sternpost was also straight, except for a few types of boat such as the early yawls. It raked aft from the aftermost part of the

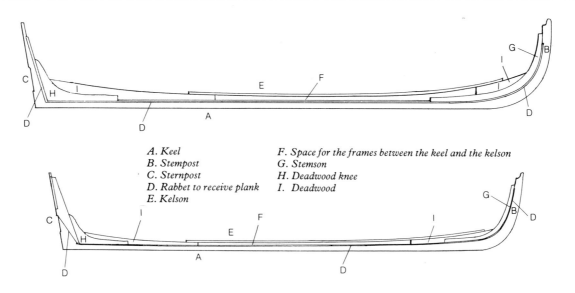

A. Keel
B. Stempost
C. Sternpost
D. Rabbet to receive plank
E. Kelson
F. Space for the frames between the keel and the kelson
G. Stemson
H. Deadwood knee
I. Deadwood

The keel, stempost and sternpost assembly of a pinnace (top) and a cutter (bottom), c1795.

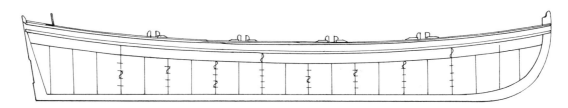

The planks of a pinnace, c1795. The vertical lines represent the frame stations. The short horizontal lines show the run of the planking. The S-shaped lines are the joins in the planking. These are always placed over frame stations.

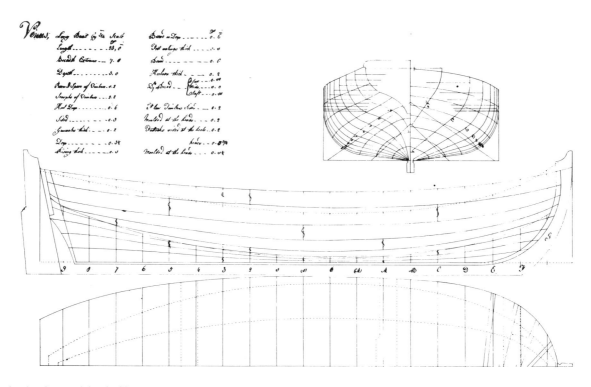

A longboat of 1758, showing the run of the planking.

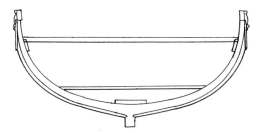

Midship section of a yawl of 1798, showing the deck which seems to have been normal in such vessels. The thwarts are supported by a strake of internal planking.

keel and was intended to form a suitable position for hanging the rudder. The stempost was curved, and it was joined to the foremost part of the keel. All three of these pieces were cut with a groove, triangular in cross section, known as the rabbet. This ran along the top of the keel on both sides, and up the innermost parts of the stempost and sternpost. Its purpose was to receive and secure the extremities of the planks which would be fitted to the hull. The sternpost was strengthened with a timber knee, which was fitted in the angle between it and the keel.

The frames were fitted next. They were placed along the keel, with one frame every 12 or 14in. The distance between them was called the room and space. The frames were cut to shape using moulds of thin wood. Normally they were made in three parts: the floor timber, which was laid across the keel, and two futtocks, one on each side, which were joined to the outermost part of the floor timber, and formed the curved part of the frame. They were joined together by scarphs – overlapping the joins – which could take several forms. A flat transom was fitted to the sternpost, its shape and size depending very much on the type of boat. A launch, for example, had a very large transom, and a pinnace a small one. The keelson, a long piece of curved timber, was now

A mid-eighteenth century longboat, with its windlass in place. Part of the planking has been omitted, which emphasises the framing.

fitted over the centres of the frames, directly above the line of the keel, stempost and sternpost.

The hull could now be planked. In carvel building, the plank was usually between $\frac{3}{4}$in and 1in thick (thinner plank was needed for clinker building).[3] Sometimes the uppermost planks used in carvel building were thicker than those below, as they had to withstand more stress. These were known as wales and were common on longboats and launches, which had to bear the strains imposed by a winch. The planks were cut to shape, so they were narrower at the bow and the stern than in midships. They were nailed to the timbers, and in carvel building there was no direct join between the adjacent planks. The lowest plank was fitted first, into the rabbet of the keel, and was known as the garboard strake.

Above the main planking was fitted a thicker piece of timber known as the gunwale. Originally it formed the uppermost limit of the side of the boat, and it was fitted with thole pins or rowlocks for the oars. After the mid-eighteenth century a removeable wash-strake was fitted on many boats, above the gunwale. It was either made up in several sections, with a space between them for each oar, or in a single piece on each side, with recesses cut for the oars.

The internal decking of the boat could be formed in several ways. A few boats, such as large pinnaces and yawls of around 1800, actually had a proper deck, raised a few inches above the keel of the boat, for their whole length, though it was not level, being higher at the bow and stern. Other boats, such as launches and smaller pinnaces, had such decking only in the stern and perhaps the bows, to raise the passengers' feet above the water in the bilge. In midships most boats had a type of internal planking, known a footwaling, resting directly on the frames of the hull. Some boats had removeable boards, known as bottom boards, burden boards, or pallating, placed over their timbers.

Internally the hull was strengthened by riders. These were similar to the frames, except that they were stronger and fewer, and were fitted later, over the footwaling, decking, and so on. They were used mainly in the heavier boats, such as longboats and launches. Breast hooks were used to strengthen the bows. These were similar to riders, but were fitted in the horizontal plane, near the top of the side. Other knees, in the horizontal plane, were fitted between the sides of the hull and the transom.

The thwarts served two purposes. As well as providing seats for the oarsmen, they braced the hull against the pressure of the water, like the deck beams of a ship. There were two types of thwart. Some were fixed, and these were reinforced by wooden knees. Loose thwarts could be removed so that casks and other large items could be stowed. Pinnaces and barges had few removeable thwarts, but about half of those on longboats and launches could be taken out, as these boats were intended to carry heavy loads.

Clinker Building

The keel, stempost and sternpost assembly was made up in the same way as in carvel build, complete with sternpost knee and rabbet. Above the keel was the hog, wider than the keel, and shaped so that it would help set the angle of the garboard strake. (The hog is not mentioned in contracts for such boats, but it is difficult to see how the shape of the hull could be formed without it, and contracts did not specify every detail of construction.)

A cutter of 1808. Although built for the Customs, it shows several typical features of construction. The system of clinker building is shown in the cross-section. Science Museum.

An early gig, of 1763. Again, it shows some detail of clinker building. Science Museum.

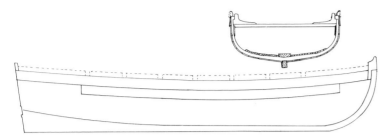

Midship section and sheer plan of a 29ft launch of 1779, showing several features of construction. The removeable upper strakes are indicated by a dashed line. Note how in the midship section they are supported by a bracket. The uppermost strake of plank below that forms a type of wale, and is angled rather like clinker build. The thwarts are supported from below by a strake of internal planking, and from above by knees. The floor also has internal planking.

Three or four moulds were then placed across the keel, to give the hull shape during its construction. It is possible that builders with enough skill would have been able to work without them, for the correct shaping of the planks would ensure that the hull was correctly formed.

The planks of a clinker-built boat had to be relatively thin, $\frac{3}{4}$in or less. The garboard strake was fitted first, and nailed to the hog. The next strake was then fitted, overlapping slightly with the garboard, and fixed directly to it. The system of fixing was known as 'clenching', and it gave clinker-work its name. A nail was driven all the way through both planks, and bent over inside the hull to keep it in place. In some cases the nail was passed through a small metal plate before being turned down. In others, it was hammered flat like a rivet. From 1783 some boats had copper nails instead of iron, because of the tendency of the latter to rust on long voyages.[4] The experiment was not entirely successful, and clinker-built boats still tended to be difficult to maintain. The planking continued in this way until the sides of the hull were completed. A cutter had nine to twelve strakes of planking on each side.[5]

The moulds were then removed, and permanent timbers were fitted to give the hull greater rigidity. These were lighter than the timbers and riders employed in carvel work, but they were made in the same way, by cutting from pieces of timber with suitable grain, to the exact shape required. Steamed frames, which were made pliable by steaming and then bent into shape, were not used until well after 1815. The hull was then completed in much the same way as a carvel-built boat. Thwarts, gunwales and other items were added. Most cutters had removeable boards on their floors, rather than permanent footwaling or decking. The Deal cutter, first used by the Navy in the 1740s, introduced the custom of fitting the removeable wash-strake above the gunwale; thereafter this was common on such vessels.

Advantages and Disadvantages

Clinker build had several important advantages. It was about a quarter of the weight of carvel build. Thus it was very suitable for boats which had to be hoisted in and out of the water in a hurry, especially those which, in the later part of the eighteenth century, were kept on davits for emergency use. It was also useful for boats which had to be hauled up on a beach, or out of the water. The system of building gave them a certain rigidity, and clinker-built boats were generally good sea boats.

On the other hand, many officers disliked clinker build because it caused difficulties in maintenance. Partly this was because ships' carpenters did not really understand it. They had mostly been trained in the royal dockyards, where its use was rare. But there were some genuine difficulties. One common complaint was that such boats became 'nail sick', that is their nails became rusty, and the hull weak. This of course was also a problem on carvel-built boats, but less so, as they had fewer nails under the water-line. One solution to this was to use copper nails, which was the practice after 1786, though it added about ten per cent to the cost of the boat. Other problems were caused by the planking itself. It was thinner than that used for carvel, to allow the nails to be rove through two planks at once. This was light but it was easier for the hull to be damaged. If this happened, or some of the planks began to decay, then the hull was very difficult to repair. In carvel build it was not too difficult to remove one of the lower planks, but in clinker build this could not be done without disturbing all those above.

As a result of this, most boats issued to naval ships were carvel-built. In the seventeenth century, clinker build seems to have been almost unknown. It came into use in the early eighteenth century, with Deal yawls and later on with cutters, but it never became standard for other boats. It was not suitable for large boats, such as longboats and launches. In 1814 it was recommended that even the cutter, the classic clinker-built boat, should be carvel built for foreign service, where repair and replacement facilities were rare.[6] Thus on balance the Navy preferred carvel build, though clinker had its uses.

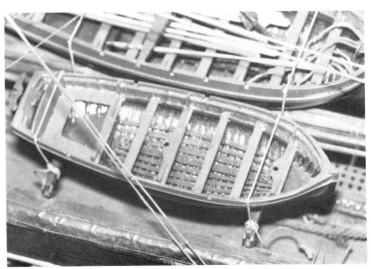

A model of a cutter of about 1800, stowed on the boat booms. It shows the internal planking of the bottom, and the holes in the thwarts for masts. Author's photograph, courtesy of NMM.

Chapter 40. Types of Boat

The Longboat

Traditionally the longboat was the largest and heaviest boat carried by a ship. Its size was necessary because it was 'ever intended to be able to carry forth and weigh her sheet anchor'.[1] In the early days the longboat was very large indeed. In 1618 the *Prince* had a boat of 52ft, just under half the length of her keel.[2] Longboat size had been reduced somewhat by 1640, when the *Sovereign*, a bigger ship than the *Prince*, had a boat of 50ft 10in and the *Prince* had one of 44ft. All ships down to the Fifth Rate carried two longboats, and the smallest was 24ft long.[3] Throughout the seventeenth century, longboats became shorter and by 1686 the largest carried was of 36ft.[4] The earliest longboats were towed behind ships but in the later seventeenth century there was a tendency to haul them aboard and this led to some reduction in length.

The demands on a longboat were very heavy. It had to be able to transport a large number of casks for replenishing the ship's water and to carry out and lay the ship's kedge and stream anchors. Since neither of the other boats carried at the time, the pinnace and the skiff, were good sea boats, the longboat had to operate in all weathers, under oar or sail. She had to be stout and large enough to carry out all these tasks, yet at the same time be light and short enough to be hoisted aboard, particularly at the beginning of the eighteenth century, when the Admiralty tried to eliminate the practice of towing astern.

It is not surprising to find a great deal of dissatisfaction with longboats in the early 1700s. In 1706 Admiral Sir Edward Whittaker wanted all the longboats of his squadron exchanged for Deal yawls, and the Admiral at Deal agreed, and wished 'that all the cruisers in England were to be supplied with Deal yawls instead of longboats'.[5] In 1709 Captain Gunman complained that 'a longboat cannot on any ways be stored aboard the said ship, but that he will be obliged in bad weather to cut her away, if he tows her by the stern.' The Navy Board held firm, and defended the longboat, as 'it hath always been judged necessary that they should do so for their safety, in carrying out an anchor upon occasion, watering the ships, etc.'[6]

There were slightly fewer complaints over the next few years. Perhaps the development of the yawl, and later the cutter, as sea boats, meant the longboat had to do less work. Nevertheless it still had to lay out anchors, and these had no tendency to become any smaller. The longboat, on the other hand, did not keep up with the increasing size of ships. In 1745, as in 1719 and 1786, the longest carried was 36ft, though the largest ships had increased in size by more than 10ft. By the 1740s the longboat was being criticised again, and it was said that a launch was 'preferable to a longboat, in the expeditious watering, carrying of stores, and towing of a ship, as well as the carrying of a great number of hands upon any occasion, with the greater conveniency for stowage upon deck.'[7] Numerous other captains preferred the launch, but still the Navy Board held firm. It was not until 1780 that as standard policy the longboat was replaced by the launch. Even so, it may not have disappeared completely by the early nineteenth century as boat establishments still allowed a longboat to be carried in place of a launch.

The early longboat, like most boats of its time, had bluff bows. It had a relatively narrow stern, though wider than that of a pinnace. Its sheer was considerable compared with its successor, the launch, and this may have contributed to its sea-keeping qualities. Usually it had a single mast and a bowsprit, and was cutter-rigged with a mainsail, fore staysail, and jib. It was equipped with a windlass to help raise anchors, and often with a moveable davit over the stern, to help lift the buoy rope. Early boats tended to live up to their name, in that they were long and narrow, with a length-to-breadth ratio of four to one. This was rather less on

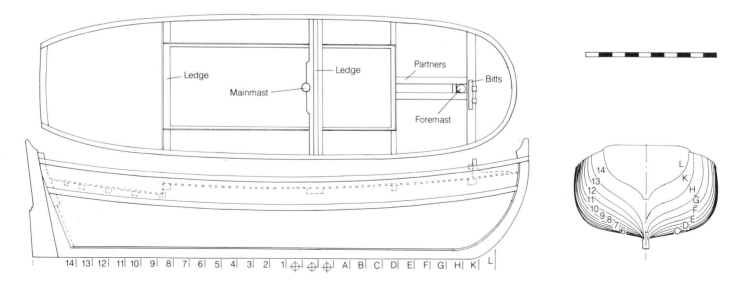

The longboat of the Royal Sovereign, *made for Admiral Aylmer in 1711. Length 38ft, breadth 11ft.*

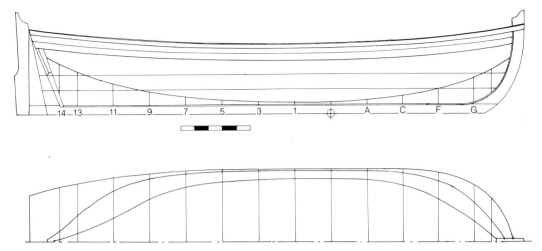
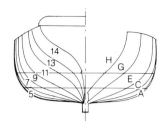

A longboat of 1758, for a First Rate. Length 26ft; breadth 10ft 4in; depth 4ft 5in.

smaller boats, and over the years it tended to diminish to a ratio of three and a half to one.

The Launch

Compared with the longboat, the launch had less sheer, and a wider stern. Its midship section was rather square, especially in the larger boats, and this made it suitable for carrying heavy and bulky loads. Under the waterline aft, the timbers of the stern rose directly out of the deadwood. There was no curved deadrise to give a smooth shape, as on other types of boat. Though it had been used occasionally as a ship's boat since as early as 1661,[8] it had originated as a dockyard craft, designed for lifting rather than sea-keeping ability. Many captains asked to be issued with them in the 1740s, and a few of these requests were granted, but the launch did not become standard until November 1780, when ships of 20 guns and more were to be supplied with launches instead of longboats, as soon as they were refitted.[9]

By about 1805, all ships except brigs and cutters were entitled to launches (though the longboat was still an acceptable alternative). The length of the launch was roughly proportional to the size of the ship, thus a small sloop would have one of 18 or 19ft and a First Rate one of 34ft.[10]

The launch had similar fittings to the longboat. It had a windlass, and a davit for raising the buoy rope of an anchor. It was usually cutter-rigged, though it seems that some could carry schooner rig, with either lug or lateen sails. In 1783 it was ordered that all launches should be equipped to row double-banked.[11]

The Pinnace

The pinnace and the barge are often confused, even in official records, and to a certain extent the two terms are interchangable. There was some measure of agreement that the barge was larger and more prestigious than the pinnace, and was mainly used for

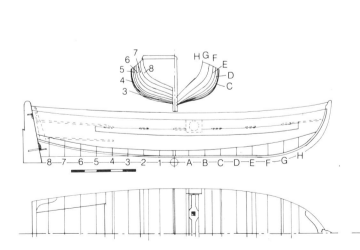

Possibly the most famous ship's boat ever – the launch of the Bounty, *into which Captain Bligh was forced by the mutineers, and made a voyage of 3000 miles.*

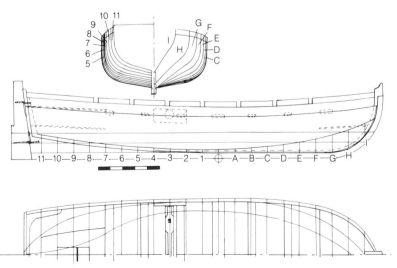

A launch of 1779. Length 29ft; breadth 8ft 7in; depth abaft 4ft 4in; midships 3ft 6in; afore 4ft 4in.

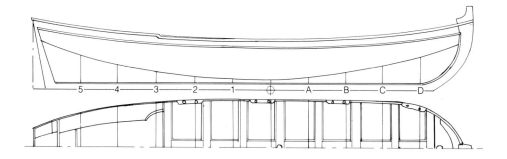
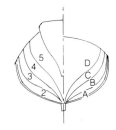

An eight-oared pinnace as made in Portsmouth, taken from a set of draughts dated 1706.

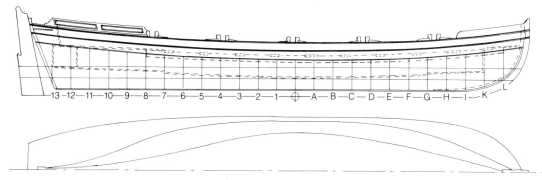
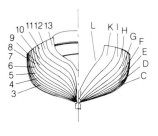

A 10-oared pinnace of 1798, made in Portsmouth. Length 32ft; breadth 6ft 7in; depth 2ft 11in.

the transport of captains and admirals, whereas the pinnace was used for junior officers. According to Falconer, writing in 1769, 'Pinnaces exactly resemble barges, only they are somewhat smaller, and never row more than eight oars; whereas a barge properly never rows less than ten.'[12] A later source states that 'barges are principally for carrying flag officers and captains, and are lined and panelled fore and aft, that they may be richly decorated if required.' Pinnaces were 'for similar purposes to the barges, but to carry officers of less rank; they are therefore not fitted up in quite so neat a style, as they are lined and panelled no further forward than the stern sheets.'[13]

The pinnace was in use throughout the whole of the period. It was established by 1618, and by 1640 all ships from the Fourth Rate upwards carried one, between 22 and 35ft long.[14] In 1686 a pinnace was carried by all vessels, including the tiny ketches. In 1745 its length ranged from 23 to 30ft.[15] Over the years, this range tended to diminish and in 1781 it seems that pinnaces were only issued in lengths of 26, 28 and 30ft.[16] By an order of 1740, all eight-oared boats were to be 28ft long, and by the 1800s, all ships of the line had a 28ft pinnace, as did large sloops, while small sloops of 200 tons carried one of 24ft.[17]

Early pinnaces were not particularly narrow, having a length-to-breadth ratio similar to that of longboats. By about 1750 it was suggested that the ratio should remain at four to one for smaller pinnaces, but for a larger pinnace it should be as much as six to one.[18] The standard 28ft pinnace of the early nineteenth century had a length-to-breadth ratio of about four and a half to one. These ratios indicate that a boat which was designed to be rowed had an optimum width for a given arrangement of oarsmen, and this relationship did not alter much as the length of the vessel was increased.

There were several important differences between pinnaces and barges, and other boats. They were narrower, particularly at

the stern, and had very small transoms. There was a backboard just inside the stern which separated the helmsman from the passenger area just forward. The latter area was known as the stern sheets, and was decked with either planks or gratings, and fitted with a thwartships bench just forward of the backboard, and longitudinal benches on each side just forward of that. Most pinnaces had a board running along the length of the centre line, at the level of the thwarts. They were rowed single-banked, with each oarsman sitting on the opposite side to his thole pin, to give him extra leverage. In the 1800s pinnaces were fitted with two masts and lateen-rigged.[19] There is little information about the rig before then, but those of the mid-eighteenth century seem to have had fittings for two masts. This is fully consistent with the lateen rig. Those of 1771 were evidently two-masted with spritsail rig, while in 1813–14 sliding gunter rig is mentioned in connection with pinnaces and barges.[20]

The Barge

The barge began to take on a separate identity from the pinnace, around 1700. It did not appear on the lists of 1640, 1655 or 1686, but by the end of the century flag officers were beginning to demand larger boats, of up to 20 oars, and these were often called barges. By 1702 many captains of Third Rates were allowed barges larger than their pinnaces. In the early years of the eighteenth century enormous barges, of up to twenty oars, were sometimes used by admirals. In 1719 ships of the Fourth Rate and above had boats with ten oars or more, though these were still called pinnaces, probably for convenience in drawing up a table.[21] This terminology was used throughout most of the eighteenth century. By an order of 1740, all ten-oared boats were to be 32ft

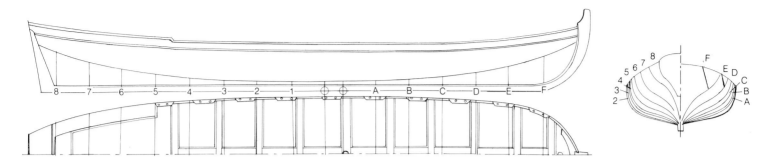

Sir George Rooke's barge in 1706. This was one of the very large barges made for admirals around that time. It is fitted for 20 oars.

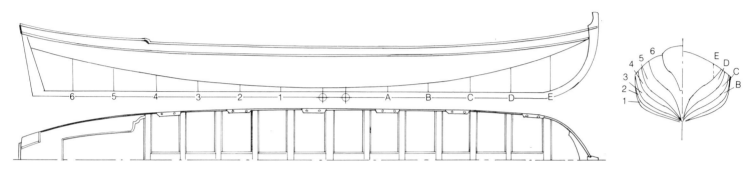

A 12-oared barge from the same period as the above. It was probably used by a senior captain or rear admiral.

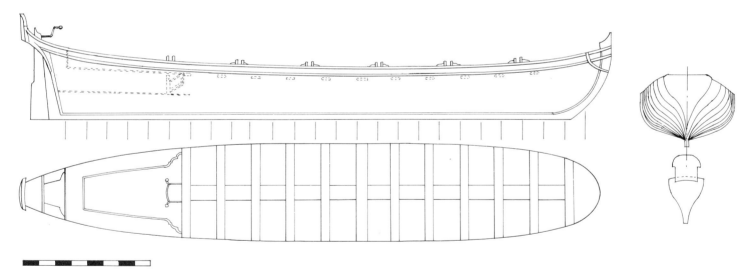

A 36ft barge with 12 oars, c1750.

long.[22] In a list of the 1800s, a 'barge or ten-oared boat of 32ft' was carried by all ships of 32 guns or more, while those of more than 64 guns also had a 28ft pinnace. Smaller 'barges or ten-oared boats' of a minimum length of 28ft were carried by ships of 20 to 28 guns.[23]

The rigging and fitting of barges was similar to that of pinnaces, though of course the former were more heavily decorated. Proportions were similar, though the issue is confused by the difference in terminology. The standard 32ft barge of the 1800s had a length-to-breadth ratio of nearly five to one.

The Skiff and Shallop

For most of the seventeenth century the skiff was the smallest boat carried by large ships. According to Boteler it was 'a nimbler boat than the longboat, and the peculiar employment of it is to row speedily upon all occasions.'[24] Mainwaring offers a slightly different definition when he suggests that it was 'for lightness, and to hoist in and out quickly.'[25] Several sources agree that the skiff was similar to the shallop, though Mainwaring implies that the form of the hull was different.

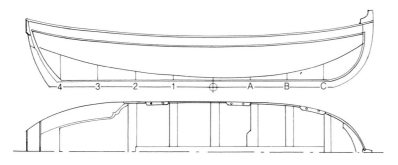
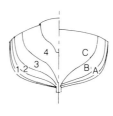

An early yawl, c1700. This one was used by Admiral Sir Clowdisley Shovell, and is presumably similar to those which came into standard use around this time.

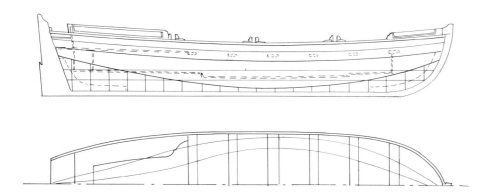

A yawl of 1798. This was typical of the new type of yawl, which replaced some cutters. Length 26ft; breadth 6ft 6in; depth 2ft 11in.

In 1640 the skiff was carried by First and Second Rates, and was between 20 and 27ft long. In 1655 it was carried by Fourth Rates and above, though the shallop was offered as an alternative. By 1686 it was again confined to the two largest rates, and all were 27ft long. Both skiff and shallop tended to die out around the end of the century, as their various roles were taken over by the barge and the yawl.

The Yawl

The yawl was probably the Navy's first clinker-built boat, dating at least from the beginning of the seventeenth century. It originated at Deal, where local builders had produced a type which was ideal for servicing both naval and merchant ships which anchored in the Downs to await a favourable wind. In this role it attracted the attention of naval officers, and a few were in service on ships in 1662. The yawl may have developed from the Norwegian 'yole', which was regarded as a highly seaworthy boat. The earliest yawls, as shown from a plan of around 1700, were unusual amongst ships' boats in that they were almost double-ended, with a sternpost that was curved rather than straight. They had only a very small transom.

The Navy was ordering some yawls from private boatbuilders as early as 1690, though it is not clear if these were intended for issue to ships.[26] It became established in 1701, when Fourth Rates were given one each, and in 1702 when ships of the first three rates were to be given one in addition to the boats already

carried. The yawl was a good sea-boat, and highly regarded by officers, who often requested them instead of longboats.

The Navy was never entirely happy about the clinker build of the yawl. The boats of 1702 were to be built 'after the manner of a Deal yawl in all respects, except the clinker work'.[27] In 1719 they were to be of 'pinnace fashion' for the larger ships, of 'Deal fashion' for the Sixth Rates, and 'sometimes Deal and sometimes pinnaces' for sloops. In 1769, those issued to frigates for Channel service were to be 'of clench work of the cutter kind', and those for foreign service were to be 'of carvel work, as more durable and easy to repair'.[28] By the end of the century, all yawls seem to have been carvel-built. By this time, and probably much earlier, the curved sternpost had been replaced by a straight one.

The standard yawl of 1800 was 26ft long, though they were constructed in other lengths. This type was unusual in that it was decked throughout its length, in three stages. Yawls usually had four, six or eight oars. Usually they were two-masted, with sprit, lateen or gunter rig at different times, like barges and pinnaces.

The Cutter

The cutter was the great success of the late eighteenth century. In shape it was not unlike the yawls, though it tended to be larger, and had a straight sternpost. It had a very sharp bow in comparison to other boats of the time, and was 'broader, deeper and shorter' than barges and pinnaces, so that it was 'fitter for sailing'.[29] This quality made it very popular with captains, and it was

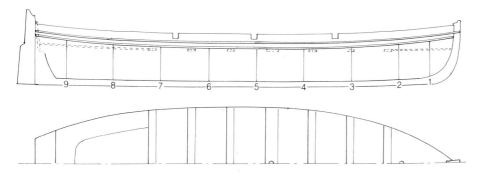
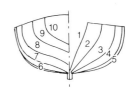

A Deal cutter used by HMS Captain *in 1762. Length 27ft; breadth 6ft 11in; depth 2ft 5in.*

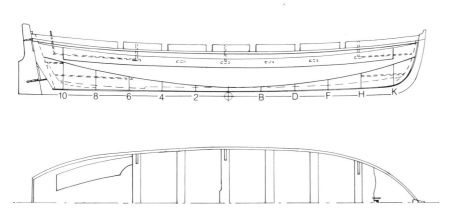
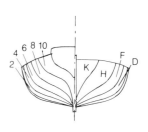

A 25ft cutter, standard for all large ships by the late eighteenth century. Length 25ft; breadth 6ft 11in; depth 2ft 5¼in.

very much in demand. Like the yawls it originated at Deal, and was originally clinker-built. Unlike the yawl, the cutter remained clinker-built; only cutters issued for foreign service were normally carvel-built.

Cutters were first used in 1740, when ships of the Third Rate and above were issued with one each to assist in pressing men. Others were provided for the ships which took part in Anson's famous circumnavigation of 1740–44. In 1767 they were available in several dimensions, from 15 to 28ft. The boats issued to frigates, however, were still known as yawls. In 1771 a 74-gun ship carried two cutters of different lengths, and after 1781 all ships of 20 guns and more carried an 18ft cutter, which later became known as a jolly boat. By the 1800s, all ships of 36 guns or more had two 25ft cutters, the only case where identical boats were carried on the same ships. Smaller vessels had a 'Deal cutter or yawl' of 22 or 24ft, and also a 'four-oared Deal cutter or jolly boat'.[30] Cutters of 1771 had two masts, of equal height, and were spritsail-rigged; by the 1800s lug rig seems to have been more common. Usually they were rowed with six oars.

The Jolly Boat

The jolly boat was quite common in the early seventeenth century. It was a small, light boat, easy to hoist in and out of the water. In 1627 they were between 14 and 20ft long. They were still in occasional use in the latter part of the seventeenth century, and in the 1680s it is documented that they were issued to First,

Second and Third Rate ships in sizes ranging from 13 to 19ft.[31]

The term jolly boat reappears towards the end of the eighteenth century, when it was used to describe small boats of 16 or 18ft. It is not clear whether it referred to the 18ft cutter, or to an alternative boat, but one authority says of cutters, 'Sometimes the smaller boats are called and used as jolly boats.' Another says that four-oared cutters were called jolly boats.[32] If it is the case that the jolly boat was merely a small cutter, then the standard boat of the period was 6½ft broad, had two masts of equal height, and was spritsail rigged.

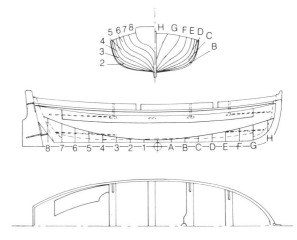

An 18ft cutter or jolly boat. Length 18ft; breadth 6ft 6½in; depth 2ft 3in.

The Cockboat

This type of small boat was rarely in use by the beginning of the seventeenth century. In the 1630s it was 'seldom regarded, being over tender-sided, and too small to be made use of in any service at sea.'[33] It was, however, possible to hoist them in and out of the water, a comparatively rare facility at that time.

The Wherry

In the early seventeenth century the wherry was classed with the cockboat as being too light and fragile to be of real use. It was regarded as a fast rowing boat, but only suitable for river use. By the 1800s it may have seen some unofficial use because the Thames waterman's wherry was adopted by some captains as their own boat. This craft had very sharp bows, and a great rake. It was clinker-built, with large and wide strakes of planking.

The Gig

This was another light boat, clinker-built, and often favoured by captains for their own use. A few were used in the 1760s, and in the 1800s 22-ft gigs were issued officially to some brigs and cutters, as an alternative to cutters and jolly boats. Others were bought privately by captains, and used unofficially. One such, of 1815, was 25ft long, 5ft 7in broad, and 2ft deep. Most gigs appear to have had six oars. The hull form of some seems to have been slightly unusual, in that the midships section continued to increase in breadth right up to the top of the side.

The Galley

The galley was a slightly bigger version of the gig, with six or eight oars. Its design was derived from a boat used by smugglers in the last quarter of the eighteenth century, and it was originally used in patrols against smuggling. It was evidently used as a ship's boat in the 1800s, being regarded as useful for raiding parties on enemy coast. However, it did not become standard type until the 1850s.

Brenton's Yawl

This was an experimental type, developed by Captain Brenton in 1808. At first the Navy Board was impressed, and it was issued to many ships in place of the launch, but this was shortlived and in March 1810 it was withdrawn from use.[34]

Lifeboats

Henry Greathead developed his lifeboat in 1789, following on the work of others, such as Rear Admiral Hunter and Lionel Lupin, and in 1808 he suggested that the Admiralty might be interested in them, as they could be used in conditions which would put other boats in severe danger. They were tested at Portsmouth, Plymouth, Deal and Yarmouth. They had built-in buoyancy, in the form of large amounts of cork, but the Admiralty found that they cost £108 each compared with £11 for a jolly boat, and lost interest.[35] It was to be many years before such boats were used on ships.

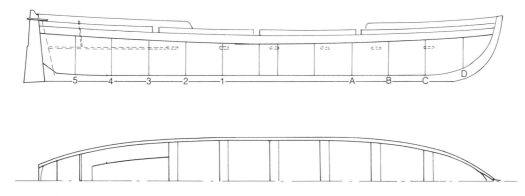
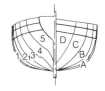

A captain's gig of 1806. Length 25ft; breadth 4ft 6in; depth 2ft 4in.

Chapter 41. Boat Fittings

Steering

The rudder of a boat was exactly the same as that of a contemporary ship, in that it was not balanced, but hinged to the sternpost by its forward edge, and it tapered from foot to head, with a large hancing just above the waterline. Its lowest edge was usually level with the bottom of the keel, and it reached high enough to allow the fitting of a tiller which could pass over the top of the sternpost. In some barges and pinnaces the transom was placed behind the rudder, but in other boats the head of the rudder was completely exposed.

The rudder was hung on the sternpost by only two gudgeons and pintles. Unlike that of a ship, it was likely to be hung and unhung every time the boat was used, and it needed to be easily removeable. The lower pintle was fitted to the sternpost rather than the rudder. It was very long, and extended almost up to the waterline. The upper one was shorter, and fitted to the rudder.

The rudder of a longboat of 1742, showing some of its painted decoration. Author's photograph.

During anchor work, for example, the rudder would sometimes have to be hung or unhung while the boat was in the water, and the system of pintles was designed to make this easier. Because the top of the lower pintle was just below the waterline, it was easy to locate and as the pintles were different lengths, it was possible to position the lower one before putting the upper one in place.

Most boats had a fairly long wooden tiller, fitted into a hole in the head of the rudder. On boats with a backboard, such as pinnaces and some cutters, the space for the tiller was very restricted, and it had to be kept short. Barges and pinnaces often had an iron tiller, which was sometimes curved to allow it to fit into the available space.

Some boats appear to have used a yoke instead of a tiller. This was defined by Falconer as 'a small board or bar which crosses the upper end of a boat's rudder at right angles, and having two small cords extending from its opposite extremities to the stern sheets of the boat, whereby she is steered as with a tiller.'[1] This had the advantage of saving space in the after part, and it could have allowed the boat to be steered by a helmsman some distance from the stern.

For extended voyages, boats must have been issued with one of the ship's spare compasses. By an order of 1802, special boat compasses could be issued, one for each boat, on the captain's request.[2]

Rowing

All ships' boats could be rowed. For some, such as barges, pinnaces, gigs and wherries, it was the primary means of propulsion, and the sails were seldom used. The number and position of the oars were an integral part of the boat's design and depended

Pinnaces coming alongside a ship in the late eighteenth century, showing oars and boathooks in use. NMM.

very much on the number and position of the thwarts. Boats could be either double- or single-banked. If single-banked, two oarsmen sat side by side on each thwart, and each operated an oar on his own side. If double-banked, one oarsman sat on each thwart, and his oar passed over the centre line of the boat and through a thole pin on the opposite side. This system reduced the number of oars available, but increased the leverage which each oarsman could apply. Pinnaces and smaller barges were usually single-banked, partly because they were too narrow to enable two men to sit side by side without getting in one another's way. Some of the very large barges used by admirals in the first half of the eighteenth century were double-banked. Other boats were usually double-banked. This was confirmed by an order of 1783, that all launches built were to be 'fitted for rowing double-banked'.[3]

The oars were made by contract, or by oar-makers employed in the dockyards. The blade was long and flat; the next part was round in cross section. The oar was square and somewhat thicker where it was intended to fit into the rowlock or thole pin, to help keep it in position. Its innermost extremity, the loom, was very thin, so that it could be held by the rower. Oars varied in length according to whether the boat was single- or double-banked.

The modern rowlock, with its swivelling crutch, did not come

A single-banked barge, c1750, showing the distribution of the oarsmen. NMM.

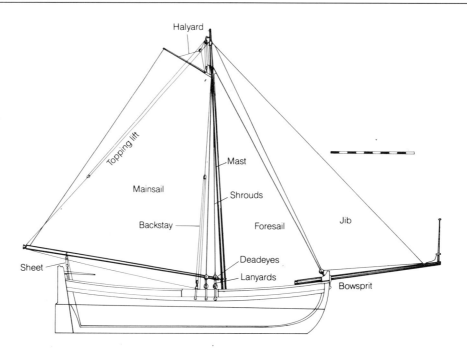

A cutter-rigged longboat, c1750.

into use until the mid-nineteenth century. Until the mid-eighteenth century, thole pins were used to stop the oar from moving backwards and forwards. These pins came in pairs, and projected upwards from the gunwale, just aft of the thwart used for each oar. The advent of the cutter with removeable wash-strakes tended to make thole pins obsolete, though they were still to be found on some of the smaller boats in 1815, and were perhaps kept on others for use when the wash-strake was not in position.

Boat hooks were issued to help in coming alongside, fending off, and in picking up objects such as anchor buoys. The standard type had an iron head, with a spike projecting forward and a hook to one side. It was fitted to a wooden pole, or spar. In the 1800s, a First Rate fitted for Channel service was allowed 12 boat hooks for its six boats, and 12 spare spars.[4]

Types of Rig

All boats were fitted for sailing, and were issued with removeable masts, spars, sails and rigging. Some, such as yawls, cutters and longboats, would have used their sails more than others, and to some extent the type of rig was tailored to the purposes of the boat. A boat could be fitted with one, two, or occasionally three masts. Several different types of rig were used over the years, and boat rigging showed a far greater variety than that of the ships which carried them.

Lateen rig was the oldest, and took its name from its Mediterranean origins. It consisted of a relatively short mast, and a long yard which was hoisted diagonally, fore and aft. The true lateen sail was triangular, but there was a variation of it known as the settee sail which had its forward corner cut off. Though like all the other boats it had a fore and aft rig, it was better suited than some for running before the wind, but it needed a large crew to operate it, mainly because the long yard had to be moved from one side to the other when going about. It seems to have been standard for barges and pinnaces, though in at least one case in

the 1800s it was offered as an alternative rig for a launch.[5] Lateen-rigged boats were usually two-masted, with the foremast well forward.

Lug rig was similar to lateen, except that the fore part of the sail was considerably reduced, so that it projected only slightly forward of the mast. Like lateen it was suitable for running, and it required a large crew, especially if the yard had to be moved from one side to the other when tacking. It seems to have been common on cutters, and was certainly standard on them in the early nineteenth century. Most lug-rigged boats had two masts, with an outrigger to extend the sail aft.

Gaff rig was so called because of the gaff which supported the sail. It projected diagonally from the mast as with lateen or lug rig, but no part of the gaff or the main sail projected forward of the mast. This made it easier to handle in going about than the other two, and it was more efficient when close to the wind, though perhaps less useful in running before it. It was used in combination with a bowsprit, and a fore staysail and a jib. The single-masted gaff rig, now known as cutter rig, was well established on longboats by the middle of the eighteenth century, and it was to remain in use for launches. Most gaff-rigged boats had only one mast, but some longboats and launches were two-masted schooner-rigged.

A spritsail was similar in shape to a gaff sail, but it was supported in rather a different way. Instead of having a gaff to which the head of the sail was laced, a sprit projected diagonally from the mast just above the deck. It passed over the middle of the sail, and its outer end supported the outer corner of the sail. The head of the sail was generally wider than in gaff rig, and the centre of gravity was kept lower by the way in which the sprit was fitted. The sail was furled by clewing it up, rather than by lowering it as with a gaff sail. This meant that it could be operated by fewer men, but it was less efficient close to the wind, and on one tack or the other the sprit would interrupt the air flow, and prevent the sail from forming the ideal shape. Most sprit-rigged boats were two-masted, apparently with masts of equal height. Such a rig was standard for yawls. An establishment of 1771 made it

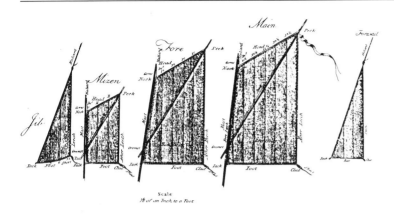

Types of boat sails in use in the 1790s, from Steel's Sailmaking, Mastmaking and Rigging.

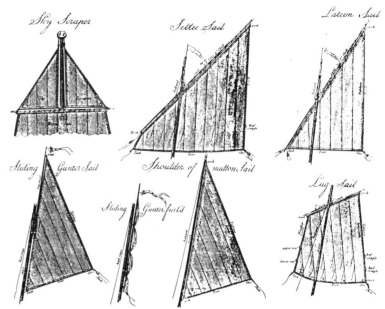

standard for barges and pinnaces, though by the end of the century it had been replaced by the lateen rig.[6]

Sliding gunter rig had a triangular sail, rather like that used by a modern yacht. It was laced to a topmast, which slid up the mainmast to raise the sail. It was used for the barge of the *San Domingo* in 1813–14, and presumably for other ships.[7] The 'leg of mutton' sail was similar, but did not have the sliding topmast. It is not clear if it was used for ships' boats during this period, though it is described in Steel's book of 1794, without any mention of where it was used. 'Shoulder of mutton' sails were slightly different, in that they had a small gaff at their heads, one-sixth of the length of the boom which extended the foot. They appear to have been in use around 1750.

had a short vertical mast, like the spritsail topsail of a ship, rising from the outer end of the bowsprit. It is unlikely that such a mast could carry a sail with any efficiency, but it could possibly fly a flag or ensign. In other cases, a flagstaff seems to have been fitted at the stern, for use when the boat was being rowed.

The mast was supported against stresses from behind and from either side by the shrouds, which were similar in principle to those of a ship. Some longboats had their sides strengthened beside the mast, to hold the deadeyes which supported the shrouds. The bowsprit was held down against the pull of its sails by a bobstay, which passed from its outermost end to a hole in the stempost of the boat. The original gaff sail, as carried in the middle of the eighteenth century, had a short gaff, which tended to become

Rigging Details

The mast of a boat, unlike that of a large ship, was made in a single piece. It was circular in cross-section, reaching its maximum diameter at the level of the boat's thwarts. It tapered after that, to about half its maximum diameter. Because boats never had topmasts, there was no need to shape the top of the mast to accommodate one. Some masts had a button on top, others were simply rounded off.

Masts were easily removeable. Around 1700 they seem to have been fitted through a hole drilled in suitably positioned thwarts, strengthened for the purpose. Presumably there was some kind of step on the keelson, to hold the foot of the mast. By the middle of the eighteenth century, the mast was usually put into a semicircular groove in the fore or after edge of the thwart, and held in place by a metal clamp.

The bowsprit was used mainly on gaff-rigged longboats and launches. It was fitted over the gunwale, to the starboard side of the stempost, where it was put through a metal frame to hold it in position. It was at its maximum thickness at this point, and it extended aft a little way so that it could be fixed to the first thwart. It tapered forward, but less than a mast. Some bowsprits

A rigged model of a mid-eighteenth century longboat. Author's photograph.

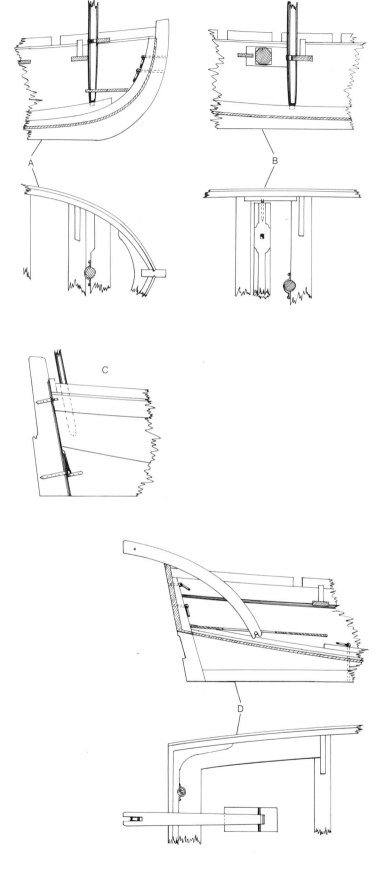

longer as the years progressed. Presumably a parrel held the end of the gaff to the mast. There is no detailed information on how lateen and lug sails were hoisted, but the principle was similar in some ways to the gaff.

Early gaff sails were loose footed, with the lower outer corner attached directly to the main sheet. Around 1750 the boom was introduced. This projected horizontally from the lower part of the mast, and helped to extend the foot of the sail. The sail was only attached to the boom at its outer corner, known as the clew, and not laced to it as it was to the gaff.

The sheet, which controlled the outer corner of the sail, presented a problem, for it had a tendency to get in the way of the tiller. In the mid-eighteenth century this was solved by putting a horse across the transom to lift it clear, and allow the sheet to move from one side to the other without interruption.

Forestays braced the mast against pressures from forward. They extended from the head of the mast to the stempost, and to the bowsprit if one was fitted. On gaff-rigged boats they were used to support staysails and jibs.

Ground Tackle

Except for longboats of the 1650s, which carried a conventional anchor, boats usually carried a grapnel. This had four arms instead of two, and so had no need of a stock. One grapnel was issued for each boat. Its weight was in proportion to the size of the boat. Thus in 1686 a First Rate's longboat, 33ft long, had a grapnel of 84lbs, while a pinnace of 33ft had one of 56lbs.[8] In the 1800s, a 74-gun ship's 32ft barge had one of 84lbs, while its 31ft launch had a grapnel of 56lbs, and each other boat had one of 40lbs.[9] Cables of suitable length were issued, and some of the larger boats had bitts for securing the anchor cable.

Windlasses and Davits

The largest grapnels were heavy enough to require some mechanical assistance in lifting them. Moreover longboats and launches were required to work with the anchors of their parent ships, and needed considerable leverage to do so. One of their more important tasks was to lift the buoy rope of an anchor which had embedded itself too firmly in the ground. Though this did not necessarily involve lifting the anchor itself, it did mean lifting the crown so that the anchor could free itself and the ship's capstan could do the work of raising it. A large anchor could weigh three tons or more, which was more than a party of seamen on a longboat could move unaided.

Clearly there was no space for a capstan on a longboat. Therefore the next best alternative, the windlass, was used. It was situated amidships, where the boat was broadest. A contract for

Details of a launch of 1787.
A. Profile and plan of the bows, showing how the foremast is wedged between two thwarts and fixed with a metal band to the upper thwart. It also shows the ringbolts used for lifting the boat.
B. Midships views, showing the fitting of the mainmast, and the windlass, which is octagonal for most of its length, but square near the holes for the bars. It also shows one of the pins about which it rotates.
C. The stern from the outside, showing the rudder fitting and the flagstaff.
D. Profile and plan of the stern, showing how the davit is fitted. It also shows the ringbolts, and the fitting of the flagstaff, offset to clear the rudder.

longboats of 1696 demanded 'a windlass well fix't'.[10] The standard mid-eighteenth century windlass was octagonal in section for most of its length, but square where the bar holes were cut. It tapered to a circular form towards its ends, where it fitted into recesses in the side of the boat, which was specially strengthened at that point. Two rows of bar holes were cut, one on each side, just out from the centre line of the boat, with four holes in each. The buoy rope would have been coiled round the centre of the windlass, and two bars could have been used at once, perhaps with several seamen pulling on each if necessary.

In some longboats, the buoy rope was hauled onboard by means of a simple sheave. The contract of 1696 demanded a 'rowle of lignum vitae at the stem and stern posts, of four and a half inches diameter, of a proper length for carrying the buoy rope.'[11] Davits, however, had been in use in the early part of the seventeenth century, and by the middle of the eighteenth century one was usually fitted to the stern. Its lower end fitted into a recess in the decking of the stern sheets, and a thwartships pin fitted through a groove in the davit. The davit itself curved over the stern, and the rudder had to be removed to make room for it. Its outer end was fitted with a sheave, through which the buoy rope passed.

Painting and Decoration

Boats were exposed to more varying conditions than anything else aboard ship, and they had to be well protected against the elements. It seems that the outsides of most boats were primed with rosin. This had good protective qualities and allowed the natural colour of the wood to show through. Other boats were painted in places. In 1676 a contractor agreed to 'prime and paint' barges and pinnaces, 'withinside to the floor, and also the ceiling if any be, and the outboard strake, together with the rails if any.'[12] Up to three coats could be applied, if needed. In 1696 a builder of longboats agreed that they should be 'paid with white stuff to the risings within board, well caulked, graved, and primed to the water's edge without board and painted within as usual.'[13] According to models of the early and mid-eighteenth century, many pinnaces and longboats had their gunwales and stern sheets painted red, and a gilt frieze along the top strake on the outside. The transoms of barges were also decorated in some cases, reflecting the status of the officers who used them. By an order of 1755, pinnaces were to be painted, except on the bottom, because they saw less service than other boats. The bottom under the pallating, and the fore and stern sheets, were to be payed with white stuff only.[14]

Other types of boat had little decoration. According to a specification of 1800, only the largest cutters, of 30 and 34ft, were to be painted, though captains had the option of having them painted aboard ship from the boatswain's stores, or supplying their own paint.[15] Where several cutters were carried, they were sometimes identified by their colours, thus in 1813 the *San Domingo* had a black and a yellow cutter.[16] This probably means that the upper strake, and perhaps the stern sheets and thwarts, were painted in these colours. The custom of covering the bottom of the boat with rosin continued until 1771, when it was ordered that white lead should be used instead.[17]

Actual decoration, in the form of carvings, seems to have been rare on boats. Lining and panelling was allowed in the stern sheets of pinnaces, and on the upper strakes of barges. This con-

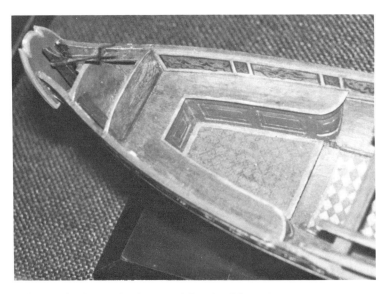

The stern of a pinnace, showing some of the painted decoration. Author's photograph, courtesy of NMM.

tained some mouldings, but by the standards of the seventeenth and eighteenth centuries it was very restrained. Any extra decoration had to be supplied by the officer who used the barge.

Armament of Boats

There is no evidence that boats were armed before the second quarter of the eighteenth century, except in that their crews often carried small arms to defend themselves when fetching water on a hostile coast, or for offensive purposes on a cutting-out expedition. In 1737 the *Centurion*, then operating off the west coast of Africa, was allowed four swivels for her longboat and in 1742 the *Burford* and *Suffolk* were allowed six swivels each for their launches. Captain Utting of the *Gosport* was refused swivels for his tops in 1744, but allowed them for his longboat.[18] After this date it seems to have become normal to carry four or six half-pounder swivels for launches or longboats. By the 1770s a 74-gun ship carried 12 such guns, though half of these would probably have been used in the tops.[19]

After 1795, swivels were replaced by a single carronade. By orders of 1794 and 1795, each launch was to be fitted with a carronade: 24- and 18-pounders for ships of the line, and 12-pounders for smaller ships.[20] The original boat carronade slide extended the whole length of the boat, so that the gun could be used at either end as required. In 1814 a new type was adopted. One slide was fitted, in either the bow or stern, to extend over several thwarts. One end was pivoted at either the bow or stern, and the other could be dropped, to lower the gun to the floor of the boat in order to improve stability.

Boat Covers

Boat covers are never shown on models, though they were certainly in use by 1778, to protect the boat when it was stowed. By the early 1800s, one was issued for each boat, except the launch, possibly because another boat was stowed inside this type.[21]

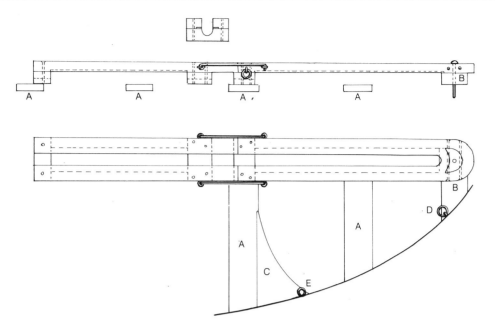

Elevation and plan of a carronade fitting proposed in 1814, arranged so that the gun could be dropped into the boat to lower the centre of gravity when needed. It also allows the gun to be rotated for aiming.
A. Thwarts.
B. A stout thwart to receive the bolt to secure the slide, one was also to be fitted close to the transom for a similar purpose.
C. A knee to receive the slide when tracked into the side – knees were also to be placed on the aft side of the after thwart.
D, E. Ring- and eyebolts for securing the carronade and slide – similar bolts were also to be placed abaft.

Chapter 42. Boat Establishments

Rules and Reality

As with guns, the naval administration continually tried to impose order on the number and types of boats carried by ships. Boats were a little easier to control in this respect than guns, in that there were fewer of them on each ship, they usually had to be replaced more often, and they were under the direct control of the Navy Board, rather than the Board of Ordnance. Nevertheless, the boat establishments must be treated with caution when being used to obtain an accurate picture of reality, for the following reasons.

Firstly, terminology varied, and the same boat might be described by different names at different times, leading the unwary into much confusion. Secondly, the boats prescribed were not always available, and sometimes a different type or size was issued. Thirdly, boats which were lost or fell into disrepair on foreign service were often replaced with what was locally available, though it might differ from what the establishment stipulated. Alternatively, boats could be made by the ship's carpenters, according to their own or the captain's ideas. In other cases, boats might be added for particular expeditions, involving, for example, the landing of troops. Finally, the personal preferences of officers might lead them to demand, and sometimes

receive, extra or unusual boats from official sources, or sometimes to supply them from their own private funds. All this must be borne in mind when considering boat establishments, especially in the seventeenth century, when the reality was often very different from the theory.

The Seventeenth Century

Throughout this period, three types of boat, the longboat, pinnace and the skiff, were normally issued. Only the largest ships carried all three, and the lists of 1618, 1640, 1670 and 1686[1] all show that only First and Second Rates should have skiffs. In 1655, however, Third Rates are also listed as having skiffs.[2] Third and Fourth Rates usually carried a longboat and a pinnace. Up to 1655, Fifth Rates were expected to carry only one boat, a longboat. In 1670 and in subsequent years, they had at least two, a longboat and a pinnace. Sixth Rates had only one boat up to 1670, but in 1686 they were allocated a longboat and a pinnace, like all rated ships below the Third Rate.

The relative lengths of boats tended to vary over the years. On the whole that of longboats was reduced. The *Sovereign* carried one of 50ft in 1640 and 1655, but only 36ft in 1686. The length of the pinnace, on the other hand, tended to increase. That carried by a typical Third Rate in 1640 and 1655 was 28ft long. By 1686 it was 31ft long, though this partly reflected the increase in size of ships of that rate. The length of skiffs also tended to increase. That carried by the typical Second Rate was 20 to 24ft long in the 1640s and '50s, while all skiffs were 27ft long in 1686.

Some variations from the establishments can be noted, and in every case ships carried more boats than officially allowed. Thus in 1660 the Third Rate *Plymouth* was said to have a longboat, a launch, a pinnace and a wherry, (though it is possible that different names were used for the same boat).[3] In 1668 the Third Rate *Monmouth* had a longboat, a barge, a shallop, a jolly boat and a yawl.[4] In 1672 the *Fairfax* had a longboat, a pinnace and a yawl.[5] On the other hand, the Second Rate *Duchess* of 1679 conformed to the establishment by carrying a longboat, pinnace and a skiff.[6] However, it is notable that most of the ships for which we have information were flagships, and these often carried more boats than the establishment stipulated. It is not unlikely that admirals managed to acquire extra boats for their own use.

The Early Eighteenth Century

The simple seventeenth century system of boat establishments began to be altered almost as soon as the new century began. The longboat had come in for much criticism because it was unable to perform all the tasks demanded of it, and could not be hoisted aboard ship. The Navy Board and Admiralty were not prepared to abolish it, however, as they could see no other vessel which was suitable for anchor work. Many officers would have liked to see the yawl substituted for the longboat, but the Navy Board, impressed with the sailing qualities of the former, was prepared to allow it to be issued in addition to the longboat. By an order of 1701, ships of 50 guns were to have a four-oared Deal yawl, and those of 60 guns were to have one of six oars. The following year, ships of the First, Second and Third Rates were also to be given Deal yawls. Thus all ships of the first two rates now had four boats, and Third Rates had three. Sixth Rates had only one, until they too were issued with a yawl in 1715. Fifth Rates still kept to the seventeenth century establishment and had a longboat and a pinnace, and were now the only vessels without a yawl.[7]

The longboat tended to become shorter, largely because it was now expected to be hauled in, and because some of its roles as a sea-boat had been taken over by the yawl. Between 1686 and 1719, longboats for each rate tended to be reduced by a foot or two, though those carried by 90-gun ships actually increased by a foot. The general reduction was all the more significant in that the ships themselves tended to increase in size over the same period. Obviously this reduction in longboat length had the most effect among the smaller ships. Fifth Rates were now issued with 26ft instead of 28ft boats.[8] These would of course be much easier to hoist and stow.

Pinnaces, on the other hand, tended to increase in size, so that in some cases they were longer than the longboat. In 1719 a Fifth Rate had a 26ft longboat and a 28ft pinnace.

The Introduction of the Cutter

Boats, like other aspects of ship design and fitting, tended to reflect the increasing range and scope of naval warfare. Until 1688 English wars were fought in the English Channel and the North Sea, within easy reach of the main naval bases. In the 1690s, the Mediterranean became established as one of the main theatres of fleet operations. In the eighteenth century the Caribbean gained steadily in importance, culminating in the 1780s, when the main fleets of France and Britain operated in the area for a time. Of

course bases were captured and built in these areas, but only after the fleet had been operating in them for some time. Moreover, these bases were far apart, and much less well equipped than the home yards. Thus a ship had to rely more on her own resources, finding her supplies wherever she could, and carrying out many of her own repairs. Thus a fuller and more versatile complement of boats was required.

The Caribbean and the Pacific gained in importance when war with Spain broke out in 1739. It was in these circumstances that the cutter was introduced. By an order of 1740, ships of the three largest rates were to have an additional boat in the form of a 25ft six-oared Deal cutter. In 1746, the most recently built Fourth and Fifth Rates were also to be equipped with a 25ft cutter.[9] In 1755, ships of the First, Second and Third Rates gained another 25ft cutter, so that Third Rates now had a total of five boats, while First and Second Rates had six.

New Classes of Ship

In the late 1750s several new and very successful classes of ship were added to the Navy, and became standard. The two-decker 74 replaced the old 70- and 80-gun ships, and the 64 replaced the 60 as the standard small ship of the line. The lower rates were now dominated by the frigates of 28, 32 and 36 guns, instead of the old 20-, 24- and 40-gun ships. At the bottom end of the scale, sloops, schooners and cutters were introduced or developed. There is no sign that a general boat establishment was issued to accommodate all these changes, but the new ships had to be given boats, and a series of orders was issued over the years.

Probably the most important order was that of 1769, which regulated the boats issued to ships of 10 to 36 guns.[10] Frigates of 28 to 36 guns had three boats each, a longboat, pinnace and a yawl. Ships of 32 and 36 guns had identical boats, a longboat of 23ft, a pinnace of 30ft, and a yawl of 24ft. Ships of 28 guns had slightly smaller boats, with longboats of 22 or 21ft, pinnaces of 28ft, and yawls of 22 or 23. Sloops of 16, 14 or 10 guns had two boats: a longboat of 19 to 16ft, and a pinnace of 26 to 24ft. However, by an earlier order of 1757, Sixth Rates on Channel service were to have a six-oared boat, presumably a cutter, in place of their ten-oared pinnace.[11]

By 1771 it seems that 74s were carrying six boats.[12] Only breadths are given in the list for this year, but from the draughts in the Admiralty collection it is not difficult to calculate the lengths. It appears a 74 could carry a longboat of 31ft, a barge or large pinnace of 32ft, a smaller pinnace of 28ft, one cutter of 25ft, and a smaller one of 18ft, and a yawl of about 25ft. This differed from past orders which allowed only one pinnace. If two cutters were in fact carried, as is suggested by the order of 1746, then a 74-gun ship would have carried seven boats, unless the yawl was intended as an alternative to one of the cutters, but this was not a regular custom until 1799.

Several orders were issued over the next few years. In 1780 launches replaced longboats in all types of ship. In 1781, all ships of 20 guns or more were allowed an 18ft cutter, which later became known as the jolly boat. In 1783 ships of 60 to 32 guns were given a barge of 32ft instead of a pinnace of 30ft. Presumably the number of oars had been increased as well as the length of the vessel, hence the different name.[13]

Other orders applied to particular types of ship. Thus in 1780 64-gun ships were to carry a launch, two pinnaces of different lengths (one presumably being a barge) and two 25ft cutters. The 38-gun frigate, a new class, was given a launch, a pinnace, and two 24ft cutters. Shortly afterwards, the 36-gun frigate was also given an extra cutter, making a total of four boats. In 1784 small 28-gun frigates were allowed a 30ft pinnace instead of a 28ft one, and in 1783 large sloops of 300 tons or more were given a 28ft pinnace instead of a 26ft one. They had already been given an 18ft cutter in 1777.[14]

The term 'cutter' also referred to a type of decked patrol vessel, used largely in activity against smugglers. It carried its own boats, and these too were sometimes called cutters. In 1779 cutters were to carry only one boat, a four-oared yawl or cutter. In 1783, they were to have an extra boat, though we are not told what size or type. Later in the same year it was ordered that their 18ft boats be replaced by 20ft ones, in peacetime at least.[15]

A Period of Stability

By the time war with France had begun in 1793, the allocation of ships' boats had fallen into regular patterns. The number of boat types and their lengths had been gradually reduced, and the establishments show some evidence of systematic thinking, so that it is not too difficult to identify the basic rules governing the issue of boats. Ships of 64 guns or more had six boats, plus an extra barge if serving as a flagship. Those of 50 to 32 guns had five boats, and Sixth Rates of 28 to 20 guns had four. Large sloops

of 300 tons and more had three boats, while smaller vessels had only two.

The dimensions of launches were directly proportional to the size of the ship, so that they could be used in raising the appropriate size of anchor. Thus 12 different lengths of launch were in use around 1805, ranging from a 34ft one for a 100-gun ship to a 16ft one for a small sloop. Pinnaces, on the other hand, took on a much more standard form. All ships of 32 guns or more had a 32ft pinnace, while those of 64 guns and more had a 28ft one. The 25ft cutter was carried by all ships down to 64 guns, while those of 50 to 28 guns had the 24ft version. All ships of more than 28 guns had the standard 18ft cutter, the jolly boat.[16]

This system seems to have survived, with some modifications, until 1815. From 1799, ships of 36 guns or more were allowed to substitute one of their 25ft cutters for a 26ft yawl. After 1794 ships of 32 to 64 guns were allowed to replace their barge with an eight-oared cutter. Between 1808 and 1810 Brenton's yawl was tested, and eventually rejected, as a substitute for the launch on medium-sized ships. A new class of 32-gun ship, with 18-pounder guns instead of 12-pounders, was developed, and equipped with a boat complement very similar to that of a 36-gun ship. Different arrangements were evolved for different types of sloops, according to their tonnage and whether they were brig or ship-rigged. A new class of cutter was equipped with a gig of 22ft, and a cutter of 22ft.[17] Apart from these, and the variations introduced by individual captains, there was little change in boat establishments between 1790 and 1815.

Chapter 43. Boat Stowage

Towing

Towing was the simplest and oldest method of transporting a ship's boat. It was probably universal in the early years of the seventeenth century, when enormous longboats, with a length of nearly half the keel of the ship, were used. Besides the advantage of enabling ships to have a very large boat, towing also made it possible to get a boat into use very quickly, without much labour. The disadvantage of towing was that it left the boat in a position where it was very vulnerable to heavy seas, strong winds, and the hazards of battle. In 1625, all the English ships on an expedition to Cadiz lost their longboats while towing them across the Bay of Biscay.[1]

A boat was towed by two ropes, a boat rope and a gust rope (spelled in a variety of ways in seventeenth-century documents). The boat rope was the thicker of the two, being 7in in circumference on a Third Rate of 1670.[2] It did the actual work of towing and was attached to the bow of the boat, and to a position on one side of the ship, perhaps as far forward as the mainmast. The gust rope was a little lighter, being 4½in in circumference on a Third Rate of 1670. It too was attached to the bow of the boat, and led forward to the other side of the ship. It was intended to 'keep the boat from sheering', and to 'save the bows of the boat, which would be torn out by the twitches which the ship under sail

would give.'[3] It was particularly important that the boat should not come too close under the stern, where it would be in danger of fouling the rudder.

It appears that the boat's rudder was unshipped whilst under tow. The evidence of paintings show it was normal to station at least one man in the boat, probably to bail out water when necessary, and to help when bringing it alongside.

By the second quarter of the seventeenth century, perhaps as a result of the Cadiz expedition of 1625, the concept of towing was being questioned. Mainwaring, writing around 1625, seems to imply that the longboat was not hoisted in. 'Other smaller boats which they carry for lightness, to hoist in and out quickly, are called skiffs and shallops ... A good longboat will live in any grown sea if the water be sometimes freed, unless the sea break very much.'[4] Boteler, writing a few years later, clearly states that the longboat could be hoisted in. It was 'the largest and strongest of all such boats as are to be hoisted into a ship.'[5] The earliest specific reference to a longboat being hoisted in comes from 1661, but there is no doubt that it was done much earlier than that.[6]

On the other hand, ships still towed their boats when necessary. In 1655 boat ropes and gust ropes were issued for both the longboat and the pinnace. By 1670, they were issued for one boat only.[7] Paintings and drawings of the battles of the Dutch Wars often show boats being towed, suggesting that they were hoisted out to allow more room to work the guns. As late as 1711 the Navy Board complained that 'there is a great expense of longboats by the ships towing 'em, and cutting 'em away upon exigencies.'[8] A well known painting from the 1750s (above, on the next page) shows a ship of the line towing both its longboat and its pinnace, though in this case the ship is clearly entering harbour, and had perhaps lowered its boats to have them ready for immediate use in mooring or anchoring.

Hoisting Boats

From about 1625 onwards there was an increasing tendency to hoist all boats aboard and this practice had probably become standard by the second half of the seventeenth century. Many drawings of ships show boats stowed in the waist, and sometimes they show the crew engaged in hoisting them in or out. In the 1700s one of the great complaints against the longboat was that it was very difficult to hoist, and in 1711 the Navy Board instructed the dockyards 'to examine on all occasions what size of boats the ship can conveniently receive and stow, though they should not agree exactly with the sizes established,' in order that the boats could be hoisted in without difficulty.[9]

Because the largest boats were stowed between the mainmast and the foremast, in the longest open space on the ship, a complicated tackle was needed for hoisting them in and out. Draughts of boats often show ringbolts fitted inside the hull, which were used to attach the ropes used in hoisting. The first stage was to raise the boat from its position admidships. Two pendants hung from the masts, one from under the top of the mainmast, the other from under the top of the foremast. When in use these were joined together by another rope known as the triatic stay, which was the same length as the boat. A tackle was hung from the lower end of each of the pendants, one to lift each end of the boat. Once the boat had been lifted, it had to be swung outboard. The main and fore yards were angled inwards towards one another, and a tackle was extended from each yardarm to one end of the boat. If the boat was heavy, the yards had to be supported with extra ropes in addition to their normal lifts. Other ropes led from the bows and stern of the boat to the deck, and were used to control its motion. The boat was swung outwards until the tackle from the yardarms took the weight, and then it was lowered into the water.

The procedure was of course reversed for hoisting the boat in. This was a cumbersome and labour intensive procedure, but a man of war had a large crew, and sometimes a captain was grateful for a means of keeping them employed. The need to brace the yards round during the process must have been an inconvenience, but as the ship had to be hove to when lowering a boat, it was not an insurmountable problem. Until the late years of the eighteenth century it was the only means of hoisting boats, and remained standard for large boats for long after that.

Stowage on Spars in the Waist

In the 1620s and '30s, when there was an increasing tendency to stow boats in the waist of the ship, between the foremast and the mainmast. Larger ships often had a grating deck built over the waist. This was constructed to protect the men in action and possibly also to stow boats. Although the well known pictures of the *Prince Royal* and the *Soveriegn of the Seas* show this area vacant, with the longboat being towed, in both the ships are close to shore, when they would probably have had their boats hoisted out to help anchor or moor.

By the middle of the century, at least one boat could be carried on booms or spare topmasts laid along the centre line of the waist. These were raised above the deck by a wooden frame known as a

A two-decker entering Harwich in the mid-eighteenth century, towing a longboat and a cutter. The boat rope and the gust rope can both be seen. NMM.

A boat being hoisted aboard a ship, c1750. Note the tackles rigged from both the yardarms and the main stay, attached to each end of the boat. NMM.

The Neptune *of 1683 carries her pinnace on fore and aft booms in the waist. The crew is preparing the boat for hoisting out.* NMM.

An eighteenth century pinnace on spare spars. NMM.

The boat gallows of a Sixth Rate, from about 1730. Author's photograph.

gallows which was erected just forward of the mainmast. The forward ends of the booms rested on the after edge of the forecastle. This arrangement lifted the boats clear of the gratings in the waist, and probably enabled the fore capstan to be used even when the boat was stowed. French ships, which stowed their boats directly on the upper deck in the waist, had to put their capstans in a less convenient position, on the forecastle.

Stowing the Other Boats

There are many paintings and models from the period between 1650 and 1750, some of which show details of the boats stowed on booms or spars in the waist. The problem is that they invariably show only one boat, usually the pinnace, stowed thus. As ships of this period carried two, three, or four boats, it is a mystery how the others were stowed. The gallows had width only for one boat, so there was no question of stowing two side by side. The pinnace or longboat was long enough to take up all the available space between the gallows and the break of the forecastle, so it would

not have been possible to stow one boat behind another. The position of the shrouds, backstays, and other pieces of rigging would have made it impossible to hoist boats at any other part of the ship, and in any case there was no room to stow them. The only other possibility is that they were stowed one on top of another.

In the mid-nineteenth century boats were 'nested'. The thwarts were removed from the lowest one, so a smaller boat could be fitted inside it. It is unlikely that this was done in the eighteenth century, or before. Although boats often had some removable thwarts, these were intended to allow the carriage of casks, and there were enough fixed thwarts to make nesting very difficult. At least one thwart was usually fixed and kneed in midships, to support the mainmast. This alone would have made nesting impossible. Another possibility is that the boats were turned upside down and stacked on top of one another. There is no evidence for this, and several factors would have made it very difficult. Most boats had a considerable sheer, which would have hindered this kind of stowage. Moreover, a ship's pinnace was often longer and narrower than her longboat, so that it would have been impossible to stow one inside another. It is possible that a yawl could be stowed inside a pinnace or a longboat, but there is no evidence of this.

At least one model[10] shows a boat permanently suspended from the hoisting tackle on the masts, so that it hangs over the centre of the waist. This may well be a product of later restoration. It seems rather unlikely that it was normal practice. A boat suspended in such a position would tend to sway dangerously with the ship, though this could be controlled to some extent by ropes. However, the boat would still be extremely vulnerable, and the slightest damage to the rigging would bring it crashing down onto the heads of the gun crews, though of course it might have been taken down and stowed during action. It is conceivable, though not very likely, that one of the boats could have been stowed in this way, perhaps held above another which was stowed on the spars.

The final possibility is that one boat was stowed directly on the upper deck, while another rested on the booms, and a third was turned upside down inside it. There were two ways of stowing a boat on the upper deck in the waist. Either it could be placed to one side, where it would seriously interfere with the guns, or it could be put directly under the boat on the booms, in which case its position would be restricted by the jeer capstan. This is hinted at in a Navy Board letter of 1744, when it was suggested that, with improvements in the main capstans, 'there will seldom be occasion for the use of the jeer, which may be unshipped and stowed between decks to make room for the stowing of the longboat out of the way of the guns.'[11] The implication is that before 1744 the longboat was stowed beside the guns in the waist at sea, and presumably hoisted out in time of battle. The other boat, the yawl, could have been stowed on the other side, or upside down inside the pinnace, which was stowed on the booms.

Athwartships Booms in the Waist

If removing the jeer capstan to allow the stowing of the longboat under the pinnace had ever been practice, it would have been necessary for only a short period. In 1744 the Navy Board authorised gangboards to be fitted in the waist, running along the sides of the hull between the quarterdeck and the forecastle, on all ships of 40 guns or more.[12] At first the gangway was to be only 1ft wide, but by the 1750s its width had increased. This may have interfered with the old system of stowing boats on the upper deck in the waist, but it soon suggested another possibility. Instead of longitudinal beams which could support only one boat efficiently, three or four beams could be placed across the waist, between the gangways. These could stow at least three boats quite efficiently. Since the complement of boats was increasing with the introduction of cutters, such a change was clearly necessary.

It is not known precisely when such booms were first introduced. They are shown, for example, on the model of the *Victory* in her original condition. Though the ship was not launched until 1765, she was begun in 1759, and the model is more likely to date from the earlier period. External fittings such as these were often not included by the modelmaker until they had been in use for some time, so it is not unlikely that they were standard by about 1750.

The early boom was a simple removeable structure. It was rectangular in cross-section, and seems to have been slightly curved to match the camber of the deck below. Each end was sup-

Removeable boat booms, on a model of the Boyne *of 1790. This method was rather old-fashioned by this date.* Author's photograph, courtesy of Science Museum.

ported by an iron crutch, placed in a hole in the gangway. Wedges were placed on the uppermost edge of the boom, shaped to match the hull section of the boat at that point, and intended to keep it from moving from side to side. It is not clear whether these were fixed or removeable, but the latter seems more likely, as models show them in place only when a boat is actually being carried, and such a system would have allowed a greater flexibility in stowage. Ringbolts were fitted to the upper sides of the booms. These were used to hold the ropes which lashed the boats in position.

Frigates were rather slower in adopting gangways and boat booms, and do not appear to have had them until the early 1800s. By the 1780s, ships of the line had adopted a more permanent system. The cross beams were now fitted under the gangways, and were part of the structure of the ship. Over the years there was a further tendency to close this space, by extending the quarterdeck and the gangways. Thus the waist was almost closed, and the forecastle and quarterdeck almost joined. Despite this, these areas still retained their separate names, and guns were never mounted on the gangways, as was practised on French and American ships in the nineteenth century.

Though the cross booms would have enabled about three boats to be stowed side by side, there was still not enough space, for five or six boats were now carried on most ships. Again we have to consider the possibility that one was stowed inside another, perhaps with the upper one turned upside down. Certainly it would have been possible to stow a small pinnace inside a longboat or a launch, or a small cutter inside a large one, and it is very likely that this was done until the development of the davit made it unnecessary. Models, however, rarely show the full complement of boats, so again it is not possible to be certain.

Quarter Davits

It is not clear when quarter davits were introduced, but they were certainly in use by about 1805. They were fitted on each side of the mizzen mast, at poop deck level, in the area of the mizzen channels. Here the boats could be lifted high out of the water,

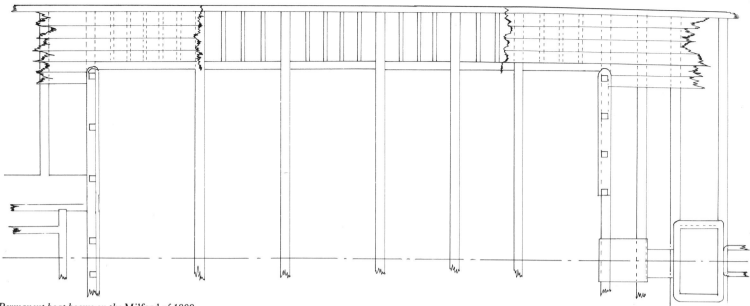

Permanent boat booms on the Milford *of 1809.*

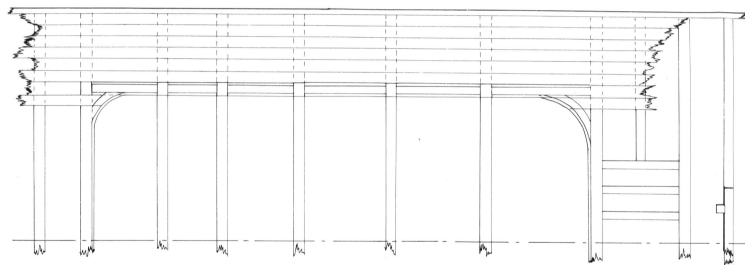

The closing of the waist and building up of the gangways round the boat booms on the Wellesley *and* Melville *of 1814.*

without obstructing anything. The mast could be used to hold the tackle which supported the davits. Each davit was a straight piece of timber, rectangular or square in cross-section. The outer end was cut square, and it was fitted with holes for two sheaves, rather like those of a cathead. The innermost end was rounded so that it could be rotatéd to raise and lower the davit. It was drilled to receive a pin, and was held against the side of the hull by two lugs, through which the pin was passed. When the boat was stowed the davit could be lifted until it was almost vertical, raising the boat above the level of the poop carronades and allowing it to be lashed against the mizzen shrouds. When the boat was lowered it was carried out clear of the mizzen channels, and could be let down directly into the water. Two davits were fitted to each quarter, one forward of the shrouds and one in the middle of them, so that the mizzen mast came halfway between them. A topping lift led through the shrouds, to a block well up the mast, where it divided into two, one part going to each davit.

Once the davits were lowered, the tackle through the sheaves at the end of the davit was used to lower the boat itself. A single block was hung on the lower end of this tackle, and a hook fitted to the block was passed through the ringbolt inside the boat. Such tackle was perhaps slow to operate in an emergency, so stoppers, like those used to release an anchor, were sometimes used.

The new system was clearly an improvement on the old. It was first commonly used to stow the two 25ft cutters of a ship of the line or a large frigate, though before long it was used on quite small vessels, such as brigs and sloops. Though it created extra space for boats the old positions in the waist were retained and used for the larger and heavier boats. The new system allowed boats to be launched very quickly indeed, with none of the complicated rigging which had to be set up to operate the old system. It is possible its introduction pre-dated 1800 quite considerably. It would have been very useful in the 1750s, when the second 25ft cutter was introduced. It is difficult to see where else this could have been stowed.

Details of the davit fitted on the 36-gun Dryad, *in 1811.*

Stern Davits

Again, the exact date of the introduction of stern davits is something of a mystery, but they can be seen on a model of a frigate of 1779.[13] In 1798 an order was issued abolishing them,[14] perhaps because they spoiled the view from the captain's cabin, or because a boat lowered from that position would be in danger of fouling the rudder. In any case, the order was not successful, and stern davits can be seen on many ships of the 1800s.

Unlike the quarter davit, the stern davit was fixed. It projected aft from the stern, sometimes being bolted to the ship's side outside the hull, above the quarter gallery. It also had sheaves in its outer end. It was particularly suitable for carrying the smallest boat, the 18ft cutter or jolly boat, which was issued to nearly all ships in the late eighteenth century. The stern davit was most useful on smaller ships, and seems to have been common on frigates.

Stern davits on the Victory. **Author's photograph.**

PART XI

Deck Fittings

Chapter 44. Hatches and Ladders

The Position of Hatchways

A sailing warship had many openings in its side, in the form of gunports, but these were designed for a specific function, and were not normally used for either men or stores to enter the ship. Three-deckers had entry ports cut in their sides, but these were reserved for the higher ranks. Men and stores entered the ship by way of the upper deck, and passed below through openings in the decks, known as hatches. These were needed for communication between decks, for instance when men were called to the upper decks to trim sails, or went below when their watch was over. They also allowed a bare minimum of light and air to reach the decks below.

The hatches were invariably rectangular in shape. They were mostly cut along the ship's centre line, especially on the gundecks where they had to be kept clear of the guns. This also reduced the risk of their being submerged if the ship heeled. As far as possible the hatches were carefully arranged so that each extended between a pair of deck beams. On most eighteenth and nineteenth century ships, this space was not large enough for the largest types of cask. Therefore at least one double-sized hatch

was fitted on each deck. The beam which should have passed through the centre of this was curved back, to join with one of the other beams, thus leaving the area free.

To give clear access to the hold, there had to be at least one run of hatches of similar size which passed through each deck, one directly above another. This was called the main hatchway. It was usually in midships, in the waist. Here there were fewer decks to penetrate, casks could be lowered directly into the roomiest part of the ship, and tackle rigged between the fore- and mainmast could be used to raise and lower them. Most ships of any size had more than one hatchway: a fore one, also in the waist, aft of the foremast, and an after one just aft of the mainmast. These, however, were mostly single hatches, without the curved deck beam.

Other hatches were for the passage of men rather than stores. They were fitted with ladders to give access between decks. Steam gratings were fitted over hatches cut in the forecastle deck, above and forward of the cooking stove. These were intended to allow the steam from the stove to escape, and were not used as access hatches.

Scuttles

Scuttles were small hatches, which each had a particular purpose. They were common on the orlop deck, where they gave access to the magazines, light rooms, and different parts of the hold, such as the fish room and the spirit room. A scuttle was

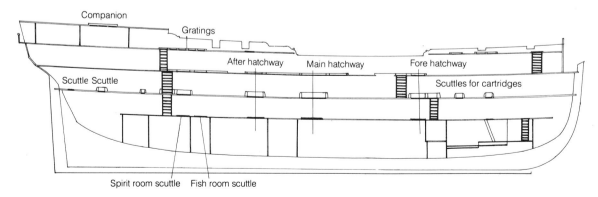

The run of the hatches and ladders of a 74-gun ship of the 1790s.

238

barely large enough for a man to pass through, and some, such as the scuttles for cartridges, were intended for passing up articles, rather than for human access. Others were used in connection with maintenance or rigging. Some were fitted in the wings to allow inspection of parts of the hold, and others, such as the top tackle scuttles, were for particular ropes to pass through the deck. Unlike other hatches, scuttles were not usually on the centre line, but were placed over the appropriate compartments. They were closed by solid wooden lids, rather than gratings which covered most hatches. Some lids, known as cap scuttles, overhung part of the coaming.

The Construction of Hatches

A hatch was not simply a hole in the deck. Its fore and after edges were defined by the deck beams, and its sides were formed by the carlines, which ran fore and aft between the deck beams. Thus most hatches conformed to the line of carlines, which were an integral part of the ship's structure.

To stop water on the deck running down the hatches, and perhaps to prevent unwary crew members from falling down an open hatch in the dark, each was surrounded by a low wooden wall. The forward and after sides were known as the head ledges, and were placed over the deck beams. The coamings formed the fore and aft sides, and were fitted above the carlines. They formed a rectangle round the hatch, the outside corners which were rounded for the sake of appearance. The inner edges of the coamings were recessed to hold the gratings and hatch covers which fitted over them. From the late eighteenth century, holes were cut in the coamings and ledges to hold round shot.

Coamings and ledges varied considerably in height, according

to the size of the ship, and their position. They could be as high as 12in on a large ship, and as small as 3in on a sloop or brig. By the late eighteenth century, much higher coamings were fitted on the gundeck than on other decks, as water was much more likely to come through the ports of that deck. The head ledges had a slightly greater camber than the deck itself, by about $1\frac{1}{2}$in.[1]

Gratings

Some hatches had solid wooden covers for security reasons, but most were covered with gratings. Ladderways were kept open in the daytime, but often covered with gratings at night, when an open hole in the deck would have been very dangerous. The main hatchways, giving access to the hold, were covered except when loading or unloading; the steam gratings were only removed for maintenance purposes.

The gratings allowed light and air to the lower decks, which was essential when the gunports were closed. They were also used in floggings when one was taken up and placed against the side of the ship, and the victim's arms and legs were tied to it. In wet weather, gratings let in too much water, so they had to be covered with tarpaulin, which was lashed round the edges of the coamings.

Essentially a grating was made up of strips of timber running fore and aft, and others running athwartships across them. The thwartships timbers, known as ledges, were the deepest. In the early nineteenth century they were approximately 3in square in cross-section. Recesses were cut at suitable intervals, to take the battens which ran fore and aft. The battens were as broad as the ledges, but they were only about $\frac{3}{4}$in deep, except for the outermost ones, which were deeper, for they gave strength to the

Gratings. The main hatch of a 70-gun ship, c1730, seen from above (left) and below (right). Note how the shallower parts of the gratings, the battens, run fore and aft. Author's photographs, courtesy of NMM.

structure, and fitted into the recess in the coaming. The grating curved upwards towards the centre line of the ship, as did the head ledge to which it was fitted. The spaces between the battens and ledges were roughly equal to their widths, but this was open to slight adjustment to allow the grating to fit into a specific space. Gratings were nearly always rectangular, except for the few oval ones fitted on the hatches above the steerage on some large ships of the late seventeenth century.[2]

Hatch Covers

Scuttles, being relatively small, and often giving access to rather sensitive areas such as the powder room, were covered with a rectangular piece of wood known as a cap scuttle. It simply fitted into a recess, or rabbet, cut into the insides of the coamings and ledges. Where greater security was needed, locks and hinges were fitted. Larger hatches which often needed to be secure, such as those to the main magazine and the spirit room were fitted with double doors, opening upwards, with two hinges on each. Such hatches were of course common on the orlop deck, to give access to the different parts of the hold. For some reason they often appear on the quarterdecks of frigate models, though it is not clear what purpose they could have served there.

Cross-section of a scuttle, showing the cap which kept it secure.

Ladders

The basic ladder was simple. 'The ladders are formed of two principal pieces, that extend from one deck to another, and are called sides, lying at as great an inclination as the breadth of the ladderway will allow, with proper head room; fitted between the sides in grooves or scores taken out of them; are pieces called the steps, lying after the deck, from seven to nine inches apart.'[3]

From the middle of the eighteenth century, the ladders which gave access to the hold and to the crew's quarters were as simple as this on most ships. Previously, there had been many variations, even in the humbler parts of the ship. Few seventeenth century ladders seem to have had entirely straight sides. The central part of those in Deane's *Doctrine* of 1670 curve downwards, and those in the Phillips print of the 1690s have various multiple curves. Early eighteenth century ladders were more likely to have straight profiles, but to curve in a different direction, for the 'bell' ladder was fashionable around this time. Its sides curved outwards towards its lower end, giving it a bell-like shape. It can be seen as late as the 1790s, on a model of a 74-gun ship.[4] On many other ladders, the steps curved outwards, possibly to provide a wider foothold, but more probably as a form of decoration.

Towards the stern of the ship, where the officers lived and worked, the ladders were more elaborate. By the late seventeenth century they usually had carved rails and bannisters. The spiral staircase appeared on ships at around this time. It was mainly used on three-deckers, where it led from the admiral's apartment, on the upper deck, to his station on the quarterdeck. It was commonly placed on the port side, and it tended, not surprisingly, to interfere with the working of the guns, particularly because it was apparently not designed to be removed in action.

Staircases were at their most elaborate at the beginning of the eighteenth century. After that, there were some attempts to simplify them, with gradual success. The number of highly decorated rails seem to have been reduced as part of the campaign against carved and joined works, which culminated in 1703. The spiral staircase survived into the 1750s. In 1757 it was found that the one fitted to the *Royal George* severely obstructed the guns, and it was ordered that it be removed. By a general order of September of that year, all winding staircases were to be taken off, as being 'very inconvenient as standing in the way of the gun on either side'.[5] They were to be replaced with ladders fitted 'at the sides leading from the lobby before the admiral's cabin up to the quarterdeck'. This caused some difficulty on some of the old three-deckers, such as the *Namur*, which had their wheels fitted, in the older fashion, aft of the mizzen mast.[6]

In the late seventeenth century, curved stairways were also fitted at the break of the poop, forecastle and quarterdeck. After a

A ladder, with some decoration, and a rail round the hatchway, on the Dorsetshire *of 1757.*

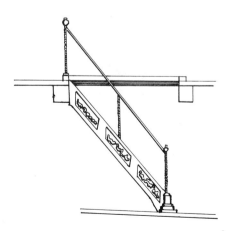

A decorated ladder, with rails, leading to the quarterdeck of the 98-gun Duke *of 1777.*

small step down, a short gangway led forward or aft from the deck. At the end of that was a staircase which curved round at about 90 degrees to the deck below. The short gangway was retained in the early eighteenth century, but the curved ladder was replaced with a straight one, leading fore and aft. After the 1740s when the longer gangways were fitted in the waist it was no longer possible for the ladders to lead that way, and they now ran inwards from the gangway.

The short gangways from the poop were largely eliminated over the first half of the eighteenth century, as the poop itself was extended to cover the steering wheel. After this, simple ladders led forward to the quarterdeck. By an order of 1808, they were to be made so that they could be moved to the centre line in action, to avoid impeding the guns.

Sometimes companionways were fitted over the heads of ladders around the officers' quarters. They can be seen on some models of the 1650s and '60s, on Dummer's drawings of a First Rate of around 1680, and less clearly on the Phillips print of the 1690s. They served only as decoration on the large ships, and disappeared in the early years of the next century, though they survived rather longer on some small vessels, such as yachts and sloops. Thus, from the early 1700s the ladder leading to the quarterdeck usually had a rail round its hatchway, and some carved work, though like all decoration this tended to be reduced over the years.

The Run of the Ladders

Despite the indulgences of some joiners and carvers, most ladders had a specific and essential function. Though there was considerable variety in their distribution about the ship over the years, certain patterns can be discerned.

A ship usually had two ladders to the orlop, one forward and one aft, reflecting the fact that the central area was mainly reserved for the cables. This may have caused some problems on frigates, where the cable tier was not connected with the fore and after platforms. Large ships normally had a ladder leading into the fore magazine, but none leading to the after powder room, or the hold. Two-deckers and frigates almost invariably had a ladder

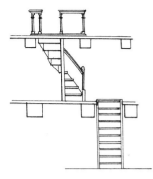

A spiral staircase and a conventional ladder on the Royal George *of 1756. She was one of the last ships to be fitted with a spiral stair.*

A curved ladder which led from the quarterdeck to the waist, on a model of the 1690s. Such ladders were common in the seventeenth century. Author's photograph.

A 'bell' ladder, on a model of a 74-gun ship of the 1790s. Author's photograph.

Left. A companion on a model of a frigate of about 50 guns, c1660. Author's photograph. *Right. A slightly later type of companion, almost buried under the coach, on a 100-gun ship c1670.* Author's photograph, courtesy of Science Museum.

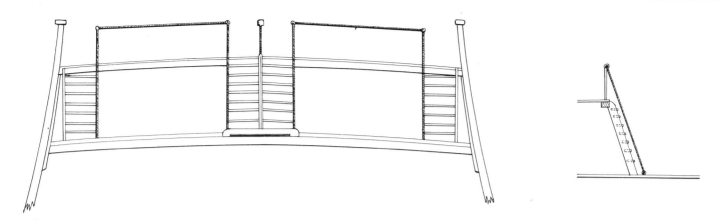

The arrangement of ladders ordered for the poop of 74-gun ships, and other ships of the line, in 1808. The side ladders could be moved to the centre line in time of action.

in midships, just forward of the main hatch, leading from the lower to the upper deck. Three-deckers had two such ladders, one above the other, linking all three main gundecks. These ladders formed the main route for the crew when called on deck. They were usually double, having two sets of steps side by side, and an extra diagonal running down the centre between them. Most ships had another ladder leading upwards from a position well forward on the deck where the galley was situated. On two-deckers and frigates it led to the forecastle, on three-deckers to the upper deck.

The arrangements of the after ladders were more varied, partly because of the whims of commanders and shipwrights. In the seventeenth century there was not a single run of ladders in this area but several, each of which served a specific function. Ships, especially the larger ones, often had too many ladders, perhaps so that the officers and the crew should take separate routes to the upper decks. The number of ladders tended to reduce after about 1760. There are signs of the development of a single route leading from the orlop to the quarterdeck. By the 1740s two ladders, one above the other, formed a direct link from the orlop to the upper deck. By the 1790s, a third had been added to carry it up to the quarterdeck.

In the seventeenth century most ladders ran fore and aft. In the eighteenth century there was an increasing tendency for them to run athwartships. This had become the most common system by the 1770s, except for those leading up to the poop.

Steps on the Sides

From about the middle of the seventeenth century, pieces of shaped timber were fixed to the sides of ships, to form steps, making it much easier than previously to enter the ship from a boat or jetty. The earlier steps often had verticals on each side, giving the whole the appearance of a ladder, but these had disappeared by the end of the century, so that each step was separate. The ladder was shaped so that the top part was wider than the bottom, and the corners were usually rounded. Often the lower part had a fairly ornate shape, which gave a slightly decorative effect. There does not seem to have been any attempt to incorporate hand-holds in the steps, but ropes were often hung down each side from above, to make climbing easier and safer. In any case, the ship's tumblehome must have been a help.

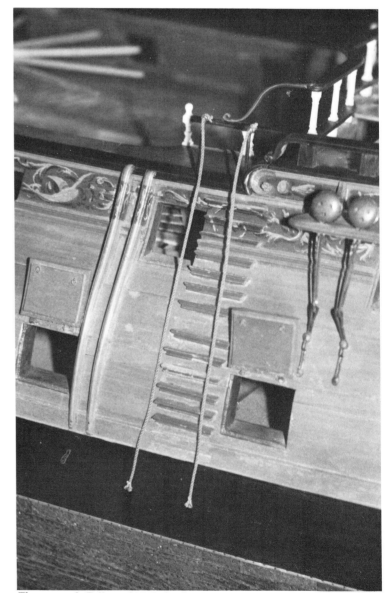

The steps on the Bellona *of 1760, showing the ropes to help entry, and the skid beams just forward, used for parbuckling casks up the side. Author's photograph, courtesy of NMM.*

The entry port and steps on the Prince *of 1670*. Science Museum.

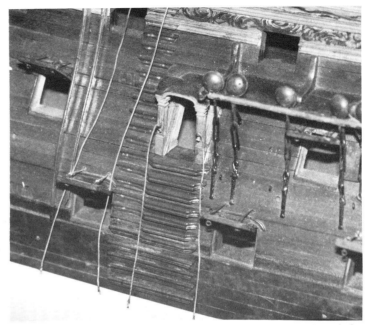
The commonest late eighteenth century type of entry port, with the double-arched roof. The steps on the ship's side lead past the port, to the gangway.
Author's photograph, courtesy of NMM.

Entry Ports

The side of the three-decker, as developed in the early part of the seventeenth century, was considered to be too high for senior officers to climb. Thus a door was cut at middle deck level. Steps on the side led to it, and continued past it up to the upper deck. Until the 1670s only one entry port was fitted, on the port side. After that they were fitted to both sides.

The entry port was usually covered with rather elaborate carving. There was often some attempt to build a roof over it. This was extended over the years, so that by the mid-eighteenth century it had a double curve shape, like that of a contemporary belfry, and it protruded several feet from the side. In the seventeenth century the roof was much smaller, and was supported by carved figures. In the eighteenth century it was supported by brackets, with some carving on their surfaces.

Companions

In the mid-eighteenth century a new type of companion began to appear over the captain's cabins on many ships. This was a structure of frames and glass, which gave light to the cabin. The earliest example is from 1746, aboard the 70-gun *Hampton Court*. Its appearance at this date may be significant, for this was when the captain's cabin was first moved from the upper deck to the quarterdeck. But the Navy Board did not approve of the new companion because it was said that it did not leave room for stationing the marines in action, and they ordered that it be replaced by 'sashes and gratings'.[7] Despite this opposition, the companion soon began to take over from the old gratings on the poop deck. It is to be seen again on the model of the *Royal George*

of 1756. Several other ships of the line were fitted with it not long afterwards.

Usually the companion had a flat top, made up of about 15 panes of glass, and sides one pane high, but there were variations. Sometimes no panes were used on the sides, and the structure was much lower. On others the top was made in two halves, at an angle, and these could be hinged upwards for ventilation.

Following an order of 1779, companions were to be fitted to frigates. They were to be 'placed over the steerage, extending two spaces of the beams, or to be kept in length about five feet, and in breadth three feet, and as much above the decks to admit the panes of the glass in the sides to be about seven inches in height'. Sloops of 300 tons were also to have companions 'afore the mizzen mast, to extend one space from beam to beam, to be three feet broad and about six inches in the sides above the deck.'[8]

The companion to the captain's cabin, on a frigate of the 1780s.
Author's photograph, courtesy of NMM.

Chapter 45. Rails and Nettings

The Need for Protection

The designer of a sailing warship had to resolve many dilemmas. One of these was to decide how high the sides should be. High topsides would allow the ship to tower over a smaller enemy, and would protect the men on her upper works. On the other hand, too much height would have a very detrimental effect on her sailing qualities, causing her to make much leeway in any but a following wind. Heavy bulwarks would also raise the centre of gravity, making the ship less stable.

In many ways the officers and men who were stationed on the upper works in time of action were the élite of the crew. The captain, first lieutenant and master directed the ship. The helmsmen were chosen from among the most reliable seamen. The gun crews on the quarterdeck and forecastle contributed relatively little to the ship's fire-power, but part of their role was to be ready to leave their guns and trim the sails when necessary, so they too were often chosen from among the best seamen. Yet these men faced the greatest risks. Because wooden warships rarely sank in action, there was no advantage in being able to abandon ship quickly, but there were many dangers, from musket shot, boarders, and debris falling down from the ship's rigging. The seaman who served the lower deck guns had a thick hull in front of him and a stout deck above, so faced none of these dangers.

Over the years various attempts were made to protect the men on the upper works in battle, and to help shelter the crew in more everyday pursuits. Most of these originated as very light structures of canvas or rope. They tended to become more solid over the years, being made of wood instead and thus became part of the ship's structure rather than the fittings. They fall naturally into two categories: those which gave lateral protection, and were an extension, however light and temporary, of the sides of the ship, and those intended to give protection from above, which developed eventually into parts of the ship's deck.

Arming Cloths

The sides of seventeenth-century warships were mounted with open rails except in the waist, where the structure was solid. The wales, rails and planks of the side had a much greater sheer than the decks. One result of this was that there were many parts of the upper decks where the men had good lateral protection – in the waist, or aft on either the quarterdeck or the poop. Conversely, some areas had very little protection. On the forecastle, or forward on the quarterdeck or the poop, the gun crews and small arms men were very exposed to enemy fire. The only attempt to remedy this was to rig cloths, known as 'fights', and later as 'armings'. In the late seventeenth century these were suspended from stanchions above the rails, and hung down to the level of the rail, leaving a gap between the rail and the top of the side, presumably for small arms to be fired.

Such cloths were used in Elizabethan times, when they replaced 'pavesses', or lines of shields. They were common in the

Stanchions for arming cloths can be seen on the poop and quarterdeck of the Portland *of 1652.* NMM.

first half of the seventeenth century, and almost universal in the second. They were made of long strips of red kersey, and in the last part of the century they had a white edging. When not in use they could be completely dismantled, or could be kept in position and furled up like a sail. Judging by paintings of the Restoration period, they were in place more often than not, but this evidence is perhaps not entirely reliable, for the best-known painting of a ship of this period, Van de Velde's *Resolution in a Gale*, shows the cloths rigged, which seems rather unlikely in the circumstances.

The cloths are most often seen round the poop and quarterdeck, where they would help cover the officers. They were also quite common round the forecastle, which was the least protected area. Sometimes they appear on the forward rail of the forecastle, above the beakhead bulkhead. Occasionally they can also be seen in the waist, giving a continuous line along the whole ship.[1] The use of these cloths declined in the eighteenth century, and they are rarely seen in paintings. By that time naval tactics had become very rigid, and close action was not encouraged so they were much less necessary. Nevertheless they appear on a painting of 1752, though they are fitted only on the poop, and cover the space under the rail, rather than above it.[2]

The Development of Hammock Netting

By the 1740s there was a gradual move towards a more daring and decisive form of tactics. Single ship actions became rather more common, and fleet tactics began to allow for the possibility of closing with the enemy, if the circumstances favoured this. This change, which was to culminate in Nelson's highly aggressive tactics sixty years later, was slow to gain momentum, but had certainly begun in the war of 1739–48.[3]

Captains began to feel the need for greater protection on the upper works. This was especially true of the smaller vessels, including the new sloops which were coming into use for escort and patrol duties. One way of achieving this was by staving the crew's hammocks in nettings which were hung from stanchions fitted above the sides of the ship. This solved two problems. First, a place was found for the hammocks when not in use, saving much room under the quarterdeck, where they had previously been stowed. Second, the men on deck were given some degree of protection, less than they would get from a solid wooden structure, but more than from an arming cloth. The hammocks could be removed and stowed elsewhere if they were likely to interfere with the sailing of the ship.

The use of hammock nettings was first noted in 1746, but it is possible that they had been in use for a few years before that. Captain Barnsley of the *Dispatch* sloop objected to them on the grounds that it was 'very prejudicial to the men's health to get their hammocks up in rainy weather, either in chase or in sight of the enemy'. He suggested instead that junk, or old rope, be made into barricades.[4] The Navy Board disagreed. 'Junk made from platting for the use of hawsers, a practice of late introduced into the navy, is extremely heavy, and as it is always continued aloft, must by its opposition to the wind be a great obstruction to sailing, especially in small vessels.'[5] Admiral Steuart suggested that 'bags filled with cork shavings, or in sheets', would be preferable, and the Navy Board was inclined to agree. They would be light and easily removeable, and they had already been tried on some sloops. But there was a fatal flaw – they did not work. The Navy

Board carried out some tests at Deptford, using bags filled with different thicknesses of cork. None of them stopped a musket ball, or even slowed it down significantly. Even when three bags were placed together, there was no effect.[6]

The Navy Board was obliged to return to hammock nettings as the best available protection. To prevent them from getting wet, an obvious solution was found. 'But as keeping the hammocks dry in the nettings may tend to the preservation of the seamen's health, . . . we humbly propose . . . that tarpaulins may be allowed to His Majesty's ships, . . . and that their commanders may be directed to cause the hammacoes to be covered therewith, whenever the weather requires it.'[7] Hammock nettings seem to have been common by about 1750, though ten years later it was complained that some ships still had large barricades of junk, which were hindering their sailing. They were to be cut down.[8]

The Fitting of Hammock Nettings

It is not clear how quickly the use of hammock nettings spread through the fleet, which ships used them in the early period, or where they were fitted on individual ships. The first definite evidence on the latter point comes from a model of the *Victory*, as she was when launched in 1765.[9] She had stanchions for nettings on each side of the poop and quarterdeck, and also at the breaks of these decks, running athwartships. They were not necessary at the taffrail of the stern, as that was high enough already. There was only a single light rail in the waist, enough to prevent men passing along the gangways from falling overboard, but not suitable for stowing hammocks. There was no attempt at protecting the forecastle. By about 1780, nettings were also being fitted in the waist, and it was ordered that these should be issued with cloths. There was little real need for protection in this area, as the

The *Victory* as built in 1765, showing the stanchions and rails for the hammock netting at the break of the quarterdeck, and the wheel and binnacle. NMM.

Part of the quarterdeck rail of a frigate of the 1770s, showing hammock stanchions outside the rail. Author's photograph.

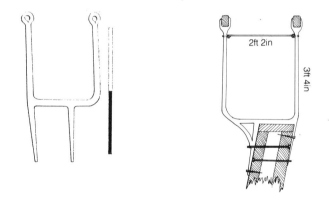

Left. A type of hammock stanchion used on some gunboats built around 1797. Right. A hammock stanchion as specified in the 1808 establishment. Wooden rails join the stanchions, and a bar is fitted over the top, hooked into a hole in one of the uprights.

The hammock nettings covered by a cloth, on a model of a frigate of around 1805. Author's photograph, courtesy of NMM.

sides were quite high already, and the gangways even gave some protection from above; perhaps the waist rails were fitted because it was becoming common to issue each man with two hammocks instead of one, and a place was needed to stow them.

The most common type of netting stanchion was crutch shaped, its lower point fitted into the ship's rail. A plan from around 1780 shows a type of rail which could be folded down when not in use. Sometimes the stanchions on the side of the poop and the quarterdeck were fitted outside the rail, with the side of the ship forming one side of the receptacle for hammocks. In this case, the hammocks would add little to the protection given already by the ship's sides, which confirms the suggestion that it was becoming as important to find a place to stow the hammocks as to strengthen the defences of the ship.

The height of the stanchions varied considerably according to where they were fitted. Those on the sides of the poop and quarterdeck often increased in height as they approached midships, to make up for the corresponding reduction of the rails at the foremost parts of these decks. Those on top of the rails at the break of the poop and quarterdeck were quite low, so that the space between them was approximately square in cross-section. In such a rail, the hammocks must have been stowed on their sides, whereas in higher structures they could have stood upright. The width of the stanchions also varied. In 1813 the captain of the *Royal Sovereign* asked that they might be 7½in wide, enough for three rolled hammocks side by side. In 1812 the captain of the frigate *Rhin* had asked that they be wide enough for two hammocks.[10]

Each arm of a hammock stanchion had a ring on top. A rope was passed through this on each of the stanchions, and was made fast at each end of the rail. One side of the hammock netting was lashed to this rope. This was wide enough to hang in the space between the stanchions, and the other side was tied to the rope on the other side of the stanchions. In 1815 wooden rails replaced the ropes between the stanchions, though it was to be some years before the whole structure was covered with wooden planks. Most stanchions were made of wood, though metal was not unknown. The cloths covering the hammocks were tarpaulin until 1780 when ordered that they be painted not tarred. In 1782 they were to be painted on one side only, to save money.[11]

Rails for Carronades

The introduction of the carronade in 1779 meant that guns were now fitted in spaces which had been unoccupied for more than 50 years, especially on the poop. The first response in the provision of protection was to build open rails round the poop, with their stanchions distributed so there was room for a number of gunports. The spaces between these ports, however, were left empty, so the rail itself gave practically no protection to the men at the guns. Provision was made for moveable barricades of junk, which could be put in place for action, but removed when necesary in order to help the ship's sailing. In 1780 the frigate *Assurance* was supplied with bundles of hoops to be fixed between the quarterdeck rails, but this experiment does not seem to have been very successful.[12] By 1794 it was customary 'to supply ships whose carronades are not fitted on the quarterdeck with some old rope and other materials to make moveable barricades round the carronades.'[13] From 1796, there was a tendency to increase the height of the bulwarks round the poop. By 1800, it was customary to fit solid bulwarks.[14]

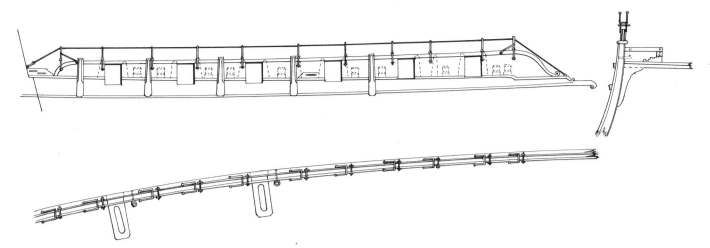

The rail of the quarterdeck of a frigate of about 1790. The rail has been built up for use with carronades, but the dashed lines show the old timberheads and stanchions. The structure of the hammock stanchions can be seen quite clearly. Slides for carronades are fitted, but the old mountings for swivel guns are still retained.

Chapter 46. Awnings and Gangways

Protection from Above

Often the seaman faced nearly as much danger from above as from the cannon-balls which might penetrate the ship's side. French gunners often attempted to disable a ship by firing into her rigging, and this caused much debris to fall. As close action became more common in the latter years of the eighteenth century, small arms, swivel guns, and even carronades were fired from the tops, to harrass the men on the decks below. Nelson himself was killed by a shot fired from the top of an enemy ship.

In such circumstances, men needed as much protection as possible over their heads. For day to day activity, protection from the weather was also useful. The steering wheel could be partly covered, and an area could be created on deck where the duty watch would be sheltered from the rain, but still within the call of its officer when needed. In warmer climates, shelter from the sun was equally necessary.

Grating Decks

In the first half of the seventeenth century, officers, gunners, and sail trimmers were protected by complete decks, made up of large gratings, placed sufficiently high over the gundecks for the men to be able to operate. The well known pictures of the *Prince* and the *Sovereign of the Seas* show such gratings. The *Prince* of

The grating decks on the Prince *of 1610.* Science Museum.

1610 had gratings over her waist, quarterdeck and forecastle. As the quarterdeck and forecastle carried no heavy guns, it can be assumed that the gratings were intended to protect the small arms men. They were built up with rails and stanchions, to raise them high enough to allow the men to operate underneath.

Such gratings were evidently standard on large English ships, and can be seen on several of them in a painting of the fleet in 1623.[1] On the *Sovereign* of 1637, they are placed over the quarter-deck, waist and forecastle as on the *Prince*, but in the case of the former they are intended to protect the gunners, for she was much more heavily armed on the upper decks. They appear to be rather low, leaving little room for the gunners. Presumably the gratings were similar in construction to hatches, though rather stouter. It is possible that the fore and aft members, which were much thinner on hatch gratings, were as strong as the thwartships timbers on the large gratings, to give extra strength. According to paintings the protective gratings had a much larger mesh, but not too large, for men are seen walking quite comfortably over them in all surviving paintings. The grating deck was taken off the *Sovereign* in 1651, on the recommendation of the master ship-wrights, after which no more is heard of them.[2]

The Waist

After the abolition of the grating deck, the waist of the ship, in particular, was very open from above. It took up nearly half the length of the ship, and often included half the gunports on the upper deck. A typical First Rate of the last quarter of the seventeenth century had 13 gunports on the upper deck. At least six of these would be in the waist, though two might be partly protected by the short gangways running from the quarterdeck to the forecastle. Apart from these gangways, the only substantial structure in the waist was the gallows, a $\top$-shaped structure just forward of the mainmast, which supported the boat booms, and the boats. The boats themselves would have provided little protection for the gunners. Even if they were not hoisted out in action, their light construction would have made them vulnerable, and they were too far inboard to be much help.

The Central Gangway

In the course of the eighteenth century the waist was to be largely closed in. This took place in several stages. The first of these involved the development of a gangway which joined the gallows to the quarterdeck. Around the beginning of the eighteenth century, many ships began to be fitted with a central gangway, extending forward from the break of the quarterdeck. It first appears on a model of 1702, though in this case it does not reach as far as the mainmast.[3] On another model, of a 70-gun ship of around 1710, it is much longer, and reaches the gallows forward of the mainmast.[4] On a model of the *Royal William* of 1719 it ends at the same point, though the gangway itself is shorter because the break of the quarterdeck is further forward.[5] By the 1730s it seemed to have been fitted to most ships, though an 80-gun ship of 1740 shows a surprising variation. In this case the whole quarterdeck has been moved forward, to stop just short of the gallows, though forward of the mainmast.[6]

The structure of the central gangway was rather light. A beam was fitted on each side, extending between the quarterdeck and

The central gangway, on a 90-gun ship of c1710. In this case it extends as far as the boat gallows, but is not connected with the mainmast. Author's photograph, courtesy of NMM.

the gallows. Between the beams were fitted several gratings, to provide a flat surface. By about 1710 the gangway had a rail on each side. The original purpose of the gangway is not clear. Because some of the early versions did not make contact with the mainmast, it is not likely to have been much help to the men operating the lines of that mast. Since it was usually covered with gratings rather than a solid deck, it would not in itself have been very useful in providing shelter from the weather, and it was too far from the guns to provide any protection for their crews. It did not always extend as far as the gallows so it could not have been intended to allow men to reach the boat on the booms in order to begin lowering it, though of course the later versions would have been helpful. It might have allowed the officer of the watch to walk further forward for a better view, but this was a minor advantage.

An order of 1728 mentions a different version of the gangway, and provides some clues as to its purpose. It refers to Sixth Rates which had very short quarterdecks which stopped some way short of the mizzen mast. They were to have awnings 'lengthened to six feet afore the wedges of the mizzen mast, and part of a bulk-head put up under the said awning, close to the wedges, to be four feet on each side of the middle of the deck, the middle panel to be deal, and a panel on each side of that to have a small sash; and from the said panels to the sides of the ship, to have painted canvas to roll up and down on occasion, and thereby part off a space of about eight feet for a conveniency for the captain, and leave six feet of awning afore that for the sheltering of men.'[7]

On larger ships the central gangway extended along the quarterdeck forward of the mainmast rather than the mizzen mast, but similar principles might have applied. It is possible that the spaces between the ship's sides and the central gangway could have been covered with canvas, allowing the men to shelter from bad weather. By the 1750s the space between the central and the side gangways was fully closed and decked over, so that, in effect, the quarterdeck was extended forward of the mainmast. The wardroom or captain's cabin was never extended into this space, and it was never used for any other purpose. It remained technically part of the waist, and was available for the shelter of the crew if needed.

The Extension of the Forecastle

In the late seventeenth century the break of the forecastle was rather irregular. It had three projections, a central one for the cook room, and one on each side for cabins. The belfry was either above the middle projection or incorporated as part of its structure. The whole area was heavily decorated and carved, especially on large ships at the end of the seventeenth century. Around 1740 the deck of the forecastle was moved back several feet, so that it now had a straight edge, and formed a canopy over the three projections. For a brief period the belfry remained in its old position, a few feet forward of the new break of the poop; it was moved aft a few years later. The three projections retained their basic shape under the deck, but they were somewhat reduced in size over the years, and the two outer ones were eventually eliminated.

Thus the length of the waist was considerably reduced in the first half of the eighteenth century. A 74-gun ship of the 1750s, which had 14 gunports on the upper deck, now had only four uncovered in the waist. Moreover, they were now beginning to enjoy a certain amount of protection from the gangways built along the side.

The Side Gangways

Short light gangways had extended forward of the poop and quarterdeck, and aft of the forecastle, for some time before the end of the seventeenth century. On larger ships each usually had a small cabin built under it, and gave some protection to the guns in the area. The first known attempt to join these gangways up, and form a continuous fore and aft gangway along each side of the waist, can be seen on a model of the *Royal William* of 1719. Evidently its main purpose was to provide an easier passage from the quarterdeck to the forecastle. The gangways had handrails on

An early example of the side gangway, on a model of a First Rate of 1719.
Author's photograph, courtesy of NMM.

each side, to make the route safer. There may have been some attempt to fit such gangways on other ships, but the Navy Board was not enthusiastic. In 1728 it ordered that 40-gun ships were to have 'only light narrow gangways next to the sides from the quarterdeck to the entering place, laid a sufficient height clear from the working of the guns'.[8] This implies that only the short gangways were authorised, and the longer ones, if they were fitted at all, were not.

The issue was raised again in the 1740s. By 1743 it seems that some captains had applied to have gangways fitted on their ships, and had been given some support by the Admiralty. The Navy Board remained sceptical, but was prepared to give way for the sake of uniformity. It was agreed that a light narrow gangway should be fitted to all the larger ships, rather than having them altered piecemeal. In February 1744 it was decided that 'if all ships of 40 guns and upwards were fitted with gangboards, to pass from the entering place to the forecastle, with a gangboard of about one foot broad, it would in our opinion be useful to pass from the quarterdeck to the forecastle.' The dockyards were to 'cause all ships of 40 guns and upwards to be fitted for the future with gangboards accordingly'.[9]

These gangboards were still very light, but they tended to become wider over the years. They were supported from underneath by iron knees. They are rarely seen on draughts of this period, because they were regarded as fittings rather than as part of the ship's structure. They served two other purposes besides the intended ones: they gave some protection to the gunners in the waist, and from the 1750s they were used to support boat booms across the waist. By about 1780 they became incorporated as part of the structure, being supported with regular deck beams, carlines and ledges.

The Extension of the Poop

The process of extending the poop deck began in 1718, when captains were allowed to build 'light boarded awnings' for the protection of the steering wheel, which was on the quarterdeck. Until the 1730s the wheel had usually been aft of the mizzen, but after that it was moved forward to improve the helmsman's view. In the 1740s the poop deck was further extended, to cover it. This created a space under the deck, forward of the bulkhead of the captain's cabin, which could be used for cabins for the captain's clerk and master, while the deck, which now extended forward of the mizzen, sheltered the quartermasters on the wheel. On frigates and smaller vessels, which had no poop, the wheel remained in a very exposed position in the middle of the quarterdeck.

Canvas Awnings

Pictures of Restoration warships often show an awning fitted over the quarterdeck. It is usually red, to match the arming cloths, and is supported some height above the deck by frames. These appear to have been quite substantial, and in at least one painting men can be seen sitting round the edges of the awning.[10] The awning was usually cambered like the deck, which suggests that it was supported by fairly strong athwartships beams, as well as by stanchions. Its purpose was presumably to protect the officers from sun and rain.

The awning reappears very early in the eighteenth century,

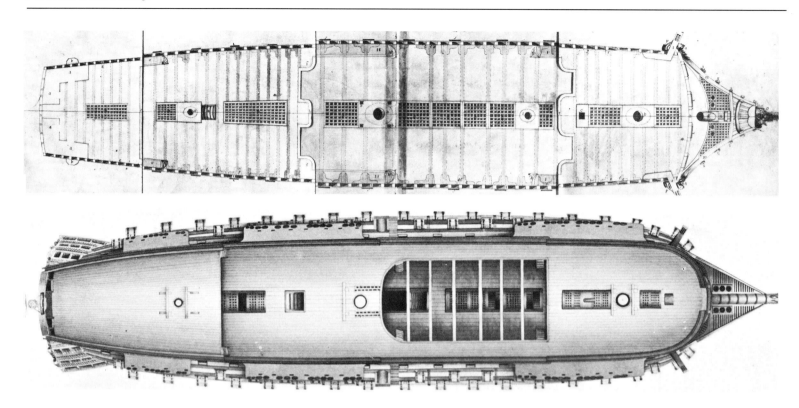

The closing of the waist. Science Museum.

Top. *The deck plan of a First Rate, c1680. The waist is completely open, except for*
the short gangways, marked H and I, which run along each side.

Bottom. *The decks of a First Rate of 1814, showing the much smaller waist, with*
wide gangways and larger quarterdeck and forecastle.

An awning over the quarterdeck of a frigate, drawn around 1670. NMM.

The structure under the awning, on a model of a late seventeenth century yacht.
Author's photograph, courtesy of NMM.

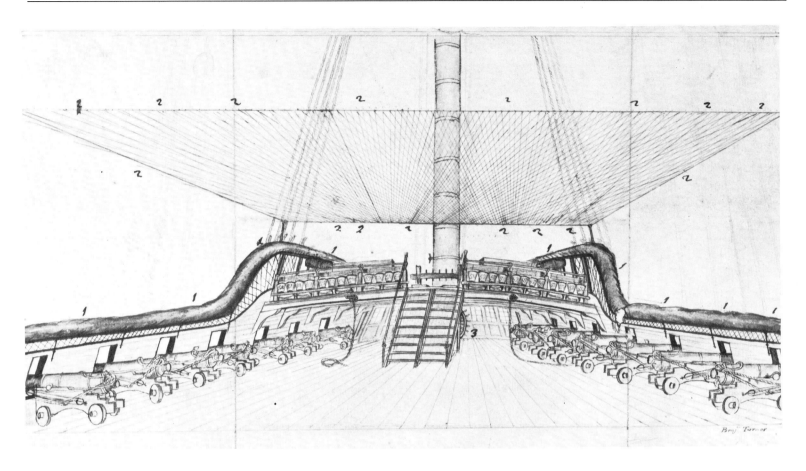

The quarterdeck of the 74-gun ship Venerable, *in 1799, showing the 'sauve tête' netting. NMM. 1. The hammock netting, covered with a tarpaulin. 2. The 'sauve tête' netting. 3. The poop ladders, moved to the centre line when the ship was in action, to avoid fouling the guns.*

when it was ordered that one was to be issued to every ship going to the West Indies.[11] Little is known about these, but the late eighteenth-century awning was certainly much more functional than its seventeenth century predecessor. It was usually made from old sails, and was unlikely to be painted. It was supported mainly by the ship's own rigging, being stretched between the shrouds of the main- and mizzen mast. It became increasingly necessary as ships served more time in the West Indies, particularly in the American War.

Guard and Boarding Nettings

From 1793, captains of virtually all ships could be issued with netting to stretch above the quarterdeck and forecastle, to protect the heads of the men from falling debris. Following an order of that year they were to be allowed 'guard nettings for the quarterdeck and forecastle, commonly called sauve têtes'. There is a hint in the order that the concept was not entirely new, and was based on long experience.[12] By an order of the following year, 74-gun ships were to have 1400 fathoms of $1\frac{1}{2}$in rope for making up the netting.[13] In 1799, because of a shortage of cordage in the yards, it was decided to 'supply good junk for making sinnet in lieu', in the

belief that it was 'by no means a bad substitute.' This seems to have become normal policy.[14]

Boarding netting is first mentioned in 1795. Like guard netting, it was to be made up on board ship, and ships of 38 guns and less were to be issued with rope of either $1\frac{1}{2}$ or 1in circumference, in quantities of 1900 fathoms for a 38-gun ship, and 1550 fathoms for a large sloop. The dockyards were asked to collect information and make suggestions about the ideal construction of the netting, and especially mesh size. None of them seem to have done this, and there is no sign of any such size being established.[15] As with guard netting, after 1799 boarding netting was made from junk rather than new rope.

Boarding netting was described as 'a netting extended fore and aft, from the gunwale to a proper height up the rigging, to prevent an enemy from boarding in time of engagement.'[16] It was only issued to frigates and smaller vessels, presumably because ships of the line were considered high enough to resist boarders. After 1804 ships were issued with large amounts of chain for the netting. A 36-gun frigate, for example, was given 138 fathoms.[17] This was more than enough to line the whole length of the hull, on both sides. It suggests that it supported both the top and the bottom of the netting, the upper chains being extended between the shrouds and other parts of the rigging, while the lower chain helped to weigh it down.

Chapter 47. Communication

Internal Communications

The internal communications of a ship of war were not very sophisticated. The most important element was the human voice, either a very loud one, as developed by the boatswain and his mates to summon the crew, or one amplified by the speaking trumpet to give orders to the hands forward, or those aloft working the sails. The voice could be supplemented by instruments. Trumpets or drums were used to draw attention to orders, or for ceremonies. The boatswain's whistle was used to transmit a code of signals which was quite sophisticated, considering the simplicity of the instrument itself.

Though none of these methods are directly connected with the fittings of a ship, there were some more permanent fixtures which aided internal communication, organisation and discipline. The ship's bell was perhaps the most important of these. It was an age when only a few of the officers (and occasionally a seaman rich with prize money) could afford watches or clocks. Yet good timekeeping was essential to the running of the ship. The watch had to be changed every four hours, and men on certain duties, such as helmsmen and look-outs, had to be relieved every half hour. Meals had to be taken, the log written, and hammocks brought up or taken down, all at a fixed time. With such enormous numbers of men crammed into a small space, every movement had to be planned carefully in advance. The men in the hold, for example, had to bring up provisions a certain time in advance of dinner. Everyone with any kind of responsibility had to be constantly aware of the time, at least to the nearest half hour.

The Bell

The ship's bell ensured that this was the case. It was rung with a certain number of strokes every half hour, in order that the men carrying out the more demanding tasks could be relieved after a period of duty. Most watches lasted for four hours, and the cycle of bell strokes began half an hour after the start of the watch, with one stroke of the bell. Two strokes were rung after an hour, and so on, until eight bells signalled the end of one watch and the beginning of another. To keep the time, the boatswain was issued with various hour glasses. In 1686, for example, a First Rate had a watch glass, which lasted for four hours; a half-watch glass, which measured the length of the dog watches of two hours each, and perhaps helped to check the accuracy of the other glasses; and 18 half-hour glasses, which told the bell ringer when to perform his task.[1]

The bell was of the usual shape. It was cast in bell metal, which is a variety of bronze. Because of this, bells often survive years under water, and some examples have been recovered from wrecks. Usually they are marked with a broad arrow, to signify government ownership, and with the date of manufacture. Unfortunately they do not carry the name of the ship to which they were issued, probably because there was a standard size of bell for each rate.[2]

The Belfry

The bell was hung in the ship's belfry, which was placed in a prominent position on deck. In the first half of the seventeenth century it was usually to be found on the quarterdeck. After about 1660 it was placed at the break of the forecastle, above the cook room. By this time the belfry had become quite an elaborate structure with a roof over the bell. About ten years later it became part of the highly decorated bulkhead of the forecastle, and its lowest part was about halfway down the bulkhead, while the uppermost part projected some way above it. By about 1690 the lowest part of the belfry was at the level of the forecastle deck where it was to remain for the next century and a half. This meant that the belfry was once again a separate structure, instead of an integral part of the bulkhead, as it had been between 1670 and 1690. It was to remain at the break of the forecastle, except for a short period in the 1740s, when the forecastle was extended aft. The bell remained in its old position for a time, until it too was moved aft to the new break of the forecastle.

There were several systems for ringing the bell. In most of these, the bell was hung under an athwartships beam within the belfry. An arm which protruded from some point in the beam was rotated to ring the bell. In the late seventeenth century, when the belfry was built halfway up the bulkhead of the forecastle, the arm led aft and had a piece of rope hanging down from it. The bell ringer stood in the waist and pulled the rope. On most eighteenth century ships the arm led from the fore or upper part of the beam, and was pulled by the ringer, who stood on the

Left. The belfry of the St Michael, *a First Rate of 1669.* Science Museum. *Right. The belfry of a First Rate of 1719, showing the wheel used to ring the bell.* Author's photograph.

The double-arch belfry, on a Third Rate of 1780.

forecastle. On some large ships, such as the *Royal William* of 1719 and the *Victory* of 1744, a wheel was incorporated within the belfry, and attached to the beam. This type of system does not seem to have been necessary on the even larger ships of later in the century. Small ships, on the other hand, simply used a rope attached to the clapper of the bell.

The belfry was a prominent feature on a ship, and it had much carving, particularly in the second half of the seventeenth century. Large ships of that period usually had a turret-shaped belfry. This was a rather complex shape. It was basically cylindrical with a conical roof, but often the carving was so elaborate that the shape was obscured. Smaller ships seem to have had an arched belfry, with vertical sides and a curved roof. Again it was heavily decorated, with figures on both the sides and the roof.

After the orders of the early eighteenth century, the carving of belfries was much reduced. From then on, two forms predominated: the single arch and the crossed arch. The single arch was obviously related to the older form of belfry found on small ships of the 1670s, but of course it was much plainer, and it tended to be deeper in the fore and aft direction. This meant that it was virtually square in its plan view. So too was the other type, with crossed arches. One arch ran fore and aft, the other athwartships, and they met in the middle. This type was already in use by 1719, and it became the most common for larger ships throughout the eighteenth and nineteenth centuries. The actual shape developed over the years, so that by the 1790s some belfries almost had a flat roof, with corners that dropped slightly.

The sides of the belfry tended to become more open over the years. Often the single arch was supported by a flat panel on each side, but the crossing arch usually had a square pillar at each corner. In the early eighteenth century the pillars on each side were joined by a panel as high as the pillars themselves, so that the sides were solid, but the front and back open. The panels tended to be reduced over the years, so that by 1720 they extended only about half way up the side. By 1800 they had disappeared altogether. A fore and aft beam was still necessary on each side, to support the rotating beam.[3]

Trumpeters' cabins on the Boyne *of 1692, and the spherical lanterns common at the time.* Author's photograph.

Trumpeters' Cabins

In the late seventeenth century ships down to the Fourth Rate carried trumpeters to help convey orders to the crew, and to give dignity to important occasions. In the orders of 1673, the trumpeters were allocated tiny cabins aft on the poop deck, close to the taffrail. Third Rates and above were allowed four cabins. Two were positioned fore and aft, and two athwartships, against the taffrail.[4] The *Boyne* of 1693, however, was a Third Rate and had only two cabins, like a Fourth Rate.[5] On other ships of this period, the cabins were beginning to develop into the topgallant roundhouse, which was eventually to replace them. The latter can be seen in its embryonic form on a model which is believed to represent the *Britannia* of 1682, after a major repair in 1700.[6] Trumpeters' cabins had largely disappeared by this time. On small ships they were dispensed with, and on the very largest they expanded, and were taken over by the master and first lieutenant. Judging by the cabins to be seen on the *Boyne* and other models, they must have been very cramped, sparse, and uncomfortable.

Voice Pipes

Often orders had to be conveyed from one deck to another with some degree of urgency. In the days of the whipstaff, helm orders often had to be passed down below from the pilot or quartermaster, and in action midshipmen acted as aides de camp to the captain. Occasionally attempts were made to develop a more sophisticated system of communication. In 1745 a committee of flag officers recommended that 'all ships have funnels or pipes fixed to go down from the quarterdeck into the gunroom, for the convenience of conning them upon the accident of the tiller rope or wheel breaking.'[7] There is no sign that this suggestion was actually implemented, but in 1777 the Navy Board ordered that 'trumpets or sounding pipes should be fitted on all three decked ships on their going to sea, for the conveniency of giving directions on the middle gun decks in time of action.'[8] Again, there is no further evidence that they were actually fitted and used.

Communication With Other Ships

Until the late eighteenth century there was very little provision aboard a warship specifically for communication with other vessels. Communication could be made by voice when ships were close enough and the weather was calm, or officers could be sent by boat from one ship to another for conferences or instructions. There was also a fairly complex system of signals, which used lights at night, flags in the daytime, and guns in fog or to draw attention to other signals. However, few special signal flags had been developed. Ensigns, jacks and pendants were hoisted in particular positions according to the message. Naturally the potential for developing such a system was limited, and it was eventually superseded as tactics became more complex. The first system of special signal flags, which could be used in combination to make a great number of pre-arranged messages, was developed by Hawke in the 1750s and 1760s, and Howe, and Admiral Kempenfeldt in the 1770s. In 1801 it was improved by Sir Home Popham, so that individual words and letters could be composed if the message was not in the standard signal book. This system was used to send Nelson's famous signal at Trafalgar, and it would not have been possible with any of the older systems.[9]

Even with the old system, a ship had to carry a wide range of flags. She needed a union flag, a red, white and blue ensign, a set of pennants, and a number of foreign flags, for use either as courtesy flags or as a *ruse de guerre*, as the situation demanded. From quite early in the eighteenth century models show flag lockers. These are fitted on the poop just inside the taffrail, in the place just previously occupied by the trumpeters' cabins. They were relatively light in construction, and were perhaps made by the ship's carpenter, as not all models have them, and there is no sign of official authorisation for them. The first appearance of what was possibly a flag locker is on a model of 1702. However, this has vertical bars along its innermost side, and it could have been

intended as a hen coop.[10] The flag locker makes an unambiguous appearance on a 60-gun ship of about 1735. In this case it is in the same position, but with a solid inner edge, and hinged lids on top.[11] This was to remain the standard form. Lockers can be seen on various other models, such as the *Royal George* of 1756.[12] On some ships of the mid-eighteenth century, the knees of the taffrail were so large that the fitting of flag lockers would have been difficult, and it is possible that they were put elsewhere. A different type of flag locker is seen aboard the 74-gun ship *San Domingo* of 1812. This was fitted at the break of the poop, and its after face had many doors, each marked with a picture of the flag it contained.[13] This form probably became necessary with the advent of a more sophisticated signalling system, which employed a greater number of flags, but there is no direct evidence of the use of the break of the poop for this purpose.

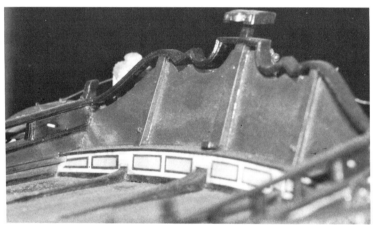

Left. A model of 1702 with what were possibly flag lockers (or poultry coops). It also shows the parallel-sided stern lanterns which were used soon after glass replaced mica. Author's photograph, courtesy of NMM. Right. Flag locker on a 60-gun ship of the 1730s.

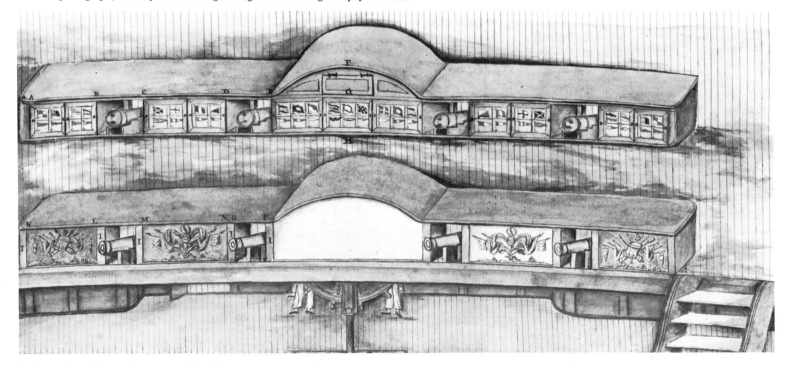

The flag locker of the San Domingo *in 1811. This example is unusual in that it is fitted at the break of the poop, rather than the taffrail. Each compartment is fitted with a picture of the flag it contains. NMM.*

Lanterns

Ships had large lanterns fitted on their sterns. These were particularly useful when sailing in a fleet at night, because they allowed the ship astern to keep her station. Large ships, of the Third Rate and above, usually carried three lanterns. In 1722 it was ordered that Fourth Rates should also have three lanterns,[14] but in 1804 it was decided that ships below the First Rate needed only two, except when they were fitted as flagships. It is clear from this order that a private ship lit only the two outer lanterns, even before the middle one was abolished.[15] These gave the following ship some indication of how far away the other ship was, and her relative aspect. The middle one served solely to identify the flagship.

In the seventeenth century, the central lantern was far bigger than the other two. It was especially large on prestige ships, such as the *Sovereign* of 1637. It was quite easy to mount this lantern centrally aft of the taffrail, but in the first half of the century the mounting of the other two caused problems. The stern itself was very narrow, so the outside lanterns had to be mounted above the quarter galleries, where they were considerably lower than the central one, and could possibly be obscured by it at certain angles. By about 1650, after the stern had become wider, they were mounted on the outer corners of the taffrail. In the early eighteenth century the stern tended to become yet wider, and the lanterns were mounted a little way in from the quarter, so that their position in relation to one another remained unaltered.

Early seventeenth-century lanterns were usually hexagonal in plan, with parallel sides. Around 1650 the spherical lantern made its appearance, and it became the most common type for the next 40 years. It was made up of scores of tiny panels of mica. Because of developments in the glass industry, larger panels of plate glass became available towards the end of the century, and in the 1690s the parallel-sided hexagonal lantern came into use again. In 1702 all ships were to be fitted with 'stern lights and gallery lights, ranging with those of the stern', made of stone-ground glass.[16] By about 1707 the lantern had developed into a standard shape, hexagonal in plan, with a base which was narrower than the top, and a curved roof which carried some decoration. This remained standard until the early nineteenth century.

Each stern lantern was supported by a bracket leading aft from the poop. Most of these were quite simple, with a horizontal arm leading out, and a short diagonal extending upwards to support the lantern. Others had several arms converging at the base of the lantern, so that it was braced from the sides and from below.

The top lantern was used by flagships, and ships in charge of a convoy. It was fitted to the after edge of the appropriate top, according to the rank of the admiral concerned: the main top for a full admiral, the fore top for a vice admiral, and the mizzen top for a rear admiral. In 1804 the Navy Board pointed out one of the disadvantages of the abolition of the central lantern: 'when a ship is appointed for a convoy, it is not unusual for one of the poop lanterns to be removed to the main top'.[17]

Typical eighteenth century glass lanterns on a Second Rate, c1710. Author's photograph, courtesy of Science Museum.

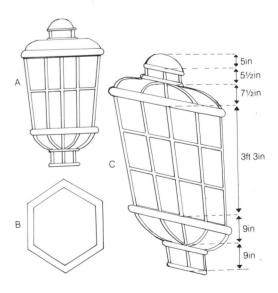

A and B. Side lantern for a First and Second Rate, c1740.
C. Main lantern for a First Rate.

Appendices

Appendix I (see Part I)

Pollard to the Navy Board, 18th December 1770. (PRO Adm 106/1191)

As the safety of His Majesty's ships and men depend on the rudder, tiller and tiller ropes, and the present method of steering His Majesty's ships being attended with many inconveniences and fatal accidents that have happened are generally known to have been by the unavoidable slack rope when the tiller is near its greatest angle, by which the men are often thrown from the steering wheel, the tiller in danger of being broke, the rudder head, pintles and braces work loose, the tiller ropes are in the way of working the guns and are in danger of being shot away.

I humble propose to your honours a model how to avoid the dangers and inconveniences that attend His Majesty's ships and men by the present method of leading the tiller ropes to the steering wheel . . .

Extract from the contract for the Bombay Castle, *1782.* (NMM Draught Room)

The rudderhead to be made long enough to receive a tiller above the upper deck, to be strapped and hooked with iron as usual, to be 2ft 2in thwartships, fore and aft 2ft 4in, and 5ft 6in broad at the lower end including a 3in back, and 4ft 6in at the lower hance. Height above the deck as the said draught agreed as aforesaid directs; to be well made, the pieces to be tabled to each other, and all but the main and bearding pieces to be fir. To have seven pair of rudder irons, the upper brace to have long straps that may turn and meet round the standard against the post; the second brace, 4ft 6in long from the rabbets, the lower one from the back of the post 7ft; to be hung Flemish fashion, and well secured with chocks above water to prevent it unhanging.

The pintles to be $3\frac{3}{8}$in diameter, all of them to be 1ft $1\frac{1}{2}$in long except the lower one; that to be 1ft $3\frac{1}{2}$in long. The straps of the rudder braces and pintles to be $4\frac{1}{2}$in broad, 2in thick in the shoulder at the return, and to have an iron strap on the back of the rudder, and a ringbolt with two rings by $1\frac{1}{8}$in diameter drove through the rudder, the rings of sufficient bigness; and to have an eye bole on each side at the ends of the wing transom with bolts of $1\frac{1}{4}$in diameter for the rudder tackles; that all, both braces and pintles, be carefully let in, that the irons bear an equal strain; that every pintle and brace have a bolt in the strap as close to the shoulder as may be drove through, with a saucer head, and well clenched on the other side; the hole for the tiller in the rudder head to be cut (both that above and that below the upper deck) of equal bigness; square on the foreside, $11\frac{1}{8}$in; on the after side, 10in; that the same tiller may fit either hole. The bearding of the rudder between the pintles and back of the stern post to be covered with lead, turned and nailed on the sides; also to lead the helm port as it is done in His Majesty's yards.

Appendix II (see Part II)

A proportion for making a main capstan, c1680. (NMM AND/31)

Suppose the barrel 5 foot long and 30 inches diameter, the length of the whelps must be $\frac{5}{9}$ of the length of the barrel, and the depth of the whelps must be $\frac{1}{2}$ the diameter of the barrel; and the breadth of the whelp alow must be the breadth of one of the squares, and aloft they must be $\frac{1}{4}$ of the square broader; the length of the surge $\frac{2}{3}$ of the length of the whelps, and cut down $\frac{1}{3}$ of the depth of the whelp; the thickness of the chocks alow, $\frac{1}{2}$ of the breadth of the square, and the upper chocks must be $\frac{1}{3}$ of the breadth of the square; the bar holes, $\frac{4}{5}$ of the breadth of the square for the holes up and down, and $\frac{8}{9}$ of the hole up and down for the bigness thwartships; the diameter of the spindle at the partners must be $\frac{4}{5}$ of the diameter of the barrel, and the diameter at the lowest end must be $\frac{1}{2}$ of the diameter of the partners (or $\frac{5}{9}$, which is something more) for letting the hoop on.

A proportion for making a jeer capstan. (NMM AND/31)

First suppose the length of the upper barrel 5 foot, and the diameter 20 inches, and the length of the lower barrel with the partners and spindle $6\frac{1}{2}$ feet. Now the length of the spindle is 6 inches, and length of the partners 2 foot; and for the diameter of the lower barrel it must be $\frac{7}{8}$ of the upper barrel; and the diameter at the partners must be $\frac{4}{5}$ or $\frac{3}{4}$ of the upper barrel, and the diameter of the spindle must be half as much as the partners be; the length of the upper whelps is $\frac{5}{9}$ or $\frac{2}{3}$ of the upper barrel, and for the diameter of the whelps $\frac{1}{2}$ of the diameter of the barrel, and the thickness of the sole of the whelps must be equal with the square of the capstan, either 10 or 12 squares; and for his thickness aloft, you must strike a circle 30 inch diameter (which is just the bigness of the barrel and whelps) and divide that circle into either 10 or 12 squares, and take one of them squares for the thickness of the whelp aloft, or else take $\frac{1}{4}$ of the first square and add to the square and that will be the thickness.

. . . with 10 holes and 6 whelps, and the holes 13 inches in thwartships. A bolt between every hole.

A proportion of anchors judged necessary for a ship of each class of the Royal Navy that are built according to the established dimensions ... Navy Office, April 1718

	Anchors proposed	
	Number	Weight [Cwt]
100 guns		
Royal Sovereign	1	81
	4	77
	1	$20\frac{1}{2}$
	1	$10\frac{1}{4}$
	1	$5\frac{1}{8}$
Royal William	1	81
	2	77
	1	72
	1	71
	1	20
	1	10
	1	5
Britannia	1	81
	4	77
	1	$20\frac{1}{4}$
	1	$10\frac{1}{8}$
	1	5
Royal George	1	$77\frac{3}{4}$
	4	$73\frac{3}{4}$
	1	$19\frac{1}{2}$
	1	$9\frac{3}{4}$
	1	$4\frac{7}{8}$
Royal Anne	1	$74\frac{1}{2}$
	4	$70\frac{1}{2}$
	1	$18\frac{5}{8}$
	1	$9\frac{1}{4}$
	1	$4\frac{5}{8}$
London	1	73
	4	69
	1	$18\frac{1}{4}$
	1	$9\frac{1}{8}$
	1	$4\frac{1}{2}$
90-gun ship	1	69
	4	66
	1	$17\frac{1}{4}$
	1	$8\frac{5}{8}$
	1	$4\frac{1}{4}$
80-gun ship	1	58
	3	55
	1	$14\frac{1}{2}$
	1	$7\frac{1}{4}$
70-gun ship	1	51
	3	48
	1	$12\frac{3}{4}$
	1	$6\frac{3}{8}$
60-gun ship	1	43
	3	41
	1	$10\frac{3}{4}$
	1	$5\frac{3}{8}$
50-gun ship	1	$34\frac{1}{2}$
	3	$32\frac{1}{2}$
	1	$8\frac{5}{8}$
	1	$4\frac{1}{4}$

	Anchors proposed	
	Number	Weight [Cwt]
40-gun ship	1	27
	3	25
	1	$6\frac{3}{4}$
	1	$3\frac{3}{8}$

Viol blocks and cat blocks. (PRO 106/30)

Dimensions of viol blocks, c1740

100 guns, 56 inches
 90 guns, 54 inches
 80 guns, 50 inches
 70 guns, 48 inches
 60 guns, 46 inches
 50 guns, 42 inches
 40 guns, 38 inches
 30 guns, 34 inches
 20 guns, 32 inches

Cat blocks, iron bound

Treble	100 guns, 24 inches
	90 guns, 22 inches
	80 guns, 20 inches
Double	70 guns, 19 inches
	60 guns, 18 inches
	50 guns, 17 inches
	40 guns, 16 inches
	30 guns, 15 inches
	20 guns, 14 inches

Anchors and cables for ships of 90 and 80 guns, c1750. (PRO Adm 95/17)

Anchors		90 guns Cwt	80 guns Cwt
By establishment	1719	69	58
	1733	$70\frac{1}{4}$	$63\frac{1}{2}$
	1741	$71\frac{3}{4}$	$65\frac{3}{4}$
	1745	$73\frac{1}{2}$	$69\frac{1}{2}$

Cables By the establishment of		90 guns Inches	80 guns Inches
	1719	$21\frac{1}{2}$	20
	1733	22	21
	1741	$22\frac{1}{2}$	$21\frac{1}{2}$
	1745	23	22

Anchors and cables supplied to the undermentioned ships. (PRO Adm 95/17)

Guns	Anchors of			Number
	Cwt	Qrs	Tons	
90 *Ramillies*	74	2	21	1
	73	2	12	1
	73	2	0	1
	72	2	0	1
	75	3	14	1
Cables of	23 inches			9
90 *Prince*	72	2	6	1
	71	3	14	1
	71	1	14	1
	71	0	0	1

Guns		Anchors of		Number
	Cwt	Qrs	Tons	
Cables of	22½ inches			9
90 *St George*	70	1	14	1
	69	0	0	1
	68	0	10	1
	66	2	4	1
	65	2	10	1
Cables of	22 inches			9
80 *Prince George*	72	1	7	1
	70	0	14	1
	69	0	0	1
	67	0	0	1
	66	2	4	1
Cables of	22 inches			1
80 *Barfleur*	70	3	0	2
	70	2	0	2
	69	3	21	1
Cables of	22 inches			9
80 *Cambridge*	71	2	0	1
	70	1	0	1
	70	0	0	1
	69	3	0	1
Cables of	22 inches			9

Methods to make capstans, c1750. (NMM SPB/20)

The main capstan barrel to be as big as the mainmast, the partners $\frac{5}{6}$ of the barrel, and carry them so low as the false partners may come under the beam. The spindle to $\frac{1}{2}$ the partners length of the viol is 3 foot or 3 foot one inch. To make a mould for your whelps, the lower end to be $\frac{1}{2}$ the barrel and the upper end $\frac{2}{3}$ of the lower. Then strike that line and divide it into 3 parts, and set off 2 of them from the lower end for the height of the surge, then divide it into 4 parts, and one of them is the depth of the surge for the tapering of your whelps. Take the bigness of your square of the barrel and divide it into four parts and set off one on each side of the square for the tapering. The round and hollow of the chocks, take $\frac{1}{2}$ the barrel, and the depth of the whelps. Where the chock is, add them together. The total is the length of the sweep. The square that goes into the drumhead is $\frac{5}{6}$ of the barrel, and so long as that the upper piece of drumhead may take hole 1 inch. The thickness of the drumhead is half the barrel, diameter twice the barrel and two inches more than. The bar holes must cut in $\frac{1}{4}$ of the drumhead, and to be brought into 12 squares.

For a jeer capstan

To be $\frac{9}{10}$ of the main capstan, or as big as the foremast. The lower barrel $\frac{9}{10}$ of the upper barrel. Length of the partners, one inch less than the upper barrel is in diameter, the bigness $\frac{5}{6}$ of the barrel. You must make the surge of your lower whelps be so high as that the viol may come above the cross piece, which height is as 7 is to 13 of the height from beam to beam. The spindle must be 1 inch bigger than $\frac{1}{2}$ the barrel. All the rest the same as the main capstan. You must make your lower whelps $\frac{4}{5}$ of the length of the lower barrel, that $\frac{3}{11}$ of the barrel gives the 12 squares, $\frac{3}{9}$ the 10 squares, and the $\frac{5}{12}$ the 8 squares. The capstan is to be broad into 10 inches square.

Dimensions thought fit for making capstans, c1750. (NMM SPB/1)

For a jeer capstan, the upper barrel not to exceed 3 foot in length, the lower end of the whelps to be half the diameter of the barrel, the whelps to surge two inches in a foot. The length of the surge, $\frac{1}{3}$ the length of the whelps, allowing 2½ or 3 inches for the stop of the head; and let the upper parts of the head be 1 inch shallower than the lower part of the head. Let all the whelps taper one and a half inches on each side in a foot deep; the partners out to be at least 2 inches on each side less than the upper barrel, and of a sufficient length to lift the capstan high enough to shift the viol. The lower barrel is convenient to be $\frac{3}{4}$ of an inch each side bigger than the partners, that the whelps may not be set too far into the barrel. The lower whelps to be $\frac{5}{9}$ of the length from the end of the upper whelps to the lower end of the lower whelps. The lower end of the [?] to be $\frac{3}{5}$ of the lower barrel, to taper in the surge 2 inches in a foot in the length of the surge. The head to follow the same tapering, allowing at least 3 inches stop. The length of the head something less than $\frac{1}{3}$ of the whelps. The spindle ought at least to be $\frac{1}{2}$ the lower barrel, the length as you please and as conveniently will serve. The drumhead ought to overhang the lower end of the whelps 2 inches round, and the thickness according to the bigness of the bar holes. The proportions differ something from the rule. But is our opinion make much handsomer capstans.

The true establishment of anchors not being known at some of the yards; these are to direct you to establish those mentioned in the enclosed account to each ship, 3rd November 1784. (PRO 106/2508)

Guns	Cwt	Number
100	81	4
	21	1
	10½	1
	5	1
90 and 98	73	4
	18	1
	9	1
	4½	1
80 of three decks	69	4
	17	1
	8½	1
74	67	4
	16	1
	8	1
70	59	4
	15	1
	7½	1
44	57	4
	15	1
	7½	1
60	53	4
	12	1
	6	1
50, large	49	4
	11	1
	5¼	1
50, small	46	4
	10½	1
	5¼	1
44 and 38	44	4
	10	1
	5	1

Guns	Cwt	Number
36 new construction	40	4
	10	1
	5	1
32	33	4
	8½	1
	4	1
28	31	4
	8	1
	4	1
24	29½	4
	7½	1
	4	1
26	25	4
	7½	1
	3½	1
Sloop of 268 to 300 tons	20	3
	7	1
	3½	1
200 tons	15	3
	6	1
	3	1
140 tons	12	3
	5	1
	3	1
Fireships	8	3
	6	1
	4	1
Brigs, iron stocked	10	2
	7	1
	3	1
Cutter of 180 tons, iron stocked	10	2
	6	1
	3	1
150 tons	9	2
	6	1
	3	1

Appendix III (see Part III)

Cleaning and graving a Fourth Rate (50 gun) and Fifth Rate ship, 1696. (NMM Adm A/1866)

	Material	Workmanship	Material	Workmanship
With black stuff	£ 13/17/0	£11/11/6	£ 10/14/1	£ 9/0/7
		£ 3/10/0		£ 2/19/6
Tallowing	£ 30/5/11	£11/11/6	£ 21/0/1	£ 9/0/7
		£ 3/10/0		£ 2/16/4
Charge of sheathing (caulking and paying is included)	£166/9/5	£33/10/7	£125/13/0	£28/7/0

The charge of graving at 3 shillings per foot for a Fourth Rate may amount to the sum of £75/14/0, and for a Fifth Rate, £56/5/0.

Navy Board report on the cost of paying with different materials, 1702. (PRO Adm 1/3592)

With black stuff:	Pitch – 2 barrels	£2/12/0
	Tar – 1 barrel	£1/0/0
		£3/12/0
With white stuff:	Rozin – 7cwt	£5/5/0
	Oil –18 gallons	£1/7/0
	Brimstone –84lbs	£0/12/9
		£7/4/9
With this new stuff:	Turpentine – 7cwt	£5/12/0
	Oil –12 gallons	£0/18/0
	Brimstone –84lbs	£0/12/9
		£7/2/9

An account of calculation of materials and workmanship for sheathing His Majesty's ship Resolution, *74 guns, 1770.* (PRO Adm 106/3472)

Sheathing board, keel, rudder and stern		1700 feet			
ditto bottom		15398 feet			
Elm, 1 inch		400 feet			
Tar		8 barrels			

		Cwt	Qr	Lbs
Hair, loose		12	3	
Brown paper sheets		26	3	
Spun yarn		3	0	
Nails, 20d		1	0	
10d		37	0	
Sharp, 10		2	0	
2		0	1	2
Round 4		0	0	16
Milled lead, no 4		4	2	16
Thrums		0	0	26
Twine		0	0	2
Leather		0	0	4
Spars, small, no	8			
Old canvas	18 yards			
Nails, scuppers		3	3	14
Baskets, brushes	6			
Baskets, ballast	6			
Baskets, broad	24			
Double buckets	4			
Single buckets	4			
Lashing	8 coils			
Oil, train	1 gallon			
Oakum		8	0	0
Paying bottom of sheathing with brown stuff;				
Brimstone		5	0	0
Pitch	9 barrels			
Tar	6 barrels			

Caulkers sheathing, workmanship	£26/0/0	
Caulkers paying, workmanship	£ 3/10/0	
Shipwrights sheathing, workmanship	£48/0/0	All at £3 per day
Total cost	£308/10/8	

Materials for coppering several ships at Deptford, November 1782. (PRO Adm 106/3472)

Particulars	Messrs Randall *Fortitude*, 74		Deptford Yard *Magnanime*, 64		Messrs Barnard *Africa*, 64		Messrs Randall *Sceptre*, 64	
	Quan.	Cwt Qr Lbs	Quan.	Cwt Qr Lbs	Quan.	Cwt Qr Lbs	Quan.	Cwt Qr Lbs
Copper sheets of:								
32lbs	35	3.0.0	6	0.2.2	61	5.0.17	61	5.0.17
28lbs	118	8.2.27	77	5.1.13	130	9.2.17	138	10.0.26
22lbs	283	16.1.16	301	17.2. 9	295	17.0. 5	298	16.3.15
Plates, lacquered, yards	226		199		252	257½		
Paper, cartridge, quires	5	97½	4	77½	3	58	3	58
Composition, barrels	1½		1½		1½		1½	
Paper, thick, dipped		7.0.0		7.0.0		7.0.0		7.0.0
Copper nails, bright head		7.2.24		8.2.27		7.2.26		6.3.21
Copper nails, for the gripe		0.0.12		0.0.12		0.0.12		0.0.12
Iron nails, 20		0.0.15		0.0.12		0.0.12		0.0.12
Nails, scuppers		0.1. 2		0.1.11		0.0.20		0.0.20
Nails, 4		0.0. 7		0.0. 7		0.0. 7		0.0. 7
3		0.0. 6		0.0. 6		0.0. 6		0.0. 6
Tar, barrels	1½		1½		1½		1½	
Spun yarn		0.2.17		0.2.18		0.2.11		0.2.11
Oakum, white		0.1. 0		0.1. 0		0.1. 0		0.1. 0
Battens, whole	32		32		32		62 [sic]	
Cost of workmanship	£ 18/7/5		£ 16/ 4/00		£ 29/16/6		£ 15/8/00	
Total cost	£240/4/2		£215/19/11		£259/0/9		£254/1/11	

Appendix IV (see Part IV)

An estimate of the charge of fitting a 70-gun ship with two chain pumps. Deptford yard, 17th October 1753. (PRO Adm 95/17)

To two chain pumps, bored, with brass rolls, plates, axletrees, winches, wheels, sprockets, chains, pump dales, scuppers, leather, with all kind of materials required for the cistern, hoods, and co., for the entire completing the same ... £35/13/11

To shipwrights and blockmakers work on fitting the said pumps in their places, making the cistern and hoods, fitting the axletrees, winches, pump dales, and doing every part incumbent on them to perform, toward the finishing the same for service ... £4/8/0

To blockmakers work, in fixing the rolls and plates at the bottom of the pumps, boring the cases for the chain above the deck, and making the square ones for ditto under the deck, fitting sprockets and squares to the wheels, leathering and reaving the chain and all that belongs to him ... £0/14/7

Total ... £40/16/6

Pump gear, agreeable to Mr Coles pumps, 23rd September 1771. (PRO ADM 1061/3551)

Guns (Months: 8 / Add for 12) — Sloops

Species	100		90		80		74		70		64		60		50		44		36		32		28		24 & 20		300 to 268 tons		200 tons	
	8	Add for 12	8	Add for 12	8	Add for 12	8	Add for 12	8	Add for 12	8	Add for 12	8	Add for 12	8	Add for 12	8	Add for 12	8	Add for 12	8	Add for 12	8	Add for 12	8	Add for 12	8	Add for 12	8	Add for 12
Axletrees	2	1	2	1	2	1	2	1	2	1	2	1	2	1	1		1		1		1		1		1		1		1	
Burrs	12	4	12	4	12	4	11	3	11	3	10	3	10	3	9	3	8	3	6	3	6	3	6	3	5	2	5	2	5	2
Chain, spare	2	1	2	1	2	1	2	1	2	1	2	1	2	1	2	1	1	1	1	1	1	1	1	1	1	1	1	1	1	1
Ditto, lengths	12	6	12	6	10	5	10	5	10	4	10	4	9	4	7	3	6	3	6	3	6	2	5	2	5	2	3	1	2	1
Bolts of the chains with forelocks	50		49		47		46		44		44		42		21		20		20		18		18		18		14		12	
Brass cleats for winches	4		4		4		4		4		4		4		3		2		2		2		2		2		2		2	
Cast iron ditto	2		2		2		2		2		2		2		2		1		1		1		1		1		1		1	
Iron bars $\frac{1}{2}$in thick and 12in long to stop the chain whilst repairing	4		4		4		4		4		4		2		2		2		2		2		2		2		2		2	
Hooks to take up chain	2		2		2		2		2		2		2		2		2		2		2		2		2		2		2	
Nuts, brass for cisterns	8		8		8		8		8		8		8		8		4		4		4		4		4		4		4	
Pumps, fitted	4		4		4		4		4		4		2		2		2		2		2		2		2		2		2	
Punch	1		1		1		1		1		1		1		1		1		1		1		1		1		1		1	
Sweep knife	1		1		1		1		1		1		1		1		1		1		1		1		1		1		1	
Wheels, fitted	1		1		1		1		1		1		1		1		1		1		1		1		1		1		1	
Bolts for the wheels with nuts	18		18		18		18		18		18		18		12		12		12		12		12		12		12		12	
Winches	2	1	2	1	2	1	2	1	1	1	1	1	1		1		1		1		1		1		1		1		1	
Forked spanner or screw key	1		1		1		1		1		1		1		1		1		1		1		1		1		1		1	

NB All 60 guns that are fitted with four chain pumps to be allowed the same proportion as 64-gun ships.

Carpenter's stores, c1805. (PRO Adm 7/580)

Pump parts for a 74-gun ship

Pumps, chain, fitted	4	Forked spanner	1
Spare axletrees	2	Hooks to take up chain	2
Bolts for chain, with forelock	46	Iron bars, $1\frac{1}{2}$ inches thick, 12 inches long	4
Bolts for wheel, with nuts	18	Nuts, brass, for cisterns	8
Burrs or saucers	11	Pinchers, pair	1
Chains	2	Punches	2
Chain lengths	10	Print	1
Chisel	1	Sweep knife	—
Cleats for winches, brass	4	Wheels, fitted	1
Cleats for winches, cast iron	2	Winches	2
Copper forelocks	50		

Appendix V (see Part V)

Cast iron ordnance brought into His Majesty's stores by John Browne, His Majesty's founder of cast iron ordnance and shot, since the beginning of His Majesty's reign, viz. (PRO SP 16/148 f16)

27th March 1625	Demi-culverin	204
	Saker	99
1st June	Demi-culverin	63
	Saker	42
6th August	Saker	20
12th August	Culverin	1
	Demi-culverin	5
	Saker	5
	Minion	3
18th February 1626	Culverin	16
	Demi-culverin	15
	Saker	3
20th February	Saker	2
20th March	Culverin	2
	Demi-culverin	10
21st March	Saker	16
24th March	Minion	18
1st June	Culverin	2 ⎫ Light ordnance
	Demi-culverin	2 ⎬ of fine metal
	Saker	2 ⎭
7th July	Minion	4
12th December	Demi-culverin	4
	Culverin	2
	Saker	4
	Demi-culverin of fine metal	3
10th January 1627	Demi-culverin	29
	Saker	10
	Demi-culverin drakes	36
17th January	Culverin	1
	Demi-culverin	7 of fine metal
21st March	Minion	12
12th March	Falcon	4
19th April	Culverin drakes	1 ⎫
	Demi-culverin drakes	7 ⎬ of fine metal
	Saker drakes	6 ⎭
10th July	Sakers	30
26th August	Minion	16
	Falcons	4
10th September	Saker	2
15th November	Culverin	2
	Demi-culverin	2 of fine metal
25th January 1628	Demi-cannon drakes	4
	Culverin drakes	31 of fine metal
	Saker drakes	5
2nd March	Demi-culverin drakes	26
	Culverin drakes	40 of fine metal
	Demi-culverin drakes	40
28th June	Saker	37
	Minion	3
2nd August	Saker drakes	20
	Minion	8

Sum total of pieces of ordnance

Culverin	28
Demi-culverin	330
Saker	267
Minion	64
Falcon	8

Drakes:

Demi-cannon	30
Culverin	72
Demi-culverin	83
Saker	31

Light ordnance of metal:

Culverin	2
Demi-culverin	14
Saker	2

Sum total of all the pieces	931
Sum total of all the weight	1143 tons, 18cwt, 2qrs

22nd April 1665. Proved and received from Mr Thomas Western, the iron ordnance of the several dimensions at touch hole, trunnion, and muzzle, following, being proved at Rye, viz. (PRO WO 47/7)

Demi-cannon of 9 foot

At touch hole Inches	At trunnion Inches	At muzzle Inches
$18\frac{3}{4}$	$16\frac{1}{2}$	$12\frac{3}{4}$
$18\frac{3}{4}$	$16\frac{1}{2}$	$12\frac{1}{4}$
$18\frac{3}{4}$	$15\frac{3}{4}$	12
$18\frac{3}{4}$	$16\frac{1}{2}$	$12\frac{1}{2}$
19	$16\frac{1}{2}$	$12\frac{1}{4}+\frac{1}{8}$
$18\frac{1}{2}$	16	$11\frac{3}{4}+\frac{1}{8}$
19	$16\frac{1}{2}$	$12\frac{1}{4}$
19	$16\frac{1}{2}$	$12\frac{1}{2}$
$19\frac{1}{8}$	$16\frac{1}{2}+\frac{1}{8}$	$12\frac{1}{4}$
19	$16\frac{1}{2}$	$12\frac{3}{4}$
$18\frac{3}{4}$	$16\frac{1}{4}$	$12\frac{1}{4}$
$19\frac{1}{4}$	$16\frac{3}{4}$	$12\frac{1}{2}$
19	$16\frac{1}{2}+\frac{1}{8}$	$12\frac{3}{4}$
19	$16\frac{1}{2}$	$12\frac{1}{4}$
19	$16\frac{1}{2}$	$12\frac{1}{8}$
$19\frac{1}{2}$	$16\frac{3}{4}$	$12\frac{3}{4}$
19	$16\frac{1}{2}$	$12\frac{1}{4}$
$19\frac{1}{4}$	$16\frac{3}{4}$	$12\frac{1}{4}+\frac{1}{8}$
19	$16\frac{1}{2}$	$12\frac{3}{4}$
19	$16\frac{3}{4}$	$12\frac{1}{4}$
19	$16\frac{1}{2}$	$12\frac{1}{4}$
$19\frac{1}{4}$	$16\frac{1}{4}$	$12\frac{1}{4}$

Gun proportions, 1782. (NMM GUN/1)

The ordnance employed in the Royal Navy are all of iron, excepting the guns on board His Majesty's ship *Royal George*, and the mortars in the bomb ketches, 1782.

The guns consist of the following natures, viz. 42, 32, 24, 18, 12, 9, 6, 4, 3, and $\frac{1}{2}$ pounders. That is, they carry balls of these several weights, by which they are also distinguished one from each other.

In the land service, the different natures have a fixed proportion assigned to each, but here, guns carrying the same ball are frequently cast of various lengths, in order to accommodate the rate of the ship designed for, and the local situation on board.

From the necessity of this variety in the lengths of ships guns, very few of them are properly proportioned to the magnitude of their shots, which all pieces of ordnance should be regulated by.

As for instance, a 24 pounder being nearly 21 diameters of its shot in length, or $9\frac{1}{2}$ feet; a 6 pounder, to be proportioned to it, should not exceed six feet, whereas many of them extend as far as 9, or 31 diameters

263

of the shot. By this mode of comparison, (supposing the 24 pounder of a proper length) it will be found that guns in general are much larger than is necessary, with regard to the ranging of their shots. Therefore the closer this proportion can be adhered to, the more advantageous it will be in serving the guns, and with less strain to the ships.

General proportion observed in the construction of guns.

Lengths

The whole length of the gun is divided into seven equal parts. The first reinforce contains two of these parts, the second, one, with a diameter of the bore added to it, which leaves the chace four parts, wanting one diameter of the bore.

The trunnions are each one diameter, and placed at three parts distant from the base ring, their axis produced being a tangent to the bottom of the bore.

The breech mouldings and cascable are equal to two calibres or more, but are never included in the estimation of the gun's length.

Thickness of metal

The heavy brass guns of all natures have a thickness of metal at the breech and vent equal to one calibre of shot, and half that substance at the muzzle. But cast iron being of a more brittle quality, those guns are allowed one seventh of the shot's calibre more.

The longest iron guns are here spoke of. The metal should be proportioned in some measure to the length of the piece.

The placing of the vent in any piece of ordnance is esteemed a material circumstance. It is generally drilled slanting into the bore, near the breech, which is looked upon as the most favourable situation for the greatest effect upon the charge. The bore or calibre of every gun exceeds the diameter of its shot by one twentieth part of the shot's diameter. This difference between them is called the windage; and is allowed for the convenience of loading the piece without obstruction. It is generally thought that one twentieth part is more than necessary, and that the effect of the shot is not only thereby lessened, but the direction of the object fixed at rendered more uncertain.

All nature of iron guns not exceeding 12 pounders are proved by loading them with a quantity of powder equal to the weight of the shot, and half that is allowed for common service, but the longer natures have the following less proportional charges:

Pounders	Proof Lbs	Service Lbs
42	25	17
32	$21\frac{1}{2}$	14
24	18	11
18	15	9

Contract made between officers of the ordnance and Samuel Walker and Co., gunfounders, 1768. (PRO Adm 7/940)

Articles of agreement made and concluded upon this 17th day of February, in the 26th year of the reign of our Sovereign Lord George the third ... in the year of our Lord 1786 ... between (the officers of the ordnance, named) and Joshua Walker, Joseph Walker, Thomas Walker, and John Crawshaw, of Rotherham in the County of York, gunfounders and co-partners, of the other part, in the manner following, that is to say;

The said Samuel Walker & Co., for the considerations hereinafter mentioned, do hereby ... promise and agree ... that they ... shall and will at their own proper costs and charges, on or before the 31st day of December 1787, cast and deliver into the charge of His Majesty's storekeeper at Woolwich Warren, 1000 tons of iron ordnance, of such natures

and dimensions as shall be marked on gauges of metal, and according to such draughts upon paper models, and other directions, as they, the said Samuel Walker & Co., shall receive from the said Principal officers of the Ordnance ... for that purpose ... All which said iron ordnance they, the said Samuel Walker & co., will mould in sand, cast the same solid, with His Majesty's crown and cypher thereon, and afterwards bore out of the same solid metal, bore the same horizontally. And also that all the metal which they, the said Samuel Walker & Co., shall use in casting the said iron ordnance shall be extracted from and out of the best and finest ore; and shall be of a close and dense texture, and of the toughest and best quality for that purpose.

And also that they ... will distinguish such iron ordnance as shall be cast from the same run of metal by cutting a particular mark thereon, and numbering the whole quantity delivered under the warrant issued for the supplying thereof in the order in which they were cast; and shall and will send a true and exact list with every parcel of iron ordnance at the time of delivery, describing such marks and numbers.

And further, that no proof or examination of the said iron ordnance shall be required, until there shall be actually in the custody of the said storekeeper fifty guns or upwards, belonging to the said Samuel Walker & Co. (if as many shall be demanded) unless the said Principal Officers or their successors shall think proper, on the delivery of a smaller quantity to prove the same.

And it is further agreed between the said parties hereto, that the proofs of such iron ordnance shall commence within two calendar months from the time of such guns being delivered to the amount in number as aforesaid, and shall furnish within one calendar month next upwards.

And further, that if upon any proof or examination, such iron ordnance shall be found to deviate from the draughts or directions which shall be given for casting the same, either above or below the dimensions therein specified, in a greater degree than what is mentioned in the schedule marked with the letter A, hereto annexed, or in case the said iron ordnance shall not sustain the proof of firing two rounds with the charges of powder mentioned in the schedule marked with the letter B, hereto also annexed, with two junk wads, and a shot of the full weight and gauge of such iron ordnance, or in case any hole or cavity shall be discovered in the bores of such iron ordnance, of one fifth of an inch in depth behind the first reinforce, or of one fourth of an inch before it, or in case, upon the water proof, to be carried on by forcing engines, the water shall penetrate from the bore through any part of the surface of the said iron ordnance; or in case there shall be any scoops, bulges, flaws or honey-combed spots in the bores, or upon any part of the surface of such iron ordnance, which shall in the opinion of the said Principal Officers ... shall and may reject, and mark as unserviceable, such iron ordnance as shall not stand such examination and proofs, or have such defects as aforesaid.

And also, that in case the mouldings of any of the said iron ordnance shall be improperly placed, or ill formed, or otherwise defective, the said Principal Officers ... shall and may reject such iron ordnance as they think proper.

And in case any of the said defects shall appear to be of such a nature as to admit of being rectified, they, the said Samuel Walker & Co. shall and will at his own proper costs and charges, rectify such defects in such manner as shall be directed, or in default thereof, such ordnance shall be rejected, and further, that in case any of the said iron ordnance shall burst upon proof, or the metal contained in the said iron ordnance shall be suspected to be of a bad, insufficient or improper quality, the said Principal officer ... in order the better to ascertain the strength of such suspected metal, shall and may direct further proofs to be made of the remainder of the said iron ordnance which shall have been cast at the same furnace, by firing the same thirty rounds with the established charge for service; and of upon such further proof, any of the said iron ordnance shall burst, the said Principal officers ... shall and may knock off the trunnions of any three pieces of the said iron ordnance, or break them in any manner they think proper, in order to make assays of the metal of which the same is composed; and in case such metal shall, upon an assay made under the direction of the inspector general of artillery, be found not to be well refined, or shall in any other respect be of improper quality for guns, the said Principal Officers ... shall and may reject all such iron ordnance as shall have been delivered into the Warren by the said Samuel Walker & co, and mark them in such manner as shall be thought fit, to prevent their being again tendered for His Majesty' service.

And further that they, the said Samuel Walker & Co. shall not, nor will at any time or times hereafter, by himself, journeymen, agents or servants, or by any other person or persons whomsoever, insert any screws or pegs in any holes, cavities or other defects whatsoever, that shall or may happen to be in any of the said ordnance. [Followed by several paragraphs on prices, delivery dates, etc]

The schedule of guns referred to in the contract, marked A

| | Government guns Fraction of an inch | | Merchant guns Fraction of an inch |
	From 42 to 18 pdr	From 12 to 4 pdr	From 42 to 4 pdr
The Bore Its diameter	$\frac{1}{30}$	$\frac{1}{40}$	$\frac{1}{20}$
Its position out of the centre or axis	$\frac{1}{2}$	$\frac{1}{3}$	$\frac{1}{2}$
Its curvature or deviation from an exact cylinder	$\frac{1}{10}$	$\frac{1}{10}$	$\frac{1}{10}$
The Vent Its diameter	0	0	$\frac{1}{20}$
Position forwards	$\frac{3}{10}$	$\frac{3}{10}$	$\frac{5}{10}$
backwards	$\frac{1}{10}$	$\frac{1}{10}$	$\frac{1}{10}$
on either side	$\frac{2}{10}$	$\frac{2}{10}$	$\frac{3}{10}$
Trunnions Diameter	$\frac{2}{10}$	$\frac{1}{10}$	$\frac{2}{10}$
Length	$\frac{3}{10}$	$\frac{2}{10}$	$\frac{4}{10}$
Position – vertically	$\frac{2}{10}$	$\frac{2}{10}$	$\frac{3}{10}$
horizontally	$\frac{3}{10}$	$\frac{2}{10}$	$\frac{3}{10}$
out of the same line	$\frac{2}{10}$	$\frac{2}{10}$	$\frac{3}{10}$
bulged	$\frac{1}{10}$	–	$\frac{1}{10}$
The exterior diameter of the piece in any part	$\frac{2}{10}$	$\frac{2}{10}$	$\frac{3}{10}$
Length of the bore	$\frac{3}{10}$	$\frac{3}{10}$	$\frac{4}{10}$
Length of the piece	$\frac{3}{10}$	$\frac{3}{10}$	$\frac{4}{10}$
Diameter of the base ring and swell of the muzzle	$\frac{1}{10}$	$\frac{1}{10}$	$\frac{3}{10}$

Honeycombs in the bore, to reject the piece. External defects or irregularities to be tolerated if not such as to endanger the piece materially.

The schedule referred to in the contract marked B

| | Charge of powder | |
Gun pdr	Lbs	Oz
42	25	
32	21	8
24	18	
18	15	
12	12	
9	9	
6	6	
4	4	
3	3	
2	2	
$1\frac{1}{2}$	1	8
1	1	
$\frac{1}{2}$		8

A table of the dimensions of iron guns made under the direction of Col. Blomefield at Carron for the British government, from the year 1796. (Scottish Record Office, GD 58/11/2). See illustration on page 96.

	32	24	18	12	9	9	6	6	6	6
AX	114	108	108	90	102	84	96	72	90	102
XY	107.2	101.45	101.75	84.25	96.48	78.48	90.956	66.97	84.96	96.957
AB	32.6	30.86	30.86	25.715	29.14	24	27.428	20.57	25.714	29.142
AC	48.9	46.29	46.29	38.571	43.71	36	41.143	30.086	38.571	43.713
AD	55.31	52.11	51.582	43.194	41.92	40.2	44.81	34.52	42.239	47.381
AE	102.24	96.82	96.7	80.639	91.2	75.24	85.726	64.51	80.448	91.076
A dia	22.24	20.93	19.68	17.86	16.65	16.44	15.01	15.06	15.02	15
B dia	20.12	19.035	17.95	16.285	15.27	15.33	13.86	13.83	13.79	13.78
C dia	19.13	18.09	17.05	15.45	14.52	14.54	13.11	13.1	13.08	13.07
D dia	19.06	18.03	17	15.41	14.45	14.5	13.08	13.05	13.04	13.03
E dia	17.38	16.49	15.55	14.06	13.27	13.22	11.95	11.88	11.92	11.85
F dia	16.3	15.55	14.68	13.24	12.49	12.46	11.24	11.18	11.23	11.19
G dia	13.31	12.45	11.67	10.5	9.8	9.78	8.79	8.78	8.77	8.77
H dia	13.2	12.35	11.565	10.42	9.72	9.72	8.71	8.7	8.7	8.7
I dia	16.45	15.46	14.25	13.301	11.5	12.24	10.975	11.46	10.475	10.72
K dia	12.43	11.57	10.08	9.7	9.03	9	8.06	8.08	8.05	8.08
A1	2.87	2.73	2.64	2.47	2.32	2.37	2.14	2.175	2.175	2.14
A2	11.06	10.31	9.5	8.43	7.76	7.78	6.97	6.875	6.95	6.98
Bore	6.41	5.823	5.292	4.623	4.2	4.2	3.668	3.668	3.668	3.668
cd	6.41	5.823	5.292	4.623	4.2	4.2	3.668	3.668	3.668	3.668
ab	6.61	6	5.42	4.75	4.35	4.35	3.8	3.8	3.8	3.8
M dia	8.81	8.02	7.33	6.36	5.8	5.8	5.05	5.05	5.05	5.05
N dia	8.77	8.02	7.23	6.36	5.73	5.73	5.05	5.03	4.98	5.05
Wt (cwts)	56	48	43	30		24		17		
Mouldings, 2Y = CG = D4 = FH = MN = 4; LP = 3; 5, 8 = ½; 7, 8 = ⅜; 9, 10 = M										
AZ	4.1	3.85	3.87	3.22	3.66	3	3.4	2.57	3.21	3.64
XQ	2.32	2.25	2.25	1.87	2.17	1.76	2.05	1.5	1.91	2.18
3, 4	.38	.38	.31	.345	.23	.32	.35	.33	.27	.3

The construction of a carronade of seven diameters. (Scottish Record Office, GD 58/11/2). See illustration on page 108.

		Calibres	16ths
Of the reinforcement	AB, $\frac{5}{12}$	2	$14\frac{2}{3}$
Of the chase and muzzle	BC, $\frac{7}{12}$	4	$1\frac{1}{3}$
Of the cascable, to the hind part of the pommel, supposing it to be completed	An	2	$0\frac{3}{4}$
Of the cup muzzle	CD		7

The thickness is reckoned from lines drawn parallel to the centre line and half a calibre distant on each side, as ab, cd.

		Calibres	16ths
Set off at the bottom of the base ring	ae		13
Set off at the entrance of the muzzle	bf		$8\frac{1}{2}$
A line joining these points determines the reinforcement, and makes the thickness at the end		8	$10\frac{15}{16}$
From g, set in towards the centre			$0\frac{1}{2}$
At the entrance of the muzzle, set off from the parallel lines			$6\frac{1}{3}$

A line joining these points determines the chase and muzzle.

		Calibres	16ths
The diameter of the pommel is	ik		13
The diameter of the pommel fillet	bm	1	$0\frac{1}{4}$
The diameter of the screw piece		1	
The thickness of the screw piece is equal to the neck of the pommel	r		$11\frac{1}{4}$
The length of the pommel	ny	1	$0\frac{1}{4}$

The length of the screw piece is determined by setting off from the point n half a calibre to [blank] on the centre line, and describing from the centre of the arch.

	Calibres	16ths
The radius for forming the neck of the pommel is		$6\frac{1}{2}$
The length of the joint	1	4
The diameter of the joint		14
The diameter of the joint belt		$6\frac{3}{4}$
The depth of the rests on the fore part of the joint measured at the centre is		5
The breadth and projection of the rests is		3
Breadth of the quoin patch	1	
Height of the quoin patch behind		5
Radius for forming the cascable is equal to the diameter of the piece at the beginning of the first curve	2	9
Width of the breeching ring		8
Breadth of the breeching ring		6
Thickness of the breeching ring		3

Mouldings	Breadth shot parts	Rising calibre parts
The base ring	$4\frac{3}{4}$	$\frac{3}{4}$
The chase ring	4	$\frac{3}{4}$
The muzzle ring	4	0
The reinforce and chase ogees	3	$\frac{1}{2}$
The pommel bead	$\frac{3}{4}$	0
The muzzle tulip	1	1
The curve at the entrance of the muzzle	–	–
The fillet at the beginning of the cascable	$\frac{3}{4}$	
The fillet before the muzzle tulip	$\frac{3}{4}$	$\frac{1}{2}$
The fillet before the muzzle ring	$\frac{3}{4}$	$\frac{1}{2}$

	Calibres	16ths
The diameter of the muzzle more than the bore		3
The radius of the cup muzzle seat is half the bore, and		$\frac{3}{4}$
The radius of the hind part of the tulip		2
The radius of the muzzle curve		2
The radius of the cup muzzle curve		$\frac{1}{2}$
The diameter of the hole in the screw piece		$6\frac{1}{2}$

Appendix VI (see Part VI)

Mary frigate, ordnance landed at Woolwich, 1660–61. (PRO 30/37/8)

Demi-cannon, iron, 20

Cwt	Qrs	Lbs
45	0	2
44	3	10
43	3	4
45	1	4
45	3	0
45	0	11
40	0	19
45	0	24
43	2	5
43	2	25
39	0	13
36	2	23
45	0	10
38	3	22
45	1	6
36	3	5
44	1	16
43	1	12
40	2	18
38	3	9

Culverin, brass, 4

Cwt	Qrs	Lbs
		3973
		4080
43	3	10
47	1	15

12-pounders, brass

Cwt	Qrs	Lbs
30	0	0
36	0	9
35	3	26
		3180
		2390
		2380
		2420
		2580
		2390
		2380
		2600
		1621
		2320

6-pounders, brass

14	2	6
		1527
		1495
		1460

3-pounders

3	0	7
3	0	15

James, Duke of York, 22 February 1663–64. (PRO WO 47/5)

Whereas I have thought fit in order to the lessening of His Majesty's charge in the office of the ordnance to reduce the complement of guns of His Majesty's ships into a lesser number when they shall be employed upon ordinary services in the narrow seas during the present peace, these are therefore to will and require that you from henceforward when you shall receive any warrant from myself for the furnishing of any of His Majesty's ships with ordnance wherein it shall be mentioned that they are intended for service in the narrow seas, you do put on board the said ships no more ordnance than are appointed for them by a list herewith sent you, of the number of guns for every ship respectively. But where it shall not be mentioned in my warrant that the ships are for the narrow seas, you are to furnish them according to the former establishment, for which this shall be your warrant, given under my hand at Whitehall.

An establishment of a proportion of guns to be borne on board His Majesty's ships for ordinary service in the narrow seas.

First Rate

Sovereign	80
Prince	70
Charles	64
Royal James	60

Second Rate

St Andrew	50
Henry	54
St George	50
James	50
London	54
Rainbow	46
Swiftsure	50
Triumph	50
Victory	46
Vanguard	44
Unicorn	44

Third Rate

Anne	40
Essex	38
Fairfax	40
Gloucester	40
Henrietta	40
Montague	40
Lion	38
Monck	38
York	40
Revenge	40
Plymouth	40
Mary	40
Dreadnought	40
Dunkirk	38

Fourth Rate

Assurance	26
Assistance	30
Adventure	26
Advice	30
Amity	26
Bristol	32
Bear	24
Centurion	30
Convertine	26
Charity	24
Diamond	30
Dover	30
Dragon	26
Elizabeth	26
Expedition	22
Elias	24
Foresight	30
Swallow	30
Guinea	26
Hampshire	30
Jersey	30
Kent	30
Leopard	32
Mary Rose	30

Fourth Rate (cont.)	
Matthias	28
Marmaduke	26
Newcastle	30
Nonsuch	26
Breda	30
Portsmouth	26
Portland	26
Antelope	30
Bonaventure	30
Phoenix	30
Providence	22
Ruby	30
Reserve	30
Sapphire	26
Crown	30
Tiger	26
Happy Return	30
Constant Warwick	26
Welcome	26
Yarmouth	32
Princess	32

Fifth Rate	
Augustine	[32]*
Guernsey	20
Briar	16
Success	22
Colchester	20
Speedwell	18
Coventry	18
Dartmouth	20
Milford	20
Forester	20
Fame	16
Garland	18
Greyhound	16
Great Gift	20
Hound	16
Hector	16

Fifth Rate (cont.)	
Lizard	14
Happy Entrance	16
Mermaid	20
Nightingale	20
Norwich	20
Oxford	18
Pearl	18
Pembroke	20
Paul	16
Roebuck	16
Eagle	20
Sophia	16
Sorlings	20
Richmond	18
Westergate	16
Dolphin	14

Sixth Rate	
Blackmoor	8
Bramble	8
Chestnut	8
Cygnet	6
Drake	10
Eaglet	4
Fox	8
Griffin	8
Hind	4
Lily	6
Martin	10
Marlin	10
Little Mary	8
Nonsuch Ketch	[8]*
Paradox	10
Rose	[6]*
Truelove	6
Little Gift	12
Hawk	4
Francis	8
Harp	8

* These vessels were no longer in service when the list was compiled.

To the principal officers and commissioners of His Majesty's Navy, 18th May 1664. (PRO 47/5)

Gentlemen,

Having perused the list of the guns by your letter, proportions to be borne on His Majesty's ships in time of war, as well as complying with the present state of His Majesty's stores as for other reasons, been induced to propound some alterations which will appear by the list herewith sent you, leaving the same to your further consideration, and to his highnesses determination.

As to the 1st rates, there is no other alteration but that instead of the whole number of cannon of 7 propounded we set down demi cannon for the chace, which we have done by reason there none in store of cannon of 7 for chace pieces, and to avoid the overcharging the ships with the extraordinary weight of these natures for the chace.

In the 2nd and 3rd rates we likewise make abatement of demi cannon and supply the chace with culverins, for demi cannon chace pieces will be altogether as heavy as ordinary cannon of 7.

In the 4th rate we take off some demi culverin cutts, in regard there are very few guns of that nature to be had, and put in their rooms sakers, of which there is plentiful numbers in store.

In the 5th rate, whereas the sakers are most of them proposed to be cutts, we make some of them to be entire sakers, in regard the stores are not provided with like quantities of cutts, and this we conceive to be of more use and service than to have them all cutts. As for the Flemish ships and prizes, we have proportioned to them 12 pounds and 8 pounds and 6 pounds instead of culverins and sakers, as being guns most proper to them, and such as they have hitherto carried.

We have likewise at the end of our list computed the want to make good the demand, as also the overplus of guns remaining, and the like in a distinct paper, according to your own proposals, together with the state of the stores in brass and iron guns, by which you may the better judge of our computation, this being all at present, we take leave as;

your humble servants,

Names of the the ships	Numbers	Cannon	Demi-cannon	Culverin	Demi-culverin	Saker	Demi-culverin cutts	Saker cutts	12-pounders
First Rate									
Sovereign	90	20	8	28	26		8		
Prince	86	20	8	28	24		6		
Charles	78	20	6	28	22		4		
Royal James	78	12	14	28	22		4		
Second Rate									
St Andrew	60		18	16	20		6		
Henry	70		22	30	16		2		
St George	64		18	16	12	14		4	
James	68		22	16	12	14	4		
London	76	12	14	26		20	4		
Rainbow	56		18	4	22	10		2	
Swiftsure	60		22	30	4		4		
Triumph	66		18	16	20	8		4	
Victory	54		18	14	10	8		4	
Vanguard	56		20	4	24	4		4	
Unicorn	56		2	16	12	4		4	
(Woolwich)	76	12	14	26	20		4		
(Portsmouth)	76	12	14	26	20		4		
Third Rate									
Anne	58		22	4	26		6		
Essex	52		12	12	22		6		
Fairfax	58		22	4	24	4	4		
Gloucester	58		22	4	24		8		
Henrietta	58		22	4	24		8		
Montague	58		22	4	24		8		
Lion	52		20	4	22		6		
Monck	54		20	4	24		6		
York	58		22	4	24		8		
Revenge	58		22	4	24		8		
Plymouth	56		22	4	24		6		
Mary	58		22	4				2	30
Dreadnought	58		22	4	24		8		
Resolution	58		22	4	24		8		
Dunkirk	54		12	12	24		6		

Names of the the ships	Numbers	Cannon	Demi-cannon	Culverin	Demi-culverin	Saker	Demi-culverin cutts	Saker cutts	12-pounders
Fourth Rate									
Assurance	36			10	12	12		2	
Assistance	44			22	16	4		2	
Adventure	36			10	16	8		2	
Advice	46			22˙	16	4		4	
Amity	36			12	14	6		4	
Bristol	48			24	16		6	2	
Centurion	46			22	14		6	4	
Diamond	46			22	14	6		4	
Dover	46			22	20			4	
Dragon	38			12	20	4		2	
Elizabeth	38			12	20	4		2	
Expedition	30			6	14	6		4	
Foresight	46			22	20			4	
Swallow	46			22	20			4	
Guinea	36			12	14	8		2	
Hampshire	40			12	16	10		2	
Jersey	48			22	20	4		2	
Kent	46			22	20			4	
Leopard	54		12	12	22	6		2	
Mary Rose	48			22	20	4		2	
Marmaduke	38			12	20	4		2	
Newcastle	48		10	12	20	4		2	
Nonsuch	38			14	16	6		2	
Breda	46			22	20			4	
Portsmouth	38			22	14			2	
Portland	46			22	20			4	
Antelope	46			22	20			4	
Bonaventure	40			12	18	8		2	
Phoenix	40			20	10	8		2	
Providence	30			6	12	8		4	
Ruby	46			22	20			4	
Reserve	46			22	20			4	
Sapphire	38			12	16	8		2	
Crown	46			22	20			4	

Names of the the ships	Numbers	Cannon	Demi-cannon	Culverin	Demi-culverin	Saker	Demi-culverin cutts	Saker cutts	12-pounders
Tiger	38			12	16	8		2	
Happy Entrance	46			22	20			4	
Constant Warwick	34			12	12	6		4	
Yarmouth	52		10	14	20	6		2	
Princess	52		10	14	20	6		2	
Fifth Rate									
Guernsey	28				20	4		4	
Success	30			10	10	6		4	
Briar	20				12	6		2	
Colchester	28				20	4		4	
Speedwell	26				16	6		4	
Coventry	22				16	2		4	
Dartmouth	28				18	6		4	
Milford	28				18	6		4	
Forester	28				18	6		4	
Garland	28				18	6		4	
Mermaid	28				20	4		4	
Nightingale	28				20	4		4	
Norwich	24				18	2		4	
Oxford	24				18	2		4	
Pearl	24				18	2		4	
Pembroke	28				20	4		4	
Eagle	26				18	4		4	
Richmond	22				16	2		4	
Dolphin	20				16			4	

Flemish [sic] ships and prizes

	Numbers	24-pounders	12-pounders	8-pounders	6-pounders	Minions or cutts or 3-pounders
Bear	42		12	10	16	4
Convertine	48		24	6	14	4
Charles	46		22	6	14	4
Elias	40		20	6	12	2
Matthias	50	8	16	16	6	4
Welcome	38		20	14		4
Great Gift	30		16	10		4
Fame	24			10	10	4
Greyhound	22			10	8	4
Hound	24			10	10	4
Hector	22			8	8	6
Lizard	20				16	4
Happy Entrance	22				16	6
Paul	28			20	6	2
Rosebush	30		12	8	8	2
Sophia	34		10	10	10	4
Sorlings	32		10	12	8	2
Westergate	30		10	10	8	2

	Ordnance demanded by this list	In store or on board	Wanting to be supplied	Overplus of guns
Cannon of 7	108	43	65	–
Demi-cannon	622	392	230	–
Culverins	1092	1268	–	176
Demi-culverins	1648	1975	–	327
Sakers	302	944	–	642
Demi-culverin cutts	158	87	71	–
Saker cutts	212	71	141	–
Minions	–	341	–	341
Minion cutts	66	32	34	–
24-pounders	8	16	–	8
12-pounders	202	462	–	260
8-pounders	166	254	–	88
6-pounders	170	440	–	270

The final establishment for the ships of the 1691 programme. (PRO WO 55/1763)

Type	No	Length	Weight	Position
Third Rates of 80 guns				
Demi-cannon	24	10ft	53cwt	Lower deck
Culverin	2	11ft	53cwt	Lower deck
Culverin	26	9ft	39cwt	Upper deck
Culverin	2	10ft	42cwt	Upper deck
6-pounder	2	9½ft	24cwt	Forecastle
6-pounder	4	7½ft	18cwt	Forecastle
6-pounder	10	7½ft	18cwt	Half deck and coach
6-pounder	6	6½ft	14cwt	Half deck and coach
3-pounder	4	6ft	7cwt	Poop
Fourth Rates of 60 guns				
24-pounder	22	10ft	46cwt	Lower deck
Demi-culverin	20	8½ft	26cwt	Upper deck
Demi-culverin	2	10ft	30cwt	Upper deck
Saker	2	9½ft	22cwt	Forecastle
Saker	2	7ft	16cwt	Forecastle
Saker	6	7½ft	16cwt	Quarterdeck and coach
Saker	6	6½ft	12cwt	Quarterdeck and coach
3-pounder	2	5½ft	6cwt	Poop

The first carronade establishment, July 1779. (PRO Adm 766/106)

Rate	Guns	Quarterdeck		Forecastle		Roundhouse		Total to each ship
		Number	Pounders	Number	Pounders	Number	Pounders	
1	100			2	12	8	12	10
2	90			4	12	6	12	10
3	74			2	12	6	12	8
3	64			2	12	6	12	8
4	50	2	24	2	12	6	12	10
5	44	8	18	2	18			10
5	38	6	18	4	18			10
5	36	4	18	4	18			8
5	32	6	18	2	18			8
6	28	4	18	2	18			6
6	24	6	12	4	12			10
6	20	6	12	2	12			8
6	Sloop	6	12	2	12			8

Navy Office, 22nd July 1782. A list of all the ships and vessels which have been supplied with carronades, prepared pursuant to an order from the Rt Hon Lords Commissioners of the Admiralty, signified by Mr Stephens letter of the 16 inst. (NMM MID/9/2)

	Quarterdeck		Forecastle		Roundhouse		Upper deck	
	No	Lbs	No	Lbs	No	Lbs	No	Lbs
100								
Victory	2	32	2	32	6	18		
98								
Duke	2	32						
Prince George	4	18			4	12	2	32
80								
Gibraltar	2	68			8	12		
74								
Ajax			2	12	6	12		
Alcide			2	12	6	12		
Alfred			2	12	6	12		
Arrogant					6	12		
Bellona					6	12		
Berwick					6	12		
Cumberland					6	18		
Dublin			2	12	6	12		
Edgar			2	12	6	12		
Fame					6	12		
Fortitude					6	12		
Ganges					4	18		
Goliath			2	12	6	18		
Magnificent			2	12	6	18		
Monarch					4	12		
Royal Oak					6	12		
Ramillies			2	12	6	12		
Vengeance					6	12		
Warrior			2	18	8	12		
Suffolk					6	18		
70								
Princessa					2	18		
68								
Monarca					4	12		
St Albans					6	12		
Anson			2	18	6	18		
Bienfaisant			2	12	6	12		
Crown					4	18		
Inflexible					6	12		
Magnanime					6	12		
Nonsuch			2	12	6	12		
Raisonable			2	18	6	18		
Vigilant					6	12		
Yarmouth			2	18	6	18		
50								
Adamant	2	18	2	18	8	12		
Assistance	2	12	2	24	6	12	2	32
Bristol	2	24	2	12	6	18		
Chatham			2	12	6	12		
Isis					6	12		
Leander	2	24			6	12		
Portland			2	18				
Renown	4	18			6	12	2	32
Warwick	2	24	2	12	4	12		

	Quarterdeck		Forecastle		Roundhouse		Upper deck	
	No	Lbs	No	Lbs	No	Lbs	No	Lbs
44								
Acteon			2	18				
Argo	4	18	2	18				
Assurance	6	18	2	18				
Diomede	6	18	2	18				
Endymion	6	18						
Mediator	6	18						
Ulysses	8	18	2	18				
					Lower Deck			
Rainbow	4	32			20	68	20	42
40								
Artois	6	18	2	18				
38								
Arethusa	4	18	2	18				
Latona	4	18						
Minerva	4	18						
La Prudente	4	18						
36								
Flora	4	18						
Leocadia	6	24	2	24				
Sta Maria	6	18	2	24				
Sta Margarita	4	18	4	18				
Monsieur	4	18	4	18				
Perseverance	2	18						
Active	4	18	2	18				
Alarm	4	18						
Amazon	6	18	2	18				
Amphion	4	18	2	18				
Ambuscade	4	18	2	18				
Apollo	4	18	2	18				
Andromanche	4	18	2	18				
Alcmene	6	18	2	32				
Boston	4	18	2	18				
Brune	4	18	2	18				
Cerberus	6	18	2	18				
Danae	4	18	2	18				
Daedalus	6	18	2	18				
Diamond	4	18	2	18				
Diana			2	18				
Eolus	4	18	2	18				
Fox	6	18	2	18				
Jason	4	18	2	18				
Juno	2	18						
Oiseau	4	18	2	18				
Orpheus	4	18						
Pearl	6	18						
Stag	6	18						
Winchelsea	6	18	2	42				
28								
Albemarle	6	18	2	18				
Aurora	4	18	2	18				
Carysfoot	4	18	2	18				
Enterprise	4	18	2	18				
Grana	4	18						
Lizard	2	18	2	18				
Maidstone	4	18	2	18				
Mercury	4	18						
Milford			2	18				
Prosperine	4	18						
Vestal	4	18						

	Quarterdeck		Forecastle		Roundhouse		Upper deck	
	No	Lbs	No	Lbs	No	Lbs	No	Lbs
26								
Camel	4	12						
24								
Amphitrite	4	12	2	12				
Champion	6	12	2	12				
Eurydice	6	12						
Garland	4	12						
Hyena	8	12	2	12				
Pandora	2	12						
20								
Ariadne	6	12	2	12				
Daphne	6	12	2	12				
Perseus	6	12	2	12				
Squirrel	6	12	2	12				
Sphinx	6	12						
Unicorn	4	12	2	12				
Myrmidon	4	12	2	24				
Sloop, 20								
Merlin	6	12						
Sloop, 16								
Fairy			4	12				
Fly	6	12	2	12				
Fury	6	12	2	12				
Lark							2	12
Pelican							2	12
Shark	4	12						
Zebra	4	12						
Sloop, 14								
Beaver	4	12	2	12				
Bustler							4	12
Cygnet	4	12						
Drake							2	12
Duguay Trouin							4	18
Martin	4	12	2	12				
Lively							2	18
Ostrich	4	12						
Racehorse							6	12
Scout	4	18						
Swan							18	18
Sloop, 12								
Alderney	4	12						
Kite							2	12
Flying Fish							2	12
Armed transport								
Raikes							10	18
Pondicherry							10	18
Manilla			2	18			8	18
							Lower Deck	
Bountiful							22	42
Armed storeship								
San Carlos	6	18	2	18				
Harriet							2	18
Minerva	6	18	2	18				
Tortoise							16	24
Fireship								
Alecto							2	18
Tisiphone							8	18
Pluto							12	18

	Quarterdeck		Forecastle		Roundhouse		Upper deck	
	No	Lbs	No	Lbs	No	Lbs	No	Lbs
Cutter								
Busy	2	12						
Brazen							12	12
Expedition							2	12
Hope							2	12
Liberty	2	18						
Pilote							2	12
Sprightly	4	12						
Surprize							2	12
True Briton							2	12
Jackal							2	12
Nimble							12	18
Hospital ship								
Lynx							2	18

Ships ordered to be supplied with carronades, of which no account has been received of their being fitted:

74 *Egmont*, to 28 carronades, 68-pdrs, for lower deck.
64 *Vigilant*, to have 2 68-pdr carronades.
36 *Belle Poule* to have 4 18-pdr carronades.
32 *Proselyte* to have 32 18-pdr carronades.
28 *Cyclops* to have 6 12-pdr carronades.
50 *Romney* to have 4 68-pdr carronades.
Sloop *Pygmy* to have 8 12-pdr carronades.
    Helena to have 4 18-pdr carronades.

Account of iron ordnance on board of his Majesty's ship Defence,
Chatham, 28th June 1803. (PRO Adm 160/154)

Cut No	Founder's marks on trunnions		Weight			Cypher	Remarks
	Letter	No	Cwt	Qrs	Lbs		
32-pounders, old pattern, 9ft 6in							
1	GS	36	54	1	9	G3	From Woolwich
2	MR		54	2	6		
3	WCo	29	54	1	14		
4	Z	97 solid	56	2	23		
5	B	bored solid	56	0	23		
6	B	bored solid	55	3	0		
7	B	bored solid	56	1	9		
8	W	bored solid	57	0	2		
9	W	240, bored solid	56	3	16		
10	Z	100 solid	56	3	16		
11	Z	Z44	56	2	23		
12	Z	39 solid	56	0	9		
13	B	GS solid	55	1	0		
14	B	GS solid	55	1	0		
15	WCo	24	54	1	20		
16	GS	25	54	0	9		
17	RF		55	0	24		
18	B	solid	55	2	0		
19	W	S	55	1	20		
20	WCo	35	55	2	14		
21	B	GS solid	55	2	14		
22	W	bored solid	57	0	9		
23	W	bored solid	56	3	23		
24	W	bored solid	56	3	16		
25	B	bored solid	56	1	2		
26	B	bored solid	56	0	16		
27	B	GS solid	55	1	0		
28	B	GS solid	55	1	0		

Cut No	Founder's marks on trunnions		Weight			Cypher	Remarks
	Letter	No	Cwt	Qrs	Lbs		
9-pounders, old pattern, 8ft 6in							
1	WCo	56	26	2	12		
2	WCo	74	26	2	26		
9-pounders, old pattern, 7ft 6in							
3	WCo	177	24	3	26		
4	WCo	58	24	1	26		
5	WCo	137	26	0	19		
6	Z	120	25	3	12		
7	WCo	62	24	3	26		
8	B	solid	26	0	26		
9	B	solid	26	0	26		
9-pounders, old pattern, 8ft 6in							
10	WCo	100	26	1	26		
11	WCo	55	26	2	26		
9-pounders, old pattern, 7ft 6in							
12	WCo	155	24	3	12		
13	WCo	100	24	2	12		
14	WCo	163	25	0	12		
15	Z	88	25	3	26		
16	WCo	57	24	2	12		
17	B	solid	26	1	12		
18	Z	112	26	3	26		
18-pounder carronade, launch							
	WGH	41	10	0	14		

Cut No	Founder's marks on trunnions		Weight			Cypher	Remarks
	Letter	No	Cwt	Qrs	Lbs		
18-pounders, old pattern, 9ft							
1	IC		41	1	4		
2	WCo	10	38	3	21		
3	WCo	8	39	2	10		
4	WCo	82	39	3	14		
5	WCo	81	39	3	0		
6	WCo	73	39	3	9		
7	Z	189 solid	42	2	21		
8	Z	197 solid	41	3	14		
9	Z	263 solid	41	2	0		
10	Z	304 solid	41	3	0		
11	Z	611 solid	41	2	14		
12	Z	560 solid	41	2	14		
13	Z	698 solid	41	2	0		
14	WCo	97	39	3	14		
15	Z	614 solid	41	1	7		
16	IC		39	0	0		
17	WCo	98	39	1	14		
18	WCo	89	39	2	14		
19	WCo	80	39	3	0		
20	WCo	137	39	3	0		
21	Z	76 solid	42	1	0		
22	Z	199 solid	42	0	14		
23	Z	274 solid	41	3	0		
24	Z	172 solid	42	0	14		
25	Z	491 solid	41	1	14		
26	Z	212 solid	41	2	14		
27	WCo	9	39	2	0		
28	WCo	129	39	0	14		

Account of iron ordnance on board of His Majesty's ship Victory,
Chatham, 8th March 1808. (PRO Adm 160/154)

32-pounders, 9ft 6in

Cut No	Letter	No	Cwt	Qrs	Lbs	Cypher	Remarks
1	WCo	79	55	2	14	NP	
2	WCo	76	55	1	14	NP	
3	WCo	84	55	1	21	NP	
4	WCo	80	55	2	7	NP	
5	WCo	74	55	2	0	NP	
6	WCo	87	55	2	0	NP	
7	WCo	73	55	2	7	NP	
8	WCo	72	55	2	21	NP	
9	WCo	126	55	3	7	NP	
10	WCo	89	55	3	0	NP	
11	WCo	89	55	2	0	NP	
12	WCo	85	55	3	0	NP	
13	WCo	77	55	3	0	NP	
14	WCo	130	55	2	21	NP	
15	WCo	127	55	2	21	NP	
16	WCo	81	55	1	14	NP	
17	WCo	90	55	2	0	NP	
18	WCo	122	55	1	21	NP	
19	WCo	78	55	2	7	NP	
20	WCo	82	55	3	0	NP	
21	WCo	123	55	2	7	NP	
22	WCo	83	55	2	7	NP	
23	WCo	69	55	2	14	NP	
24	WCo	125	55	3	7	NP	
25	WCo	131	55	3	0	NP	
26	WCo	70	55	3	0	NP	
27	WCo	75	55	3	0	NP	
28	WCo	68	55	3	14	NP	

18-pounders, 9ft

Cut No	Letter	No	Cwt	Qrs	Lbs	Cypher	Remarks
1	WCo	412	41	3	14	NP	
2	WCo	339	41	2	7	NP	
3	WCo	129	42	2	14	NP	
4	WCo	420	41	3	14	NP	
5	WCo	414	42	0	14	NP	
6	WCo	399	42	0	14	NP	
7	WCo	419	41	3	0	NP	
8	WCo	352	43	0	0	NP	
9	WCo	564	42	2	15	NP	
10	WCo	416	41	3	14	NP	
11	WCo	571	42	2	1	NP	
12	WCo	408	41	3	14	NP	
13	WCo	406	41	3	14	NP	
14	WCo	404	41	3	14	NP	
15	WCo	415	41	2	14	NP	
16	WCo	556	42	1	14	NP	
17	none	25	42	2	0	NP	
18	WCo	578	42	2	1	NP	
19	WCo	579	42	2	1	NP	
20	WCo	576	42	2	1	NP	
21	WCo	574	42	2	15	NP	
22	WCo	395	42	0	14	NP	
23	WCo	400	42	0	14	NP	
24	WCo	405	42	1	0	NP	
25	WCo	126	42	2	14	NP	
26	WCo	534	42	2	1	NP	
27	WCo	583	42	2	1	NP	
28	none	38	42	2	14	NP	1795
29	WCo	409	41	3	14	NP	
30	WCo	183	41	3	21	NP	

12-pounders, 9ft

Cut No	Letter	No	Cwt	Qrs	Lbs	Cypher	Remarks
1	B	solid	34	1	0	NP	
2	B	solid	34	1	0	NP	
3	WCo	111	34	3	15	NP	
4	WCo	114	34	3	14	NP	
5	WCo	108	34	3	1	NP	
6	WCo	107	34	3	7	NP	
7	WCo	106	34	2	15	NP	
8	WCo	105	34	2	22	NP	
9	WCo	22	34	3	16	NP	
10	B	solid	34	1	15	NP	
11	WCo	121	34	0	21	NP	
12	WCo	56	34	2	14	NP	
13	B	solid	34	1	15	NP	
14	WCo	57	34	3	14	NP	
15	B	solid	34	0	15	NP	
16	B	solid	34	0	1	NP	
17	B	solid	34	0	1	NP	
18	WCo	118	34	2	25	NP	
19	WCo	76	34	1	21	NP	
20	WCo	119	34	3	7	NP	
21	WCo	115	34	3	0	NP	
22	WCo	80	34	3	1	NP	
23	WCo	23	34	3	16	NP	
24	B	solid	34	1	15	NP	
25	S	4	34	3	0	NP	
26	WCo	19	34	3	2	NP	
27	S	6	34	2	14	NP	
28	S	7	34	3	14	NP	
29	S	8	34	3	14	NP	
30	WCo	9	35	0	14	NP	

12-pounders, 8½ft

Cut No	Letter	No	Cwt	Qrs	Lbs	Cypher	Remarks
31	WCo	165	32	3	10	NP	
32	WCo	486	28	3	15	NP	

12-pounders, 7ft 6in

Cut No	Letter	No	Cwt	Qrs	Lbs	Cypher	Remarks
33	WCo	431	28	3	15	NP	
34	none	34	32	3	23	NP	1798
35	WCo	491	28	3	15	NP	
36	WCo	444	28	3	15	NP	

32-pounder carronades

Cut No	Letter	No	Cwt	Qrs	Lbs	Cypher	Remarks
1	HCo	233	17	3	11		
2	HCo	228	17	3	21		
3	W&G	1099	17	3	24		
4	G	320	17	3	14		
5	Clyde	1205	17	3	7		1805
6	Clyde	1207	17	3	7		1805
7	G	321	17	3	7		
8	G	323	17	3	14		
9	G	292	17	3	4		
10	G	311	17	3	21		

18-pounder, launch

Cut No	Letter	No	Cwt	Qrs	Lbs	Cypher	Remarks
none	FK	55	9	3	21		

Appendix VII (see Part VII)

Gunners' stores for selected ships, 22nd January 1654–55. (PRO WO 47/3)

	Sovereign 1st Rate	James 2nd Rate	Fairfax 3rd Rate	Bristol 4th Rate	Nightingale 5th Rate	Truelove 6th Rate
Brass and iron ordnance						
Cannon of 7	19dr					
Demi-cannon	9	6	22dr			
Culverins	28	30	4	24		
Demi-culverins	30	24	26	6	18	
Sakers	5dr	4	8	8	4	8
Minions						2
Falcons						2
12-pdr bullet	4	2				
3-pdr bullet				2		
	95	66	60	40	22	12
Round shot for						
Cannon of 7	540					
Demi-cannon	240	200	800			
Culverins	900	900	160	720		
Demi-culverins	900	800	1040	180	540	
Sakers	150	150	320	240	120	240
Minions						60
Falcons						60
12-pdr bullet	120	60				
3-pdr bullet				60		
Double-headed hammered shot						
Culverin	360	360	250	290		
Demi-culverin	360	280	320	72	200	
Saker		100	100	100	60	40
Tin cases						
Demi-culverin	180	150	150	40	100	
Saker	30	50	60	56	60	40
Ladles and sponges for						
Cannon of 7	6					
Demi-cannon	4	2	6			
Culverins	8	10	2	10		
Demi-culverins	8	8	8	2	5	
Sakers	2	2	3	3	2	4

	Sovereign 1st Rate	*James* 2nd Rate	*Fairfax* 3rd Rate	*Bristol* 4th Rate	*Nightingale* 5th Rate	*Truelove* 6th Rate
Minions						1
Falcons						1
12-pdr bullet		1				
3-pdr bullet				1		
Ladle staves	24	14	14	10	6	6

Cases of wood for cartouches

	Sovereign 1st Rate	*James* 2nd Rate	*Fairfax* 3rd Rate	*Bristol* 4th Rate	*Nightingale* 5th Rate	*Truelove* 6th Rate
Cannon of 7	25					
Demi-cannon	12	12	44			
Culverins	45	64	8	36		
Demi-culverins	45	48	52	12	36	
Sakers	8	8	16	16	8	16
Minions						4
Falcons						4
12-pdr bullet	6					
3-pdr bullet				4		
Funnels of plate	7	3	4	2	2	1
Corn powder (barrels)	330	203	180	100	40	14
Match (cwt)	16	12	12	10	6	3
Matchlock muskets	200	80	80	40	20	20
Snaphance muskets	100	40	40	20	20	10
Bandoliers	300	120	120	60	40	30
Blunderbusses	20	12	10	7	4	3
Pistols (pairs)	30	20	20	10	8	4
Long pikes	150	40	40	30	20	10
Half pikes	50	40	20	30	20	10
Bills	30	20	20	10	4	4
Hatchets	100	40	40	40	20	12
Swords	300	120	120	60	40	30
Musket shot (cwt)	20	15	15	10	6	4
Shot lead (cwt)	5	4	4	3	1	1
Crows of iron	130	90	90	50	22	12
Tackle hooks (pairs)	220	150	140	90	50	30
Ladle hooks (pairs)	80	40	50	30	20	10
Linch pins (pairs)	100	50	60	30	20	10

	Sovereign 1st Rate	James 2nd Rate	Fairfax 3rd Rate	Bristol 4th Rate	Nightingale 5th Rate	Truelove 6th Rate
Spikes	300	300	250	130	100	40
Forelocks (pair)	150	100	100	40	30	20
Sledges	2	2	2	1	1	1
Great melt ladles	2	2	2	1	1	1
Small ladles	4	4	4	2	2	1
Nails of sorts	10,000	10,000	10,000	4000	4000	600
Beds	110	76	80	40	28	14
Quoins	220	150	160	80	50	28
Trucks (pairs)	12	12	12	10	6	3
Axletrees	20	12	12	10	6	3
Tampions	800	700	700	500	300	200
Pulleys (pairs)	220	190	190	120	50	30
Heads and rammers (pairs)	110	76	76	50	30	16
Formers	14	12	10	10	6	4
Budge barrels	10	3	3	2	2	1
Tanned hides	15	10	10	8	4	2
Sheepskins (dozens)	6	6	6	4	2	1
Baskets (dozens)	2	2	2	1½	1	½
Canvas (ells)	500	400	300	150	80	30
Paper royal (reams)	5	4	5	50*	30*	20*
Oil (gallons)	6	6	6	3	2	1
Tallow (cwt)	3	2	1	1	1	1
Starch (lbs)	12	8	8	6	4	2
Needles (dozen)	10	8	6	6	4	2
Thread (yds)	12	8	8	6	4	2
Lanterns, ordinary	10	6	6	5	3	2
Dark lanterns	2	2	2	1	1	1
Muscovia [glass?]	7	4	4	3	2	1
Wad hooks	8	10	10	7	4	3
Hand crow levers	100	60	60	40	22	12
Powder horns	100	66	60	40	22	12
Priming irons	100	66	60	40	22	12
Linstocks	96	66	60	40	22	12
Wire (yds)	10	10	8	6	4	3

*Quires

	Sovereign 1st Rate	*James* 2nd Rate	*Fairfax* 3rd Rate	*Bristol* 4th Rate	*Nightingale* 5th Rate	*Truelove* 6th Rate
Hand crows	2	1	1	1		
Breechings (cwt)	7	6	6	5	2	1
Tackles	14	12	12	10	4	3
Port ropes Port tackles	4	4	4	2	2	2
Junk (cwt)	50	40	30	20	10	3
Marline (yds)	60	60	50	50	36	10
Twine	15	12	12	12	6	4
Total value	£2873/8/1	£1860/7/11	£1786/17/1	£1076/12/5	£440/18/7½	£176/3/5

Dimensions of ships carriages, axletrees and trucks for the different lengths of guns, according to the new regulation, 1721. (RAI ms)

	Ft Pdr	10.0 42	10.0 32	10.0 24	9.6 18	9.6 12	9.6 9	9.0 6	7.6 5¼	7.6 4
Bottoms										
Total length			6.4	6.3	5.11	5.8¼	5.6½	5.3		
Fore axletrees centre from the fore part			0.10	0.9	0.9	0.8	0.7	0.7		
Hind axletrees centre from the hind part			1.2⅛	1.2⅛	1.1⅜	1.0¾	1.0½	1.0		
Total breadth before			2.8½	2.5½	2.3	2.0½	1.10½	1.8		
Total breadth behind			3.1¾	2.11	2.8	2.5¾	2.3½	2.0¼		
Circle's semi-diameter			5.0	4.0	3.6	3.3	3.0	2.9		
Keyhole's length			0.5	0.5	0.5	0.4	0.4	0.4		
Bottom's thickness			0.6	0.5½	0.5	0.4¾	0.4	0.3½		
Length for a 9ft 6in gun										
Do for a 9ft gun										
Do for an 8ft 6in gun										
Do for an 8ft gun										
Do for a 6ft gun										
Brackets										
Total length			5.6½	5.5½	5.2	4.11¾	4.10¼	4.7		
Breadth, gun deck			1.9¾	1.8¾	1.8⅛	1.5⅜	1.4½			
Breadth, upper deck			1.8¾	1.7⅜	1.7⅛	1.4⅛	1.3¼	1.1⅝		
Thickness			0.6	0.5½	0.5	0.4⅜	0.4	0.3½		
Step's length			0.7⅛	0.7	0.6½	0.6½	0.6¼	0.6		
Do depth			0.4⅛	0.4	0.3¾	0.3¼	0.3⅛	0.2¾		
Trunnions centre from the fore part			0.11	0.10½	0.10½	0.9	0.8	0.8		

	Ft	10.0	10.0	10.0	9.6	9.6	9.6	9.0	7.6	7.6
	Pdr	42	32	24	18	12	9	6	5¼	4
Trunnions sinking of the centre			0.1⅛	0.1⅛	0.1	0.1	0.1	0.1		
Trunnions semi-diameter			0.3¼	0.2⅞	0.2⅝	0.2⅜	0.2⅛	0.1⅞		
Length for a 9ft 6in gun										
Length for a 9ft gun										
Length for a 8ft 6in gun										
Length for a 8ft gun										
Length for a 6ft gun										
Transom										
Total length			1.10	1.8	1.6½	1.5	1.3¼	1.1¾		
Do in the clear at the transom's centre										
Total breadth			1.0	0.11	0.11	0.9½	0.9	0.8		
Facing each way			0.1½	0.1½	0.1½	0.1½	0.1½	0.1½		
Transom's clear from the bottom			0.1	0.1	0.1	0.1	0.1	0.1		
Axletrees										
Fore axletree's total length			4.3¾	4.3	3.11½	3.7¾	3.4¾	3.1¼		
Hind axletree's total length			5.1½	4.6½	4.3	3.11	3.8½	3.4¼		
Arm's length			0.11⅜	0.9¾	0.9¼	0.8⅝	0.8¼	0.7¾		
Arm's thickness			0.6⅜	0.6	0.5¾	0.5¼	0.5	0.4½		
Fore bed's length			2.11	2.7½	2.5	2.2½	2.0¼	1.9¾		
Hind bed's length			3.2	2.0	2.8½	2.5¾	2.4	2.0¾		
Bed's depth			0.7⅜	0.7½	0.7¼	0.6¾	0.6	0.5½		
Bed's thickness			0.6⅝	0.6¼	0.6	0.5½	0.5¼	0.4¾		
Trucks										
Fore truck's height from the gun deck			1.10	1.8	1.8	1.6	1.4			
Do for the upper deck, etc			1.8	1.6	1.6	1.4	1.2	1.2		
Hind truck's height from the gun deck			1.7	1.5	1.5	1.4	1.2			
Do for the upper deck, etc			1.5	1.3	1.3	1.2	1.0	1.0		
Truck's thickness			0.6	0.5½	0.5	0.4¾	0.4	0.3½		

Memoranda

The brackets to be set half an inch within the bottom, as in the plan.
The distance between the bottom now to be a third of the bottom's length.
The bracket spike to be in the inside between the hind part of the transom and the break of the first step.
The fore part of the transom to fall in the centre of the trunnion.
The hind spike to be in the middle between the centre of the hind axletree and centre of the bracket centre spike.
The fore spike to be in the middle between the centre of the fore axletree and breast of the carriage
NB The keyhole's breadth is 3 inches from the 42 to the 18 pounder, and from the 12 pounder downwards is 2½, and expressed in the draught by the letters NO

Dimensions of beds and quoins for ship carriages

	42 pdr and co	18 pdr and co	6[?] pdr and co
Beds			
Total length	3.4	3.0	2.0
Do behind the sole	0.2	0.1$\frac{1}{2}$	0.1
Breadth before	1.1	1.0	0.10$\frac{1}{2}$
Do behind	1.2	1.1	0.11$\frac{1}{2}$
Thickness of the sole	0.2$\frac{1}{2}$	0.2	0.1$\frac{1}{2}$
Thickness before	0.2	0.1$\frac{1}{2}$	0.1$\frac{1}{4}$
Sole for do			
Length	1.2	1.1	0.11$\frac{1}{2}$
Depth	0.7	0.6$\frac{1}{2}$	0.6
Thickness	0.4$\frac{3}{4}$	0.4	0.3
Coins			
Total length	1.6	1.3	1.0
Do breadth	0.10	0.9	0.7
Greatest thickness	0.5	0.3$\frac{1}{2}$	0.3
Do lesser	0.1$\frac{1}{2}$	0.1$\frac{1}{4}$	0.1
Holes distance from the end			
Do breadth			
Do depth at the square part			

Dimensions of iron work for bodies of ship carriages

	42 pdr Ft.In	32 pdr Ft.In	24 pdr Ft.In	18 pdr Ft.In	12 pdr Ft.In	9, 8 pdr Ft.In	6, 5$\frac{1}{4}$ pdr Ft.In
A. Axletree bolts							
Total length		1.5	1.4	1.3$\frac{1}{4}$	1.1$\frac{7}{8}$	1.0$\frac{3}{4}$	1.0
Do thickness	0.1$\frac{3}{8}$	0.1$\frac{3}{8}$	0.1$\frac{3}{8}$	0.1$\frac{1}{4}$	0.1$\frac{1}{4}$	0.1$\frac{1}{8}$	0.1$\frac{1}{8}$
Heads, diameter	0.2	0.2	0.2	0.1$\frac{7}{8}$	0.1$\frac{7}{8}$	0.1$\frac{3}{4}$	0.1$\frac{3}{4}$
Squares, thickness							
Thickness at the crown							
Hind axletree bolts, total length		1.9$\frac{1}{8}$	1.8	1.7	1.5$\frac{1}{8}$	1.3$\frac{7}{8}$	1.2$\frac{1}{4}$
B. Joint bolts							
Total length		1.1	1.0$\frac{1}{2}$	1.0$\frac{1}{4}$	0.11$\frac{1}{4}$	0.10$\frac{5}{8}$	0.9$\frac{1}{4}$
Do thickness	0.1$\frac{1}{8}$	0.1$\frac{1}{8}$	0.1	0.1	0.0$\frac{15}{16}$	0.0$\frac{15}{16}$	0.0$\frac{7}{8}$
Joint's diameter	0.1$\frac{7}{8}$	0.1$\frac{7}{8}$	0.1$\frac{3}{4}$	0.1$\frac{3}{4}$	0.1$\frac{5}{8}$	0.1$\frac{5}{8}$	0.1$\frac{1}{2}$
C. Eye bolts							
Total length		1.2$\frac{3}{4}$	1.1$\frac{3}{4}$	1.1	1.0	0.11$\frac{1}{4}$	0.10$\frac{1}{4}$
Do thickness	0.1$\frac{1}{8}$	0.1$\frac{1}{8}$	0.1	0.1	0.0$\frac{15}{16}$	0.0$\frac{15}{16}$	0.0$\frac{7}{8}$

Dimensions of iron work for bodies of ship carriages (cont.)

	42 pdr Ft.In	32 pdr Ft.In	24 pdr Ft.In	18 pdr Ft.In	12 pdr Ft.In	9, 8 pdr Ft.In	6, 5¼ pdr Ft.In
Head's length		$0.2\frac{3}{4}$	$0.2\frac{5}{8}$	$0.2\frac{3}{8}$	$0.2\frac{1}{4}$	$0.2\frac{1}{8}$	0.2
Do greatest breadth		$0.2\frac{1}{2}$	$0.2\frac{3}{8}$	$0.2\frac{1}{4}$	$0.2\frac{1}{8}$	$0.2\frac{1}{8}$	0.2
Do lesser							
D. Riveting bolts							
Total length of the transom bolt		$2.11\frac{3}{4}$	$2.8\frac{3}{4}$	2.6	$2.3\frac{1}{2}$	$2.1\frac{1}{2}$	1.10
Do thickness	$0.1\frac{1}{2}$	$0.1\frac{1}{2}$	$0.1\frac{1}{2}$	$0.1\frac{1}{4}$	$0.1\frac{1}{4}$	$0.1\frac{1}{8}$	$0.1\frac{1}{8}$
Head's diameter	$0.2\frac{1}{2}$	$0.2\frac{1}{2}$	$0.2\frac{1}{2}$	$0.2\frac{3}{8}$	$0.2\frac{3}{8}$	$0.2\frac{1}{4}$	$0.2\frac{1}{4}$
Squares, thickness							
Thickness at the crown							
Bed bolt's length		3.1	$2.10\frac{1}{8}$	$2.7\frac{1}{4}$	2.5	$2.2\frac{3}{4}$	$1.11\frac{1}{2}$
E. Breeching rings with eyes							
Total length		$0.11\frac{3}{4}$	0.11	$0.10\frac{1}{2}$	$0.9\frac{3}{8}$	0.9	$0.9\frac{1}{4}$
Do thickness	$0.1\frac{1}{8}$	$0.1\frac{1}{8}$	0.1	0.1	$0.0\frac{15}{16}$	$0.0\frac{15}{16}$	$0.0\frac{7}{8}$
Head's diameter	$0.3\frac{1}{2}$	$0.3\frac{1}{2}$	$0.3\frac{1}{4}$	$0.3\frac{1}{4}$	0.3	0.3	$0.2\frac{3}{4}$
Ring hole's do	$0.1\frac{1}{2}$	$0.1\frac{1}{2}$	$0.1\frac{1}{4}$	$0.1\frac{1}{4}$	$0.1\frac{1}{8}$	$0.1\frac{1}{8}$	0.1
Ring's total diameter	$0.7\frac{1}{4}$	0.7	$0.6\frac{1}{2}$	0.6	$0.5\frac{1}{2}$	$0.5\frac{3}{16}$	$0.4\frac{1}{2}$
Ring's thickness	$0.1\frac{1}{8}$	$0.1\frac{1}{8}$	0.1	0.1	$0.0\frac{15}{16}$	$0.0\frac{15}{16}$	$0.0\frac{7}{8}$
F. Loops							
Total length							
Head's diameter	0.4	0.4	$0.3\frac{3}{4}$	$0.3\frac{3}{4}$	$0.3\frac{1}{2}$	$0.3\frac{1}{2}$	$0.3\frac{1}{4}$
Head and shank thickness	$0.1\frac{1}{8}$	$0.1\frac{1}{8}$	0.1	0.1	$0.0\frac{15}{16}$	$0.0\frac{15}{16}$	$0.0\frac{7}{8}$
G. Cap-squares							
Total length when turned		$1.7\frac{1}{2}$	$1.5\frac{1}{2}$	$1.4\frac{1}{2}$	1.3	1.2	1.1
Do breadth	$0.5\frac{1}{2}$	$0.4\frac{3}{4}$	$0.4\frac{3}{10}$	0.4	$0.3\frac{3}{8}$	$0.3\frac{1}{8}$	0.3
Do thickness	$0.0\frac{5}{8}$	$0.0\frac{5}{8}$	$0.0\frac{5}{8}$	$0.0\frac{1}{2}$	$0.0\frac{1}{2}$	$0.0\frac{3}{8}$	$0.0\frac{3}{8}$
Length before the trunnion		$0.8\frac{3}{4}$	0.7	$0.6\frac{3}{4}$	$0.6\frac{1}{4}$	$0.5\frac{1}{2}$	0.5
Do behind the trunnion		$0.6\frac{1}{2}$	0.6	$0.5\frac{1}{2}$	0.5	$0.4\frac{1}{2}$	$0.4\frac{1}{4}$
H. Square spikes							
Total length	1.2	1.2	1.0	1.0	0.10	0.10	0.8
Greatest thickness	$0.1\frac{1}{4}$	$0.1\frac{1}{4}$	0.1	0.1	$0.0\frac{3}{4}$	$0.0\frac{3}{4}$	$0.0\frac{5}{8}$
Head's breadth	$0.1\frac{1}{2}$	$0.1\frac{1}{2}$	$0.1\frac{1}{2}$	$0.1\frac{1}{2}$	$0.1\frac{1}{4}$	$0.1\frac{1}{4}$	$0.1\frac{1}{4}$

The ordnance stores carried by the Invincible, Monarch *and* Terrible, *74-gun ships captured from the French in 1747.* RUSI/6

A proportion of ordnance and ordnance stores for the following ships, which are not gunned agreeable to the establishment in 1746

	Invincible, Monarch, Terrible	
	Foreign service	Channel service (if different)
Adzes of copper	2	
Aprons of lead, large	92	
small	15	
Axle-trees, fore:		
32-pounder (ft. in)	2	
18-pounder	2	
9-pounder	1	
hind;		
32-pounder	2	
18-pounder	2	
9-pounder	1	
Armourers tools		
Vices, standing	2	
hand	2	
Wrenches	1	
Stakes	1	
Hammers, hand	2	
small	3	
Punches and cold chisels	12	8
Iron braces	1	
Square bits of sorts	3	2
Screw plates with seven taps	1	
Drills of sorts	12	8
Drill boxes	1	
Drill bows	1	
Drill string – knots	2	
Breast pieces	1	
Rubbers, poise, 3lbs	2	1
Files of sorts:		
Hand	3	2
Large bastard	1	
8d Bastard	2	
Large flat smooth	1	
12d smooth	1	
9d smooth	1	
6d smooth	1	
3d smooth	1	
6d rough	9	6
2d rough	12	8
Slitting	1	
File handles	24	18
Emery, coarse, lbs	4	3
fine	4	3

	Foreign service	Channel service (if different)
Burnishers	1	
Lock nails	300	150
Side nails	50	25
Breech nails	25	20
Spring hooks	1	
Forge tongs, small, pairs	1	
Wiping rods, musket	2	1
pistol	1	
Chests for the tools, with padlock and key	1	
Baskets	25	
Bayonets	300	
Beds, spare:		
32-pounders	4	
18-pounders	4	
9-pounders	2	
Quoins, spare:		
32-pounders	4	
18-pounders	4	
9-pounders	2	
Belts for:		
cartouche boxes	230	
swords	230	
Blocks, spare, pairs:		
10in single	7	
10in double	7	
8in single	7	
8in double	7	
6½in single	8	
Boxes for:		
grape shot	72	
hand grenades	10	
cartridges, musket	32	
pistol	8	
Breechings:		
7½in	56	
5½in	45	
4½in	24	
Budge barrels	4	
Cartridges of paper:		
32	2464	1904
18	3300	2400
9	1760	1280
½	864	744
Carriages, ship, with one bed and quoin		
to each:		
32-pounder	28	
18-pounder	30	
9-pounder	16	
Cartouche boxes	230	

	Foreign service	Channel service (if different)
Cases of wood for cartridges:		
32-pounder	70	
18-pounder	75	
9-pounder	40	
Quoins for quoining guns of the new pattern	64	
Crows of iron, $5\frac{1}{2}$ft	58	
$4\frac{1}{2}$ft	16	
Drivers of copper	2	
Drums complete	3	
Flints for muskets	5400	
for pistols	700	
Forelockeys	148	
Frogs for bayonets	230	
Funnels of plate	2	
Fuses, fixed, for hand grenades	20	
Halberds	2	
Hand crow levers, of; 6ft	87	
5ft	24	
Hand grenades, fixed	200	
Handscrews, large	2	
Heads, spare,		
32-pdr	14	
18-pdr	15	
9-pdr	8	
Rammers, spare,		
32-pdr	14	
18-pdr	14	
9-pdr	8	
Hides, tanned	13	11
Hoops, copper, for		
whole powder barrels	1608	1460
budge barrels	16	
hazel, pieces	4	
Junk: tons, cwt	7.0	5.0
Ladles, complete with staves,		
32-pdr	4	
18-pdr	4	
9-pdr	2	
$\frac{1}{2}$-pdr	2	
Sponges, complete with staves:		
32-pdr	8	
18-pdr	8	
9-pdr	4	
$\frac{1}{2}$-pdr	2	
Ladle hooks, pairs	20	
Lanterns, muscovy	3	
ordinary or tin	5	
dark	2	
Linchpins, pairs	7	

	Foreign service	Channel service (if different)
Match: Qrs, Cwt	9.0	7.0
Marline, skeins	42	
Measures, copper, for powder to fill cartridge:		
32-pdr	2	
18-pdr	2	
9-pdr	2	
$\frac{1}{2}$-pdr	2	
Melting ladles	1	
Muskets for marines	70	
for ships company, bright barrelled	184	
black barrelled	46	
Musket rods	150	
Muzzle lashings, 2in	28	
Nails,		
40d	150	
30d	150	
20d	250	
10d	500	
6d	1000	
Oil, sweet, gallons	21	
Ordnance,		
32-pdr	28	
18-pdr	30	
9-pdr	16	
$\frac{1}{2}$-pdr	12	
Paper, fine, reams	6	
Pen mauls	2	
Pikes, strong	100	
Pistols with ribs, pairs	70	
Pole axes	60	
Port ropes,		
3in	30	
$2\frac{1}{2}$in	12	
2in	6	
Port tackles	42	
Powder, in copper headed whole barrels	402	365
in half barrels	–	–
Powder horns	111	
Priming irons	333	
Rope sponges with hammer heads:		
32-pdr	28	
18-pdr	30	
9-pdr	16	
Runners for port tackles, $2\frac{1}{2}$in	28	
Scabbards for swords	230	
for bayonets	300	
Sheepskins to coat sponges, doz.	7	

	Foreign service	Channel service (if different)		Foreign service	Channel service (if different)
Shot, round:			Tompions for guns:		
32-pdr	2240	1680	32-pdr	112	
18-pdr	3000	2100	18-pdr	120	
9-pdr	720	600	12-pdr (sic)	64	
grape,			9-pdr	64	
32-pdr	140				
18-pdr	210		Tarred rope, spare		
9-pdr	112		7in: cables, fath	1.0	
$\frac{1}{2}$-pdr	144		5$\frac{1}{2}$in	0.65	
double headed,			3in	2.0	
32-pdr	84		2$\frac{1}{2}$in	1.65	
18-pdr	90		2in	1.0	
9-pdr	48				
for muskets, cwt	19.0		Thimble straps		
pistol, cwt, qrs	3.3		2in	33	
			1$\frac{1}{2}$in	54	
Slings for muskets	230				
			Thimbles, double, for the breeching:		
Spikes,			32-pdr	33	
10$\frac{1}{2}$in	64		18- and 12-pdr	35	
9in	64		9- and 6-pdr	19	
Sponge tacks	4000		Trucks, pairs, fore:		
			32-pdr	4	
			18-pdr	4	
Staves, spare, for ladles	14		9-pdr	2	
Swords	230		Trucks, pairs, hind:		
			32-pdr	2	
			18-pdr	2	
Tackles, complete, with blocks and hooks:			9-pdr	1	
3in	84				
2$\frac{1}{2}$in	90		Vices of copper	2	
2in	48				
Tackle hooks, large, pairs	36		Wadhooks with rammers and staves:		
			32-pdr	8	
			18-pdr	8	
Tallow, cwt, qrs	1.3	1.2	9-pdr	4	
			$\frac{1}{2}$-pdr	2	

Appendix VIII (see Part VIII)

The officers of Chatham Dockyard to the Navy Board, 22nd November 1701. (PRO Adm 95/15)

The practice of making hammocks at this yard at first was that each sailmaker should make, for a single day's work, four and a half; or nine for a double day. After we had tried this some time, we reduced them to the allowance of 4d for making each hammock, and according to the number that each man made in a day, it was allowed him in the Clerk of the Cheque's book in a single day, night and tide, for in the summer time they generally wrought from four in the morning to nine at night, and for the making this allowance we had the connivance and approbation of the late Surveyor of the Navy, and Sir Edmond Gregory. And this method is still observed here, and if your honours will please to call for a contract made by Commissioner St. Lo at Plymouth with one Mr Pentyre, a sailmaker there, you will find he gave much more, for, to our best remembrance he had 6d for each hammock.

Your honours may please to understand that each hammock made here consists of two breadths of duck, and is $2\frac{1}{4}$ yards long, is tabled round with a small line, and had 12 holes in each end. And that our sailmakers, without any other allowance, are obliged to reduce all irregular sails into a square to mend such holes as they find, and so the whole sail is converted without any loss or disadvantage.

These are the places in every of Her Majesty's ships which are to be glazed with stone ground glass, and no other, 8th October 1702. (PRO Adm 106/2507)

	Rates					
	1	2	3	4	5	6
All stern lights and gallery lights in the quarter, ranging with those of the stern	•	•	•	•	•	•
In the wardroom, a light to each of the lieutenant's cabins, standing against the bulkhead	•	•				
In the great coach or steerage:						
The bulkhead	•	•	•	•	•	•
A light in each of the bulkhead cabins	•	•	•	•	•	•
Sash over the oval tables	•	•	•	•	•	•
In the great cabin:						
Screen bulkhead to the bedplace	•	•	•	•	•	•
If an admiral's ship, sashes to convenient places for books and papers in the withdrawing room	•	•	•			
Upper coach or roundhouse:						
The bulkhead	•	•	•	•		
Small lights to each cabin at the bulkhead	•	•	•	•		
Secretary's office (if admiral's ship) sashes to convenient nests or presses for papers	•	•	•			
On the quarterdeck:						
Companion for the whipstaff	•	•	•	•		
Upper great cabin:						
If a flagship, screen bulkheads for the captain's bedplace	•	•				

	Rates					
	1	2	3	4	5	6
Poop or topgallant roundhouse:						
The bulkhead	•	•	•			
Bulkhead of the forecastle:						
A small light to the Boatswain's and Carpenter's cabins	•	•	•	•	•	•
Scuttles through the side:						
In the cabins at the bulkhead of the upper coach	•	•	•			
In the upper coach or the cuddy on each side	•	•				
In the bulkhead cabins of the great coach or steerage	•	•	•	•	•	
In the great coach or steerage, two on each side	•	•	•			
In the lobby betwixt the great coach and great cabin bulkheads on each side	•	•	•			
Betwixt the bulkhead of the great cabin and screen bulkhead one on each side	•	•	•	•	•	
In the bulkhead cabins at the forecastle	•	•	•	•	•	
In the cook's cabin at the forecastle	•	•	•	•	•	
In the Lieutenant and gunner's cabins at the gunroom bulkhead	•	•	•	•	•	
Glass in the cookroom lights	•	•	•			

A contract for making seamen's bedding, 1760. (NMM POR/A/21)

Contracted and agreed on the 21st April 1760, with the Principal Officers and Commissioners of His Majesty's Navy, for and on behalf of His Majesty by me, Abraham Chambers of London, warehouseman. And I do hereby bargain and sell to His Majesty, and oblige myself free of all charge to His Majesty, to supply His Majesty's ships and vessels with all such bedding for seamen employed in His Majesty's service at sea, as shall be demanded by the said Principal Officers and Commissioners.

The bedding to be of the quality and dimensions following, and in all respects agreable to the pattern produced to me, the said contractor, and sealed with the seal of this office, at the rate of 11/6 a bed, bolster, blanket and coverlet.

The bed to be 5ft 10in long and 2ft 3in broad, measured by the seam when made; the bolster as long as the bed is broad, and 1ft 5in in breadth, to be made of good Bremen cloth, or other cloth of equal goodness, and good clean sweet wool and white flocks, proportioned according to the said pattern bed; and on no account whatsoever to mix with the said wool and flocks, any hip wool, shank wool or pitch mark, arising from wool coming from the dressings of fellmongers. The bed not to have less than 12 tacks, and with the bolster to weigh 10lbs, at the rate of 5/6 each bed and bolster.

The coverlet to be Yorkshire, of 6 quarters broad and 6ft long, well wrought; and not to weigh less than 3lbs, at the rate of 2/6.

The blanket to be of the same size with the coverlet, well wrought, and not to weigh less than 2lbs 11oz, at the rate of 3/6 each. [followed by several clauses on delivery, terms of payment, etc.]

The furniture taken home by Admiral Rodney in the Gibraltar, *1781, having been carried in the cabin of his flagship* Sandwich *in the previous campaign.* (PRO 30/20/17)

Cabin furniture
One large and one small cot, complete.
One mahogany bedstead, complete.
One small mahogany bedstead, complete.
One field bedstead, complete.
One large mahogany dining table, with two leaves to fit occasionally.
One small table.
One card table.
Four scrutoires with drawers complete.
Two mahogany chests with deal cases.
Two large trunks.
One deal chest.
Two mahogany trays.
Three mahogany knife cases with knives and forks.
Four decanter stands.
One mahogany prospector case.
Two sofas with four pillows.
One large green covered chair.
One night stool with pan.
One mahogany hat box.
One mahogany dressing glass.
22 small painted chairs.
12 green chairs.
Eight pieces of calico.
Three pieces of fine linen.
38 large table cloths.
12 small table cloths.
43 napkins.
12 counterpanes.
One palapo.
Four pair of large sheets.
Two pair of small sheets.
Five pillow cases.
Four large mattresses and one small.
One small feather bed.

One large bolster.
Two large pillows.
One small bolster and a pillow case.
Three large blankets.
Three small blankets.
One set of curtains for the large bed.
One set of curtains with mosquito nettings.
One set of curtains for the field bed.
Six covers for the sofas.
Two covers for the large chairs.
One cloak lined with fur.
30 silver table spoons.
Two soup ladles.
16 tea spoons.
One pair of silver tongs.
Four salt cellars with spoons.
Five plated candlesticks.
One pair of snuffers.
One set of castors, complete.
One set of castors, not complete.
One tea kitchen, imperfect.
One tea board.
Two waiters.
One small mahogany tea board.
One iron chest.

Kitchen furniture
Two filtering stones with cases.
Two large water jars.

Glass and china
One box of china plates and dishes.
One box of china tea cups and saucers.
One box of china blue white and stone stone [*sic*] plates.
One box of china plates with glass runners of GBR.

Appendix IX (see Part IX)

Measures, c1680. (NMM AND/31)

Gauging all manner of vessels, wine and oil cask, commonly in use, being full gauge, ought to be of the contents following:

Rundlett holdeth	18½ gallons
Barrel of half hogshead	31½ gallons
Tierce	42 gallons
Hogshead	63 gallons
Tertian or puncheon	84 gallons
Pipe or butt	126 gallons
Tunn	252 gallons

Navy Office, 1st May 1757. Dimensions of double kettles for a ship of each class according to their complement of men, viz. (PRO Adm 95/17)

Guns	100	90	80	74	70	64	60	50	40	36	32	30	28	24
Number of men	850	750	650	580	520	500	420	350	280	240	220	210	200	160
Whole length of both parts in the clear, thwartships inches	78	74⅛	69¾	64½	61¾	61	55¼	53¼	50¼	46½	45½	44	43½	53
Breadth, fore and aft	51¼	49¼	47	46½	44	43½	41	38½	36	33½	31¼	30½	30	29
Depth	30	29	28	27½	27	26¾	26½	24½	21⅛	21	21	20¾	20¼	20
Least part, thwartships	29½	27¾	26¼	24	23¼	22⅞	21	20¼	19⅛	17½	17	16½	16¼	16
No. of gallons:														
Large	266	235	202	183	162	157	129	108	88	77	66	61	58	55
Small	159	140	122½	109	98	93	81	69	52	43	39	36	34	33

Dimensions of iron firehearths for a ship of each class in the Royal Navy, according to their complements of men. (PRO Adm 95/47)

Guns	100	90	89	74	70	64	60	50	40	36	32	30	28	24
Men	850	750	650	580	520	500	420	350	280	240	220	210	200	160
	Ft.In	Ft.In	Ft.In	Ft.In	Ft.In	Ft.In	Ft.In	Ft.In	Ft.In	Ft.In	Ft.In	Ft.In	Ft.In	Ft.In
Length fore and aft to the fore part of the range, from out to out	7.5½	7.3	7.1	6.11	6.8	6.7½	6.3	6.0	5.9	5.7½	5.5¼	5.4½	5.4	5.0½
Breadth thwartships	7.5½	7.1	6.9¾	6.4¼	6.1	6.0	5.5	5.2	5.0	4.9½	4.8½	4.7	4.6½	4.4
Height from the deck to the under part of the kettle	2.6	2.6	2.6	2.6	2.5	2.5	2.5	2.4½	2.3¼	2.3¼	2.3¼	2.3¼	2.3¼	2.3
Height from the deck to the top of the wing of the chimney	5.11¼	5.10½	5.9½	5.5½	5.5½	5.5	5.4½	5.1	4.9	4.9	4.9	4.9	4.9	4.9
Height from the deck to the top of the fixed part of the chimney	6.1¼	6.0½	5.11½	5.7½	5.7½	5.7	5.6½	5.3	4.11	4.11	4.11	4.11	4.11	4.11
Fixed part of the chimney: thwartships	2.7½	2.6½	2.5½	2.5	2.4½	2.2	2.0	1.10	1.8	1.7	1.6	1.6	1.6	1.6
Fixed part of the chimney: fore and aft	1.9	1.8	1.7	1.6½	1.6	1.5½	1.5	1.4	1.3	1.3	1.3	1.3	1.3	1.2
Depth of the range	2.1	2.1	2.1	2.1	2.1	2.1	2.0	2.0	2.0	2.0	2.0	2.0	2.0	1.11

Weights and dimensions of copper kettles and round kettles. 7th August 1777. (PRO Adm 106/2508)

Having agreed with Mr Forbes that the copper kettles and round kettles demanded from the date hereof for His Majesty's ships shall be of the dimensions and weight undermentioned; they are to direct and require you to demand and receive them of these weights and dimensions in future

| Rate | Guns | Length, In | Width, In | Depth, In | Kettle cover | | Top, In | Bottom, In | Deep, In | Round, not to be under | Kettles not to exceed |
| | | | | | Not to weigh less than | Not to exceed | | | | | |
					Cwt.Qr.Lbs	Cwt.Qr.Lbs				Cwt.Qr.Lbs	Cwt.Qr.Lbs
1	100	78	$51\frac{1}{4}$	30	13.3.19	15.0.19	14	12	12	0.0.26	0.1.5
2	90 & 84	$74\frac{1}{8}$	$49\frac{1}{4}$	29	12.1.19	13.2.19	15	13	13	0.1.3	0.1.10
3	80 & 74	$65\frac{1}{2}$	47	$27\frac{1}{2}$	10.2.19	11.2.19	16	14	14	0.1.8	0.1.17
3	64	61	$43\frac{1}{2}$	$26\frac{3}{4}$	9.1.1	10.0.0	17	15	15	0.1.2	0.1.20
4	60	$55\frac{1}{4}$	41	$26\frac{1}{2}$	8.3.0	9.2.0	18	16	16	0.1.16	0.1.25
Large	50	$53\frac{1}{2}$	$38\frac{1}{2}$	$24\frac{1}{2}$	8.0.1	8.3.0	19	17	17	0.1.22	0.2.3
5	44	$50\frac{1}{4}$	36	$21\frac{7}{8}$	7.0.14	7.3.0	20	18	18	0.2.0	0.2.9
5	36	$46\frac{1}{2}$	$33\frac{1}{2}$	21	6.1.16	7.0.0	21	19	19	0.2.6	0.2.14
5	32	$45\frac{1}{2}$	$31\frac{1}{4}$	21	5.2.12	6.0.12	22	20	20	0.2.12	0.2.21
6	28	$43\frac{1}{2}$	30	$20\frac{1}{4}$	5.0.1	5.2.0	23	21	21	0.2.18	0.2.27
6	24	42	28	21	4.0.27	4.2.20	24	22	21	0.2.24	0.3.6
6	20	39	27	22	4.0.23	4.2.7	25	23	22	0.3.0	0.3.10
Sloops	16 & 14	37	23	20	3.2.10	3.3.10	26	24	23	0.3.4	0.3.14
Sloops	10 & 8	33	21	20	3.0.10	3.1.10	27	25	24	0.3.9	0.3.20
							28	26	25	0.3.14	0.3.24
							29	27	26	0.3.19	1.0.2
							30	28	26	0.3.24	1.0.8
							31	29	26	1.0.0	1.0.13
							32	30	27	1.0.6	1.0.20

The bottom to be made in one piece without a seam, and the handles of the covers to be of wrought copper, and not of cast metal.

Chimneys, of 1st and 2nd rates, the copper of the lower part to weigh 9lbs per foot, superficial
of upper part, 7.
of hood, 6.
3rd and 4th rates, lower part, 8
of upper, 7
of hood, 6
5th and 6th rates and sloops, the copper of the whole chimney, 7
of hood, 6
And the handles of the hoods to made of best wrought copper.
These round kettles for the navy to be hammered both bottom and sides, and not spotted as formerly.
The ears to be made of the best wrought copper, and not of cast metal, and where wires and nails shall be necessary, those also to be of wrought copper.
And the ears, wires and nails of all surgeon's pots to be made in the same manner, without any iron.

Firehearths, 23rd January 1787. (PRO Adm 106/2508)

These are to direct and require you to charge the carpenters of His Majesty's ships, when supplied with a Brodie's firehearth with each particular mentioned in the enclosed accounts, to make a notation on the indent, in copy of the supply that is given to the carpenter, that the said articles must be particularised on the survey of his remains, as he will be made to account for every one of them.
A firehearth of the new construction, with kitchen range, a folding top bar, 2 sliding racks for spits, a trivet bar, and 2 swing cranes with a stay to each, 2 ovens which are heated without any extra fuel, 2 square iron boilers with 2 covers to each, 2 brass cocks with set screws to plugs; a circular plate with 2 sliding rods and sockets for the mouth of hearth funnel.
A best smoke jack fixed in the funnel of hearth, with 2 chains for ditto.
A ventilator fixed in the hearth.
2 iron tubes or funnels with covers to ditto, fixed in the covers of boilers, to receive the still.

1 spare brass cock, with screw cuts in ditto. Set screw to plug for boiler.
1 pair of spare cheeks for range.
4 screw double dish plates for mending boilers in case of accidents by balls, and co.
Single square ditto without screws.
2 double nail wrenches.
4 large screwed bolts and nuts for fixing hearth to deck.
1 circular fender with bottom plate and 4 of 6.
1 shovel, 1 poker, 1 pair tongs and 2 rakes to clean flues round boiler.
2 spits with iron wheels and 3 collars, 1 spit with crank handle and 2 collars.
1 cuckhold or spit fork, with a set screw to fasten in spits.
l large square plate with a round hole with a flange on centre to fix round and secure the funnel or chimney of hearth to the deck.
N.B., stewing stoves with trivets and grates, furnace bars and bottom plates as undermentioned [See table that follows.]

Classes of ships in no of guns	100, 90	84, 80	74, 64	50	44	38, 36, 32, 28	24, 20	16, 14	10, 10
No of stewing stoves	7	6	5	4	4	3	2	1	1
No of grates to the stewing stoves	14	12	10	8	8	6	4	2	2
No of trivets to the stewing stoves	7	6	5	4	4	3	2	1	1
No of furnace bars in each set	16	14	14	6	6	6	6	5	4
No of plates in the additional bottom	4	4	4	4	2	2	2	1	1

Extras;
These are sent with each hearth; 1 set of square furnace bars
1 cast iron spare rack for range

An estimate of the weight carried on board His Majesty's ship Vengeance *when completed for four months, with the quantity of each specie, c1800.* (NMM SPB/15)

Provisions & co	Leaguers	Butts	Puncheons	Hogsheads	Half hogsheads	Barrels	Firkins	Tons	Cwt	Qrs	Lbs
Beef, 19152lbs			3	7		31		8	11		
Pork, 19376lbs			11	11		44		8	13		
Bread, 67224lbs								30			24
Butter, 3337lbs							48		29	3	5
Cheese, 4809lbs					33			2	2	3	21
Oatmeal, 229 bushels				26				6	10		
Peas, 196 bushels				24				6			
Raisins, 3273lbs							32	1	9		25
Vinegar, 504 gallons				8				2			
Beer, 100 butts		100						50			
Water	120	226	14	11	Ten tons of small casks kept in hand for quarters			219			
Brandy, 256 gallons			3					1			
Rum, 2279 gallons			26					8	12	3	12
Wine, 1729 gallons		14	2					7	12	3	12
Flour, 13772lbs				27				6	2	3	24
Suet, 672lbs							13		6		

Necessaries
Coals, 15 chaldrons — 20 Tons
Wood, 20 chords — 6 Tons
Candles

Furniture
Masts and spars
Rigging, standing and running
Cables, 7 of 22in and one of 13½in, including viol and messenger — 46 Tons 19 Cwt

Anchors: best bower, 67cwt. Small bower, 67cwt. Sheet, 67cwt. Spare, 67cwt. Stream, 16cwt. Kedge, 8cwt. — 14 Tons 12 Cwt

Grapnels, boat: one 84lbs, one 56lbs, and one 40lbs. — 1 Cwt 2 Qrs 12 Lbs

Boats: one launch, one barge, one pinnace, two cutters and one jolly-boat.

Ballast: iron, 80 tons, shingle, 307 tons. — 387 Tons

Guns: lower deck 78 tons 8cwt.
upper deck, 56 tons.
quarter deck and forecastle, 22 tons 11cwt. — 156 Tons 18 Cwt

Gun carriages: 7 tons 8cwt.
5 tons 12cwt.
2 tons 14cwt. — Leaguers 15, Butts 14

Establishment of iron ballast, 12th March 1796. (NMM POR/A/39)

Guns	Tons	Guns	Tons	Guns	Tons	Guns	Tons
120	340	50	85	32, built with fir	110	Sloops as brigs, 300 tons and	
100	300	44	85	32, small class	80	upwards	30
98	250	38	90	28	75	Built with fir	40
80	200	38, built with fir	130	24	70	Brigs, small	25
74, large class	150	36	85	20	60	Fireships	65
74, common class	130	36, built with fir	120	Sloops of 400 tons and upwards	65	Bombs	20
64	90	32, large class	90	Sloops, 300 to 390 tons	60	Cutters	20

Appendix X (see Part X)

Dimensions of pinnaces and jolly boats, c1680. (NMM AND/31)

		1st	2nd	3rd	4th	5th	6th	1st	2nd	3rd
		Ft In	Ft In	Ft In	Ft In	Ft In	Ft In	Ft In	Ft In	Ft In
Keel	Length of the keel	27 6	27 0	26 6	25 0	23 6	20 0	19 7	17 10	13 3
	Depth of the same	4	4	4	4	4	4	4	4	4
	Breadth of the midships	4	4	4	4	4	4	4	4	4
	Breadth abaft	2½	2½	2½	2½	2½	2½	2½	2½	2½
	Length of the scarph	1 4	1 4	1 4	1 4	1 4	1 2	1 2	1 2	1 1
Stem	Rake and sweep of the stem	4 9	4 6	4 6	4 4	4 3	4 2½	4 3	4 2	3 9
	Height from the bottom of the keel	5 0	4 11	4 10	4 9	4 7	4 5	4 2	4 1	3 7
	Fore and aft at the head	9	9	8	7	6	5	5	5	5
	Sided aloft and alow	3	3	3	3	3	3	3	3	3
Post	Rake of the post	1 4	1 4	1 3	1 2	1 2	1 0	1 0	1 0	1 0
	Fore and aft at the head	0 4	0 3½	0 3½	0 3½	0 3½	3	3	3	3
	Fore and aft alow	1 4	1 4	1 4	1 4	1 2	1 1	1 1	1 1	1 0
	Thwartships at the head	3	3	3	3	3	3	3	3	3
	Height of the height of breadth line from the upper edge of the keel — Fore	3 5	3 4	3 3	3 2	3 1	3 0	3 0	2 11	2 10
	Midships	2 7	2 7	2 6	2 6	2 5	2 4	2 4	2 3	2 2
	Abaft	3 10	3 9	3 8	3 6½	3 5½	3 4	3 4	3 3½	3 3
	Dead rising	1	1	1	1	1	1	1	1	1
	Rising abaft	2 2	2 1	2 0	1 10	1 9	1 6	1 6	1 6	1 6
	Rising afore	2 0	1 11	1 10	1 9	1 8	1 5	1 5	1 5	1 5
	Breadth in the midships	6 0	5 10	5 8	5 4	5 6	5 4	5 6	5 4	5 2
	Breadth at the touch of the stem	5 2	5 1	5 0	5 0	4 10	4 6	5 0	4 10	4 0
	Breadth at the transom	2 3	2 3	2 2	2 2	2 0	2 0	2 0	2 0	2 0
	Breadth of the floor	2 0	1 11	1 10	1 10	1 9	1 9	1 9	1 9	1 9
	Sweep of the bends	1 10	1 10	1 9	1 8	1 7	1 6	1 6	1 5	1 4½
	Foreside of the ⊕ from the touch	it is 1ft afore the middle of the keel for rowing								
	Room and space	1 2	1 2	1 2	1 2	1 2	1 2	1 2	1 2	1 2
	Timbers sided	1½	1½	1½	1½	1½	1½	1½	1½	1½
	Depth upon the keel	2½	2½	2½	2½	2½	2½	2½	2½	2½
Timbers	Timbers in and out at the breadth	1½	1½	1½	1½	1½	1½	1½	1½	1½
	Length of the scarph	1 6	1 6	1 6	1 6	1 6	1 6	1 6	1 6	1 6
Plank	Thickness of the stuff alow	1	1	1	1	1	1	1	1	1
	Thickness of the two upper strakes	¾	¾	¾	¾	¾	¾	¾	¾	¾
Gunwales	Depth of the gunwale	4	4	4	4	4	4	4	4	4
	Breadth of the same	1½	1½	1½	1½	1½	1½	1½	1½	1½
Thwarts	Depth of the kneed thwarts	1¼	1¼	1¼	1¼	1¼	1¼	1¼	1¼	1¼
	Breadth of the same, and iron knees	6	6	6	6	6	6	6	6	6
	Number of the same	5	5	5	5	4	3	3	3	3

		1st	2nd	3rd	4th	5th	6th	1st	2nd	3rd
		Ft In	Ft In	Ft In	Ft In	Ft In	Ft In	Ft In	Ft In	Ft In
Thwarts	Depth of the loose thwarts	1	1	1	1	1	1	1	1	1
	Breadth of the same	6	6	6	6	6	6	6	6	6
	Number of the same	5	5	5	4	4	4	4	3	3
Oars	Length of the oars	17	17	16 6	16 6	16 0	15 6	15 6	15 0	14 6
	Number of the same	10	10	10	10	9	8	7	6	6
Keelson	Breadth of the Keelson	7	7	7	6	6	6	6	6	6
	Depth of the same	1½	1½	1½	1½	1½	1½	1½	1½	1½
Masts	Foreside of the foremast from the [?]	1 4	1 4	1 4	1 4	1 4	1 4	1 4	1 4	1 3
	Length of the mainmast and place in the [?]	18 0	17·6	17 0	16 6	16 4	16 0	16 0	15 6	15 0
	Diameter in the partners	4	4	3¾	3¾	3½	3½	3½	3½	3½
	Length of the sprit	20 0	19 6	19 0	18 6	18 4	18 0	18 0	17 0	16 6
	Diameter of the same	2½	2½	2½	2¼	2¼	2¼	2¼	2¼	2¼
	Length of the foremast	14 0	12 6	11 6	10 6	9 6	9 10	11 0	10 6	10 0
	Diameter of the same	3½	3½	3½	3½	3¼	3¼	3¼	3¼	3
	Length of the sprit	16 0	14 6	13 0	12 0	11 0	10 6	12 0	11 8	11 0
	Diameter of the same	2½	2¼	2	2	2	1½	2	2	2
Rudder	Rudder fore and aft alow	1 4	1 3¼	1 3	1 3	1 2	1 2	1 2	1 2	1 1
	Fore and aft at the head	5	5	5	5	5	5	5	5	4½
	Thickness of the same	1	1	1	1	1	1	1	1	1

Dimensions and scantlings of boats, 19th November 1690. (PRO Adm 95/13)

	Longboats						Pinnaces			Yawls
Length of boat, feet	35, 34	33, 32	31, 30	29, 28	27, 26, 25	24, 23, 22, 21	35, 34, 33, 32, 31	30, 29, 28, 27, 26	25, 24, 23 22, 21	24, 23, 22, 21, 20, 19, 18, 17
Keel										
Deep	7	6½	6	5½	5	4	4½	4	3½	3¼
Broad	6	5½	5	4½	4	3½	4	3½	3	2¾
Stem										
Thick	5	5	4½	4	3½	3¼	3½	3	3	2½
Broad	8	7	7	6½	6	5½	6	5½	4½	4
Post										
Fore and aft, aloft	5	4½	4½	4	3½	3	3½	3	2½	4
alow	12	10	9½	9½	9	8½	10	10	9½	9
Thwartships	5	4½	4	3¾	3½	3	3	3	2½	2¼
Board, thick on the upper strake										
Oak										
Elm	1¼	1¼	1¼	1	1	1	1	1	1	¾
Wainscot	1	1	1	1	1	1	¾	¾	¾	¾
Thwarts, thick										
Main	4	3½	3½	3½	3	2½	2	2	2	1½
Loose	2	2	2	2	1½	1½	1½	1½	1½	1½
Gunwales										
Thick	3	3	3	3	3	2½	1½	1½	1½	1¼
Deep	4½	4	4	3½	3¼	3	4½	4	3½	3¼
Risings										
Thick	1½	1½	1¼	1¼	1¼	1	1	1	¾	¾
Broad	7	6½	6	6	5½	5	4	4	3½	3½
Footwaling										
Thick	1½	1½	1¼	1¼	1¼	1	1	1	¾	¾
Broad	7	6½	6	6	5½	5	4	4	3½	3½

	Longboats						Pinnaces			Yawls
Keelson										
Thick	3	3	2½	2	2	1½	1½	1½	1½	1½
Broad	10	10	9½	9	8½	8	8	7	6½	6
Timbers										
Thick	2¾	2½	2½	2½	2¼	2	1½	1½	1½	1¼
In and out	2½	2¼	2¼	2	2	1¾	1½	1½	1½	1¼
Distance or room	11	12	12	12	12	12	11½	11	11	10½
Wales										
Thick	3	3	3	3	2½	2½				
Deep	4	4	3¾	3½	3	3¾				
Scarph of the timbers (feet)	2½	2½	2½	2⅓	2⅙	2⅙	24 (inches)	20	20	18
Windlass, square (inches)	11	10	10	9	8	7½				

Contract for longboats, 1696. (PRO Adm 106/3069)

Contracted this 21st day of August 1696 with the Principal Officers and Commissioners of His Majesty's Navy, for and on behalf of His Majesty by me, John Tanner of Dover, shipwright; And I do hereby bargain and sell to His Majesty, and oblige myself to build and deliver into His Majesty's stores at Deal, in three months time from the date hereof, three longboats of the dimensions and scantlings undermentioned, by one in each month, and to be finished and fully completed according to the several conditions following, viz.–

Longboats of

Length Ft.In	Breadth Ft.In	Depth Ft.In	
32.0	9.0	3.6	One, to row with ten oars
29.0	8.2	3.6	One, to row with nine oars
27.6	7.5	3.3½	One, to row with seven oars

	Longboats		
	of 32ft	of 29ft	of 27ft 6in
	In	In	In
Keel, deep	6½	5½	5
broad	5½	4½	4
Stem, thick	5	4	3½
broad	7	6½	6
Post, fore and aft, aloft	4½	4	3½
alow	10	9½	9
thwart	4½	3¾	3½
Board, wainscot, thick	1¼	1	1
elm, the upper strake, thick	1	1	1
Thwarts, main, thick	3½	3½	3
loose, thick	2	2	1½
Gunwales, thick	3	3	3
deep	4	3½	3¼
Risings, thick	1½	1¼	1¼
broad	6½	6	5½
Footwaling, thick	1½	1¼	1¼
broad	6½	6	5½
Keelson, thick	3	2½	2
broad	10	9	8½

	Longboats		
	of 32ft	of 29ft	of 27ft 6in
	In	In	In
Timbers, thick	2½	2½	2¼
in and out	2¼	2	¼
Distance or room	12	12	12
Wales, thick	3	3	2½
deep	4	3	3
Scarphs of the timbers	30	28	26
Windlass, square	10	9	8

The longboats to have three bands of oaken riders of 3 or 4 inches thick, well fixed; and two substantial ringbolts through the stem, and two through the stern post, and one through each side in the middle bands of riders; a rudder well made and hung; roll of lignum vitae at the stem and stern posts of 4½ inches diameter, of a proper length for carrying the buoy rope, fixed with iron pins; sheets before and abaft, with convenient benches; four thwarts, to be fastened with 4 inch knees and bolted with 3 bolts of ¾; laid with burden boards to the footwale; paid with white stuff to the risings within board; well caulked, graved and primed to the water edge without board, and painted within as usual.

And I do further oblige myself that all the said boats shall be carvel, wrought well and in workmanlike manner with good sound oak materials, dry and well seasoned oak plank, and no elm save in the upper strake …

[followed by several lines on terms of payment and delivery]

Proportions for a pinnace, c1750. (NMM SPB/2)

Let the length of the keel be what it will. The proportionable breadth for a short boat is $\frac{1}{4}$ of the length of the keel, but for a long pinnace you must allow $\frac{1}{5}$ or $\frac{1}{6}$, and for their depth allow an inch to every foot of the length. The height of the sheer afore and abaft is $\frac{3}{4}$ of the breadth, and the transom 6 inches above that. But of the boat be very long, let the depth be $\frac{7}{8}$ of an inch to every foot of the length. Rake the stem $\frac{1}{2}$ the breadth, and the post $\frac{1}{4}$ of its length. Breadth of the transom $\frac{2}{3}$ or $\frac{3}{4}$ of the main breadth. Length of the hancing to be $\frac{1}{3}$ of the length of the boat. As for the rising and height of breadth, place them as you please. To find the place to the midship flat, let off $\frac{8}{15}$ of the length of the boat from abaft.

Rule for finding longboat's length and breadth

For the breadth, as you increase one foot in length so increase 3 inches in breadth. For the depth, from 30 to 36 foot, as you increase one foot in length so increase one inch in depth. Line $\frac{5}{14}$ from afore the sheer 4 inches to 2 foot, and from 24 to 30, $\frac{3}{4}$ of an inch in depth.

Length Ft In	Breadth Ft In	Depth Ft In
Longboats		
36 0	10 3	4 4
35 0	10 0	4 3
34 0	9 9	4 2
33 0	9 6	4 1
32 0	9 3	4 0
31 0	9 0	3 11
30 0	8 9	3 10
29 0	8 6	3 $9\frac{1}{4}$
28 0	8 3	3 $8\frac{1}{2}$

Length Ft In	Breadth Ft In	Depth Ft In
Longboats cont.		
27 0	8 0	3 $7\frac{3}{4}$
26 0	7 9	3 7
25 0	7 6	3 $6\frac{1}{4}$
24 0	7 3	3 $5\frac{1}{2}$
Pinnaces		
34 0	6 3	2 7
32 10 oars	6 2	2 $6\frac{1}{2}$
29 0	5 10	2 5
28 8 oars	5 10	2 5
10 Yawl	5 10	2 4

The dimensions aforesaid by the Navy board's warrant in April 1740. All 10 oared boats to be 32 feet long, and 8 oared boats to be 28 feet long. Also, first second and third rates to have an additional boat 25 foot long to row with 6 oars, and building in the manner of Deal yawls of 18 foot. Yawls of 21 foot fitted with a trunk, of 18 with 4 oars for a 40 gun ship.

Boat's mast

The mast to be 3 times the breadth of the boat in feet, having regards to the boat being built, the foremast if any to be $\frac{4}{9}$ of the mainmast. The diameter is $\frac{7}{10}$ of an inch to a yard. The sprit a foot longer and above $\frac{2}{5}$ of an inch to a yard.

Shoulder of mutton sails

The mast to be 4 times the breadth of the boat. Diameter, $\frac{2}{3}$ of an inch to a yard in length, allowing $\frac{3}{4}$ of the length of the mast for the length of the boom. For diameter, $\frac{5}{7}$ of an inch to a yard in length at the biggest end, and at the small end $\frac{1}{2}$ the biggest end, where you fay the length of the gaff $\frac{1}{6}$ of the boom.

The davits

To be $\frac{7}{12}$ of an inch in a foot in length in the middle, and $\frac{3}{4}$ of the middle at each end, and length is $\frac{5}{6}$ of the ship's main breadth.

Agreement for building cutters at Deal 13th October 1755. (PRO Adm 106/3257)

For Deal cutters of … Ft long	To be Broad Ft.In	To be Deep Ft.In	Strakes, each $\frac{3}{4}$ or $\frac{5}{8}$ of an inch thick No	To have timbers on a side No	Thwarts for rowing No	Masts and sprits No	At s;d per foot
25	$6.8\frac{1}{2}$	$2.6\frac{1}{2}$	10	26	6	2	10/0
24	6.8	2.8	10	25	6	2	10/0
23	$6.7\frac{1}{2}$	$2.7\frac{1}{2}$	10	24	6	2	10/0
22	6.7	2.7	10	23	6	2	10/0
21	6.6	$2.6\frac{1}{2}$	10	22	6	2	10/0
19	$6.3\frac{1}{2}$	2.6	10	20	5	1	9/6
18	6.2	2.6	9	19	5	1	9/0
16	6.1	2.5	9	17	4	1	8/0

Besides the aforementioned, a rudder properly fitted, a ringbolt through the stem and another through the stern post, a breast hook and plate to the stem of each, and an apron to the stems of all above 18 feet in length.
For fitting back boards to cutters of 25 and 24 feet in length – 2/6
Burden boards to cutters from 25 to 21 feet inclusive – 5/0
And to those under 21 feet – 4/0
Fixing two additional ringbolts through the keel, if required – 2/0
Fixing a fast wash strake above the gunwale in the same manner as the boats used by the people of Deal, if required – 1/6 per foot.

Dimensions of the masts and yards for the boats undermentioned, proposed for a 74-gun ship, 1771. (PRO Adm 106/2508)

	Longboat of 10ft broad		Barge 6ft 10in broad		Pinnace 6ft 6in broad		Yawl 6ft 4in broad		Cutters of 7ft 4in broad		Cutters of 6ft 2in broad	
	Length	Diam	Length	Diam	Length	Diam	Length	Diam	Length	Diam	Length	Diam
Mast to the hounds	30.0	$7\frac{1}{2}$										
Bowsprit before the stem	15.0											
scarph	5.0	6										
Boom	23.4	$5\frac{1}{8}$										
Gaff	9.9	$3\frac{7}{8}$										
Mainmast			16.0	4	15.3	$3\frac{7}{8}$	$14.10\frac{3}{4}$	$3\frac{3}{4}$				
Sprit			18.0	$2\frac{1}{4}$	17.2	$2\frac{1}{8}$	16.8	2				
Foremast			16.0	4	15.3	$3\frac{7}{8}$	14.10	$3\frac{3}{4}$				
Sprit			18.0	$2\frac{1}{4}$	17.2	$2\frac{1}{8}$	16.8	$1\frac{7}{8}$				
Foremast									20.2	$4\frac{5}{8}$	17.0	4
Mizzen mast									12.7	$3\frac{1}{8}$	10.6	$2\frac{5}{8}$
Fore yard									10.1	$2\frac{1}{2}$	8.6	$2\frac{1}{8}$
Mizzen sprit									14.2	$1\frac{3}{4}$	11.10	$1\frac{5}{8}$
Outrigger									8.5	$2\frac{3}{8}$	7.0	2

Canon for masting boats

Longboats

Mast to the hounds = to the breadth multiplied by 3.
Head = to $\frac{1}{16}$ if the length of the mast to the hounds
Bowsprit before the stem, $\frac{1}{2}$ the length of the [mast?].
Boom, $\frac{7}{9}$ of the length of the mast to the hounds.
Gaff, $\frac{5}{12}$ of the length of the boom.

Diameters

The mast $\frac{1}{4}$ of an inch to a foot in length to the hounds.
Bowsprits, $\frac{3}{10}$, boom $\frac{51}{32}$, and the gaff $\frac{2}{5}$ of an inch to a foot.

Barges, pinnaces and yawls

Main and foremast = equal to the breadth multiplied by 2.35 [?].
Sprit = to the length of the mast and $\frac{1}{8}$ of that length more.

Diameters

Mast, $\frac{1}{4}$ of an inch to a foot in length.
Sprit, $\frac{1}{8}$ of an inch to a foot in length.

Cutters

Foremast = to the breadth multiplied by 2.75.
Mizzen mast, $\frac{5}{8}$ of the foremast.
Foreyard, $\frac{1}{2}$ of the foremast.
Mizzen sprit, proportioned as the yawls.
Outrigger, $\frac{5}{18}$ of the mizzen mast.

Diameters

Foremast, $\frac{3}{13}$ of an inch to a foot in length.
Mizzen mast, $\frac{1}{4}$ of an inch to a foot in length.
Fore yard, $\frac{1}{4}$ of an inch to a foot in length.
Outrigger, $\frac{5}{18}$ of an inch to a foot in length.

Boats carried, c1805, with later amendments. (Extracted from PRO Adm 7/579)

Type of ship	Barge or 10-oared boat of ft	Longboat or launch ft	Pinnace ft	Deal cutters ft	4-oared Deal cutter, cutter or jolly boat ft
100 guns	32	34	28	25 × 2[1]	18
98 or 90	32	33	28	25 × 2[1]	18
80	32	32	28	25 × 2[1]	18
74	32	31	28[2]	25 × 2[1]	18
64	32[3]	30	28	25 × 2[1]	18
50	32[3]	29		25 × 2[1]	18
44	32[3]	26[4]		25 × 2[1]	18
40	32[3]	26[4]		25 × 2[1]	18
38	32[3]	26[4]		25 × 2[1]	18
36	32[3]	25[4]		25 × 2[1]	18
32	30	23[4,5]		24[6]	18
28	28	22[4]		24	18
24	28	21[4]		Cutter 22 or yawl 26	18
20	28	21[7]		22	18

	Longboat or launch	Pinnace or 6-oared cutter	Deal cutter	Pinnace	4-oared Deal cutter or yawl
Sloops of 361 tons plus	18 or 19[8,9]			28[8]	18[10]
Sloops, 268 to 341 tons	18 or 19[8,4]			28[8]	18[8,10]
Brigs, 200 tons			24 & 20		16
Fireships	19[8]		22[8]		18
Bombs	19	25			18
Sloops, 200t	16[4]			24[8]	
Cutters			20[11]		
Brigs, 158t			22 or 24		16[12]

Note.
1. To be allowed a yawl of 26ft in lieu of a cutter, on captain's application.
2. Or 6-oared cutter.
3. To be allowed 8 oared cutter in lieu of barge, on captain's application.
4. In lieu of Brenton's yawl, Admiralty order, 15 March 1810.
5. NB, 32-gun ships carrying 18-pounders are to be allowed a launch of 25ft.
6. 18-pounder 32s also allowed Deal cutter of 25ft.
7. In lieu of 8-oared cutter, Admiralty order, 15 March 1810.
8. If rigged as a ship.
9. Sloops of 400 tons plus have launch or longboat of 2ft.
10. Sloops rigged as brigs of about 313 tons plus are allowed–
    Cutter – 24ft
    Cutter – 20ft
    Cutter or jolly boat – 16ft.
    Brig sloops, 282 tons–
    Cutter – 24ft
    Cutter – 18ft
    Cutter or jolly boat – 16ft.
11. The new cutters of 200 and 193 tons to have;
    Gig – 22ft
    Cutter – 16ft
12. Or a gig of 22ft.

Boat fittings for 8 months, c1805. (Extracted from PRO Adm 7/579)

	100 guns	74 guns	36 guns	Sloop, 360 tons
Boat covers	1[1]	1[1]	1[1]	1[1]
Boat compasses	1[2]	1[2]	1[2]	1[2]
Grapnels, boat				
For barge	112lbs	84lbs	70lbs	
For launch	56lbs	56lbs	48lbs	
Other boats	40lbs each	40lbs each	35lbs each	36lbs each
Boat hooks	12	12	6	3
Boat sails[3]				
Barges and pinnaces, lateen	2 each	2 each	2 each	2 each
Yawls, spritsails	2	2	2	
Cutters, lugsails	2	2	2	
Longboats, sloop sails, main, fore and jib	1 each	1 each	1 each	1 each
Boat hook spars	12	10	6	3
Oars				
Barge or pinnace	36	36	20	16
Longboat or launch, if single banked	16	16	12	8
if double banked	26	26	20	14
Cutter	28	28	24	6

Notes.
1. One for each boat, except the launch or longboat.
2. On captain's application. (AO 24/12/1802)
3. Agreeable to the established dimensions of the respective masts.

Dimensions of HMS Domingo's *boats, spars, sails, etc c1813.* (NMM WQB/3)

	Pinnace	First yawl	Second yawl	Barge	Black and yellow cutter
Boats dimensions in feet					
Length	28.11	26.5	28.5		
Breadth	7.4	7.5	7.3		
Depth	3.0	3.0	2.10½		
Dimensions of masts and yards, & co, in feet					
Mainmast, length	15.0	15.6	15.0	16.6	16.6
diameter	0.4½	0.4¼	0.4¼	0.4½	0.4¼
Main yard, length	18.6	18.6	18.6	20.4	15.6
diameter	0.3	0.3	0.3	0.3½	0.2½
Foremast, length	14.2	14.2	14.2	16.4	
diameter	0.42	0.4¼	0.4¼	0.4½	
Fore yard, length	16.6	16.6	16.6	22.2	
diameter	0.3	0.3	0.3	0.3½	
Mizzen mast, length	17.3	17.3	17.3	15.6	
diameter	0.3¼	0.3¼	0.3¼	0.3¼	
Boomkin, length	10.3	10.3	10.3	9.9	
diameter	0.2½	0.2½	0.2½	0.2½	
Bowsprit, length	8.6	8.6	8.6		
diameter	0.2½	0.2½	0.2½		
Sails, described.					

	Dimensions in feet				No of cloths in		No of canvas
	Head	Foot	Leech	Luff	Head	Foot	
Launch:							
Schooner foresail	7.0	17.0	16.0	17.0			
mainsail	7.5	15.0	21.6	18.0			
Lug, mizzen	8.8	10.8	15.8	7.6			
jib		10.4	9.0	13.6			
Launch							
Lateen, full		38.0	38.0	52.0			
reduced		38.0	33.0	49.0			
Pinnace:							
Sliding gunter, jib		7.6	9.3	12.6			
foresail		10.10	20.0	20.6			
mainsail		13.0	21.0	21.0			
mizzen		8.6	13.6	12.8			
First yawl: Sails as per pinnace							
Second yawl: ditto							
Gig:							
Lug sail	11.5	15.0	13.6	12.0			Duck
Barge:							
Sliding gunter, jib		8.6	10.0	13.6			
foresail		15.6	24.0	25.0			
mainsail		13.10	23.0	25.6			
mizzen		7.0	12.6	12.6			
Black and yellow cutter:							
Lug sail		15.6	12.6	8.0	11.0		

Appendix XI (see Part XI)

The lanterns of the Royal Sovereign. *Officers of Woolwich dockyard to the Navy Board, 25th June 1701.* (PRO Adm 95/15)

Rt. Hons,

As directed by your honour's orders of the 31st May last, we put a valuation (to the best of our judgements) on the Royal Sovereign's lanterns, the lights being of stone ground glass, for which a blank bill was made out to Mr. Nicholas Pickering, the 27th March 1701 as follows, viz–
Lanterns of 9ft 6in high and 4ft 4in diameter, one – £37
Lanterns of 8ft 2in high and 3ft 9in diameter, two – £29 each
Upright top lantern of 6ft 6in high and 2ft 10in diameter, one – £15

We humbly subscribe.

Notes

Abbreviations used in the Notes

BL: British Library
CPSD: Calendar of State Papers, Domestic
IJNA: *International Journal for Nautical Archaeology*
MM: *The Mariner's Mirror*, the journal of the SNR
NMM: National Maritime Museum
NRS: Navy Records Society
PRO: Public Record Office
RAI: Royal Artillery Institution
SNR: Society for Nautical Research

Chapter 1. Rudders

1. A W Sleeswyck and L Th Lehmann, 'Pintle and Gudgeon and the Development of the Rudder', *MM*, Vol 68, pp279–303
2. NRS, *Tangier Papers of Samuel Pepys*, Vol LXXIII
3. *Deane's Doctrine of Naval Architecture, 1670*, ed Brian Lavery, p80
4. NRS, *The Life and Works of Sir Henry Mainwaring*, Vol LVI, p214
5. Ibid, p226
6. This is implied in a print issued around 1700, which is reproduced in Brian Lavery's *Ship of the Line*, Vol II, p29
7. W Falconer, *Marine Dictionary*, 1769, pp153–54

Chapter 2. Tiller and Whipstaff

1. For example, the model of a 60-gun ship in the Science Museum. Inv 1939–248
2. Mainwaring, op cit, pp255–56
3. Ibid, p214
4. See the article by Jean Boudriot in *Neptunia*, No 129
5. Op cit, p239
6. For example, on the model of the *Boyne* in the NMM, No 1692–1
7. Op cit, p256
8. NMM SPB/8; PRO Adm 106/3069–3070
9. John Fincham, *Outline of Shipbuilding*, Part IV, p54
10. SNR Occasional Publication, No 6, *A Treatise on Shipbuilding*, 1958
11. NMM SPB/8

Chapter 3. The Steering Wheel

1. Nos 1702–1, 1703–1
2. NMM SPB/8
3. NMM Draughts, Nos 4605, 4598
4. See John Harland, 'The Early History of the Steering Wheel', *MM* Vol 58, pp41–68
5. PRO Adm 106/1191, 18 December 1771. See appendix p 257
6. PRO Adm 1/1495
7. See article by L G Carr Laughton, 'HMS Victory – Report of a Search among the Admiralty Records', *MM*, Vol 10, 1924, p207
8. PRO Adm 12/161, 59–5, 14 March 1813
9. For illustrations, see John Harland's article in *MM*, Vol 58, pp41–68

Chapter 4. Navigational Fittings

1. *Admiralty Regulations and Instructions*, 1808, p190
2. PRO Adm 106/2520, 1 February 1809
3. Captain John Smith, *A Sea Grammar*, 1627, p83
4. *MM*, Vol 61, No 2, May 1975, pp185–86
5. PRO Adm 106/3574, September 1814
6. NMM AND/33; BL Manuscripts, Stowe 436
7. BL Stowe 436
8. Blanckley, *Naval Expositor*, 1750, p41
9. PRO Adm 106/2508, 15 September 1779
10. PRO Adm 106/1062, 15 March 1747/8
11. Rodney Papers, PRO/30/20/6, 31 December 1757
12. NMM POR/A/51, 24 October 1808

Chapter 5. Anchors

1. Mainwaring, op cit, p88. Sutherland, *Shipbuilding Unveiled*, 1717, Vol 1, p22. Burney, *Universal Dictionary of the Marine*, 1815, pp10–13
2. Laughton, op cit, p192
3. Richard Pering, *A Treatise on the Anchor*, 1819, p39
4. D Baugh, *British Naval Administration in the Age of Walpole*, 1966, p309

5. B Pool, *Navy Board Contracts*, p101
6. NRS *The Sergison Papers*, ed Merriman, 1949, Vol LXXXIX, pp162–63
7. J E Horsley, *Tools of the Maritime Trades*, 1978, pp235–40
8. NRS *Sergison*, p159
9. Burney, op cit, p15
10. John Harland, *Seamanship in the Age of Sail*, p237
11. Laughton, op cit, p193
12. *Marine Dictionary*, op cit, p9
13. SNR Occasional Publication No 3, *Lengths of Masts and Yards, 1640*, pp17–19
14. E Hayward, *Sizes and Lengths of Rigging*, 1655, pp49–50
15. PRO Adm 106/2508, 14 September 1779
16. NMM AND/33
17. SNR Occasional Publication No 3, op cit. Hayward op cit. NMM AND/33
18. *Ship of the Line*, Vol 1, pp109, 207
19. PRO Adm 106/2509, 3 November 1784
20. NMM AND/33. *Ship of the Line* Vol 1, p199
21. NMM AND/33
22. Pering, op cit, especially p24
23. PRO Adm 106/1942, 24 September 1815

Chapter 6. Capstans

1. M Oppenheim, *History of the Administration of the Royal Navy*, 1896, pp80, 127
2. Compiled from lists in Frank Fox, *Great Ships*, 1980
3. Edition of Coronelli's *Gli Argonauti* in the NMM
4. NMM Draughts No 6226, Box 67
5. Copy of the 1719 Establishment in NMM Draught Room, giving full details of scantlings. Reproduced in Peter Goodwin's *The Construction and Fitting of the Sailing Man of War 1650–1850*, 1987, pp241–59
6. See Brian Lavery, *Ship of the Line*, Vol II, p29
7. Fincham, *Outline of Shipbuilding*, Vol IV, p43
8. Falconer, op cit, p75
9. NMM ER/3/6
10. *Ducane Manuscripts*, Historical Manuscripts Commission, 1905, p40

Chapter 7. Cables and Accessories

1. PRO Adm 106/2520, 11 May 1809
2. Henry Bond, *The Boate Swain's Art*, 1642, p18
3. SNR Occasional Publication No 3, p19. Hayward, op cit, p31. NMM AND/33. BL Stowe 436.
4. Falconer, op cit, p58
5. PRO Adm 106/2508, 14 September 1779, 27 March 1781.
6. BL Stowe 436
7. For example, Steel's *Mastmaking, Sailmaking and Rigging*, 1794
8. NMM AND/33; BL Stowe 436
9. *Deane's Doctrine*, pp104, 106, 108. BL Stowe 436.
10. Based on several draughts in the NMM, especially No 977, of the orlop deck of the *Wellesley* and *Meville* of 1814
11. BL Stowe 436. Laughton, op cit, p192
12. PRO Adm 106/2512, 11 June 1799
13. Mainwaring, p251

14. BL Stowe 436
15. PRO Adm 91/2, 24 June 1738
16. Laughton, op cit, p203
17. BL Stowe 436
18. PRO Adm 7/579
19. A Bugler, *HMS Victory, Building, Restoration and Repair*, 1966, p74
20. Various letters in PRO Adm 1/684, 1/747, 12/146, and 106/2522

Chapter 8. Anchor Tackle

1. NMM AND/33
2. NMM Draught Room, contract for the *Bombay Castle*, 1779
3. Hayward, op cit, p13 etc
4. NMM AND/33
5. PRO Adm 7/479, Adm 12/161, 59–1, 11 February 1813, etc

Chapter 9. Graving and Paying

1. Bugler, op cit, p12 et seq
2. Sutherland, *Shipbuilding Unveiled*, p ix. NRS *The Jacobean Commissions of Enquiry, 1608 and 1618*, ed McGowan, Vol 116, 1971, p275
3. Pepys, *Memoires of the Royal Navy*, p20
4. Act of Parliament, 6 Annae c 65. See also NRS *Queen Anne's Navy*, ed Merriman, Vol CIII, 1961, pp 344–46
5. PRO Adm 1/3592
6. NMM SER/105
7. NMM ADM/A/1893, 1 June 1702
8. NRS *Naval Administration, 1715–50*, ed Baugh, Vol 120, 1977, p245
9. Ibid, p371
10. Baugh, *Naval Administration in the Age of Walpole*, p216
11. Progress Books, especially PRO Adm 180/2
12. *Marine Dictionary*, p36
13. PRO Adm 106/2508, 6 May 1677
14. NMM SER/105
15. PRO SP 18/91, f18, 4 December 1654
16. Ibid, f1, 1 May 1654
17. T Hale, *Account of Several New Inventions*, 1691, p5
18. NRS *Catalogue of the Pepysian Manuscripts, Vol IV*, ed Tanner, Vol LVII, p523
19. NRS *The Naval Miscellany*, Vol XL, ed Laughton, p147
20. PRO Adm 1/3592
21. Progress Books, PRO Adm 180/2
22. PRO Adm 2/200, 31 March 1737
23. *Calendar of State Papers, Domestic*, 1657–58, p405, 6 August 1657
24. CSPD 1657–8, p537, 1 March 1657/8
25. PRO SP 18/91, f1, 1 May 1654
26. PRO Adm 1/3549, 28 August 1679
27. NMM POR/J1
28. PRO Adm 106/2508, 5 December 1759
29. PRO Adm 1/3601. NMM ADM/A/1837, 4 December 1696
30. PRO Adm 1/3638
31. PRO Adm 95 series, especially 95/94, passim

Chapter 10. Wood and Lead Sheathing

1. Richard Hawkins, *Observations*, quoted in Hodges and Hughes, *Select Naval Documents*, 1922, p10
2. NRS *Naval Administration*, pp210–11
3. PRO Adm 95/94, 16 March 1770
4. PRO SO 18/91, f1, 1 May 1654
5. Hawkins, op cit, p10
6. NRS *Boteler's Dialogues*, ed W G Perrin, Vol LXV, p104
7. PRO SP 18/90, f190. NRS *Naval Administration*, p211
8. PRO 106/2507, 24 January 1727/8
9. NMM MID/9/1
10. NRS *Queen Anne's Navy*, p81
11. NRS *Sergison*, p110
12. PRO Adm 2/185, 28 August 1707
13. PRO Adm 2/195, 14 November 1721
14. PRO Adm 1/3639. 27 April 1726
15. NMM MID/9/1
16. NRS *Sergison*, p112
17. Based on Progress Books, especially PRO Adm 180/2
18. PRO Adm 1/3638, 25 September 1724
19. Sutherland, *Shipbuilding Unveiled*, 1717, Pt II, p185
20. NRS *Sergison*, p111
21. PRO Adm 106/2507, 18 February 1727/8
22. NMM SER/105
23. NMM POR/J/1
24. NRS *The Naval Miscellany Vol II*, ed Laughton, Vol XL, p148
25. PRO Adm 106/30, 18 November 1674, 14 December 1674, 6 January 1674/5
26. NRS *Sergison*, pp86–103
27. NRS *Monson's Tracts, Vol IV*, Vol XLV, p52
28. Hawkins, op cit, p10
29. Hale, op cit, pp72–73
30. Ibid, pp6–7
31. PRO SP 16/298, f63
32. Hale, p75
33. Ibid, p7
34. PRO Adm 106/38, 21 March 1677/8. Cancelled on the 28th. (BL Addit Mss, 9328)
35. PRO Adm 106/312, 19 April 1675
36. Hale, p76
37. NRS *Naval Miscellany V*, ed Rodger, pp134–35
38. Ibid, p134

Chapter 11. Copper Sheathing

1. NRS *Queen Anne's Navy*, pp80–81
2. Parts of the false keel have been recovered by the *Invincible* (1758) Committee
3. PRO Adm 95/17, 16 October 1759
4. PRO Adm 95/93, 23 October 1761
5. NMM Adm B/172, 31 June 1763
6. PRO Adm 2/236, 28 May 1766
7. PRO Adm 95/94, 16 March 1770
8. Article by R J B Knight 'The Introduction of Copper Sheathing to the Royal Navy', *MM* Vol 59, pp299–309
9. PRO Adm 12/54. 8 January 1777. Knight, op cit, p300
10. Knight, op cit, p308, n 6

11. NMM MID/9/1, RUSI/86, f15. (See Appendix in Brian Lavery, *Ship of the Line*, Vol I)
12. Knight, op cit, p299
13. NMM MID/9/1
14. PRO Adm 106/2508, and Knight, op cit, passim
15. Knight, op cit, p304
16. PRO Adm 95/93
17. See *Ship of the Line*, Vol I, p207 for the *Bedford*, and PRO Adm 106/3472, 24 September 1781, and PRO Adm 106/2508, 2 October 1781
18. PRO Adm 106/2508, 22 September 1779
19. PRO Adm 106/2508, 2 October 1781
20. Ibid, 31 January 1781
21. NRS *The Barham Papers Vol I*, ed Laughton, Vol XXXII, 1906, p254
22. Knight, op cit, p303
23. NMM MID/9/1
24. Knight, op cit, p306

Chapter 12. Pumps and Drainage

1. *Bombay Castle* contract, op cit
2. See, for example, NMM Draughts, No 694lb
3. Mainwaring, op cit, p180
4. For example, in PRO Adm 106/3070–1, and NMM SPB/8
5. See T J Oertling, 'The Chain Pump', *IJNA* 11: 2, 1982, pp113–24
6. *European Magazine*: Papers on Shipbuilding, 1795, Vol II, p96
7. Oertling, op cit, p115
8. NMM AND/33
9. PRO Adm 95/13, 11 September 1717
10. For example, Blanckley, op cit, p125
11. PRO Adm 95/13, 11 September 1717
12. For example, in NMM SPB/33, *Reports on the Coles Bentinck Pump*. Oertling, op cit, p115
13. NMM AND/33, SPB/28, AND/31
14. There does not seem to have been a specific order to cover this. These conclusions are based on the study of many draughts and models, especially those in the NMM

Chapter 13. The Improved Chain Pump, and the Brake Pump

1. *European Magazine*: Papers on Shipbuilding, 1795. Vol II, p94
2. BL Pamphlets, 816 m7
3. Robert Gardiner, 'Fittings for Wooden Warships', *Model Shipwright*, No 17, 1976, p100. PRO Adm 12/128
4. NMM SPB/33
5. Ibid
6. Ibid
7. Ibid
8. PRO Adm 106/2508, 6 January 1773
9. Ibid
10. PRO Adm 106/2508, 1 February 1774

11. Blanckley, op cit, p124
12. PRO Adm 106/2507, 2 March 1742/3
13. BL Stowe 436, PRO Adm 7/579
14. PRO Adm 95/96, 20 December 1779, 106/2509, 26 August 1789
15. PRO Adm 106/3472
16. PRO Adm 106/2507, 2 March 1742/3
17. PRO Adm 106/2508, 11 February 1758
18. PRO 30/20/6, 17 June 1757. PRO Adm 106/2508, 6 September 1771
19. PRO Adm 106/2533, 6 September 1771
20. PRO Adm 95/96, 9 April 1779
21. NMM Draughts No 7643, in *Ship of the Line*, Vol II, p119

Chapter 14. The Supply of Guns

1. H C Tomlinson, *Guns and Government*, passim
2. Ibid
3. NRS *Monson IV*, op cit, p45
4. C Ffoulkes, *The Gun-founders of England*, 1937. E Straker, *Wealden Iron*, 1931
5. A R Hall, *Ballistics in the Seventeenth Century*, 1952. Straker, Ffoulkes, op cit
6. For Fuller, see *Sussex Archaeological Collections*, Vol LXVII, 1926, pp25–54
7. Council for the Preservation of Business Archives, *Minutes relating to Messrs Samuel Walker and Co*, 1951
8. PRO WO 47/22, 12 May 1705
9. PRO WO 47/28, 5 July 1715
10. *Sussex Archaeological Collections*, Vol LXVII, op cit, p30. *Gunfounding in the Eighteenth Century*, op cit, p51
11. PRO Adm 160/154
12. PRO Supp 5/52
13. *Sussex Archaeological Collections*, Vol LXVII, op cit, p47
14. Council for the Preservation of Business Archives, op cit
15. Charles Derrick, *Memoirs of the Rise and Progress of the Royal Navy*

Chapter 15. Materials: Brass and Iron

1. From the Anthony Roll, reproduced in *The Mary Rose*, by Margaret Rule, 1981, pp26–27
2. NRS *Papers Relating to the Spanish War*, ed Corbett, Vol XI, p300
3. Oppenheim, op cit, p159
4. Ibid
5. *Deane's Doctrine*, p105
6. Compiled from SNR Occasional Publication, No 7, *List of English Men of War, 1509–1649*, by R C Anderson
7. M Lewis, *Armada Guns*, p180. PRO Adm 160/150
8. Oppenheim, op cit, p157
9. Derrick, op cit, pp37, 61
10. PRO SP 16/11, 7 December 1625
11. CSPD Addendum, 1625–49, p59, 6 December 1625
12. CSPD 1625–26, p320, 28 April 1626
13. PRO SP 16/230
14. PRO WO 55/1685
15. PRO WO 55/1691/2
16. PRO WO 47/2, 18 May 1653
17. Derrick, op cit, p80
18. PRO WO 47/2
19. PRO SP 16/148, f16
20. PRO WO 47/4, 29 September 1657
21. PRO WO 47/6
22. PRO WO 47/2
23. PRO WO 47/2, 4 October 1652
24. Compiled from PRO 30/37/5
25. PRO WO 47/6, 31 July 1663
26. PRO WO 47/8, 13 February 1665/6, and CSPD 1670, p556
27. PRO WO 47/6, 11 November 1664
28. *Deane's Doctrine*, pp104–13
29. PRO WO 47/6, 14 March 1662/3
30. NRS *Journals and Narratives of the Third Dutch War*, ed Anderson, Vol LXXXVI, pp188–89
31. PRO SP 16/230. *Deane's Doctrine*, p105
32. Magdalene College, Cambridge, Pepysian Library Sea Mss, 2266, f109
33. Povey, *Sea Gunner's Companion*, 1702, p8
34. PRO WO 55/1736
35. Isle of Thanet Archaeological Unit, *Interim Report*, 1979
36. NMM GUN/1
37. R F Johnson, *The Royal George*, pp6–7

Chapter 16. The Shape of Guns

1. H L Blackmore, *The Armouries of the Tower of London, Part I, Ordnance*, 1976, pp 223–24
2. Muller, *Treatise on Artillery*, 1768, p41
3. PRO WO 47/6, 27 July 1664
4. PRO Supp 5/2
5. PRO Supp 5/53, 5 February 1795
6. Blackmore, op cit, p228
7. Ibid
8. PRO SP 16/148, f16
9. CSPD 1629–31, pp389–90
10. PRO SP 16/43, f84
11. NRS *Boteler*, p260
12. Quoted in Blackmore, op cit, p228
13. PRO WO 55/1692
14. PRO SP 16/345, f71
15. PRO SP 16/43, f84
16. Oppenheim, op cit, p262
17. PRO WO 47/2, 12 July 1653
18. BL Addit Mss 32466
19. For example NRS *Boteler*, pp129–30, Povey, op cit, p7
20. PRO WO 47/2, 13 February 1652/3
21. PRO WO 47/2, 12 July 1653
22. PRO WO 47/6 23 November 1664
23. NRS *Tangier Papers of Samuel Pepys*, ed Chappell, Vol LXXIII, p247
24. From Frank Fox, *Great Ships*, 1980, p194
25. PRO WO 55/1736
26. PRO WO 55/1762
27. Fox, op cit, p194
28. PRO WO 55/1692
29. BL Addit Mss 32466, 17 February 1648/9. PRO WO 47/6, 14 July 1665, 29 March 1665/6

Chapter 17. The Proportions of Guns

1. From an unpublished paper by Charles Trollope, with permission
2. Royal Artillery Institution Manuscripts, G3 f43
3. Trollope paper, supra
4. Rees, *Cyclopaedia*, 1819, vol VI
5. Ibid
6. Blomefield's letter books in PRO Supp 5/52–3, and WO 47/108, etc
7. PRO Supp 5/43, November 1794
8. WO 55/1823
9. NMM GUN/12, and other lists
10. J F Guilmartin, *Gunpowder and Galleys*, 1974, and *The Cannon of the Batavia and Sacramento*, *IJNA* 11, pp133–44. R Barker, *Comments upon Guilmartin*, in *IJNA* 12; 1, 1983, pp67–74
11. Benjamin Robins, quoted in Falconer, *Marine Dictionary*, p68 et seq
12. NMM GUN/1
13. PRO WO 55/1740
14. Muller, *Treatise on Artillery*, 1768

Chapter 18. Types of Gun

1. Corbett, *Drake and the Tudor Navy*, Vol 1, pp 362–70. See also Blackmore, op cit, pp218–48 for definitions
2. PRO WO 47/8, 12 April 1666, 15 May 1666
3. NRS *Papers Relating to the First Dutch War, Vol V*, Vol XLI, p230
4. John Sellar, *The Sea Gunner*, 1691, pp139–40
5. *Sea Gunner's Companion*, op cit, p4
6. Blackmore, op cit, p221
7. Fox, op cit, p184
8. Laughton, op cit, p208
9. Ibid
10. PRO WO 47/4, 26 September 1657
11. PRO WO 55/1736
12. PRO WO 47/2, 12 July 1653
13. NRS *Pepysian Catalogue I*, p236. NMM SER/110
14. NMM GUN/1
15. Blackmore, op cit, p221
16. PRO SP 16/194, 15 March 1631/2
17. PRO WO 47/5
18. PRO WO 47/8
19. Fox, op cit, pp 184–86
20. Ibid, p194
21. PRO WO 55/1715 NMM SER/88, GUN/1, and others
22. Oppenheim, op cit, p157. PRO 30/37/5. Fox, op cit, p194
23. PRO WO 47/5
24. Burney, *Universal Dictionary of the Marine*, p69
25. Oppenheim, op cit, p157
26. PRO WO 55/1715, 1736
27. PRO WO 55/1715
28. NMM GUN/1
29. Compiled from PRO 30/37/5
30. PRO WO 55/1740
31. Ibid
32. NMM GUN/1
33. Blackmore, op cit, p241
34. For example, PRO WO 47/7, 27 June 1665
35. PRO WO 55/1648, 2 April 1647
36. *IJNA*, 13, 1, 1984, pp66–68
37. PRO WO 55/1745
38. PRO Adm 2/250, 14 August 1779
39. PRO Adm 160/150

Chapter 19. Carronades

1. Campbell, *Carron Company*, pp82–89
2. PRO Adm 12/67, 25 April 1795
3. For experiments with the 100-pounder, see NMM MID/9/2
4. Campbell, op cit, p97
5. Ibid, pp98–99
6. Ibid, pp99–101
7. NMM MID/9/2
8. PRO Adm 2/249
9. PRO Adm 106/2207, 18 December 1779
10. Ibid, 22 January 1780
11. Ibid, 8 March 1780
12. NMM MID/9/2, 21 October 1780
13. PRO Adm 106/2207, 9 March 1780
14. PRO Adm 7/940
15. NMM MID/9/2, 5 December 1781, 16 January 1780
16. PRO WO 55/1742
17. PRO Adm 7/940, Supp 5/54
18. PRO Adm 7/940, Burney, p77
19. NMM Draughts, Nos 6680, 7790
20. PRO Adm 7/940
21. NMM MID/9/2
22. Ibid
23. NMM RUSI/64
24. PRO Adm 2/252, 5 May 1780. Supp 5/54, 1 April 1796
25. PRO Adm 2/252, 1 March 1780. NMM MID/9/2
26. Compiled from PRO Adm 180/23, and other lists
27. PRO Adm 7/940
28. PRO Supp 5/54, 2 December 1796
29. NMM ADM/Y/5, 10 and 23 December 1806
30. R Gardiner, 'Fittings for Wooden Warships', *Model Shipwright*, No 20, 1977, p342

Chapter 20. Early Armaments

1. NRS Boteler, p259
2. NRS Mainwaring, p131
3. NRS Boteler, pp296–97
4. Ibid, p296
5. Derrick, op cit, pp31–33
6. See list in *Ship of the Line*, Vol I, pp193–94
7. PRO WO 55/1692
8. See *Ship of the Line* Vol I Ch 2, for discussion of this
9. PRO WO 66/1691, 1648, and WO 47/3, 22 January 1653/4
10. Ibid
11. Oppenheim, op cit, p341. PRO WO 55/1650
12. PRO WO 47/3, 22 January 1654/5. PRO SP 18/30, 24 December 1652
13. PRO WO 47/3, 47/5, Fox, op cit, p184
14. *Deane's Doctrine of Naval Architecture, 1670*, 1981, p104
15. PRO WO 47/3, 22 January 1653/4
16. PRO WO 47/3, 18 October 1655

17. PRO WO 47/5, 22 February 1663/4
18. Ibid
19. Fox, op cit, pp184–86
20. NRS *Journals and Narratives of the Third Dutch War*, Vol LXXXVI, pp188–91

Chapter 21. The Establishments

1. NRS *Samuel Pepys's Naval Minutes*, ed Tanner, Vol LX, p61
2. *Catalogue of Pepysian Manuscripts*, Vol I, p233
3. BL Egerton 2522, Addit 29733
4. *Catalogue of Pepysian Manuscripts*, Vol IV, p419
5. Ibid, p426
6. Ibid, p426
7. Ibid, p233
8. Ibid, p549
9. Fox, op cit, pp191–94
10. PRO WO 55/1763
11. NMM Adm 2/176, 6 November 1695
12. NMM SER/83, pp242–44. 2 August 1699
13. For guns actually borne in 1693–94, see Brian Lavery, *Ship of the Line* Vol I, pp197–99, and in 1698, PRO WO 55/1736
14. Outline proposals in NRS *Queen Anne's Navy*, pp66–67. Full details in NMM SER/110
15. Various letters in PRO Adm 1/3999
16. Based on data found in the ordnance papers at Priddy's Hard, Portsmouth, and supplied by D J Lyon of the NMM
17. NRS *Naval Administration*, pp202–03
18. For establishment, see Derrick, p273
19. PRO WO 55/1739, 1740
20. PRO WO 55/1740
21. *Ship of the Line* Vol I, pp81–83
22. PRO Adm 7/339, 28 April 1733
23. Derrick, pp274–75
24. BK Addit Mss 28156, p237
25. PRO Adm 7/340, 25 March 1743
26. Derrick p275

Chapter 22. Types of Ship

1. See *Ship of the Line*, Vol I, especially chapters IX and X, for a discussion of this process
2. For gun arrangements, see *Ship of the Line*, Vol I, pp175–190
3. Laughton, op cit, p208
4. MM XVIII, pp201–03
5. *Ship of the Line* Vol I, pp183–90
6. See *European Magazine*: Papers on Shipbuilding, Vol II, p 16, for criticisms of the 64-gun ship.
7. Derrick pp149, 171, 177
8. Ibid, p210

Chapter 23. The Age of the Carronade

1. PRO Adm 7/677, 28 July 1779. James, *Naval History of Great Britain*, Vol I, p38
2. PRO Adm 7/677, 18 January 1779

3. Ibid, 14 December 1779, January 1780
4. PRO Adm 7/677
5. PRO Adm 7/677, 21 January 1782
6. Ibid, 25 November 1782
7. NMM MID/9/2
8. James, op cit, Vol I, p423
9. PRO Adm 2/274, 19 November 1794
10. PRO WO 55/1832
11. Ibid
12. See Padfield, *Guns at Sea*, pp109–10, for examples
13. PRO Adm 7/677, 22 April 1795
14. Ibid, 17 March 1797
15. Ibid, 4 June 1799
16. Ibid, 21 February 1800
17. Ibid, 16 July 1804, 24 June 1805
18. Ibid, 17 and 27 March 1797
19. Ibid, 4 June 1799

Chapter 24. Gun Carriages

1. F Howard, *Sailing Ships of War*, pp76–81. M Rule, *The Mary Rose*, pp159–62
2. See Chapter 18 for the later use of the swivel mounting
3. L G Carr Laughton, 'Gunnery Frigates and the Line of Battle', *MM*, Vol 14, 1928
4. Smith, *Sea Grammar*, p61
5. Rule, op cit, pp158–61
6. Illustrations in Padfield, *Guns at Sea*, pp66–67
7. See Howard, op cit, p150 for an example
8. Shown in Sellar, the Keltridge Draughts in the NMM, and in a drawing in the Danish Archives. (See *Ship of the Line*, Vol 1, p51)
9. Royal Artillery Institution Manuscripts, G3 n la
10. Ibid
11. PRO MPHH 703, f6, pt1, plan of Landguard Fort, 1732
12. See Padfield, op cit, especially pp137–146, for discussion of this point
13. See F L Robertson, *The Evolution of Naval Armament*, pp140–159, for a discussion of the advantages and disadvantages of the carronade carriage.
14. PRO Adm 106/3472
15. PRO Adm 1/4014. Illustrations in Howard, op cit, p214
16. PRO Adm 1/3526, 28 July 1803
17. Ibid
18. PRO Adm 1/3527, 12 January 1805
19. PRO Adm 7/410, 11 July 1804
20. NMM ADM/Y/3, 27 November 1805
21. PRO Adm 7/410, 30 July 1805. 2/308, 7 September 1805
22. PRO Adm 2/308, 26 July 1805. NMM ADM/A/2990
23. NMM draughts, 6680

Chapter 25. Powder, Shot, and Stores

1. *The British Explosives Industry*, Vol 1, pp28–29. International Congress of Applied Chemistry, 1909
2. A Perceval, *The Faversham Gunpowder Industry*, 1967
3. NRS *Mainwaring*, pp200–01
4. *The British Explosives Industry*, op cit, pp36, 43.

5. Blackmore, op cit, p224
6. Ibid, p224
7. RAI ms, G3 n 1a
8. PRO Adm 160/150
9. PRO WO 47/3
10. RAI ms, G3 n 1a
11. PRO Adm 160/150
12. Burney, *Universal Dictionary of the Marine*, p78
13. PRO WO 47/3
14. RAI ms, G3 n 1a
15. Brian Lavery, *Ship of the Line*, Vol I, p208, on the *Bedford*
16. Blackmore, op cit, p221
17. NRS *Boteler*, p201
18. PRO WO 55/1650
19. Burney, *Universal Dictionary of the Marine*, 1815 p468
20. See Blackmore, op cit, pp191, 198–99
21. Burney, *Universal Dictionary of the Marine*, p214
22. Falconer, *Marine Dictionary*, 1769, p171
23. Brian Lavery, *Ship of the Line*, Vol I, p208
24. NRS *Boteler*, p201
25. Falconer, op cit, p266
26. RAI ms, G3 n 1a
27. NRS *Mainwaring*, p225
28. Smith, *Sea Grammar*, p66
29. Falconer, op cit, p310
30. PRO WO 47/3, 55/1745
31. PRO Adm 160/150
32. Smith, *Sea Grammar*, p68
33. NRS *Mainwaring*, p242
34. PRO WO 47/3, PRO Adm 160/150
35. PRO WO 55/1650
36. PRO WO 55/1745
37. Ibid

Chapter 26. Gun Tackle and Equipment

1. Howard, p46
2. Models in NMM with gunports in the waist, 1698–2, 1702–1, 1705–1; without gunports in the waist 1703–1, 1710–1, 1715–1, 1715–3.
3. PRO Adm 106/2508, 28 November 1778
4. Ibid, 6 May 1782
5. PRO Adm 106/2509, 7 May 1789
6. PRO Adm 12/133, 59-2, 4 January 1808, 2 November 1808
7. PRO WO 55/1740
8. PRO WO 55/1745
9. NMM GUN/12
10. Padfield, *Guns at Sea*, p108
11. PRO WO 55/1740
12. PRO Adm 1/578, 5 April 1749
13. PRO WO 55/1745
14. PRO WO 55/1740
15. PRO WO 55/1745
16. I am indebted to Frank Fox for drawing my attention to this point
17. *Exercise of the Great Guns* 1765(?) in the British Library
18. PRO Adm 160/150
19. NRS *Boteler*, p201
20. PRO WO 47/3. PRO Adm 160/150
21. *Ship of the Line*, Vol II, p180

22. PRO Adm 160/150
23. Burney, *Universal Dictionary of the Marine*, 1815, pp112, 184
24. PRO Adm 160/150
25. PRO Adm 106/2508, 10 June 1779
26. Blackmore, op cit, p233
27. PRO WO 47/46, 22 October 1755
28. Padfield, op cit, pp111–15
29. PRO Adm 160/150

Chapter 27. Magazines

1. *Deane's Doctrine*, p75
2. PRO WO 47/3, 55/1650. RAI ms, G3 n 1a. PRO Adm 7/677
3. For example, *Assistance*, 23 June 1710, and *Orford*, 8 August 1709, in PRO Adm 106/3070–1
4. Sutherland, *Shipbuilder's Assistant*, p412
5. PRO Adm 106/3551, 18 April 1716
6. NMM draughts, for example Nos 1362, *Chatham*; 1779, *Diamond*; 2747, *Fox* and *Solebay*; 502, *Humber*
7. PRO Adm 106/3070
8. PRO Adm 106/3072
9. PRO Adm 106/3551, 29 August 1716
10. PRO Adm 106/3070–1, passim
11. NRS *Sergison Papers*, pp113–15
12. PRO Adm 1/2277, 23 March 1701–02
13. NMM POR/A/5, 9 May 1715
14. PRO Adm 106/3551, 18 April 1716
15. NMM POR/A/9, 1 February 1733–34
16. PRO Adm 95/91, 10 March 1737–38
17. NMM Draught Room, contract for the *Bombay Castle*, 168/114
18. PRO Adm 106/2508, 21 April 1780
19. Laughton, op cit, p203
20. Ibid, p203
21. Ibid, p203
22. Draught of a model of a 70-gun ship in Wilton House, near Salisbury.
23. Laughton, op cit, p206

Chapter 28. General Layout

1. *Catalogue of Pepysian Manuscripts*, I, p239, for 1677. For 1800, various manuscripts in the NMM, especially the quarter bill of the *Goliath* in WQB/11. Also *Observations and Instructions*, by 'A Captain in the Royal Navy'
2. M Lewis, *A Social History of the Navy*, 1960, pp396–97
3. NMM Draught Room, print showing the hammock arrangement of the *Vengeance*, dated 1796

Chapter 29. The Layout of Cabins

1. Quoted in Oppenheim, op cit, p206
2. Smith, *Sea Grammar*, p38
3. NRS *Boteler*, p257
4. *Ship of the Line*, Vol II, p176
5. *Barlow's Journal*, ed Lubbock, 1934, pp257–58
6. NRS *Boteler*, pp257–58

7. *Deane's Doctrine*, p118
8. *Catalogue of Pepysian Manuscripts*, Vol I, p189
9. NMM AND/33
10. *Catalogue of Pepysian Manuscripts*, Vol I, pp200–01
11. NRS *The Tangier Papers of Samuel Pepys*, Vol LXXIII, p120
12. *Catalogue of Pepysian Manuscripts*, Vol I, p189
13. See M Lewis, *The Navy of Britain*, passim, for discussion of this
14. PRO Adm 106/2508, 24 June 1757, quoted in *Ship of the Line*, Vol II, p177
15. Ned Ward, *Wooden World Dissected*, 1707, reprint 1929, p68
16. *Mangin's Journal*, in NRS XLI, *Five Naval Journals, 1789–1817*, ed Thursfield, p11
17. NMM POR/A/44, 1 February 1802
18. *Catalogue of Pepysian Manuscripts*, Vol I, pp190–91
19. Laughton, op cit, p196
20. NMM POR/A/8, 2 November 1728
21. Falconer, op cit, pp236–37. Burney, *Universal Dictionary of the Marine*, p337
22. Phillips print in the Print Room of the NMM
23. Cyril Field, *Britain's Sea Soldiers*, Vol I, p130
24. NMM Draughts, 4598, 4600
25. NMM Draughts, No 8022a
26. United States Naval Academy Museum, *Catalogue of the Henry Huddleston Rogers Collection of Ship Models*, pp14–15
27. Ibid, pp10–11. NMM model No 1719–1, 2, 3
28. PRO Adm 91/2

16. PRO Adm 106/2508, 24 June 1757
17. Pamphlet in the Admiralty Library, quoted in *Britain's Sea Soldiers*, Vol 1, pp129–30
18. Laughton, op cit, p195.
19. NMM Draughts, Nos 3000,606
20. Laughton, op cit, p195
21. NMM POR/A/51, 24 October 1808
22. *Mangin's Journal*, op cit, pp9–10
23. Article by Colin Martin in *IJNA*, 7: 1, 1979, p34
24. PRO Adm 106/2507, 8 October 1702
25. Ibid
26. NMM AND/33
27. PRO 30/20/17
28. NMM POR/A/6, 18 March 1717/8
29. BL Stowe 436
30. *Mangin's Journal*, op cit, p10
31. NMM AND/33
32. PRO Adm 106/3069
33. PRO Adm 106/2534, 12 June 1797. PRO Adm 7/581
34. PRO Adm 7/581
35. *Mangin's Journal*, op cit, p11
36. PRO 30/20/17
37. *Mangin's Journal*, op cit, p13
38. W H Long, *Naval Yarns*, p119
39. PRO Adm 95/90, 2 November 1719
40. PRO Adm 106/2533, f247

Chapter 30. Captains and Admirals

1. NRS *Boteler*, p76
2. Ibid
3. NMM models, 1670–1
4. NMM POR/A/14, 6 February 1744/5
5. PRO Adm 95/12
6. PRO Adm 106/2508, 24 June 1757
7. Ibid
8. BL Addit Mss 9328, 15 June 1708
9. PRO Adm 106/2508, 3 March 1772

Chapter 31. The Structure and Fitting of Cabins

1. PRO Adm 106/3069
2. PRO Adm 106/2508, 8 November 1779
3. NRS *Boteler*, p257
4. *Ship of the Line*, Vol II, p176
5. *Deane's Doctrine*, p118
6. NMM POR/A/6, 18 March 1717/8
7. PRO Adm 95/90, 2 November 1719
8. NMM POR/A/14, 6 February 1744/5
9. PRO Adm 95/12
10. Ibid
11. PRO Adm 106/2508, 24 June 1757
12. Ibid
13. PRO Adm 174/35. 14 December 1802
14. Historical Manuscripts Commission, *Ducane*, p40
15. NMM POR/AI4, 6 February 1744–45

Chapter 32. Hammocks

1. NRS *Barham* Vol I, p42
2. Samuel Leech, *A Voice from the Middle Deck*, 1844, p37
3. NMM WQB/3
4. C J Marcus, *Quiberon Bay*, p189
5. *Observations and Instructions*, op cit, p29
6. Oppenheim, op cit, p134
7. Ibid, p235.
8. Burney, *Universal Dictionary of the Marine*, 1815, pp184, 90, 212
9. *Observations and Instructions*, op cit, p48
10. BL Stowe 431, etc
11. BL Stowe 436
12. NMM WQB/40
13. BL Stowe 436
14. NMM POR/A/21, 15 September 1760
15. NMM POR/D/12, 10 March 1757
16. Tobias Smollet, *Roderick Random*, p153
17. NMM RUSI/110a. *Vengeance* print, op cit
18. NMM RUSI ER/3/11
19. Leech, op cit
20. PRO Adm 106/2508, 5 March 1754
21. *Vengeance* print, op cit
22. Leech, op cit, p37
23. NMM RUSI/110a
24. NMM RUSI ER/3/11. WQB/40
25. NMM RUSI ER/3/11
26. WQB/40
27. Ibid

Chapter 33. The Messes

1. *Marine Dictionary*, op cit, p192
2. Leech, op cit, p37
3. NMM WQB/40
4. NMM RUSI/110.
5. Vegeance print, op cit
6. Falconer, op cit, p36
7. NRS *The Health of Seamen*, ed Lloyd, Vol 107, pp265–66
8. NRS *Barham I*, p42. NMM RUSI ER/3/11
9. *Mangin's Journal*, op cit, p10
10. PRO Adm 106/3472
11. BL Stowe 436
12. PRO Adm 95/17, 95/92, 106/2533, Laughton, op cit, p207
13. Lewis, *A Social History of the Navy*, p348
14. NRS *Barham I*, p42.

Chapter 34. Hold Stowage

1. NRS *Boteler*, pp77, 108. NRS *Mainwaring*, p92
2. *Trinity House Transactions*, London Records Society, Vol XIX, 1983, p88
3. BL Stowe 431
4. *Catalogue of Pepysian Manuscripts*, Vol IV, p353
5. PRO Adm 95/17, 24 August 1752. 95/65, no 1
6. PRO Adm 95/17
7. Harland, *Seamanship in the Age of Sail*, 1984, p49
8. Burney, *Universal Dictionary of the Marine*, p30
9. Many plans from the late eighteenth century are collected in PRO Adm 106/3122
10. PRO Adm 95/65, No 1
11. D Spinney, *Rodney*, pp132–33
12. NMM POR/A/39, 12 March 1796
13. *Admiralty Regulations and Instructions*, *1808*, p183.
14. Ibid, p183
15. Article on the *Dartmouth* by Colin Martin in *IJNA* 7: 1, 1979, p35.
16. PRO Adm 106/2533, f100. 106/1881, 1 April 1796
17. NRS *Pepys's Naval Minutes*, pp242–43. See *Ship of the Line*, Vol I, pp32–34 for criticism of this.
18. NMM SPB/15
19. *Catalogue of Pepysian Manuscripts*, Vol I, p166
20. NMM SPB/15
21. *Catalogue of Pepysian Manuscripts*, Vol I, p166
22. PRO Adm 106/2508, 8 January 1776
23. *Admiralty Regulations and Instructions*, *1808*, p185
24. PRO Adm 106/2538, 19 August 1686, 20 October 1692
25. PRO Adm 1/1548. NRS Vol XCVII, *Dillon's Narrative*, Vol II, pp283–84
26. PRO Adm 106/2266, 21 April 1815
27. PRO Adm 1/3175, 26 January 1812

Chapter 35. Store Rooms

1. NMM POR/A/51, 17 August 1808
2. Laughton, op cit, p204
3. PRO Adm 106/2536
4. NMM POR/A/51, 24 October 1808

Chapter 36. Cooking

1. NRS *Mainwaring*, pp131–32
2. NRS *Boteler*, pp90–1
3. NRS *Jacobean Commissions*, p289
4. NMM POR/D/12, 1 and 19 March 1757
5. NMM AND/33
6. NMM AND/31
7. NMM POR/A/6, 18 March 1717–18
8. NRS *Naval Administration*, p211
9. PRO Adm 95/17, 1 May 1757
10. PRO Adm 106/2508, 7 August 1777
11. Laughton, op cit, p202
12. PRO Adm 106/2508, 23 January 1787
13. PRO Adm 1/1547, 11 December 1809, 1/4833, 12 January 1810
14. NMM POR/A/51, 24 October 1808
15. NMM POR/A/18, 12 November 1755
16. PRO Adm 106/2508, 7 September 1779
17. NMM POR/A/51, 24 October 1808
18. PRO Adm 106/3574
19. NRS *Health of Seamen*, p263.

Chapter 37. Sanitary and Medical Arrangements

1. Lewis, *A Social History of the Navy*, pp420–21
2. *The Journal of James Yonge*, 1963, p33
3. Smith, *Sea Grammar*, p10
4. Ibid, p36
5. J Munday, *Heads and Tails, the Necessary Seating*, in NMM Monographs and Reports No 36, 1978, pp125–40
6. Ibid, p125
7. Ibid
8. PRO 30/20/17
9. Munday, op cit, p136
10. Burney, *Universal Dictionary of the Marine*, p417
11. Laughton, op cit, p195
12. L Wright, *Clean and Decent*, 1960, pp106–08. J S Hellyer, *The Principles and Practice of Plumbing*, 1891, pp194–98.
13. Ward, *Wooden World Dissected*, p62
14. NMM POR/A/15, 22 July 1809
15. NRS *Health of Seamen*, p70
16. Smollet, op cit, p153
17. NRS *Health of Seamen*, p71
18. Ibid, p158.
19. NMM Draughts, Mulgrave Collection, in *Ship of the Line*, Vol II, p133
20. NRS *Health of Seamen*, p186
21. Ibid, p262
22. Ibid, pp262–63
23. NMM POR/A/51, 4 May 1808

Chapter 38. The Uses of Boats

1. *Jeremy Roche's Journal* in *Three Sea Journals of Stuart Times*, ed Ingram, 1936, p117
2. James, *Naval History of Great Britain*, Vol V, pp370–71
3. Ibid, Vol II, pp405–11

4. Ibid, Vol IV, pp279–80
5. PRO Adm 1/340, passim.
6. See NRS *The Keith Papers, Vol III*, Vol XCVI, 1955, pp265–89
7. W E May, *The Boats of Men of War*, NMM Monographs and Reports No 15, 1974, p7
8. Ibid, p7

Chapter 39. Boat Construction

1. NMM AND/33
2. Whole-moulding is discussed in Mungo Murray, *Treatise on Shipbuilding and Naval Architecture*, 1765; M Stalkaart, *Naval Architecture*, 1781, and A Rees, *Naval Architecture*, 1818, reprinted 1970
3. Various contracts for boats, eg PRO Adm 106/3257, m 106/3069, 95/18, 95/13, and NMM AND/31
4. PRO Adm 106/2508, 29 April 1783
5. PRO Adm 106/2508, 21 July 1779; 106/3257, 13 December 1755
6. PRO Adm 106/3574

Chapter 40. Types of Boat

1. NRS *Mainwaring*, p103
2. May, op cit, p2
3. SNR Occasional Publication, No 3, p30
4. NMM AND/33
5. PRO Adm 106/3250, 4 May 1706
6. May, op cit, p6
7. Ibid, p9
8. Ibid, p9
9. Ibid, p10
10. PRO Adm 7/579
11. PRO Adm 106/2509, 9 January 1783
12. Falconer, op cit, p39
13. Fincham, *Outline of Shipbuilding*, IV, p20
14. SNR Occasional Publication, No 3, p31
15. W Mountaine, *The Seaman's Vade Mecum*, 1745, p262
16. Howard, op cit, p225
17. PRO Adm 7/579
18. NMM SPB/20
19. PRO Adm 7/579
20. NMM WQB/3
21. NMM SPB/37a
22. NMM SPB/20
23. PRO Adm 7/579
24. NRS *Boteler*, p195
25. NRS *Mainwaring*, p103
26. PRO Adm 106/3069
27. May, op cit, p6
28. NMM SPB/37a, PRO Adm 106/2508, 18 July 1769
29. *Marine Dictionary*, op cit, p39
30. PRO Adm 7/579. May, op cit, p7. PRO Adm 106/2508, 19 September 1771. Howard p225
31. NMM AND/33
32. Burney, *Universal Dictionary of the Marine*, p47
33. NRS *Boteler*, pp196–97
34. May, op cit, p12. PRO Adm 2/272, 15 March 1810
35. May, op cit, p16. PRO Adm 12/144, 16 January 1810

Chapter 41. Boat Fittings

1. Falconer, op cit, p328
2. PRO Adm 7/579
3. PRO Adm 106/2509, 9 January 1783
4. PRO Adm 7/579
5. NMM WQB/3
6. PRO Adm 106/2508, 17 September 1771
7. NMM WQB/3
8. NMM AND/33
9. PRO Adm 7/579
10. PRO Adm 106/3069
11. Ibid
12. Ibid
13. Ibid
14. PRO Adm 106/2507, 3 July 1755
15. PRO Adm 95/18, 1 April 1800
16. NMM WQB/3
17. PRO Adm 106/2508, 6 December 1771
18. PRO Adm 1/1696, 7 August 1744
19. PRO Adm 160/150
20. PRO Adm 7/677
21. PRO adm 7/579

Chapter 42. Boat Establishments

1. NRS *Jacobean Commissions*, p115. SNR Occasional Publication No 3, p30. *Deane's Doctrine*, pp104–113. NMM AND/33
2. Hayward, *Sizes and Lengths of Rigging*, p53
3. May, op cit, p5
4. Ibid, p5
5. NRS *Third Dutch War*, p188
6. May, op cit, p6
7. Ibid, pp6, 8
8. NMM SPB/37a
9. May, op cit, p7. Howard, op cit, p224.
10. PRO Adm 106/2508, 18 July 1769
11. Howard, op cit, p224.
12. PRO Adm 106/2508, 6 December 1771
13. PRO Adm 106/2509, 1 August 1783
14. Howard, op cit, p225. PRO Adm 106/2509, 17 July 1783, 12 January 1784
15. PRO Adm 106/2508, 16 June 1779
16. BL Stowe 436
17. PRO Adm 7/579

Chapter 43. Boat Stowage

1. May, op cit, p2
2. *Deane's Doctrine*, p98
3. NRS *Mainwaring*, p103
4. Ibid
5. NRS *Boteler*, p195
6. May, op cit, p3
7. Hayward, *Sizes and Lengths of Rigging*, pp13–14. *Deane's Doctrine*, pp91–103
8. BL Addit mss 9328, 13 March 1711/12

9. Ibid
10. Glasgow Museum of Transport, model of the *Orford*
11. HMC *Ducane*, op cit, pp40–41
12. PRO Adm 106/2507, 28 February 1743/4
13. Bristol City Museums, model of the *Arethusa*
14. Laughton, op cit, p193

Chapter 44. Hatches and Ladders

1. Some details of the construction of hatches are given in *The Ship-wright's Vade-Mecum*, 1805, pp294–95
2. NMM Models, 1702-1, 1681-1
3. Fincham, *Outline of Shipbuilding*, IV, p80
4. NMM Model No 1790-2
5. PRO Adm 106/2508, 19 September 1757
6. NMM POR/D/12, 6 January 1758
7. NMM POR/A/8, 11 September 1746
8. PRO Adm 106/2508, 11 May 1779

Chapter 45. Rails and Nettings

1. Various pictures in Frank Fox, *Great Ships*, 1980
2. Cleveley painting in the NMM, but this does not represent the *Buckingham* as catalogued. See *Ship of the Line*, Vol I, p86
3. NRS *Fighting Instructions*, ed Corbett, Vol XXIX, 1905, passim.
4. NMM ADM/B/133, 7 August 1746
5. Ibid
6. Ibid, 26 September 1746
7. Ibid
8. NMM POR/A/20, 19 May 1760
9. NMM model No 1765-1
10. PRO Adm 174/59, 29 June 1813, 9 September 1812
11. NMM model No 1780-2. PRO Adm 106/2508, 15 March 1782
12. PRO Adm 174/35
13. BL Stowe 436
14. Laughton, op cit, pp188, 202

Chapter 46. Awnings and Gangways

1. By Vroom in the NMM. Reproduced in *Ship of the Line*, Vol I, p14.
2. E H H Archibald, *The Wooden Fighting Ship*, p24
3. NMM model No 1702-1
4. Model in the Kreigstein collection, displayed temporarily in the NMM in 1983–84
5. NMM models Nos 1719-1,2,3
6. NMM model No 1740-1
7. NMM POR/A/8, 16 April 1727/8
8. PRO Adm 106/2507, 14 February 1727/8
9. PRO Adm 106/2507, 28 February 1743/4
10. Van de Velde drawing No 1187 in the NMM. Reproduced in Fox, p63
11. PRO Adm 106/2507, 16 July 1701
12. PRO Adm 106/2510, 5 June 1793
13. PRO Adm 106/2510, 20 January 1794
14. PRO Adm 106/2512, 2 February 1799
15. PRO Adm 106/2511, 6 November 1795
16. Burney, *Universal Dictionary of the Marine*, 1815, p319
17. PRO Adm 106/2515, 5 April 1804

Chapter 47. Communication

1. NMM AND/33
2. See Isle of Thanet Archaeological Unit, *Interim Report*, 1979, for the bell of the *Stirling Castle*
3. See L G Carr Laughton, *Old Ship Figureheads and Sterns*, for various drawings of belfries.
4. *Catalogue of Pepysian Manuscripts*, Vol I, pp189–92
5. NMM model No 1692-1
6. H H Rogers, *Collection of Ship Models*, pp10–11
7. PRO Adm 95/12
8. Laughton, op cit, p207
9. See Archibald, op cit, pp59–62, for a summary of signalling history.
10. NMM model No 1702-1
11. NMM model No 1735-1
12. NMM model No 1756-1
13. NMM WQB/3
14. PRO Adm 106/2508, 7 June 1722
15. PRO Adm 174/38, 21 February 1804
16. PRO Adm 106/2507, 8 October 1702
17. PRO Adm 106/2233, 26 January 1804

Select Bibliography

Contemporary Works in Modern Reprints

BURNEY, W *Universal Dictionary of the Marine*, 1815, reprinted 1970
DEANE, SIR ANTHONY, *Deane's Doctrine of Naval Architecture, 1670*, ed B Lavery, reprinted 1981
FALCONER, W *Marine Dictionary*, 1769, reprinted 1970
HAYWARD, E *Sizes and Lengths of Rigging*, 1655, reprinted 1967
HODGES AND HUGHES *Select Naval Documents*, 1922
LONDON RECORDS SOCIETY, Vol XIX, *Trinity House Transactions*, 1983
LONG, W H *Naval Yarns*, 1899, reprinted 1973
MOUNTAINE, W *The Seaman's Vade Mecum*, 1745, reprinted 1971
PEPYS, SAMUEL *Memoires of the Royal Navy*, 1690, reprinted 1906
REES, A *Naval Architecture*, 1818, reprinted 1970
SMITH, CAPTAIN JOHN *A Sea Grammar*, 1627, ed Goell, reprinted 1970
SNR OCCASIONAL PUBLICATION No 3, *Lengths of Masts and Yards, 1640*, 1931
SNR OCCASIONAL PUBLICATION No 6, *A Treatise on Shipbuilding, c 1625*, 1958
STEEL, DAVID *Mastmaking, Sailmaking and Rigging*, 1794, reprinted 1932
WARD, NED *Wooden World Dissected*, 1707, reprinted 1929

Other Contemporary Works

Admiralty Regulations and Instructions, 1808
BLANCKLEY, THOMAS *The Naval Expositor*, 1750
BOND, HENRY *The Boate Swain's Art*, 1642
DERRICK, CHARLES *Memoirs of the Rise and Progress of the Royal Navy*, 1806
Exercise of the Great Guns 1765(?) in the British Library
FINCHAM, JOHN *Outline of Shipbuilding*, 1822, 1852
HALE, T *Account of Several New Inventions*, 1691
MURRAY, MUNGO *A Treatise on Shipbuilding and Naval Architecture*, 1765
Observations and Instructions, by 'A Captain in the Royal Navy', 1807
PERING, RICHARD *A Treatise on the Anchor*, 1819
POVEY, *Sea Gunner's Companion*, 1702
REES, A *The Cyclopeadia*, 1819
SELLAR, JOHN *The Sea Gunner*, 1691
STALKAART, MARMADUKE *Naval Architecture*, 1781
SUTHERLAND, WILLIAM *Shipbuilding Unveiled*, 1717

Navy Records Society Publications

Vol 11, *Papers Relating to the Spanish War*, ed J S Corbett
Vol 29, *Fighting Instructions 1530–1816*, ed J S Corbett
Vol 40, *The Naval Miscellany*, ed J K Laughton
Vol 41, *Papers Relating to the First Dutch War, Vol V*
Vol 45, *The Naval Tracts of Sir William Monson, Vol IV*, ed M Oppenheim
Vol 56, *The Life and Works of Sir Henry Mainwaring*, ed G E Mainwaring
Vol 57, *Catalogue of the Pepysian Manuscripts, Vol IV*, ed Tanner
Vol 65, *Boteler's Dialogues*, ed W G Perrin
Vol 73, *The Tangier Papers of Samuel Pepys*, ed E Chappell
Vol 76, *Journals and Narratives of the Third Dutch War*, ed Anderson
Vol 89, *The Sergison Papers*, ed R D Merriman
Vol 91, *Five Naval Journals, 1789–1817*, ed R G Thursfield
Vol 96, *The Keith Papers, Vol III*
Vol 97, *Dillon's Narrative, Vol II*
Vol 103, *Queen Anne's Navy*, ed R D Merriman
Vol 107, *The Health of Seamen*, ed Lloyd
Vol 116, *The Jacobean Commissions of Enquiry 1608 and 1618*, ed A P Mcgowan
Vol 120, *Naval Administration, 1715–50*, ed D A Baugh
Vol 124, *Naval Miscellany V*, ed Rodger

Secondary Works on Naval History and Administration

BAUGH D A *British Naval Administration in the Age of Walpole*, 1965
CORBETT, J S *Drake and the Tudor Navy*, 2 vols, 1898
FIELD, CYRIL *Britain's Sea Soldiers*, 2 vols, 1924
JAMES, WILLIAM *Naval History of Great Britain*, 6 vols, various editions
LEWIS, MICHAEL *The Navy of Britain*, 1948
   A Social History of the Navy, 1960
MARCUS, GEOFFREY J *Quiberon Bay*, 1960
OPPENHEIM, MICHAEL *History of the Administration of the Royal Navy, 1509–1660*, 1896
POOL, BERNARD *Navy Board Contracts, 1660–1832*, 1966

Secondary Works on Shipbuilding and Fitting

Ships in General
ANDERSON, R C *List of English Men of War 1509–1649*, SNR Occasional Publication No 7
ARCHIBALD, E H H *The Wooden Fighting Ship*, 1968
BUGLER, A R *HMS Victory: Building, Restoration and Repair*, 1966
FOX, FRANK *Great Ships: The Battlefleet of King Charles II*, 1980
HOWARD, FRANK *Sailing Ships of War, 1400–1860*, 1979
JOHNSON, R F *The Royal George*, 1971
LAUGHTON, L G C *Old Ships Figureheads and Sterns*, 1925
LAVERY, BRIAN *Ship of the Line*, 2 vols, 1983–84
MAY, W E *The Boats of Men of War*, NMM Monographs and Reports No 15, 1974
ROBERTSON, F L *The Evolution of Naval Armament*, 1921, reprinted 1968
RULE, MARGARET *The Mary Rose*, 1982

Ship Models
NATIONAL MARITIME MUSEUM *Catalogue of Ship Models to 1815*, nd, *c*1980
THE SCIENCE MUSEUM *Sailing Ships, their History and Development*, 2 vols, several editions since 1930
UNITED STATES NAVAL ACADEMY MUSEUM *Catalogue of the Henry Huddleston Rogers Collection of Ship Models*, 1971

Other Technical Topics
HARLAND, JOHN *Seamanship in the Age of Sail*, 1984
HELLYER, J S *The Principles and Practice of Plumbing*, 1891
HORSLEY, J *Tools of the Maritime Trades*, 1978
WRIGHT, L *Clean and Decent*, 1960

Secondary Works on Guns and Related Subjects

BLACKMORE, H L *The Armouries of the Tower of London, Part I, Ordnance*
CAMPBELL, *Carron Company*
COUNCIL FOR THE PRESERVATION OF BUSINESS ARCHIVES *Minutes relating to Messrs Samuel Walker and Co*, 1951
FFOULKES, C *The Gun-founders of England*, 1937
GUILMARTIN, J F *Gunpowder and Galleys*, 1974
HALL, A R *Ballistics in the Seventeenth Century*, 1952
The British Explosives Industry, Vol I, International Congress of Applied Chemistry, 1909
LEWIS, M *Armada Guns*, 1961
MULLER *Treatise on Artillery*, 1768
PADFIELD, P *Guns at Sea*, 1973
PERCEVAL, A *The Faversham Gunpowder Industry*, 1967
STRAKER, E *Wealden Iron*, 1931
TOMLINSON, H C *Guns and Government*, 1979

Biography and Memoirs

BARLOW, E *Barlow's Journal 1659–1703*, ed Lubbock, 2 vols, 1934
ROCHE, JEREMY *Jeremy Roche's Journal* in *Three Sea Journals of Stuart Times*, ed Ingram, 1936
SMOLLETT, TOBIAS *Roderick Random* (fiction)
YONGE, JAMES *The Journal of James Yonge*, 1963

Periodicals

International Journal of Nautical Archaeology
The Mariner's Mirror
Model Shipwright
Nautical Research Journal
Warship

Manuscripts

Public Record Office, Kew and Chancery Lane
Admiralty Records, especially Adm 106, Navy Board Records, Adm 95 series
Controller's office, miscellaneous, and Adm 7, Admiralty miscellaneous
War Office Records, especially WO 55, miscellaneous
State Papers, SP, especially for 1640 to 1673

National Maritime Museum, Greenwich
Official records: ADM/A, ADM/B, etc
Dockyard records, especially POR (Portsmouth) series
SPB (shipbuilding) series
Numerous personal and semi-official papers

British Library, London
Several collections of private papers, eg Anson and Norris

Pepys Library, Magdalene College, Cambridge
Pepys papers, official and semi-official

INDEX

Reference to illustrations and captions are given in *italics*.